READINGS
IN THE HISTORY OF
MATHEMATICS EDUCATION

READINGS
IN THE HISTORY OF
MATHEMATICS
EDUCATION

edited by
JAMES K. BIDWELL
and
ROBERT G. CLASON
Central Michigan University

NATIONAL COUNCIL
OF TEACHERS OF MATHEMATICS

Washington, D.C.

Contents

Preface   xi

Acknowledgments   xiii

1   Beginnings of the Art of Teaching Mathematics

(1828–1890)

Comment   1

William Slocomb

    The American Calculator (1831)   3

Comment   13

Warren Colburn

    First Lessons in Arithmetic (1825)   14

    "Teaching of Arithmetic" (1830)   24

Comment   38

Charles Davies

    The Logic and Utility of Mathematics (1850)   39

    University Arithmetic (1870)   62

Comment   69

Edward Brooks

The Philosophy of Arithmetic (1880)   70

Mental Science and Methods of Mental Culture (1883)   76

Comment   91

Wentworth [Mathematical Series]

How to Teach Number (1885)   93

Levi Seeley

Grube's Method of Teaching Arithmetic (1888)   100

W. M. Welch

How to Organize, Classify and Teach a Country School
   (1889)   112

William James

The Principles of Psychology (1890)   118

2   Emergence of National Organizations as a Force in Mathematics Education

(1891–1919)

Comment   127

National Education Association

Report of the Committee on Secondary School Studies (1893)   129

Report of the Committee of Fifteen on Elementary
   Education (1895)   142

Comment   151

James A. McLellan and John Dewey

The Psychology of Number (1895)   152

Comment   163

James A. McLellan and A. F. Ames

The Public School Arithmetic for Grammar Grades (1902)   164

Comment   168

William W. Speer

Primary Arithmetic (1897)   169

National Education Association

"Report of Committee on College-Entrance Requirements"
(1899)   189

American Mathematical Society

"Report of the Committee of the Chicago Section of the
American Mathematical Society" (1899)   195

Comment   210

David Eugene Smith

The Teaching of Elementary Mathematics (1900)   211

John Perry

Discussion on the Teaching of Mathematics (1901)   220

Eliakim Hastings Moore

"On the Foundations of Mathematics" (1902)   246

J. W. A. Young

*The Teaching of Mathematics in the Elementary and the
Secondary School* (1906)   256

David Eugene Smith

The Teaching of Arithmetic (1909)   274

**International Commission on the Teaching of
Mathematics**

*Mathematics in the Elementary Schools of the
United States* (1911)   280

*Mathematics in the Public and Private Secondary Schools
of the United States* (1911)   328

3

The "1923 Report"
and Connectionism in Arithmetic

(1920–1937)

Comment   361

National Education Association

The Problem of Mathematics in Secondary Education (1920)   363

Mathematical Association of America

The Reorganization of Mathematics in Secondary Education
(1923)   382

Comment   460

Edward L. Thorndike

The Psychology of Arithmetic (1924)   461

Frederick B. Knight

in Twenty-ninth Yearbook of the National Society for
the Study of Education (1930)   478

George D. Birkhoff and Ralph Beatley

"A New Approach to Elementary Geometry" (1930)   495

William A. Brownell

"Psychological Considerations in the Learning and the
Teaching of Arithmetic" (1935)   504

4   Prewar and Postwar Reforms

(1938–1959)

Comment   531

Progressive Education Association

Mathematics in General Education (1938)   534

Comment   567

Leo J. Brueckner

in *Child Development and the Curriculum* (1939)   568

Carleton Washburne

in *Child Development and the Curriculum* (1939)   577

**Mathematical Association of America
and National Council of Teachers of Mathematics**

The Place of Mathematics in Secondary Education (1940)   586

National Council of Teachers of Mathematics

"The Second Report of the Commission on Post-War Plans"
(1945)   618

University of Illinois Committee on School Mathematics

"The University of Illinois School Mathematics Program"
(1956)   655

College Entrance Examination Board

Program for College Preparatory Mathematics (1959)   664

Preface

This book is offered in the hope that it will allow the reader to obtain, more directly than would otherwise be possible, a cohesive view of the evolution of mathematics education in the United States. While names, dates, facts, and general conclusions are readily available in secondary sources, original statements give a more incisive view of the era when they were made than résumés, which are necessarily condensed and indirect. Two noteworthy examples of primary sources that illuminate their times are an address by John Perry in England, which is said to be the origin of general mathematics courses in this country, and Warren Colburn's discussion of discovery teaching. If one attempts to broaden his knowledge of the evolution of mathematics education by investigating even the more commonly cited sources, the delays encountered in locating them unavoidably detract from the continuity of the study. Furthermore, libraries of new and developing institutions may lack sources of significance for this purpose. By offering this book, then, we hope to make the lessons of history more readily accessible.

In selecting the readings we have focused on mathematics education in public schools in the United States, grades K–12. We have been guided by several criteria:

First, we have included large portions of major committee and commission reports. These describe existing conditions and make recommendations for improvement. Notable among these reports is *The Reorganization of Mathematics in Secondary Education*, published in 1923 and commonly known as "the 1923 Report." Because of the importance of this report, the entire first part of it has been included in this book.

Second, we have given priority to sources that are less likely than others to be currently available. As a consequence, the present cycle of reform is given less attention than it might otherwise have been given. This de-emphasis of modern developments is dictated also by their profusion and by the lack of historical perspective.

Third, in addition to sources generally accepted as landmarks, we have included less well known sources in an attempt to elucidate further the methods of teaching mathematics used or advocated in various periods, and to examine more closely differences and similarities of approach, as well as for the intrinsic interest of this material. For example, Edward Brooks's statement of faculty psychology puts later objections to the theory in clearer perspective. In the selection of readings from such sources, of course, the interests and knowledge of the editors are paramount factors; someone else would no doubt make other selections and stress other themes.

It has not been our purpose to be exhaustive but rather to bring ideas into sharper focus and to emphasize historical continuity. For the period before 1900, which may be less familiar to the reader than the present century, brief biographical sketches of some men prominent in school mathematics are given. Because of the lack of comprehensive reports for this era, selections from textbooks and from advice to teachers are included along with more philosophical statements. We hope that this will clarify the intended application of the theory, which is expounded in sometimes rather abstruse prose.

To indicate the context from which selections from larger works were made, title pages and tables of contents are included. The original typographic styles, reflecting the tastes of different periods, have been followed whenever it was feasible to show such variety; but only title pages, contents pages, and an occasional listing of names are given as photographic reproductions.

When a selection is not quoted in its entirety, omissions are indicated by editorial explanation or by ellipses vertically displayed.

The arrangement of the readings is primarily chronological. Another arrangement would have involved a classification scheme and assignment of wide-ranging selections to the proper classes. The difficulties of agreement on any such arrangement accounts for the chronological plan. However, since this arrangement can obscure evolution in a particular area, we have interspersed some connective commentary. We trust that this commentary will not detract from the main purpose, which is to offer historical statements concerning mathematics education, and even to approximate their original form.

We wish to express to Arthur F. Coxford, Jr., of the Publications Committee of the National Council of Teachers of Mathematics, our appreciation for his suggestions and assistance. We extend our thanks also to the National Council for its willingness to publish this book as a service to the mathematics education community.

J. K. B.
R. G. C.

Acknowledgments

Grateful acknowledgment is made for permission to reprint extracts from the sources named below.

Child Development and the Curriculum, edited by Guy Montrose Whipple. Thirty-eighth Yearbook of the National Society for the Study of Education, pt. 1. 1939. Reprinted by permission of the Society.

Mathematics in General Education, by a committee of the Progressive Education Association. Copyright 1938 by the Progressive Education Association.

The Principles of Psychology, vol. 2 (1923 ed.), by William James. Copyright 1890, 1923, by Henry Holt and Company. Reprinted by permission of Holt, Rinehart & Winston, Inc.

The Problem of Mathematics in Secondary Education: A Report of the Commission on the Reorganization of Secondary Education. Department of the Interior Bureau of Education Bulletin, 1920, no. 1. Reprinted by permission of the U.S. Office of Education (formerly the Bureau of Education).

The Psychology of Arithmetic, by Edward L. Thorndike. Published 1922 by The Macmillan Company.

The Reorganization of Mathematics in Secondary Education, by the National Committee on Mathematical Requirements of the Mathematical Association of America, 1923. Reprinted by permission of the Association.

Report of the Commission on Mathematics. Vol. 1, Program for College Preparatory Mathematics. Copyright 1959 by College Entrance Examination Board. Reprinted with permission of the College Entrance Examination Board, New York.

Report of the Society's Committee on Arithmetic, edited by Guy Montrose Whipple. Twenty-ninth Yearbook of the National Society for the Study of Education. 1930. Reprinted by permission of the Society.

The Teaching of Mathematics in the Elementary and the Secondary School, by J. W. A. Young (New York: Longmans, Green & Company, 1924). Reprinted by arrangement with David McKay Company, Inc.

The University of Illinois School Mathematics Program, by the UICSM Project Staff. 1956. Reprinted by permission of the University of Illinois Press.

PART ONE: 1828–1890

Beginnings of the Art of Teaching Mathematics

The first group of readings traces American mathematics education from a time when the main concern was arithmetic for business applications through a stage characterized by an upsurge in the concern with pedagogy to a period when mathematics was taught for mental discipline. The first selection, from an arithmetic text written before Warren Colburn's ideas had become broadly influential, illustrates the "rule method," which was the primary approach to arithmetic teaching in colonial times. As the difficulty level suggests, arithmetic was not a subject for young children.

The appearance in 1821 of the first edition of Colburn's *First Lessons in Arithmetic on the Plan of Pestalozzi, with Some Improvements* marked the beginning of widespread concern with pedagogy in arithmetic teaching. The contrast to earlier methods is evident in the second selection here, Colburn's 1830 address to the American Institute of Instruction.

In the mathematics teaching of the mid-nineteenth century, three developments can be singled out to characterize some aspects of the evolution. First, the mental-discipline theme, recognized by Colburn, was expanded and formalized. Charles Davies spoke of strengthening different faculties by studying mathematics, and Edward Brooks offered a detailed analysis of these mental components and the way each was to be "cultivated." Second, arithmetic was increasingly formalized into a logical system complete with definitions, principles, and theorems—a contrast to the pre-Colburn rule method and Colburn's discovery approach. This recognition of the importance of logical structure has its modern counterpart; however, the mathematical structure of Davies and Brooks differs from modern structure in the physical nature of the basis. In the mid-nineteenth century school mathematics was still the science of quantity and geometry the science of space. Basing mathematics on quantity allowed mathematical and psychological theory to mesh better then than at any later time: one initially learned mathematics from quantitative reality through the faculties of perception and intuition, then extended the knowledge through such faculties as reasoning and imagination. A third and related point in the development of mathematics teaching from Colburn's time to the late nineteenth century was extension of the use of manipulative objects in early number work. The emphasis on using physical things (cubes, beans, corn, buttons, etc., were suggested) was as great as, or greater than, this emphasis in any more recent widely used approach. Thus, although we may consider the old faculty theory archaic, at least in primary grades the application of the theory was not far from current practice.

The final selection of this section is from William James's *The Principles of Psychology*. It marks the beginning of the impact of the "new" psychology on mathematics teaching, a psychology that eventually evolved into a theory that destroyed the faculty hypotheses and caused extensive reevaluation of what mathematics should be taught and why. In the selection included here James argued that number is psychological rather than real in nature— in the words of a cliché that developed shortly afterward: "Number is not got from things; it is put into them." This was in keeping with the evolving pragmatic philosophy: number is created by man to serve him; that is, mathematics is a tool. John Dewey's pedagogical application of this point of view is included in Part Two of this book.

The opening selection in this first group of readings is from *The American Calculator*, first published in 1828. The approach is reasonably typical of the colonial period. This text was used with older students (beginning at about the age of eleven). It was complete in itself, not one book of a series such as the texts that evolved in later years. The indication in the preface that the rules should be understood suggests some influence of a newer pedagogy; but the fundamental position of the rule is evident, as is well illustrated by the rule for addition that is included here.

2

THE

AMERICAN CALCULATOR,

OR,

A CONCISE SYSTEM

OF

PRACTICAL ARITHMETIC;

CONTAINING

ALL THE RULES NECESSARY FOR TRANSACTING THE
COMMON BUSINESS OF LIFE;

TOGETHER WITH

QUESTIONS FOR EXAMINATION,

UNDER EACH OF THE RULES.

INTENDED FOR

THE USE OF SCHOOLS, AND YOUNG MEN

WHO MAY BE DESIROUS OF OBTAINING FURTHER KNOWLEDGE OF
THIS SCIENCE.

TO WHICH IS ADDED, A SHORT SYSTEM OF
BOOK-KEEPING.

BY WILLIAM SLOCOMB.

Philadelphia:
PUBLISHED BY WILLIAM DAVIS.
SOLD BY BOOKSELLERS GENERALLY, THROUGHOUT THE UNITED STATES,
AND BY WILLIAM SLOCOMB, MARIETTA, OHIO.
. . . .
1831.

PREFACE.

In offering the following pages to the public, the author feels it incumbent on him to state some of the reasons, which have induced him to add another, to the numerous treatises on Arithmetic now in use.

Having been engaged, for more than twenty years, in the business of teaching, I have found it of great importance, that every thing relating to the science of Arithmetic, should be presented to the mind of the young learner, in as simple and concise a manner as possible, unencumbered with terms not readily understood by him; and that the principles embraced under each rule, should, as far as practicable, be at once presented to the mind in a plain, familiar manner, instead of being divided into a number of Cases, tending rather to confuse than enlarge the understanding. For this purpose, many of the rules found in this work were written for the benefit of my own pupils, without the most distant idea, at the time, of their ever being published. The questions also which are inserted at the close of each rule, are such as I have long been in the practice of asking my scholars, or requiring them to put to each other, in a class formed for the purpose, and from which much good has resulted, in rendering the principles contained in the rules familiar to the mind. These questions should be repeated, till the learner is able to answer them readily, not only in the natural order in which they stand, but also when put promiscuously, embracing several rules in the same lesson.

We find in all the Arithmetics now in use, a large proportion of the questions stated in *English Money*, and consequently much of the time of the pupil is wasted, without adding scarcely any thing to his stock of useful knowledge. The time has arrived, when accounts in our country should no longer be kept in that currency. In this work, therefore, the whole of the calculations are in *Federal Money*, except in the *Compound Rules* where *English Money* is introduced with the weights and measures, and in a few other cases where it seemed necessary, as in Practice, &c.

The several rules are arranged in that order in which they seemed best calculated to reflect light on each other, and so as not to require a large and separate explanation. The previous rules open the way to those which follow in so plain and easy a manner, that the pupil may proceed without much obstruction, and gradually acquire a connected and enlarged view of the whole science.

In the whole of this work, two things have been kept constantly in view:

4

viz. to furnish our schools with a plain and easy system of Arithmetic, unencumbered by useless questions, or such as would have a tendency to puzzle, rather than improve the learner: and also, to put into the hands of those young men, who, from their peculiar situation in a new country, could not, at the proper age, enjoy the advantages of a common school education, the means of acquiring, without the aid of a teacher, such a knowledge of this useful science, as to be able, without embarrassment, to transact the common business of life. For the purpose of enabling them to do this with greater facility, an explanation of the first example under each rule, will be found generally through the work.

If I might be allowed to invite the attention of the reader to any particular portion of this treatise, I would mention the method of calculating *Interest*, the rule of *Practice*, the *Illustration* of the reason and nature of the *Roots*, the *Application* under the rules generally, and the *Promiscuous Questions* at the close of the work. Of these, a large number is inserted as a kind of supplement to the foregoing rules, for the purpose of affording the learner an opportunity for exercising his judgment, in the method of operation, without having any particular rule before him. Every teacher who has had even but little practice, must have seen the great importance of such a course.

The work is, with diffidence, submitted to the public. That it is perfect, is not pretended; but it is hoped but few errors will be found in it, as every question has been carefully wrought by myself, and also by one of my most accurate pupils. Should it help to facilitate the progress of youth in acquiring a knowledge of Arithmetic, my object is attained. I have only to request that it may not be condemned unexamined.

WM. SLOCOMB.

NOTICE TO THE SECOND EDITION.

The very favorable reception, and rapid sale, of the first edition of this work, have induced the author carefully to revise, and somewhat to enlarge it for a second, and, if possible, to render it still more deserving of public patronage.

He has now the satisfaction of saying, that in every instance, so far as his knowledge extends, where the work has been introduced, it has met the approbation of teachers, and others interested in the education of youth, many testimonials of which have, unsolicited, been kindly forwarded to him.

The greatest care has been taken to prevent errors from appearing in this edition; yet some may have escaped notice. Should any be discovered, the author will be under obligations to any one who will point them out to him, that they may be corrected in future editions.

Marietta, Ohio, May, 1830.

A WORD OF ADVICE TO LEARNERS.

Never take your slate in hand till you understand the rule by which your question is to be wrought; nor call on your teacher for assistance till you have made a thorough trial by yourself, remembering that the most useful knowledge is that which is gained by your own study and reflection.

Never leave a rule, and the operations under it, till you thoroughly understand it; and not only see that the answers are produced, but also know the reasons *why* they are.

Remember that idleness and sloth are great enemies to improvement, therefore drive them far from you. The season of youth will soon pass, and with it the best, and usually the only opportunity for preparing yourself for a useful and respectable station in society.

10

CONTENTS.

Extraction of the Cube Root 123
Demonstration of the Cube
  Root................. ib.
Application of the Cube Root 124
Single Fellowship........ 127
Double Fellowship....... 128
Barter................. 129
Loss and Gain.......... 130
Duodecimals........... 131
Addition of Duodecimals.. 132
Subtraction of Duodecimals. 134
Multiplication of Duodeci-
  mals................ 135
Application of Duodeci-
  mals................ ib.
Measurement of Duodecimals 136
Measurement of Lumber
  of boards and plank... ib.
  of shingles........... 137
  of squared timber..... 138
  of round timber...... 139
Artificers' work......... 140
Carpenters' and Joiners'
  work................ 142

Masons' work....... 144
Bricklayers' work.... 145
Plasterers' work..... ib.
Pavers' work....... 148
Painters' work...... 150
Glaziers' work...... 151
Canal work........ 152
Measurement of Land 153
Equation of Payment. 155
Alligation Medial... 157
Alligation Alternate. 158
Position............ ib.
Single Position..... 160
Double Position..... 163
Gauging............ ib.
Mechanical Powers.. 164
The Lever......... 166
The Wheel and Axle 167
The screw......... 168
Promiscuous Questions ib.
Problems.......... 169
Book Keeping...... 180
            181

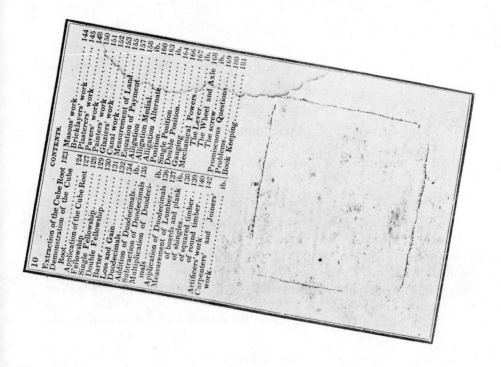

CONTENTS.

Introduction............ Page 11
Numeration of characters... 13
Explanation of characters.. ib.
Simple Addition.......... 15
Application of Simple Addi-
  tion................. 16
Simple Subtraction....... 17
Application of Simple Sub-
  traction.............. 18
Simple Multiplication.....
Application of Simple Multi-
  plication............. 22
Simple Division.......... 23
Application of Simple Divi-
  sion.................
Federal Money........... 27
Application of Federal Money 29
Addition of Federal Mo-
  ney................. 30
Subtraction of Federal Mo-
  ney................. ib.
Multiplication of Federal Mo-
  ney................. 31
Division of Federal Money.. 32
Promiscuous Questions in
  Federal Money......... 34
Federal Addition.........
Compound Addition....... 40
Application of Compound Ad-
  dition............... 41
Compound Subtraction.... 43
Application of Compound
  Subtraction........... 44
Reduction................ 47
Application of Reduction... 49
Compound Multiplication.. 52
Compound Division....... 54
Compound Fractions...... 55
Decimal Fractions........ 56
Addition of Decimal Frac-
  tions................ ib.
Subtraction of Decimal Frac-
  tions................ 57
Multiplication of Decimal
  Fractions of Decimal Fractions

Reduction of Decimal Frac-
  tions................ 58
Rule of Three Direct...... 62
Single Rule of Three Inverse 67
Single Rule of Questions in Di-
  rect Rule of Three..... 69
Promiscuous and Inverse Proportion 71
Vulgar Fractions......... 74
Practice Trett........... 76
Tare and Tret...........
Interest on Notes, Bonds, &c. 84
Interest on Notes........ 85
Compound Interest....... 93
Discount, Commission, and
  Exchange............. 94
Insurance............... 96
Brokerage.............. 101
Practice................ 103
Tare and Tret........... ib.
Reduction of Vulgar Frac-
  tions................ 109
Addition of Vulgar Frac-
  tions................ 110
Subtraction of Vulgar Frac-
  tions................ 111
Multiplication of Vulgar
  Fractions............. ib.
Division of Vulgar Frac-
  tions................ 112
Rule of Three Direct in Vul-
  gar Fractions.......... 113
Rule of Three Inverse in
  Vulgar Fractions....... 114
Application of Vulgar Frac-
  tions................ ib.
Involution............... 115
Evolution of the Square... 116
Extraction of the Square
  Root................
Demonstration of the Square
  Root................ ib.
Application of the Square
  Root................ 119

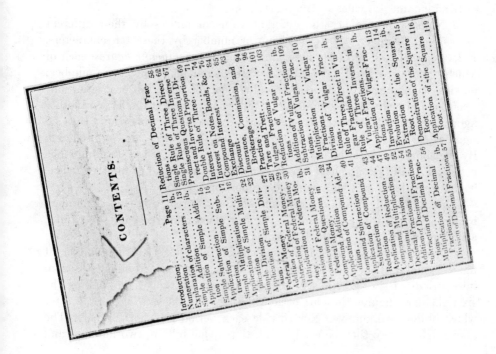

Arithmetic.

INTRODUCTION.

a Arithmetic is the Art, or Science, which treats of numbers, and consists of two kinds, *theoretical* and *practical.*

b The THEORY of Arithmetic explains the nature and quality of numbers, and demonstrates the reasons of practical operations.

c PRACTICAL ARITHMETIC shows the method of working by numbers, so as to be most useful and expeditious for business.

The first thing which should engage the attention of the learner, is

NUMERATION,

With which he should be well acquainted, before entering upon the study of the fundamental rules of Arithmetic.

d Numeration teaches the different value of figures by their different places, and to read or write any sum or number by these ten characters, 1, 2, 3, 4, 5, 6, 7, 8, 9, 0. The first nine are called *significant figures,* each of which standing by itself, invariably expresses a particular or certain number; but in a combination of figures, its value depends upon its local situation: thus, 5 standing by itself signifies *five;* but when placed at the left of another figure, or 0, it *e*] is increased in value, in a tenfold proportion; thus 50 signifies *ten times five,* or *fifty;* and 500, *ten times fifty,* or *five hundred.* By the above example the use of the cipher is obvious. When standing alone it has no signification; but when placed at the right hand of another figure, it increases that figure in a ten-fold proportion.

The value of figures in conjunction, and how to read any sum or number, by giving to each figure its proper value, will be rendered easy, by careful attention to the [table on the following page].

In order to assist the learner in enumeration, when the *f*] number of figures is large, the following directions may be of use. Point off the sum into periods of six figures each, commencing at the right hand, calling the six right hand figures the *unit* period, the next six the *million* period, after which billion, trillion, &c. Next divide each period into half periods. The above figures may then be easily read, thus—One billion, two hundred and

TABLE.

Billions	Hundred thousand of millions	Ten thousand of millions	Thousand millions	Hundred millions	Ten millions	Millions	Hundred thousands	Ten thousands	Thousands	Hundreds	Tens	Units
1,	2	6	4,	0	7	9,	4	9	8,	3	4	5

sixty-four thousand and seventy nine million, four hundred and ninety-eight thousand, three hundred and forty-five.

Thus by the use of ten characters the whole operation in Arithmetic is performed, and every thing may be reckoned which can be numbered.

After the foregoing table has been carefully studied, and is well understood, the learner will do well to write a few figures upon his slate, and enumerate them,. without looking at the table, gradually increasing the number till·he is able to read at least ten or twelve figures. He may then write the following numbers in figures:—

Six hundred and twenty five.

Three thousand two hundred and forty nine.

One hundred and twenty thousand eight hundred and forty.

{ Two millions, three hundred and twenty-seven thousand, six hundred and thirty-four.

{ Seven hundred and sixty-nine thousand, four hundred twenty-four millions, two hundred and three thousand, five hundred and twenty-eight.

{ Two billions, three hundred twenty-one thousand, nine hundred and three millions, sixty-five thousand, one hundred and forty-three.

Explanation of the Characters made use of in this Work.

= The sign of equality; as 100 cts. = to 1 dollar

+ The sign of addition; as $4 + 5 =$ to 9. That is, four added to five are equal to nine.

— The sign of subtraction; as $9 - 5 = 4$. That is, five taken from nine leaves four.

× The sign of multiplication; as $5 \times 4 = 20$. That is, four times five are equal to twenty.

÷ or) (The sign of division; as 4)20(5, or $20 \div 4 = 5$. That is, twenty

9

divided by four, the quotient is five.

: :: : The sign of proportion; or 2 : 4 :: 6 : 12. That is, as two is to four, so is six to twelve.

FUNDAMENTAL RULES OF ARITHMETIC.

g These are four, *Addition, Subtraction, Multiplication,* and *Division;* they may be either simple or compound.

h They are called *principal,* or *fundamental rules,* because all other rules and operations in arithmetic, are the various uses and repetitions of these four rules.

QUESTIONS.

a What is Arithmetic?

b What is the theory of Arithmetic?

c What is practical Arithmetic?

d What is Numeration?

e How are figures increased in value by being placed at the left hand of another figure or cipher?

f What directions are given to facilitate the reading of figures?

g What are the fundamental rules of Arithmetic?

h Why are they called principal or fundamental rules?

SIMPLE ADDITION.

a Simple Addition is the putting together of two or more numbers of the same denomination, so as to make them one whole number, called *sum*, or *amount*.

RULE.

b Place the numbers to be added one under another, with units under units, tens under tens, &c. and draw a line below them.

c Begin the addition with the unit column, and having added all the figures, consider how many tens are contained *d*] in their sum, and placing the excess under the unit column, carry as many to the next column as there are tens in the one added. Proceed in like manner to add the other columns, carrying as before, and set down the full sum of the last column.

PROOF

e Reckon the figures from the top downwards, and if the work be right, the amount of the last addition will correspond with the first.

f Note.—The reason for carrying for *ten* in all simple numbers, will be evident from what has been taught in Numeration. It is because 1 in a superior column, is equal to 10 in the inferior: thus, 1, by itself, is one; but place it in a superior column, or, which is the same thing, place a cipher at the right hand of it, thus 10, and it is ten.

ADDITION AND SUBTRACTION TABLE.

1	2	3	4	5	6	7	8	9	10	11	12
2	4	5	6	7	8	9	10	11	12	13	14
3	5	6	7	8	9	10	11	12	13	14	15
4	6	7	8	9	10	11	12	13	14	15	16
5	7	8	9	10	11	12	13	14	15	16	17
6	8	9	10	11	12	13	14	15	16	17	18
7	9	10	11	12	13	14	15	16	17	18	19
8	10	11	12	13	14	15	16	17	18	19	20
9	11	12	13	14	15	16	17	18	19	20	21
10	12	13	14	15	16	17	18	19	20	21	22

When you would add two numbers, look for one of them in the left hand column, and the other at top; and under the top number you will find their sum: as 6 and 4 are 10.

When you would subtract, find the number to be subtracted in the left hand column; in the same line to the right, find the number from which it is to be taken, and directly over it at top, you will find the difference; as 6 taken from 10, leaves 4.

EXAMPLES.

(1)	(2)	(3)
4635	429764	65420276
2463	343043	35067543
1650	976436	76424675
6784	637580	34647890
15532	2386823	211560384 Sum or am't.
15532	2386823	211560384 Proof.

(4)	(5)	(6)
947634	6879476	3754589465
765427	4035204	7436062741
231032	7694346	3567453587
421543	5960465	9432785043
634689	2347653	4763241635
724576	4600764	5037856342

(7)	(8)	(9)
5434275	64	6407564
640350	245	54367
24766	4357	540374
3453	27564	796
646	154034	3547
34	4734565	24345
1	26785630	9427654

APPLICATION.

1. Suppose a farm to produce 340 bushels of wheat, 1746 bushels of corn, 239 bushels of oats: what is the whole product of the farm?   Ans. 2325.

2. Suppose you freight a boat with 143 barrels of flour, 75 barrels of potatoes, 106 barrels of pork, and 56 barrels of beans: how many barrels would you then have on board?   Ans. 380.

3. A gentleman left his sons 3600 dollars, his daughters 1375 dollars, his grand-children 570 dollars, the American Bible Society 4600 dollars, the Orphan Asylum 500 dollars: what was the amount of his estate?

Ans. $10645.

．
．
．

WARREN COLBURN

Warren Colburn (1793–1833) was raised on a farm in Massachusetts.[1] In 1810 his family moved to Pawtucket, where he worked five years in factories to gain experience with machinery. From 1816 to 1820 he attended Harvard, where he excelled at mathematics, and taught school during the winter months. After leaving Harvard he continued teaching for two and a half years in Boston. For the remainder of his life he was superintendent successively at two different manufacturing companies and lectured widely on scientific subjects.

Colburn's mental processes were described as not rapid; he reached conclusions only after patient and painstaking effort. Possibly this accounts in part for his understanding of children's difficulties and for the teachability of his *First Lessons in Arithmetic on the Plan of Pestalozzi, with Some Improvements* (1821). This book in its many editions and revisions is credited with being the most popular arithmetic text ever published. In 1913 it was still selling several thousand copies a year.

The first Colburn selection is from the 1825 edition of *First Lessons.* This is followed by the reprinting of a lecture he gave in 1830 on the teaching of arithmetic.

1. Walter S. Monroe, *Development of Arithmetic as a School Subject,* U.S. Bureau of Education Bulletin no. 10 (Washington, D.C., 1917), pp. 51–56.

First Lessons

IN

ARITHMETIC,

ON THE

PLAN OF PESTALOZZI.

WITH SOME IMPROVEMENTS.

➤➤◆❀◆◄◄

BY WARREN COLBURN.

➤➤◆❀◆◄◄

STEREOTYPED BY T. H. CARTER & CO. BOSTON.

Boston:

PUBLISHED BY CUMMINGS, HILLIARD, & CO.

Sold by Booksellers generally throughout the country.

1825.

PREFACE.

As soon as a child begins to use his senses, nature continually presents to his eyes a variety of objects; and one of the first properties which he discovers, is the relation of number. He intuitively fixes upon *unity* as a measure, and from this he forms the idea of more and less; which is the idea of quantity.

The names of a few of the first numbers are usually learned very early; and children frequently learn to count as far as a hundred before they learn their letters.

As soon as children have the idea of more and less, and the names of a few of the first numbers, they are able to make small calculations. And this we see them do every day about their playthings, and about the little affairs which they are called upon to attend to. The idea of more and less implies addition; hence they will often perform these operations without any previous instruction. If, for example, one child has three apples, and another five, they will readily tell how many they both have; and how many one has more than the other. If a child be requested to bring three apples for each person in the room, he will calculate very readily how many to bring, if the number does not exceed those he has learnt. Again, if a child be requested to divide a number of apples among a certain number of persons, he will contrive a way to do it, and will tell how many each must have. The method which children take to do these things, though always correct, is not always the most expeditious.

The fondness which children usually manifest for these exercises, and the facility with which they perform them; seem to indicate that the science of numbers, to a certain extent, should be among the first lessons taught to them.[1]

To succeed in this, however, it is necessary rather to furnish occasions for them to exercise their own skill in performing examples, than to give them rules. They should be allowed to pursue their own method first, and then they should be made to observe and explain it, and if it was not the best, some improvement should be suggested. By following this mode, and making the examples gradually increase in difficulty; experience proves, that, at an early age, children may be taught a great variety of the most

1. See on this subject two essays, entitled *Juvenile Studies,* in the Prize Book of the Latin school, Nos. I and II. Published by Cummings & Hilliard, 1820 and 1821.

15

useful combinations of numbers.

Few exercises strengthen and mature the mind so much as arithmetical calculations, if the examples are made sufficiently simple to be understood by the pupil; because a regular, though simple process of reasoning is requisite to perform them, and the results are attended with certainty.

The idea of number is first acquired by observing sensible objects. Having observed that this quality is common to all things with which we are acquainted, we obtain an abstract idea of number. We first make calculations about sensible objects; and we soon observe, that the same calculations will apply to things very dissimilar; and finally, that they may be made without reference to any particular things. Hence from particulars, we establish general principles, which serve as the basis of our reasonings, and enable us to proceed step by step, from the most simple to the more complex operations. It appears, therefore, that mathematical reasoning proceeds as much upon the principle of analytic induction, as that of any other science.

Examples of any kind upon abstract numbers, are of very little use, until the learner has discovered the principle from practical examples. They are more difficult in themselves, for the learner does not see their use; and therefore does not so readily understand the question. But questions of a practical kind, if judiciously chosen, show at once what the combination is, and what is to be effected by it. Hence the pupil will much more readily discover the means by which the result is to be obtained. The mind is also greatly assisted in the operations by reference to sensible objects. When the pupil learns a new combination by means of abstract examples, it very seldom happens that he understands practical examples more easily for it, because he does not discover the connexion, until he has performed several practical examples and begins to generalize them.

After the pupil comprehends an operation, abstract examples are useful, to exercise him, and make him familiar with it. And they serve better to fix the principle, because they teach the learner to generalize.

From the above observations, and from his own experience, the author has been induced to publish this treatise; in which he has pursued the following plan, which seemed to him the most agreeable to the natural progress of the mind.

GENERAL VIEW OF THE PLAN.

Every combination commences with practical examples. Care has been taken to select such as will aptly illustrate the combination, and assist the imagination of the pupil in performing it. In most instances, immediately after the practical, abstract examples are placed, containing the same numbers and the same operations, that the pupil may then more easily observe

16

the connexion. The instructer should be careful to make the pupil observe the connexion. After these are a few abstract examples, and then practical questions again.

The numbers are small, and the questions so simple, that almost any child of five or six years old is capable of understanding more than half the book, and those of seven or eight years old can understand the whole of it.

The examples are to be performed in the mind, or by means of sensible objects, such as beans, nuts, &c. or by means of the plate at the end of the book. The pupil should first perform the examples in his own way, and then be made to observe and tell how he did them, and why he did them so.[2]

The use of the plates is explained in the Key at the end of the book. Several examples in each section are performed in the Key, to show the method of solving them. No answers are given in the book, except where it is necessary to explain something to the pupil. Most of the explanations are given in the Key; because pupils generally will not understand any explanation given in a book, especially at so early an age. The instructer must, therefore, give the explanation *viva voce*. These, however, will occupy the instructer but a very short time.

The first section contains addition and subtraction, the second multiplication. The third section contains division. In this section the pupil learns the first principles of fractions and the terms which are applied to them. This is done by making him observe that one is the half of two, the third of three, the fourth of four, &c. and that two is two thirds of three, two fourths of four, two fifths of five, &c.

The fourth section commences with multiplication. In this the pupil is taught to repeat a number a certain number of times, and a part of another

2. It is remarkable, that a child, although he is able to perform a variety of examples which involve addition, subtraction, multiplication, and division, recognises no operation but addition. Indeed, if we analyze these operations when we perform them in our minds, we shall find that they all reduce themselves to addition. They are only different ways of applying the same principle. And it is only when we use an artificial method of performing them, that they take a different form.

If the following questions were proposed to a child, his answers would be, in substance, like those annexed to the questions. How much is five less than eight? Ans. Three. Why? because five and three are eight. What is the difference between five and eight? Ans. Three. Why? because five and three are eight. If you divide eight into two parts, such that one of the parts may be five, what will the other be? Ans. Three. Why? because five and three are eight.

How much must you give for four apples at two cents apiece? Ans. Eight cents. Why? because two and two are four, and two are six, and two are eight.

How many apples, at two cents apiece, can you buy for eight cents? Ans. Four. Why? because two and two are four, and two are six, and two are eight.

We shall be further convinced of this if we observe that the same table serves for addition and subtraction; and another table which is formed by *addition*, serves both for multiplication and division. In this treatise the same plate serves for the four operations.

This remark shows the necessity of making the pupil attend to his manner of performing the examples and of explaining to him the difference between them.

time. In the second part of this section the pupil is taught to change a certain number of twos into threes, threes into fours, &c.

In the fifth section the pupil is taught to find ½, ⅓, ¼, &c. and ⅔, ¾, ⅘, &c. of numbers, which are exactly divisible into these parts. This is only an extension of the principle of fractions, which is contained in the third section.

In the sixth section the pupil learns to tell of what number any number, as 2, 3, 4, &c. is one half, one third, one fourth, &c.; and also, knowing ⅔, ¾, ⅖, &c. of a number, to find that number.

These combinations contain all the most common and most useful operations of vulgar fractions. But being applied only to numbers which are exactly divisible into these fractional parts, the pupil will observe no principles but multiplication and division, unless he is told of it. In fact, fractions contain no other principle. The examples are so arranged, that almost any child of six or seven years old will readily comprehend them. And the questions are asked in such a manner, that, if the instructer pursues the method explained in the Key, it will be almost impossible for the pupil to perform any example without understanding the reason of it. Indeed, in every example which he performs, he is obliged to go through a complete demonstration of the principle by which he does it; and at the same time he does it in the simplest way possible. These observations apply to the remaining part of the book.

These principles are sufficient to enable the pupil to perform almost all kinds of examples that ever occur. He will not, however, be able to solve questions in which it is necessary to take fractional parts of unity, though the principles are the same.

After section sixth, there is a collection of miscellaneous examples, in which are contained almost all the kinds that usually occur. There are none, however, which the principles explained are not sufficient to solve.

In section eight and the following, fractions of unity are explained, and, it is believed, so simply as to be intelligible to most pupils of seven or eight years of age. The operations do not differ materially from those in the preceding sections. There are some operations, however, peculiar to fractions. The two last plates are used to illustrate fractions.

When the pupil is made familiar with all the principles contained in this book, he will be able to perform all examples, in which the numbers are so small, that the operations may be performed in the mind. Afterwards he has only to learn the application of figures to these operations, and his knowledge of arithmetic will be complete.

The Rule of Three, and all the other rules which are usually contained in our arithmetics, will be found useless. The examples under these rules will be performed upon general principles with much greater facility, and with a greater degree of certainty.

The following are some of the principal difficulties which a child has to encounter in learning arithmetic, in the usual way, and which are seldom overcome. First, the examples are so large, that the pupil can form no conception of the numbers themselves; therefore it is impossible for him to comprehend the reasoning upon them. Secondly, the first examples are usually abstract numbers. This increases the difficulty very much, for even if the numbers were so small, that the pupil could comprehend them, he would discover but very little connexion between them, and practical examples. Abstract numbers, and the operations upon them, must be learned from practical examples; there is no such thing as deriving practical examples from those which are abstract, unless the abstract have been first derived from those which are practical. Thirdly, the numbers are expressed by figures, which, if they were used only as a contracted way of writing numbers, would be much more difficult to be understood at first, than the numbers written at length in words. But they are not used merely as words, they require operations peculiar to themselves. They are, in fact, a new language, which the pupil has to learn. The pupil, therefore, when he commences arithmetic is presented with a set of *abstract* numbers, written with *figures*, and so large that he has not the least conception of them even when expressed in *words*. From these he is expected to learn what the figures signify, and what is meant by addition, subtraction, multiplication, and division; and at the same time how to perform these operations with figures. The consequence is, that he learns only one of all these things, and that is, how to perform these operations on figures. He can perhaps translate the figures into words, but this is useless since he does not understand the words themselves. Of the effect produced by the four fundamental operations he has not the least conception.

After the abstract examples a few practical examples are usually given, but these again are so large that the pupil cannot reason upon them, and consequently he could not tell whether he must add, subtract, multiply, or divide, even if he had an adequate idea of what these operations are.

The common method, therefore, entirely reverses the natural process; for the pupil is expected to learn general principles, before he has obtained the particular ideas of which they are composed.

The usual mode of proceeding is as follows. The pupil learns a rule, which, to the man that made it, was a general principle; but with respect to *him*, and often times to the instructer himself, it is so far from it, that it hardly deserves to be called even a mechanical principle. He performs the examples, and makes the answers agree with those in the book, and so presumes they are right. He is soon able to do this with considerable facility, and is then supposed to be master of the rule. He is next to apply his rule to practical examples, but if he did not find the examples under the rule, he would never so much as mistrust they belonged to it. But finding them there, he applies his rule to them, and obtains the answers, which are in the book, and this satisfies him that they are right. In this manner he proceeds from rule to rule through the book.

When an example is proposed to him, which is not in the book, his sagacity is exercised, not in discovering the operations necessary to solve it; but in comparing it with the examples which he has performed before, and endeavoring to discover some analogy between it and them, either in the sound, or in something else. If he is fortunate enough to discover any such analogy, he finds what rule to apply, and if he has not been deceived in tracing the analogy, he will probably solve the question. His knowledge of the principles of his rules, is so imperfect, that he would never discover to which of them the example belongs if he did not trace it by some analogy, to the examples which he had found under it.

These observations do not apply equally to all; for some will find the right course themselves, whatever obstacles be thrown in their way. But they apply to the greater part; and it is probable that there are very few who have not experienced more or less inconvenience from this mode of proceeding. Almost all, who have ever fully understood arithmetic, have been obliged to learn it over again in their own way. And it is not too bold an assertion to say, that no man ever actually learned mathematics in any other method, than by analytic induction; that is, by learning the principles by the examples he performs; and not by learning principles first, and then discovering by them how the examples are to be performed.

In forming and arranging the several combinations the author has received considerable assistance from the system of Pestalozzi. He has not however had an opportunity of seeing Pestalozzi's own work on this subject, but only a brief outline of it by another. The plates also are from Pestalozzi. In selecting and arranging the examples to illustrate these combinations, and in the manner of solving questions generally, he has received no assistance from Pestalozzi.

Arithmetic.

Part I.

SECTION I.

A.[1] 1. How many thumbs have you on your right hand? how many on your left? how many on both together?

2. How many hands have you?

3. If you have two nuts in one hand and one in the other, how many have you in both?

4. How many fingers have you on one hand?

5. If you count the thumb with the fingers, how many will it make?

6. If you shut your thumb and one finger and leave the rest open, how many will be open?

7. If you have two cents in one hand, and two in the other, how many have you in both?

8. James has two apples, and William has three; if James gives his apples to William, how many will William have?

9. If you count all the fingers on one hand, and two on the other, how many will there be?

10. George has three cents, and Joseph has four; how many have they both together?

11. Robert gave five cents for an orange, and two for an apple, how many did he give for both?

12. If a custard cost six cents, and an apple two cents; how many cents will it take to buy an apple and a custard?

13. If you buy a pint of nuts for five cents, and an orange for three cents, how many cents would you give for both? how many more for the nuts than for the orange?

14. If an ounce of figs is worth six cents, and a half a pint of cherries is worth three cents; how much are they both worth?

15. Dick had five plums, and John gave him four more; how many had he then?

1. For the manner of solving questions, and the explanation of the plates, see the key at the end of the book. The first questions in this section are intended for very young children. It will be well for the instructer to give a great many more of this kind. —Older pupils may omit these.

16. How many fingers have you on both hands?

17. How many fingers and thumbs have you on both hands?

18. If you had six marbles in one hand, and four in the other; how many would you have in the one, more than in the other? how many would you have in both hands?

19. David had seven nuts, and gave three of them to George, how many had he left?

20. Two boys, James and Robert, played at marbles; when they began, they had seven apiece, and when they had done, James had won four; how many had each then?

21. A boy, having eleven nuts, gave away three of them, how many had he left?

22. If you had eight cents, and your papa should give you five more, how many would you have?

23. A man bought a sheep for eight dollars, and a calf for seven dollars, what did he give for both?

24. A man bought a barrel of flour for eight dollars, and sold it for four dollars more then he gave for it; how much did he sell it for?

25. A man bought a hundred weight of sugar for nine dollars, and a barrel of flour for seven dollars, how much did he give for the whole?

26. A man bought three barrels of cider for eight dollars, and ten bushels of apples for nine dollars; how much did he give for the whole?

27. A man bought a firkin of butter for twelve dollars, but, being damaged, he sold it again for eight dollars; how much did he lose?

28. A man bought three sheep for fifteen dollars, but could not sell them again for so much by eight dollars; how much did he sell them for?

29. A man bought sixteen pounds of coffee, and lost seven pounds of it as he was carrying it home, how much had he left?

30. A man bought nineteen pounds of sugar, and having lost a part of it, he found he had nine pounds left; how much had he lost?

31. A man owing fifteen dollars, paid nine dollars of it, how much did he then owe?

32. A man owing seventeen dollars, paid all but seven dollars; how much did he pay?

    B. 1. Two and one are how many?

2. Two and two are how many?

3. Three and two are how many?

4. Four and two are how many?

5. Five and two are how many?

6. Six and two are how many?

7. Seven and two are how many?

8. Eight and two are how many?

9. Nine and two are how many?

10. Ten and two are how many?
11. Two and three are how many?
12. Three and three are how many?
13. Four and three are how many?
14. Five and three are how many?
15. Six and three are how many?
16. Seven and three are how many?
17. Eight and three are how many?
18. Nine and three are how many?
19. Ten and three are how many?
20. Two and four are how many?
21. Three and four are how many?
22. Four and four are how many?
23. Five and four are how many?
24. Six and four are how many?
25. Seven and four are how many?
26. Eight and four are how many?
27. Nine and four are how many?
28. Ten and four are how many?
29. Two and five are how many?
30. Three and five are how many?
31. Four and five are how many?
32. Five and five are how many?
33. Six and five are how many?
34. Seven and five are how many?
35. Eight and five are how many?
36. Nine and five are how many?
37. Ten and five are how many?
38. Two and six are how many?
39. Three and six are how many?
40. Four and six are how many?
41. Five and six are how many?
42. Six and six are how many?
43. Seven and six are how many?
44. Eight and six are how many?
45. Nine and six are how many?
46. Ten and six are how many?
47. Two and seven are how many?
48. Three and seven are how many?
49. Four and seven are how many?
50. Five and seven are how many?
51. Six and seven are how many?

.
.
.

23

Teaching of Arithmetic

By Warren Colburn

I have been requested to address the convention on the subject of teaching arithmetic. I have accepted the invitation with extreme diffidence, believing there would be many gentlemen present much more competent to this task than myself. The subject is certainly an important one in every point of view, whether we consider its application to the affairs of life, or its effect as a discipline of the mind, or the time which is usually devoted to it.

With regard to its application, there are very few persons, either male or female, arrived at years of discretion, who have not occasions daily to make use of arithmetic in some form or other in the ordinary routine of business. And the person the most ready in calculation is much the most likely to succeed in business of any kind. As our country becomes more thickly peopled, and competition in the various branches of business becomes greater, and further progress is made in the arts, and new arts are discovered, knowledge of all kinds is brought into requisition; and none more so than that of arithmetic, and the higher branches of mathematics, of which arithmetic is the foundation.

Arithmetic, when properly taught, is acknowledged by all to be very important as a discipline of the mind; so much so that even if it had no practical application which should render it valuable on its own account, it would still be well worth while to bestow a considerable portion of time on it for this purpose alone. This is a very important consideration, though a secondary one compared with its practical utility.

The fact that the study of arithmetic is allowed to occupy so large a portion of time in all our schools shows sufficiently the degree of importance attached to the subject by all classes of people. And that it does occupy so large a portion of time is another very strong reason for attention to the mode of teaching it, that the time may be employed to the best advantage.

This is the text of an address delivered by Warren Colburn before the American Institute of Instruction in Boston, August 1830. It is reprinted here from the *Elementary School Teacher* 12 (June 1912): 463–80.

As the demand for all kinds of knowledge is increasing, and new branches of learning are almost daily brought within the compass of the ordinary means of education, it becomes highly important that those kinds which require considerable labor for their acquirement should be made to occupy as little time as may be consistently without sacrificing the advantage of learning them well.

It may not seem improper here to introduce a few remarks concerning the relative advantages of the old and new systems of teaching arithmetic. For though most teachers at the present time prefer the new system, and the majority of the community are decidedly in favor of it, yet there are persons, and some whose opinions are entitled to high respect, who strongly object to the new system and give a decided preference to the old. To such we ought at least to be able to give a reason why we prefer the new system.

For this we shall appeal to facts; they are stubborn things, and the side which they favor must prevail. It must be allowed by all that previous to the introduction of the new system fewer persons learned arithmetic than at present. At least, fewer made any considerable progress in it. Very few females pretended to study it at all, and the number of either sex that advanced much beyond the four primary rules was very inconsiderable. And the learner was very seldom found who could give a satisfactory reason for any operation which he performed. The study of it used to be put off to a very late period. Scholars under twelve or thirteen years of age were not considered capable of learning it, and generally they were not capable. Many persons were obliged to leave school before they were old enough to commence the study of it.

At present the study of arithmetic is very general with both sexes and among all classes. It is taught to advantage even to the very youngest scholars in school and made to fill a portion of time which used to be left unoccupied. And most scholars now have a thorough knowledge of arithmetic at an earlier age than it used formerly to be commenced. And scholars who cannot give a satisfactory reason for their operations are now as rare as were formerly those who could.

But perhaps the advocate for the old system will say, "I grant that it was a little more difficult, and on that very account it was a better exercise for the mind, and when it was learned, it was learned more thoroughly." But in this we shall again find the facts on our side. It cannot be pretended that those who did not study it at all had their minds exercised by it; nor can much more be claimed for those who pretended to learn it. In those two classes, we have seen, was comprehended a very large proportion of the scholars. And with regard to the remainder, a very little observation will show that the advantage is in favor of the new system. I believe most teachers who have understood and taught well the new system will give it as their opinion that most scholars who have studied arithmetic well have

25

learned more of other things, and learned them better, than they would have done if they had not studied arithmetic at all or had studied it the old way. And in this class of teachers we shall find a great number who have been successful both on the old and new systems. It will pass for no argument at all, at the present time, for a man, however well skilled in arithmetic he may be himself, to come forward and say, "I have tried your system, and could not succeed with it at all; therefore it is good for nothing." The reply to such a one is, "You have not taken the trouble to understand the system; therefore you have not given it a fair trial." And we are sure that a sufficient number of successful teachers on the new system can be produced to justify such an answer. Those who do not believe that pupils taught by the new system are as ready and expert in the use of figures and in calculation generally as those taught in the old way have only to go into the best schools taught on the two systems and examine for themselves. Unless they will do this, they will not be convinced; and if they do, we do not fear for the result.

We believe also that we have reason on our side as well as facts. By the old system the learner was presented with a rule which told him how to perform certain operations on figures, and when these were done he would have the proper result. But no reason was given for a single step. His first application of his rule was on a set of abstract numbers, so large that he could not reason on them if he had been disposed to do so. And when he had got through and obtained the result, he understood neither what it was nor the use of it. Neither did he know that it was the proper result, but was obliged to rely wholly on the book, or more frequently on the teacher. As he began in the dark, so he continued; and the results of his calculation seemed to be obtained by some magical operation rather than by the inductions of reason.

By the new system the learner commences with practical examples on which the numbers are so small that he can easily reason upon them. And the reference to sensible objects gives him an idea at once of the kind of result which he ought to produce and suggests to him the method of proceeding necessary to obtain it. By this he is thrown immediately upon his own resources, and is compelled to exert his own powers. At the same time he meets with no greater difficulty than he feels himself confident to overcome. In this way every step is accompanied with complete demonstration. Every new example increases his powers and his confidence. And most scholars soon acquire such a habit of thinking and reasoning for themselves that they will not be satisfied with anything which they do not understand in any of their studies.

Instead of studying rules in the book, the reason of which he does not understand, the scholar makes his own rules; and his rules are a generalization of his own reasoning, and in a way agreeable to his own associations.

We conclude, then, that the new system is preferable to the old. We now come to the question, What is the best mode of teaching the new system? This is a question frequently asked and frequently discussed. In the way that the question is usually considered, it does not admit of an answer. It may be briefly stated to be his who teaches the best. But then it will be found to be the best only in his hands. For any other teacher, another method would be better; so that the method must be suited to the teacher; and the teacher again, to be successful, must adapt his method to the scholar. For until mankind are all made to think alike, and act alike, and look alike, it will be worse than useless—it will be absolutely injurious—to endeavor to make them teach alike or learn alike: I mean in the detail. For there are a few general principles, some of which I shall endeavor by and by to explain, which are applicable to all and must be attended to by all who wish to be successful in teaching. The best method for any particular instructor is that by which he can teach the best. It is that which is suited to his particular mode of thinking, to his manners, to his temper and disposition; and generally, also, it will be modified by the character of his school. So that if I am to give an instructor particular directions with regard to teaching, I must see him in his school and see him teach. Then my instructions would not tend to change his manner, but to improve it if it were faulty.

Teachers are very apt to pride themselves upon some plan which they have discovered for keeping up the attention of the scholars, or of directing their attention to some important point, or of making them remember certain things, or of explaining certain difficult subjects, or of exciting emulation among their pupils, and many other things of the like kind—which, they suppose, if it were generally known and adopted, would be a great improvement, not being aware that the thing is peculiarly adapted to themselves, and to themselves only, and that if another person were to attempt the same thing he would fail. Many have felt so much confidence in improvements of this kind, mistaking a particular case in which they have been successful for a general principle, that they have been at the pains to prepare books adapted to those particular modes, with the greatest expectations of success. But such books always fail of general success, not because the methods were not good and successful in the authors' hands, but because others cannot enter into the spirit of them. Such books, if they are not used in precisely the way that the authors intended, cannot be used at all.

By these remarks, however, I would by no means discourage any teacher from communicating his method to others. On the contrary, I would encourage everyone to do it, whatever his methods may be. For though others should not think proper to adopt them exactly, yet they may frequently draw hints from them to improve their own. And the very fact of a teacher's giving so much attention to his own methods as to be able to explain them to others will be very useful to himself, and often the cause of improvement in them. But no one should feel disappointed because others do not adopt his plans; neither should he despise the plans of others, though he does not choose to adopt them himself.

Without giving any very particular directions with regard to modes of teaching, I will state a few general principles that will apply to almost all modes; and whoever will pursue his own mode according to them, will teach successfully. Most of them are applicable to all other subjects as well as to arithmetic. And, if in the course of the lectures, you may have heard them from others, or may hear them hereafter—which I dare say will be the case —they will not be injured by the repetition.

The first precept which I shall enjoin upon you is to teach but one thing at a time. This is a grand point in arithmetic and in all other branches. Select the principle which you intend to teach the pupil, and apply yourself strictly and exclusively to that, until he is master of it. For as certainly as you endeavor to fix upon his mind two or more things at once, you distract his attention and blend the things together in his mind, so that he does not get a distinct idea of either; and neither of them will be learned well. In teaching any one point, therefore, all others should be kept entirely out of sight, except those which he already knows. These may be referred to at any time for illustration, or for showing the connection. Be sure that the pupil is master of the principle before he is allowed to leave it, let it require what time it will, unless he becomes weary of it and his mind gets confused; in which case, leave it entirely for the present, and take it up afresh at some other time. If the learner is allowed to pass from one point to another when the first is but partially learned, he soon acquires a habit of learning things imperfectly, which it is very difficult afterward to break up. It begets habits of inattention, of thinking loosely and carelessly, and of not fixing anything in his mind as it should be. And if the teacher thinks to remedy this evil by constantly calling up those things which have been poorly learned, he will find himself disappointed; for he will only confirm the habit instead of curing it.

Almost every instructor succeeds in teaching some things, and almost everyone partially fails in some things; that is, there are some things which he does not teach to his own satisfaction. If he will refer to them, he will perceive that in those things in which he does succeed, his scholars are made thorough as they proceed; and that he is in the habit of seizing the important points, and keeping them distinct, both in his own mind and in the minds of his pupils. But in those things in which he does not succeed, he lets them pass from step to step, without becoming perfect in any of them, and he is probably endeavoring to make up the deficiency by a constant repetition of the things which they have so passed. With many teachers, English grammar would be a familiar illustration of the latter mode of proceeding. The old method of teaching grammar was very faulty in this respect. The learner was first required to commit the grammar to memory, without understanding it at all, or being expected to understand it. And then he was put to parsing all parts of speech at once. Of the success of that mode many of you, I dare say, are able to judge from experience in learning, if not in teaching by it. Many persons still find the subject a difficult one to teach, and the difficulty will generally be found to arise chiefly from the fault I have been speaking of; that is, of endeavoring to teach too many things at once.

In arithmetic this difficulty does not happen exactly in the same way, though in this it is very likely to happen. In grammar, teachers frequently endeavor purposely to teach several things at once; but in arithmetic they do not do it intentionally. They endeavor to teach only one thing at a time; but they are in too great haste to get along, and they do not make their scholars perfect in one thing before they let them pass to another. Hence there is necessarily a reference to what is past while what is past is still imperfectly understood, and the scholar is kept in continual confusion.

I repeat, therefore, Teach but one thing at a time, and be sure that that one thing be learned before another is attempted. If by mistake the scholar is found to have passed some essential point without learning it, he should be put back to it again and be made to learn it; but on no account should he try to learn it by reference. When such a case has taken place, the scholar will show it by failing to get his lessons, by getting into difficulties too often, and requiring too many explanations. If it cannot readily be discovered what it is that he has neglected, he should be examined backward, until a place is found where he meets with no difficulty, and then let him proceed from that. But it is by far the best way that the scholar should be made thorough as he goes, and it is the only way to be successful. It is also the easiest and most expeditious.

By teaching one thing at a time I would not be understood to mean that the scholar should not study different subjects on the same day. It is necessary for most scholars to be attending to several subjects at the same time; for young persons cannot well be made to apply themselves to the same thing long at a time. A change, therefore, is necessary as a relief to the mind, and a judicious teacher will not keep his pupils upon any one exercise longer than he can keep their attention upon it.

Whatever subject you are teaching, keep this precept in view: to teach only one point of it at once, and apply yourself strictly to that, until the learner is master of it, and then give him another. Be careful, in the selection, to choose the easiest first, and then the next easiest, and so on. And where one thing depends on another, make them follow each other as much as possible in the order of dependence. You cannot always decide, by your own judgment, what is the easiest. This must be discovered by trial on the scholars. It will often be found that the thing which one scholar will learn the easiest first will not be the same for another. Also, what is easiest with one teacher will not always be so with another. Each teacher should satisfy himself, by experiment, what order he succeeds best with, and then pursue it as nearly as he can, varying only when the learner requires it. It is not always necessary to pursue the precise order of the textbook. The order of the book should be followed in preference to any other, unless the teacher feels very sure that some other order succeeds better with him.

The learner should never be told directly how to perform any operation in arithmetic. Much less should he have the operation performed for him. I know it is generally much easier for the teacher, when a scholar finds a question a little too difficult and comes for assistance, either to solve the question for him, or tell him directly how to do it. In the old method this generally was done. Not infrequently the teacher took the question and solved it at home in the evening if he could and gave the scholar the solution the next day to copy into his book. Now by this generally no effect was produced on the scholar, except admiration of the *master's* skill in *ciphering.* He himself was none the wiser for it.

If the learner meets with a difficulty, the teacher, instead of telling him directly how to go on, should examine him and endeavor to discover in what the difficulty consists; and then, if possible, remove it. Perhaps he does not fully understand the question. Then it should be explained to him. Perhaps it depends on some former principle which he has learned but does not readily call to mind. Then he should be put in mind of it. Perhaps it is a little too difficult. Then it should be simplified. This may be done by substituting smaller numbers, or by separating it into parts and making a distinct question of each of the parts. Suppose the question were this: *If 8 men can do a piece of work in 12 days, how long would it take 15 men to do it?* It might be simplified by putting in smaller numbers, thus: *If 2 men can do a piece of work in 3 days, how long would it take 5 men to do it?* If this should still be found too difficult, say, *If 2 men can do a piece of work in 3 days, how long will it take 1 man to do it?* This being answered, say, *If 1 man will do it in 6 days, how long will it take 3 men to do it? In what time would 4 men do it? In what time would five men do it?* By degrees, in some such way as this, lead him to the original question. Some mode of this kind should always be practiced; and by no means should the learner be told directly how to do it, for then the question is lost to him. For when the question is thus solved for him, he is perfectly satisfied with it, and he will give himself no further trouble about the mode in which it is done.

When the learner begins to require assistance too often, it is an indication that something has not been learned thoroughly. He should then go back to some place that he does perfectly understand, and review.

All illustrations should be given by practical examples having reference to sensible objects. Most people use the reverse of this principle and think to simplify practical examples by means of abstract ones. For instance, if you propose to a child this simple question: *George had five cents, and his father gave him three more, how many had he then?* I have found that most persons think to simplify such practical examples by putting them into an abstract form and saying, *How many are five and three?* But this question is already in the simplest form that it can be. The only way that it can be made easier is to put in smaller numbers. If the child can count, this will hardly be necessary. No explanation more simple than the question itself can be given, and none is required. The reference to sensible objects, and to the action of giving, assists the mind of the child in thinking of it, and suggests immediately what operation he must perform; and he sets himself to calculate it. He has not yet learned what the sum of those two numbers is; he is therefore obliged to calculate it in order to answer the question; and he will require some little time to do it. Most persons, when such a question is proposed, do not observe the process going on in the child's mind; but because he does not answer immediately, they think that he does not understand it, and they begin to assist him, as they suppose, and say, How many are five and three? Cannot you tell how many five and three are? Now this latter question is very much more difficult for the child than the original one. Besides, the child would not probably perceive any connection between them. He can very easily understand, and the question itself suggests it to him better than any explanation, that the five cents and three cents are to be counted together; but he does not easily perceive what the abstract numbers five and three have to do with it. This is a process of generalization which it takes children some time to learn.

In all cases, then, especially in the early stages, it will be perplexing and rather injurious to refer the learner from a practical to an abstract question for the purpose of explanation. And it is still worse to tell him the result, and not make him find it himself. If the question is sufficiently simple, he will solve it. And he should be allowed time to do it and not be perplexed with questions or interruptions until he has done it. But if he does not solve the question, it will be because he does not fully comprehend it. And if he cannot be made to comprehend it, the question should be varied, either by varying the numbers, or the objects, or both, until a question is made that he can answer. One being found that he can answer, another should be made a little varied, and then another, and so on, till he is brought back to the one first proposed. It will be better that the question remain unanswered than that the child be told the answer, or assisted in the operation any further than may be necessary to make him fully understand the question.

Some children, when a question is proposed, instead of thinking of it, and trying to solve it, will endeavor to guess at the result. This should be checked immediately.

It has often been asked whether the plates which sometimes accompany

Colburn's *Intellectual Arithmetic,* or anything else of a similar nature, are of any use to the learner. I think myself that they have very little effect upon his progress. At first, before he is familiar with the addition and multiplication tables, some kind of counters seem to be necessary; but it is not important what they are. The plates are very convenient, but I believe the fingers do about as well as anything. If the scholar is allowed any helps of this kind, he should be left to manage them entirely by himself, and in his own way. Any helps by which the work is partly done for the scholar are certainly injurious. It is by his own efforts, that a child is to learn if he learns at all. The teacher cannot learn for him. Neither will he labor himself, if the teacher will endeavor to do the work for him. You might, with as much propriety, expect that his muscles would be strengthened by seeing others exercise in the gymnasium as to expect a child's mind to be strengthened and improved when the teacher does the work for him. The teacher may assist him in understanding the question, but not in the operation— not even in arranging his counters; for to do this, is to do for him the most important part of the solution.

It is best that the learner should be exercised for some time in solving practical questions involving addition and multiplication before he commits to memory the addition and multiplication tables. He should understand the use of them, and be able to make them, before he is required to learn them, and then he should be made to learn them thoroughly. It is not well for a child to commit anything to memory that he does not understand, for he thereby acquires a habit of repeating it without attending to the sense; and it is more difficult to make him attend to the sense afterward, when he repeats it, than if he had not seen it before. At least, this is generally the case. There may be exceptions. I might refer again to the subject of grammar as furnishing the most familiar instance of this. For example, it is very easy for a scholar, when properly taught, to learn the distinction of cases in the pronouns. And yet I have had scholars who had learned their grammar before they came under my care, so as to repeat it by heart, in parsing the word *him,* call it in the nominative case; and still persist in calling it so, after being required to decline it five or six times in succession. Arithmetic, or any other subject, would furnish examples enough of the difficulty of making the scholars attend to the sense sufficiently to understand a rule or principle when they have first committed it without understanding it. But grammar, perhaps, affords the most striking instances of it.

I shall now endeavor to explain a principle which I consider to be a very important one. It is one less generally understood than any that I have mentioned or shall mention. Many teachers have practiced upon it very well without having particularly thought of it. Many of you, I presume, have both thought of it and practiced upon it. But there are many who do not observe it, either in theory or practice. This principle depends on the association of ideas. I shall not enter here into a discussion of the principle of association. I leave it to the metaphysician to determine whether there are any general laws which regulate it or not. I shall confine myself to one simple matter of fact concerning it and the practical consequences to be derived from it.

The fact is this, that two persons never have exactly the same associations of ideas. I mean, they never associate their ideas in exactly the same order. The consequence is that no two persons think of the same proposition alike. Hence a proposition expressed in certain terms may be very clear and intelligible to one person and very obscure or altogether unintelligible to another. And perhaps, with a very slight change of terms, the case would be entirely changed. It would be intelligible to the latter and unintelligible to the former. An explanation which is very clear and lucid to one will often convey no idea at all to another. When a proposition is made for two persons to reason upon, they will often take it up and manage it very differently in their minds. When the subject is such as to admit of demonstration, as is the case with mathematics, they will generally come to the same conclusions. But on other subjects their conclusions will sometimes agree and sometimes not.

There are several practical results to be derived from this. First, it is very important that a teacher should be able readily to trace, not only his own associations, but those of all his pupils, when he hears them recite their lessons. When a proposition or question is made to a scholar, he ought to be able to discover at once whether the scholar understands it or not. If he does not understand it, the teacher should be able to discover the reason why, and then he can apply the remedy. This is to be done only by questioning the scholar, and tracing his associations, and finding what he is thinking about, and how he is thinking about it. Without doing this, the teacher is as likely to perplex the scholar as to assist him by his explanations. And it is a very common thing to see scholars perplexed in this way.

Secondly, when the scholar does not understand the question or proposition, he should be allowed to reason upon it in his own way, and agreeably to his own associations. Whether his way is the best or not, on the whole, it is the best way for him at first, and he ought by no means to be interrupted in it or forced out of it. The judicious teacher will leave him to manage it entirely by himself, and in his own way, if he can. Or if he meets with a little difficulty, but is still in a way that will lead to a proper result, he will apply his aid so as to keep him in his own way. When the scholar has been through the process in his own way, he should be made to explain how he has done it; and if he has not proceeded by the best way, he should be led by degrees into the best way. Many teachers seem not to know that there is more than one way to do a thing, or think of a thing; and if they find a scholar pursuing a method different from their own, they suppose of course he must be wrong, and they check him at once, and endeavor to force him into their way, whether he understands it or not. If such teachers would have patience to listen to their scholars and examine their operations, they would frequently discover very good ways that had never occurred to them before. Nothing is more discouraging to scholars than to interrupt them when they are proceeding by a method which they perfectly comprehend, and which they know to be right; and to endeavor to force them into one which they do not understand, and which is not agreeable to their way of thinking. And nothing gives scholars so much confidence in their own powers and stimulates them so much to use their own efforts as to allow them to pursue their own methods and to encourage them in them.

It is very important for teachers to lead their scholars into the habit of attending to the process going on in their own minds while solving questions, and of explaining how they solve them. Unless the teacher possesses the faculty of tracing the associations of others, he cannot make them do it effectually. But the teacher who does possess this faculty perfectly will get an explanation out of anybody that has any thoughts and can be made to speak on the subject upon which he is questioned. He can take one of his scholars, or any other person, and make him trace out and explain a process of reasoning which has passed in his mind, but of which he was not at all aware, and concerning which, if left to himself, he could give no account. He seems to have the thoughts of his scholars under his control. He will not only find out *what* they are thinking about, and *how* they are thinking of it, but he is able to turn their thoughts into almost any channel he pleases. And it is next to impossible for one person to direct the current of another's thoughts on any subject, unless he knows the channel in which they are already flowing.

This subject also suggests a hint with regard to making books, and especially those for children. The author should endeavor to instruct, by furnishing the learner with occasions for thinking and exercising his own reasoning powers, and he should not endeavor to think and reason for him. It is often very well that there should be a regular course of reasoning in the book on the subject taught; but the learner ought not to be compelled to pursue it, if it can possibly be avoided, until he has examined the subject and come to a conclusion in his own way. Then it is well for him to follow the reasoning of others, and see how they think of it.

I will now say a few words concerning recitations. They are of very great importance in instruction in a great many points of view; and it is very essential that they be well conducted. They are the principal means which the teacher has to know what progress the scholars are making. It is chiefly at recitations that one scholar can compare himself with another; consequently they furnish the most effectual means of promoting emulation. They are an excellent exercise for the scholar, for forming the habit of expressing his ideas properly and readily. The scholar will be likely to learn his lesson more thoroughly when he knows he shall be called upon to explain it. They give him an opportunity to discover whether he understands his subject fully or not, which he will not always be sure of, until he is called upon to give an account of it. Recitations in arithmetic, when properly conducted, produce a habit of quick and ready reckoning on the spur of the occasion, which can be produced in no other way except in the business of life; and then only when the business is of a kind to require constant practice. They are therefore a great help in preparing scholars for business.

Directions concerning recitations must be general. Each teacher must manage the detail of them in his own way.

In the first place, the scholar should be thoroughly prepared before he attempts to recite. No lessons should be received by the teacher that are not well learned. If this is not insisted on, the scholar will soon become careless and inattentive.

It is best that the recitations, both in intellectual and written arithmetic, should be in classes, when practicable. It is best that they should be without the book, and that the scholar should perform the examples from hearing them read by the teacher. Questions that are put out to be solved at the recitation should be solved at the recitation, and not answered from memory. The scholars should frequently be required to explain fully and clearly the steps by which they solve a question and the reasons for them. Recitations should be conducted briskly and not suffered to lag and become dull. The attention of every scholar should be kept on the subject, if possible, so that all shall hear everything that is said. For this it is necessary that the questions pass around quickly, and that no scholar be allowed a longer time to think than is absolutely necessary. If the lesson is prepared as it should be, it will not take the scholar long to give his answer. It is not well to ask one scholar too many questions at a time; for by that there is danger of losing the attention of the rest. It is a good plan, when practicable, so to manage the recitation that every scholar shall endeavor to solve each question that is proposed for solution at the time of recitation. This may sometimes be done by proposing the question without letting it be known who is to answer it until all have had time to solve it, and then calling upon someone for the answer. No further time should be allowed for the solution; but if the scholar so called on is not ready, the question should be immediately put to another in the same manner.

There is one point more which I shall urge, and it is one which I consider the most important of all. It is to make the scholars study. I can give no directions how to do it. Each teacher must do it in his own way, if he does it at all. He who succeeds in making his scholars study will succeed in making them learn, whether he does it by punishing, or hiring, or persuading, or by exciting emulation, or by making the studies so interesting that they do it for the love of it. It is useless for me to say which will produce the best effects upon the scholars; each of you may judge of that for yourselves. But this I say, that he who makes his scholars study will make them learn; and he who does not will not make them learn much or well. There never has been found a royal road to learning of any kind, and I presume there never will be. Or if there should be, I may venture to say that learning so obtained will not be worth the having. It is a law of our nature, and a wise one too, that nothing truly valuable can be obtained without labor.

There are some facilities for learning at the present day, perhaps, which were not formerly known. These serve to render study less irksome, but they do not render it less necessary. They enable the scholar to obtain more knowledge with an equal quantity of labor, but they do not enable him to obtain any valuable knowledge without labor. If scholars were to learn wholly by the assistance of the teacher, without any efforts of their own, they would acquire habits of idleness and inactivity which would be more injurious to them than their learning would be beneficial; and they would be little able to make any progress in learning after leaving school. But the scholar who is made to apply himself closely, and to learn by his own efforts, acquires habits of diligence and perseverance which will be useful to him through life. And he learns (which is of more advantage than the immediate subject of his studies) how to learn by his own efforts, without the aid of a teacher.

I have now briefly noticed what I consider the essential points to be attended to in teaching arithmetic. Many of them, as I observed before, are not peculiar to arithmetic but apply equally to all subjects. And I dare say you will hear some of them much more ably discussed during the course. But there are many essential points of a good instructor that cannot be taught by lecture. This I will not undertake to describe. One point more, however, I will remark: that to teach a subject well, it is necessary for the teacher to understand it well himself, and to take an interest in it; otherwise he will not make it interesting to his scholars.

Allow me to close with a few remarks, expressing, though imperfectly, the interest I feel in the occasion that has brought us together. There have been, in every age, a few persons who have felt the importance of the subject of education. But generally the numbers have been few. The business of teaching, except in great seminaries, has not been considered as one of the most honorable occupations, but rather degraded; so that few persons of talents would engage in it. Even in our own country and age, it has been too much the case that persons with a little learning, and unwilling to work and unfit for anything else, have turned schoolmasters, and have been encouraged in it. They have been encouraged in it because the pay of school teachers, in most instances, has been just sufficient to obtain that class of persons, and no other but one, which, with few exceptions, is not much better. I mean such as engage in the business of teaching for a short time, in order to discharge a few debts previous to entering on a profession.

But a new era, I trust, is now opened upon us. The community at large is beginning to feel the importance of the subject, and to show an interest in it. The fact of there being so many persons, both teachers and others, and many of them from distant parts of the country, collected here on this occasion, is a sufficient proof that the interest is neither small nor confined to one section of the country. A few years ago it would have been impossible to assemble such a number of persons for such a purpose. It seems now to be generally agreed that the business of teaching ought to be considered as a profession; and that the persons engaging in it ought to be instructed expressly for it, as for a profession. And institutions are getting up for that purpose. Your assembling here in this way, for mutual instruction on this important subject, though it will not supply the place of regular institutions for it, will greatly promote the general object and hasten on the period of their adoption. I rejoice, therefore, to see this meeting. Though at present engaged in a pursuit very different from yours, I cheerfully accepted the proposals to deliver a lecture before you; not because I felt that I could do the subject justice, but because I was glad of the opportunity of contributing my mite, however small, to the promotion of so great a cause. I hope, therefore, that you will improve the opportunity you now have of receiving and communicating information, and that you will lay the foundation of a great work of which not only your own immediate neighborhoods, but our country at large, and not our country only, but the whole world, shall feel the influence.

CHARLES DAVIES

Charles Davies (1798–1876) taught mathematics at the United States Military Academy at West Point, at Trinity College in Connecticut, and at Columbia College. He is credited with the first American book on mathematics teaching methods, *The Logic and Utility of Mathematics with the Best Methods of Instruction Explained and Illustrated* (1850), from which the first selections below are taken. He also wrote or translated from the French mathematics texts ranging from primary arithmetic through the calculus. Some of his books were in print well into the twentieth century.

Also included here are the preface and first page of Davies's *University Arithmetic*. The preface contains a description of a reasonably typical graded series of arithmetic texts of the era. While we may now consider arithmetic a rather mundane subject for the university, this book is more sophisticated than the word *arithmetic* suggests. It contains a more thorough section on repeating decimals than most modern texts for teacher training, and it also has a section on continued fractions.

THE

LOGIC AND UTILITY

OF

MATHEMATICS,

WITH THE BEST METHODS OF INSTRUCTION EXPLAINED
AND ILLUSTRATED.

BY CHARLES DAVIES, LL. D.

~~~~~~~~~~~~~~~

NEW YORK:
PUBLISHED BY A. S. BARNES & CO.,
NO. 51 JOHN-STREET.
CINCINNATI:—H. W. DERBY & COMPANY.
1850.

CONTENTS.

***

INTRODUCTION.

PAGE
OBJECTS AND PLAN OF THE WORK...... 11

BOOK I.
LOGIC.

CHAPTER I.

DEFINITIONS—OPERATIONS OF THE MIND—TERMS DEFINED. 27

SECTION
Definitions ...... 1—6
Operations of the Mind concerned in Reasoning ...... 6—13
Abstraction ...... 13—14
Generalization ...... 14—22
Terms—Singular Terms—Common Terms 15
Terms—Common Terms ...... 16—20
Classification 20
Nature of Common Terms 21
Science 22
Art 22

CHAPTER II.

SOURCES AND MEANS OF KNOWLEDGE—INDUCTION...... 41

PAGE
SECTION
Knowledge 23
Facts and Truths ...... 24—27
Intuitive Truths 27
Logical Truths 28
Logic 29
Induction ...... 30—34

CHAPTER III.

DEDUCTION—NATURE OF THE SYLLOGISM—ITS USES AND AP-
PLICATIONS...... Page 54

SECTION
Deduction 34
Propositions ...... 35—40
Syllogism ...... 40—43
Analytical Outline of Deduction ...... 43—67
Aristotle's Dictum ...... 54—61
Distribution and Non-distribution of Terms ...... 61—67
Rules for examining Syllogisms 67
Of Fallacies ...... 68—71
Concluding Remarks ...... 71—75

BOOK II.
MATHEMATICAL SCIENCE.

CHAPTER I.

QUANTITY AND MATHEMATICAL SCIENCE DEFINED—DIFFER-
ENT KINDS OF QUANTITY—LANGUAGE OF MATHEMATICS
EXPLAINED—SUBJECTS CLASSIFIED—USE OF MEASURE
DEFINED—MATHEMATICS A DEDUCTIVE SCIENCE....Page 90

SECTION
Quantity ...... 75—79
Number ...... 79—81
Space ...... 81—87
Analysis ...... 87—91
Language of Mathematics ...... 91—94
Quantity of Mathematics ...... 94—97
Pure Mathematics ...... 97—101
Comparison of Quantities 101
Axioms or Formulas for inferring Equality 102
Axioms or Formulas for inferring Inequality 102

CHAPTER II.

ARITHMETIC—SCIENCE AND ART OF NUMBERS

PAGE
117

SECTION I.

SECTION
First Notions of Numbers ...... 104—107
Idea of Numbers Generalized ...... 107—110
Unity and a Unit Defined 110
Simple and Denominate Numbers ...... 111—113
Alphabet—Word—Grammar 113
Arithmetical Alphabet 114
Spelling and Reading in Addition ...... 115—120
Spelling and Reading in Subtraction ...... 120—129

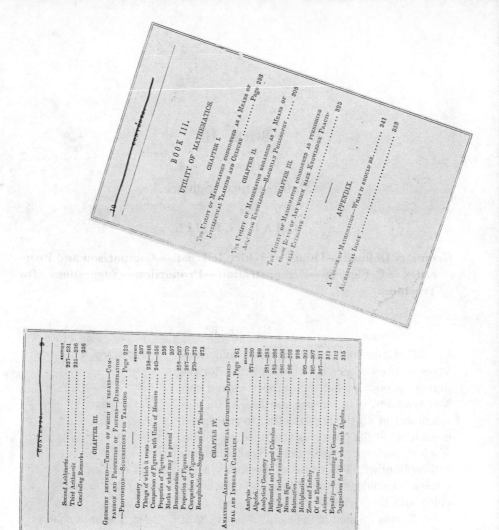

10   CONTENTS.

BOOK III.

UTILITY OF MATHEMATICS.

CHAPTER I.

THE UTILITY OF MATHEMATICS CONSIDERED AS A MEANS OF INTELLECTUAL TRAINING AND CULTURE .... Page 293

CHAPTER II.

THE UTILITY OF MATHEMATICS REGARDED AS A MEANS OF ACQUIRING KNOWLEDGE—BACONIAN PHILOSOPHY 303

CHAPTER III.

THE UTILITY OF MATHEMATICS CONSIDERED AS FURNISHING THOSE RULES OF ART WHICH MAKE KNOWLEDGE PRACTICALLY EFFECTIVE 308

APPENDIX.

A COURSE OF MATHEMATICS 325

ALPHABETICAL INDEX—WHAT IT SHOULD BE 341

.... 353

CONTENTS.   9

	SECTION
Second Arithmetic	227—231
Third Arithmetic	231—236
Concluding Remarks	236

CHAPTER III.

GEOMETRY DEFINED—THINGS OF WHICH IT TREATS—COMPARISON AND PROPERTIES OF FIGURES—DEMONSTRATION—PROPORTION—SUGGESTIONS FOR TEACHING .... Page 223

	SECTION
Geometry	237
Things of which it treats	238—246
Comparison of Figures with Units of Measure	249—256
Properties of Figures	256
Marks of what may be proved	257
Demonstration	258—267
Proportion of Figures	267—270
Comparison of Figures	270—273
Recapitulation—Suggestions for Teachers	273

CHAPTER IV.

ANALYSIS—ALGEBRA—ANALYTICAL GEOMETRY—DIFFERENTIAL AND INTEGRAL CALCULUS .... Page 261

	SECTION
Analysis	271—280
Algebra	280
Analytical Geometry	281—283
Differential and Integral Calculus	282—286
Algebra further considered	286—296
Minus Sign	296—298
Subtraction	298
Multiplication	299—302
Zero and Infinity	302—307
Or the Equation	307—311
Axioms	311
Equality—its meaning in Geometry	312
Suggestions for those who teach Algebra	315

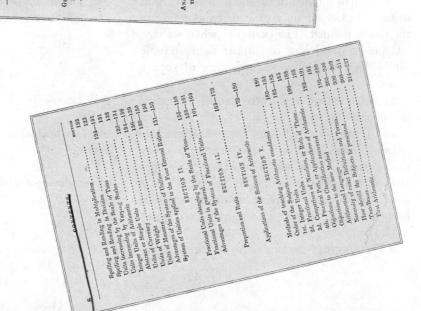

8   CONTENTS.

	SECTION
Spelling and Reading in Multiplication	122
Spelling and Reading in Division	123
Spelling and Reading the Scale of Tens	124—131
Units increasing by Varyed Scales	132
Units Units of Arithmetic	132—134
Integer Units of Arithmetic	134—136
Abstract or Simple Units	136—139
Abstract or Currency	139—150
Units of Weight	150
Units of Measure—Units	151—155
Units of Measure—Ground Rules	
Advances of the System of Units applied to the Four Ground Rules	

SECTION II.

	155—158
System of Units applied to the Scale of Tens	158—161
	161—163

SECTION III.

Fractional Units changing by the Scale of Tens	
Fractional Units in general	
Fractional Units of the System of Fractional Units	163—172
Advantages of the System of Fractional Units	

SECTION IV.

	172—180
Proportion and Ratio	180

SECTION V.

Applications of the Science of Arithmetic	
Methods of teaching Arithmetic considered	180—183
Applications of the Science of Arithmetic	183—185
Order of the Subjects	185
1st. Integer Units or Rule of Three	186—188
2d. Fractional Units or Applications of Arithmetic	189—191
3d. Comparison of Numbers or Applications of Arithmetic	191
4th. Practical Classification answered	193—200
Objections to the new Method	200—206
Arithmetical Language and Terms	206—209
Necessity of exact Definitions and Terms	209—214
How should the Subjects be presented	214—257
How-Books	
Text-Books	
First Arithmetic	

BOOK II.

Mathematical Science.

CHAPTER III.

Geometry Defined—Things of Which It Treats—Comparison and Properties of Figures—Demonstration—Proportion—Suggestions for Teaching.

GEOMETRY

§ 237. GEOMETRY treats of space, and compares portions of space with each other, for the purpose of pointing out their properties and mutual relations. The science consists in the development of all the laws relating to space, and is made up of the processes and rules, by means of which portions of space can be best compared with each other. The truths of Geometry are a series of dependent propositions, and may be divided into three classes:

1st. Truths implied in the definitions, viz. that things do exist, or may exist, corresponding to the words defined. For example: when we say, "A quadrilateral is a rectilinear figure having four sides," we imply the existence of such a figure.

2d. Self-evident, or intuitive truths, embodied in the axioms; and,

3d. Truths inferred from the definitions and axioms, called Demonstrative Truths. We say that a truth or proposition is proved or demonstrated, when, by a course of reasoning, it is shown to be included under some other truth or proposition, previously known, and from which is said to *follow;* hence,

A DEMONSTRATION is a series of logical argu-

Geometry.

Its science.

Its truths.
Of three kinds.

1st. Those implied in the definitions.

2d. Axioms.

3d. Demonstrative truths.

When demonstrated.

Demonstration.

ments, brought to a conclusion, in which the major premises are definitions, axioms, or propositions already established.

§ 238. Before we can understand the proofs or demonstrations of Geometry, we must understand what that is to which demonstration is applicable: hence, the first thing necessary is to form a clear conception of space, the subject of all geometrical reasoning.

Subjects of Geometry.

The next step is to give names to particular forms or limited portions of space, and to define these names accurately. The definitions of these names are the definitions of Geometry, and the portions of space corresponding to them are called Figures, or Geometrical Magnitudes; of which there are three general classes:

Names of forms.

Figures.
Three kinds.

1st. Lines;
2d. Surfaces;
3d. Solids.

First.
Second.
Third.

§ 239. Lines embrace only one dimension of space, viz. length, without breadth or thickness. The extremities, or limits of a line, are called points.

Lines.

There are two general classes of lines—straight lines and curved lines. A straight line is one which lies in the same direction between any two of its points; and a curved line is one which constantly changes its direction at every point. There is but one kind of straight line, and that is fully characterized by the definition. From the definition we may infer the following axiom: "A straight line is the shortest distance between two points." There are many kinds of curves, of which the circumference of the circle is the simplest and the most easily described.

Two classes: Straight and Curved.

One kind of straight line:

many of curves.

§ 240. Surfaces embrace two dimensions of space, viz. length and breadth, but not thickness. Surfaces, like lines, are also divided into two general classes, viz. plane surfaces and curved surfaces.

Surfaces:

Plane and Curved.

43

A plane surface is that with which a straight line, any how placed, and having two points common with the surface, will coincide throughout its entire extent. Such a surface is perfectly even, and is commonly designated by the term "A plane." A large class of the figures of Geometry are but portions of a plane, and all such are called plane figures.

A plane surface:

Perfectly even.

Plane Figures.

§ 241. A portion of a plane, bounded by three straight lines, is called a triangle, and this is the simplest of the plane figures. There are several kinds of triangles, differing from each other, however, only in the relative values of their sides and angles. For example: when the sides are all equal to each other, the triangle is called equilateral; when two of the sides are equal, it is called isosceles; and scalene, when the three sides are all unequal. If one of the angles is a right angle, the triangle is called a right-angled triangle.

A triangle, the most simple figure.

Kinds of triangles.

§ 242. The next simplest class of plane figures comprises all those which are bounded by four straight lines, and are called quadrilaterals. There are several varieties of this class:

1st. The mere quadrilateral, which has no mark, except that of having four sides;

2d. The trapezoid, which has two sides parallel and two not parallel;

3d. The parallelogram, which has its opposite sides parallel and its angles oblique;

4th. The rectangle, which has all its angles right angles and its opposite sides parallel; and,

5th. The square, which has its four sides equal to each other, each to each, and its four angles right angles.

Quadrilaterals.

1st species.

2d species.

3d species.

4th species.

5th species.

§ 243. Plane figures, bounded by straight lines, having a number of sides greater than four, take names corresponding to the number of sides, viz. Pentagons, Hexagons, Heptagons, &c.

Other Polygons.

44

§ 244. A portion of a plane bounded by a curved line, all the points of which are equally distant from a certain point within called the centre, is called a circle, and the bounding line is called the circumference. This is the only curve usually treated of in Elementary Geometry.

Circles:

the circumference.

§ 245. A curved surface, like a plane, embraces the two dimensions of length and breadth. It is not even, like the plane, throughout its whole extent, and therefore a straight line may have two points in common, and yet not coincide with it. The surface of the cone, of the sphere, and cylinder, are the curved surfaces treated of in Elementary Geometry.

Curved Surfaces:

their properties.

§ 246. A solid is a portion of space, combining the three dimensions of length, breadth, and thickness. Solids are divided into three classes:

1st. Those bounded by planes;

2d. Those bounded by plane and curved surfaces; and,

3d. Those bounded only by curved surfaces.

The first class embraces the pyramid and prism with their several varieties; the second class embraces the cylinder and cone; and the third class the sphere, together with others not generally treated of in Elementary Geometry.

Solids.

Three classes.
1st class.
2d class.

3d class.
What figures fall in each class.

§ 247. We have now named all the geometrical magnitudes treated of in elementary Geometry. They are merely limited portions of space, and do not, *necessarily*, involve the idea of matter. A sphere, for example, fulfills all the conditions imposed by its definitions, without any reference to what may be within the space enclosed by its surface. That space may be occupied by lead, iron, or air, or may be a vacuum, without at all changing the nature of the sphere, as a geometrical magnitude.

It should be observed that the boundary or limit of a geometrical magnitude, is another geometrical magnitude, having one dimension less. For example: the boundary or limit of a solid,

Magnitudes named.

What they are.

A sphere.

Need not be material.

Boundaries of solids.

45

which has three dimensions, is always a surface which has but two: the limits or boundaries of all surfaces are lines, straight or curved; and the extremities or limits of lines are points.

Examples.

§ 248. We have now named and shown the nature of the things which are the subjects of Elementary Geometry. The science of Geometry is a collection of those connected processes by which we determine the measures, properties, and relations of these magnitudes.

Subjects named.

Science of Geometry.

COMPARISON OF FIGURES WITH UNITS OF MEASURE.

§ 249. We have seen that the term measure implies a comparison of the thing measured with some known thing of the same kind, regarded as a standard; and that such standard is called the unit of measure. The unit of measure for lines must, therefore, be a line of a known length: a foot, a yard, a rod, a mile, or any other known unit. For surfaces, it is a' square constructed on the linear unit as a side: that is, a square foot, a square yard, a square rod, a square mile; that is, *a square described on any known unit of length.*

Measure.

Unit of measure
For Lines, A Line.

For Surfaces,
A Square.

The unit of measure, for solidity, is a solid, and therefore has three dimensions. It is a cube constructed on a linear unit as an edge, or on the superficial unit as a base. It is, therefore, a cubic foot, a cubic yard, a cubic rod, &c. Hence, there are three units of measure, each differing in kind from the other two, viz. a known length for the measurement of lines; a known square for the measurement of surfaces; and a known cube for the measurement of solids. The measure or contents of any magnitude, belonging to either class, is ascertained by finding how many times that magnitude contains its unit of measure.

For Solids,
A Cube.

Three units of measure:

A Line,
A Square,
A Cube.
Contents:
how ascertained.

§ 250. There is yet another class of magnitudes with which Geometry is conversant, called

Angles. They are not, however, elementary magnitudes, but arise from the relative positions of those already described. The unit of this class is the right angle; and with this as a standard, all other angles are compared.

§ 251. We have dwelt with much detail on the unit of measure, because it furnishes the only basis of estimating quantity. The conception of number and space merely opens to the intellectual vision an unmeasured field of investigation and thought, as the ascent to the summit of a mountain presents to the eye a wide and unsurveyed horizon. To ascertain the height of the point of view, the diameter of the surrounding circular area and the distance to any point which may be seen, some standard or unity must be known, and its value distinctly apprehended. So, also, number and space, which at first fill the mind with vague and indefinite conceptions, are to be finally measured by units of ascertained value.

§ 252. It is found, on careful analysis, that every number may be referred to the unit one, as a standard, and when the signification of the term ONE is clearly apprehended, that any number, whether large or small, whether integer or fractional, may be deduced from the standard by an easy and known process.

In space, also, which is indefinite in extent, and exactly similar in all its parts, the faculties of the mind have established ideal boundaries. These boundaries give rise to the geometrical magnitudes, each of which has its own unit of measure; and by these simple contrivances, we measure space, even to the stars, as with a yardstick.

§ 253. We have, thus far, not alluded to the difficulty of *determining* the exact length of that which we regard as a standard. We are presented with a given length, and told that it is

Angles:

Their unit.

Importance of the unit of measure:

Space indefinite without it:

and always measured by it.

Every number may be referred to the unit one.

Space:

Its ideal boundaries.

Conception of the unit of measure:

called a foot or a yard, and this being usually
done at a period of life when the mind is satisfied with mere facts, we adopt the conception
of a distance corresponding to a name, and then
by multiplying and dividing that distance we
are enabled to apprehend other distances. But
this by no means answers the inquiry, What is
the standard for measurement?

*At first, a mere
impression.*

Under the supposition that the laws of physical nature operate uniformly, the unit of measure in England and the United States has been
fixed by ascertaining the length of a pendulum
which will vibrate seconds, and to this length
the Imperial yard, which we have also adopted
as a standard, is referred. Hence, the unit of
measure is referred to a natural standard, viz. to
the distance between the axis of suspension and
the centre of oscillation of a pendulum which
shall vibrate seconds in vacuo, in London, at the
level of the sea. This distance is declared to
be 39.1393 *imperial inches;* that is, 3 imperial
feet and 3.1393 inches. Thus, the determination of the unit of length demands the application of the most abstruse science, combined with
accurate observation and delicate experiment.

How determined.

What it is.

Its length.

*Difficulties of deter-
mining it.*

Could this distance, or unit, have been exactly
ascertained before the measures of the world
were fixed, and in general use, it would have
afforded a standard at once certain and convenient, and all distances would then have been
expressed in numbers arising from its multiplication or exact division. But as the measures
of the world (and consequently their units) were
fixed antecedently to the determination of this
distance, it was expressed in measures already
known; and hence, instead of being represented
by 1, which had already been appropriated to
the foot, it was expressed in terms of the foot,
viz. 39.1393 inches, and this is now the standard
to which all units of measure are referred.

*What should have been
called one.
Other numbers derived
from it.*

Why it is not so.

What now represents it.

§ 254. The unit of measure is not only important as affording a basis for all measurement,
but is also the element from which we deduce

*Unit of measure the
basis of the unit of
weight.*

the unit of weight. The weight of 27.7015 cubic
inches of distilled water is taken as the standard,
weighing exactly one pound avoirdupois, and
this quantity of water is determined from the
unit of length; that is, the determination of it   *What it is.*
reaches back to the length of a pendulum which
will vibrate seconds in the latitude of London.

§ 255. Two geometrical figures are said to be   *Equivalent figures.*
equivalent, when they contain the same unit of
measure an equal number of times. Two figures
are said to be equal when they can be so applied   *Equal figures.*
to each other as to coincide throughout their
whole extent. Hence, equivalency refers to   *Equivalency:*
measure, and equality to coincidence. Indeed,   *Equality.*
coincidence is the only test of geometrical equal-
ity. All equal figures are of course equivalent,
though equivalent figures are by no means equal.   *Their difference.*
Equality is equivalency, with the further mark
of coincidence.

.
.
.

SUGGESTIONS FOR THOSE WHO TEACH GEOMETRY.

1. Be sure that your pupils have a clear ap-   *Suggestions.*
prehension of space, and of the notion that Ge-   *First.*
ometry is conversant about space only.
2. Be sure that they understand the significa-
tion of the terms, lines, surfaces, and solids, and   *Second.*
that these names indicate certain portions of
space corresponding to them.
3. See that they understand the distinction between a straight line and a curve; between a   *Third.*
plane surface and a curved surface; between a
solid bounded by planes and a solid bounded by
curved surfaces.
4. Be careful to have them note the charac-
teristics of the different species of plane figures,   *Fourth.*
such as triangles, quadrilaterals, pentagons, hexagons, &c.; and then the characteristic of each
class or subspecies, so that the name shall recall,
at once, the characteristic properties of each
figure.

49

5. Be careful, also, to have them note the characteristic differences of the solids. Let them often name and distinguish those which are bounded by planes, those bounded by plane and curved surfaces, and those bounded by curved surfaces only. Regarding Solids as a genus, let them give the species and subspecies into which the solid bodies may be divided. *Fifth.*

6. Having thus made them familiar with the things which are the subjects of the reasoning, explain carefully the nature of the definitions; then of the axioms, the grounds of our belief in them, and the information from which those self-evident truths are inferred. *Sixth.*

7. Then explain to them, that the definitions and axioms are the basis of all geometrical reasoning: that every proposition must be deduced from them, and that they afford the tests of all the truths which the reasonings establish. *Seventh.*

8. Let every figure, used in a demonstration, be accurately drawn, by the pupil himself, on a blackboard. This will establish a connection between the eye and the hand, and give, at the same time, a clear perception of the figure and a distinct apprehension of the relations of its parts. *Eighth.*

9. Let the pupil, in every demonstration, first enunciate, in general terms, that is, without the aid of a diagram, or any reference to one, the proposition to be proved; and then state the principles previously established, which are to be employed in making out the proof. *Ninth.*

10. When in the course of a demonstration, any truth is inferred from its connection with one before known, let the truth so referred to be fully and accurately stated, even though the number of the proposition in which it is proved, be also required. This is deemed important. *Tenth.*

11. Let the pupil be made to understand that a demonstration is but a series of logical arguments arising from comparison, and that the result of every comparison, in respect to quantity, contains the mark either of equality or inequality. *Eleventh.*

12. Let the distinction between a positive and negative demonstration be fully explained and clearly apprehended.

Twelfth.

13. In the comparison of quantities with each other, great care should be taken to impress the fact that proportion exists only between quantities of the same kind, and that ratio is the measure of proportion.

Thirteenth.

14. Do not fail to give much importance to the *kind* of quantity under consideration. Let the question be often put, What kind of quantity are you considering? Is it a line, a surface, or a solid? And what kind of a line, surface, or solid?

Fourteenth.

15. In all cases of measurement, the unit of measure should receive special attention. If lines are measured, or compared by means of a common unit, see that the pupil perceives that unit clearly, and apprehends distinctly its relations to the lines which it measures. In surfaces, take much pains to mark out on the blackboard the particular square which forms the unit of measure, and write unit, or unit of measure, over it. So in the measurement of solidity, let the unit or measuring cube be exhibited, and the conception of its size clearly formed in the mind; and then impress the important fact, that, *all measurement consists in merely comparing a unit of measure with the quantity measured; and that the number which expresses the ratio is the numerical expression for that measure.*

Fifteenth.

16. Be careful to explain the difference of the terms *Equal* and *Equivalent,* and never permit the pupil to use them as synonymous. An accurate use of words leads to nice discriminations of thought.

Sixteenth.

CHAPTER IV.

Analysis—Algebra—Analytical Geometry— Differential and Integral Calculus

.
.
.

SUGGESTIONS FOR THOSE WHO TEACH ALGEBRA.

1. Be careful to explain that the letters employed, are the mere symbols of quantity. That of, and in themselves, they have no meaning or signification whatever, but are used merely as the signs or representatives of such quantities as they may be employed to denote. *Letters are but mere symbols.*

2. Be careful to explain that the signs which are used are employed merely for the purpose of indicating the five operations which may be performed on quantity; and that they indicate operations merely, without at all affecting the nature of the quantities before which they are placed. *Signs indicate operations.*

3. Explain that the letters and signs are the elements of the algebraic language, and that the language itself arises from the combination of these elements. *Letters and signs elements of language.*

4. Explain that the finding of an algebraic formula is but the translation of certain ideas, first expressed in our common language, into the language of Algebra; and that the interpretation of an algebraic formula is merely translating its various significations into common language. *Algebraic formula:* *Its interpretation.*

5. Let the language of Algebra be carefully studied, so that its construction and significations may be clearly apprehended. *Language.*

6. Let the difference between a coefficient and an exponent be carefully noted, and the *Coefficient, Exponent.*

52

office of each often explained; and illustrate frequently the signification of the language by attributing numerical values to letters in various algebraic expressions.

7. Point out often the characteristics of similar and dissimilar quantities, and explain which may be incorporated and which cannot.

Similar quantities.

8. Explain the power of the minus sign, as shown in the four ground rules, but very particularly as it is illustrated in subtraction and multiplication.

Minus sign.

9. Point out and illustrate the correspondence between the four ground rules of Arithmetic and Algebra; and impress the fact, that their differences, wherever they appear, arise merely from differences in notation and language: the principles which govern the operations being the same in both.

Arithmetic and Algebra compared.

10. Explain with great minuteness and particularity all the characteristic properties of the equation; the manner of forming it; the different kinds of quantity which enter into its composition; its examination or discussion; and the different methods of elimination.

Equation.
Its properties.

11. In the equation of the second degree, be careful to dwell on the four forms which embrace all the cases, and illustrate by many examples that every equation of the second degree may be reduced to one or other of them. Explain very particularly the meaning of the term root; and then show, why every equation of the first degree has one, and every equation of the second degree two. Dwell on the properties of these roots in the equation of the second degree. Show why their sum, in all the forms, is equal to the coefficient of the second term, taken with a contrary sign; and why their product is equal to the absolute term with a contrary sign. Explain when and why the roots are imaginary.

Equation of the second degree.

Its forms.

Its roots.

Their sum.

Their product.

12. In fine, remember that every operation and rule is based on a principle of science, and that an intelligible reason may be given for it.

General Principles:

Find that reason, and impress it on the mind of your pupil in plain and simple language, and by familiar and appropriate illustrations. You will thus impress right habits of investigation and study, and he will grow in knowledge. The broad field of analytical investigation will be opened to his intellectual vision, and he will have made the first steps in that sublime science which discovers the laws of nature in their most secret hiding-places, and follows them, as they reach out, in omnipotent power, to control the motions of matter through the entire regions of occupied space.

Should be explained.

They lead to general laws.

BOOK III.

Utility of Mathematics.

CHAPTER I.

The Utility of Mathematics Considered as a Means of Intellectual Training and Culture.

§ 316. THE first efforts in mathematical science are made by the child in the process of counting. He counts his fingers, and repeats the words one, two, three, four, five, six, seven, eight, nine, ten, until he associates with these words the ideas of one or more, and thus acquires his first notions of number. Hence, the idea of number is first presented to the mind by means of sensible objects; but when once clearly apprehended, the perception of the sensible objects fades away, and the mind retains only the abstract idea. Thus, the child, after counting for a time with the aid of his fingers or his marbles, dispenses with these cumbrous helps, and employs only the abstract ideas, which his mind embraces with clearness and uses with facility.

First efforts.

Counting of sensible objects.

Generalization.

Abstraction.

§ 317. In the first stages of the analytical methods, where the quantities considered are represented by the letters of the alphabet, sensible objects again lend their aid to enable the mind to gain exact and distinct ideas of the things considered; but no sooner are these ideas obtained than the mind loses sight of the things themselves, and operates entirely through the instrumentality of symbols.

Analytical method:

Uses sensible objects at first.

§ 318. So, also, in Geometry. The right line may first be presented to the mind, as a black

Geometry.

55

mark on paper, or a chalk mark on a blackboard, to impress the geometrical definition, that
"A straight line does not change its direction
between any two of its points." When this definition is clearly apprehended, the mind needs
no further aid from the eye, for the image is
forever imprinted.

*First impressions by
sensible objects.*

§ 319. The idea of a plane surface may be
impressed by exhibiting the surface of a polished
mirror; and thus the mind may be aided in
apprehending the definition, that "a plane surface is one in which, if any two points be taken,
the straight line which joins them will lie wholly
in the surface." But when the definition is
understood, the mind requires no sensible object
to aid its conception. The ideal alone fills the
mind, and the image lives there without any
connection with sensible objects.

*A plane.
Definition:*

How illustrated.

Its true conception.

§ 320. Space is indefinite extension, in which
all bodies are situated. A solid or body is any
portion of space embracing the three dimensions
of length, breadth, and thickness. To give to
the mind the true conception of a solid, the aid
of the eye may at first be necessary; but the
idea being once impressed, that a solid, in a
strictly mathematical sense, means only a portion of space, and has no reference to the matter with which the space may be filled, the mind
turns away from the material object, and dwells
alone on the ideal.

*Space.
Solid:*

How conceived.

What it really is.

§ 321. Although quantity, in its general sense,
is the subject of mathematical inquiry, yet the
language of mathematics is so constructed, that
the investigations are pursued without the slight-
est reference to quantity as a material substance.
We have seen that a system of symbols, by
which quantities may be represented, has been
adopted, forming a language for the expression
of ideas entirely disconnected from material ob-

Quantity:

*Language:
How constructed.*

Symbols:

jects, and yet capable of expressing and representing such objects. This symbolical language, at once copious and exact, not only enables us to express our known thoughts, in every department of mathematical science, but is a potent means of pushing our inquiries into unexplored regions, and conducting the mind with certainty to new and valuable truths.

Nature of the language:

What it accomplishes.

§ 322. The nature of that culture, which the mind undergoes by being trained in the use of an exact language, in which the connection between the *sign* and the *thing signified* is unmistakable, has been well set forth by a living author, greatly distinguished for his scientific attainments.[1] Of the pure sciences, he says:

Advantages of an exact language.

"Their objects are so definite, and our notions of them so distinct, that we can reason about them with an assurance that the words and signs of our reasonings are full and true representatives of the things signified; and, consequently, that when we use language or signs in argument, we neither by their use introduce extraneous notions, nor exclude any part of the case before us from consideration. For example: the words space, square, circle, a hundred, &c., convey to the mind notions so complete in themselves, and so distinct from every thing else, that we are sure when we use them we know and have in view the whole of our own meaning. It is widely different with words expressing natural objects and mixed relations. Take, for instance, *Iron.* Different persons attach very different ideas to this word. One who has never heard of magnetism has a widely different notion of iron from one in the contrary predicament. The vulgar who regard this metal as incombustible, and the chemist, who sees it burn with the utmost fury, and who has other reasons for regarding it as one of the most combustible bodies in nature; the poet, who uses

Herschel's views.

Exact language prevents error.

Mathematical terms exact.

Different in regard to other terms.

How iron is regarded by the chemist:

The poet:

1. Sir John Herschel. Discourse on the study of Natural Philosophy.

it as an emblem of rigidity; and the smith and engineer, in whose hands it is plastic, and moulded like wax into every form; the jailer, who prizes it as an obstruction, and the electrician, who sees in it only a channel of open communication by which that most impassable of obstacles, the air, may be traversed by his imprisoned fluid,— have all different, and all imperfect notions of the same word. The meaning of such a term is like the rainbow—everybody sees a different one, and all maintain it to be the same."

The jailer:
The electrician.

Final illustration.

"It is, in fact, in this double or incomplete sense of words, that we must look for the origin of a very large portion of the errors into which we fall. Now, the study of the abstract sciences, such as Arithmetic, Geometry, Algebra, &c., while they afford scope for the exercise of reasoning about objects that are, or, at least, may be conceived to be, external to us; yet, being free from these sources of error and mistake, accustom us to the strict use of language as an instrument of reason, and by familiarizing us in our progress towards truth, to walk uprightly and straightforward, on firm ground, give us that proper and dignified carriage of mind which could never be acquired by having always to pick our steps among obstructions and loose fragments, or to steady them in the reeling tempests of conflicting meanings."

Incomplete meaning the source of error.

Mathematics free from such errors.

Requires a strict use of language.

Results.

§ 323. Mr. Locke lays down two ways of increasing our knowledge:

Two ways of acquiring knowledge.

1st. "Clear and distinct ideas with settled names; and,

2d. "The finding of those which show their agreement or disagreement;" that is, the searching out of new ideas which result from the combination of those that are known.

In regard to the first of these ways, Mr. Locke says: "The first is to get and settle in our minds determined ideas of those things, whereof we have general or specific names; at least, of so many of them as we would consider and im-

First.

Ideas of things must be distinct.

prove our knowledge in, or reason about." * * *
"For, it being evident, that our knowledge cannot exceed our ideas, as far as they are either imperfect, confused, or obscure, we cannot expect
to have certain, perfect, or clear knowledge."

Reason.

§ 324. Now, the ideas which make up our
knowledge of mathematical science, fulfil exactly these requirements. They are all impressed on the mind by a fixed, definite, and
certain language, and the mind embraces them
as so many images or pictures, clear and distinct in their outlines, with names which suggest at once their characteristics and properties.

*Why it is so in
mathematics.*

§ 325. In the second method of increasing
our knowledge, pointed out by Mr. Locke, mathematical science offers the most ample and the
surest means. The reasonings are all based on
self-evident truths, and are conducted by means
of the most striking relations between the known
and the unknown. The things reasoned about,
and the methods of reasoning, are so clearly
apprehended, that the mind never hesitates or
doubts. It comprehends, or it does not comprehend, and the line which separates the known
from the unknown, is always well defined. These
characteristics give to this system of reasoning
a superiority over every other, arising, not from
any difference in the logic, but from a difference
in the things to which the logic is applied. Observation may deceive, experiment may fail, and
experience prove treacherous, but demonstration
never.

Second.

*Why mathematics offer
the surest means.*

*Characteristics of the
reasoning.*
Its advantages.

Demonstration certain.

"If it be true, then, that mathematics include
a perfect system of reasoning, whose premises
are self-evident, and whose conclusions are irre-
sistible, can there be any branch of science or
knowledge better adapted to the improvement
of the understanding? It is in this capacity,
as a strong and natural adjunct and instrument
of reason, that this science becomes the fit subject of education with all conditions of society,

*Mathematics includes a
certain system.*

*An adjunct and instru-
ment of reason;*

whatever may be their ultimate pursuits. Most sciences, as, indeed, most branches of knowledge, address themselves to some particular taste, or subsequent avocation; but this, while it is before all, as a useful attainment, especially adapts itself to the cultivation and improvement of the thinking faculty, and is alike necessary to all who would be governed by reason, or live for usefulness."[2]

and necessary to all.

§ 326. The following, among other considerations, may serve to point out and illustrate the value of mathematical studies, as a means of mental improvement and development.

Considerations of the value of mathematics.

1. We readily conceive and clearly apprehend the things of which the science treats; they being things simple in themselves and readily presented to the mind by plain and familiar language. For example: the idea of number, of one or more, is among the first ideas implanted in the mind; and the child who counts his fingers or his marbles, understands the art of numbering them as perfectly as he can know any thing. So, likewise, when he learns the definition of a straight line, of a triangle, of a square, of a circle, or of a parallelogram, he conceives the idea of each perfectly, and the name and the image are inseparably connected. These ideas, so distinct and satisfactory, are expressed in the simplest and fewest terms, and may, if necessary, be illustrated by the aid of sensible objects.

First. They give clear conceptions of things.

Example.

They establish clear relations between definitions and things.

2. The words employed in the definitions are always used in the same sense—each expressing at all times the same idea; so that when a definition is apprehended, the conception of the thing, whose name is defined, is perfect in the mind.

Second. Words are always used in the same sense.

There is, therefore, no doubt or ambiguity either in the language, or in regard to what is affirmed or denied of the things spoken of; but all is certainty, both in the language employed and in the ideas which it expresses.

Hence, it is certain.

2. Mansfield's Discourse on the Mathematics.

3. The science of mathematics employs no definition which may not be clearly comprehended—lays down no axioms not universally true, and to which the mind, by the very laws of its nature, readily assents; and because, also, in the process of the reasoning, no principle or truth is taken for granted, but every link in the chain of the argument is immediately connected with a definition or axiom, or with some principle previously established.

Third. It employs no definition or axiom not evident and clear.

The connection evident.

4. The order established in présenting the subject to the mind, aids the memory at the same time that it strengthens and improves the reasoning powers. For example: first, their are the definitions of the names of the things which are the subjects of the reasoning; then the axioms, or self-evident truths, which, together with the definitions, form the basis of the science. From these the simplest propositions are deduced, and then follow others of greater difficulty; the whole connected together by rigorous logic—each part receiving strength and light from all the others. Whence, it follows, that any proposition may be traced to first principles; its dependence upon and connection with those principles made obvious; and its truth established by certain and infallible argument.

Fourth. The order strengthens different faculties.

How ideas are presented.

How the deductions follow.

Propositions traced to their sources.

5. The demonstrative argument of mathematics produces the most certain knowledge of which the mind is susceptible. It establishes truth so clearly, that none can doubt or deny. For, if the premises are certain—that is, such that all minds admit their truth without hesitation or doubt, and if the method of drawing the conclusions be lawful—that is, in accordance with the infallible rules of logic, the inferences must also be true. Truths thus established may be relied on for their verity; and the knowledge thus gained may well be denominated SCIENCE.

Fifth. Argument the most certain.

Reasons.

Such knowledge science.

· · ·

UNIVERSITY ARITHMETIC,

EMBRACING THE

SCIENCE OF NUMBERS,

AND

GENERAL RULES FOR THEIR APPLICATION.

By CHARLES DAVIES, LL.D.,

AUTHOR OF PRIMARY, INTELLECTUAL, AND SCHOOL ARITHMETICS; ELEMENTARY
ALGEBRA; ELEMENTARY GEOMETRY; PRACTICAL MATHEMATICS; ELEMENTS
OF SURVEYING; ELEMENTS OF ANALYTICAL GEOMETRY; DESCRIPTIVE
GEOMETRY; SHADES, SHADOWS, AND PERSPECTIVE; DIFFER-
ENTIAL AND INTEGRAL CALCULUS; AND LOGIC AND
UTILITY OF MATHEMATICS.

A. S. BARNES & COMPANY,
NEW YORK AND CHICAGO.

1870

PREFACE.

SCIENCE, in its popular signification, means knowledge reduced to order; that is, knowledge so classified and arranged as to be easily remembered, readily referred to, and advantageously applied. More strictly, it is a *knowledge of laws, relations, and principles.*

ARITHMETIC is the science of numbers, and the art of applying numbers to all practical purposes. It is the foundation of the exact and mixed sciences, and an accurate knowledge of it is an important element either of a liberal or practical education.

It is the first subject, in a well-arranged course of instruction, to which the reasoning faculties of the mind are applied, and is the guide-book of the mechanic and man of business. It is the first fountain at which the young votary of knowledge drinks the pure waters of intellectual truth.

It has seemed, to the author, of the first importance that this subject should be carefully treated in our Elementary Textbooks. In the hope of contributing something to so desirable an end, he has prepared a series of arithmetical works, embracing four books, entitled, Primary Arithmetic; Intellectual Arithmetic; Practical Arithmetic; and University Arithmetic— the latter of which is the present volume.

PRIMARY ARITHMETIC. This first-book is adapted to the capacities and wants of young children. Sensible objects are employed to illustrate and make familiar the simple combinations and relations of numbers. Each lesson embraces one combination of numbers, or one set of combinations.

INTELLECTUAL ARITHMETIC. This work is designed to present a thorough analysis of the science of numbers, and to form a complete course of mental arithmetic. I have aimed to make it accessible to young pupils by the simplicity and gradation of its methods, and to adapt it to the wants of advanced students by a scientific arrangement and logical connection, in all the higher processes of arithmetical analysis.

PRACTICAL ARITHMETIC. Great pains have been taken, in the preparation of this book, to combine *theory* and *practice;* to explain and illustrate principles, and to apply them to the common business transactions of life— to make it *emphatically a practical work.* The student is required to demonstrate every principle laid down, by a course of mental reasoning, before deducing a proposition or making a practical application of a rule to examples. He is required to fix and apprehend the *unit* or *base* of all numbers, whether integral or fractional—to reason with constant reference to this base, and thus make it the *key* to the solution of all arithmetical questions. It is hoped, that the language used in the statement of principles, in the definition of terms, and in the explanation of methods, will be found to be clear, exact, brief, and comprehensive.

UNIVERSITY ARITHMETIC. This work is designed to answer another object. Here, the entire subject is treated as a *science*. The pupil is supposed to be familiar with the simple operations in the four ground rules, and with the first principles of fractions, these being now taught to small children, either orally or from elementary treatises. This being premised, the language of figures, which are the representatives of numbers, is carefully taught, and the different significations of which the figures themselves are susceptible, depending on the manner in which they are written, are fully explained. It is shown, for example, that the simple numbers in which the value of the unit increases from right to left according to the scale of tens, and the Denominate or Compound numbers in which it increases according to a varying scale, belong to the same class of numbers, and that both may be treated under the same rules. Hence, the rules for Notation, Addition, Subtraction, Multiplication, and Division, have been so constructed as to apply equally to all numbers. This arrangement, which the author has not seen elsewhere, is deemed an essential improvement in the science of Arithmetic.

In developing the properties of numbers, from their elementary to their highest combinations, great labor has been bestowed on classification and arrangement. It has been a leading object to present the entire subject of arithmetic as forming *a series of dependent and connected propositions:* so that the pupil, while acquiring useful and practical knowledge, may at the same time be introduced to those beautiful methods of reasoning which science alone teaches.

Great care has been taken to demonstrate every proposition—to give a complete analysis of all the methods employed, from the simplest to the most difficult, and to explain fully the reason of every rule. A full analysis of the science of Numbers has developed but *one law; viz., the law which connects all the numbers of arithmetic with the unit one, and which points out. the relations of these numbers to each other.*

In the Appendix, which treats of Units, Weights, and Measures, &c., the methods of determining the Arbitrary Unit, as well as the general law which prevails in the formation of numbers, are fully explained. I cannot too earnestly recommend this part of the work to the special attention of Teachers and pupils.

In fine, the attention of Teachers is especially invited to this work, because *general methods* and *general rules* are employed to abridge the common arithmetical processes, and to give to them a more *scientific* and *practical* character. In the present edition, the matter is presented in a new form; the arrangement of the subjects is more natural and scientific; the methods have been carefully considered; the illustrations abridged and simplified; the definitions and rules thoroughly revised and corrected; and a very large number and variety of practical examples have been added. The subjects of Fractions, Proportion, Interest, Percentage, Alligation, Analysis, and Weights and Measures, present many new and valuable features, which are not found in other works.

A Key to the present work has also been published for the use of such Teachers as may desire it,—prepared with great care, containing not only the answers and solutions of all the examples, but a full and comprehensive *analysis* of the more difficult ones.

The author has great pleasure in acknowledging the interest which Teachers have manifested in the success of his labors: they have suggested many improvements, both in rules and methods, not only in his elementary, but also in his advanced works. The recitation-room is the final tribunal, and the intelligent teacher the final judge, before which all text-books must stand or fall.

COLUMBIA COLLEGE, }
  May, 1864.   }

Multiplication of Common Fractions...... 145-148
Division of Common Fractions...... 148-152
Complex Fractions...... 152
Applications in Fractions...... 152-155

DUODECIMALS.
Principles and Rules...... 155-164

DECIMAL FRACTIONS.
Definition of Decimals, &c......
Decimal Numeration Table—First Principles, &c...... 164
Addition of Decimals...... 165-170
Subtraction of Decimals...... 170-173
Multiplication of Decimals...... 173-175
Contractions in Multiplication...... 175-177
Division of Decimals...... 177-179
Contractions in Division...... 179-184
Reduction of Common Fractions to Decimals...... 184-186
Reduction of Denominate Decimals...... 186-190
Repeating Decimals—Definition of, &c...... 190-191
Reduction of Repeating Decimals...... 191-195
Addition of Repeating Decimals...... 195-201
Subtraction of Repeating Decimals...... 201
Multiplication of Repeating Decimals...... 201
Division of Repeating Decimals...... 203
203

CONTINUED FRACTIONS.
Definitions and Principles...... 200-206

RATIO AND PROPORTION.
Ratio Defined...... 206
Compound Ratio...... 207
Simple Proportion...... 209
Direct and Inverse Proportion...... 211
Single Rule of Three...... 214-220
Double Rule of Three...... 221-225
Partnership...... 225-230

CONTENTS.

FIRST FIVE RULES.
Notation...... 13
Expressing Numbers...... 14?
Roman and Numeration...... 14-24
Notation and Numeration of Numbers...... 24
Notation and Nature of Numbers...... 25-28
Scales...... 28
Integral Units...... 29
Properties of the 9's...... 30-34
Reduction...... 31-44
Addition...... 44-54
Subtraction...... 54-68
Multiplication...... 68-87
Division...... 87-90
Practice and Time...... 90-94
Longitude and Time...... 94-103
Applications in the Four Rules...... 103
Properties of Numbers...... 100-105
Divisibility of Numbers...... 100-100
Cancelation...... 100-10U
Least Common Multiple...... 111-115
Greatest Common Divisor......

COMMON FRACTIONS.
Definition of, and First Principles...... 115-119
The six Kinds of Fractions...... 119-120
Six Principles...... 120-121
Reduction of Common Fractions...... 121-123
Reduction of Denominate Fractions...... 132-125
Addition of Common Fractions...... 135-149
Subtraction of Common Fractions...... 140-143

11

CONTENTS.

PERCENTAGE.

PAGE

Percentage Defined and Illustrated 231–236
.... 237–241
Partial Loss 242–244
.... 245–253
.... 253–256
Partial Payments 256–257
.... 258–259
.... 260–261
.... 262–264
.... 264–266
.... 267–272
.... 272–275
.... 275–277
.... 278
.... 279–281

APPLICATIONS.

.... 281–284
.... 284–294
.... 295
.... 296–301
.... 302–306
.... 306–307
Custom-house Business 308–310
Tonnage of Vessels 311
.... 312–319
.... 320–323

POWERS AND ROOTS.

.... 329
.... 331
Extraction of Square Root 334–333
Cube Root 338–339

ARITHMETICAL PROGRESSION.

Definition of, &c. 339
Different Cases 340–344

12

CONTENTS.

GEOMETRICAL PROGRESSION.

PAGE

Definition of, &c. 344
Different Cases 345–348

ANALYSIS.

Analysis and Promiscuous Examples 348–369

MENSURATION.

Mensuration of Surfaces 370–375
Mensuration of Volumes 375–380
Gauging 381–383
Mechanical Powers 384–392
Questions in Natural Philosophy 392–398

APPENDIX.

Different Kinds of Units 399–403
Abstract Units 403
Units of Currency 404–408
Linear Units 408–409
Units of Surface 410
Units of Volume 410
Units of Weight 411–413
Units of Time 416–418
Miscellaneous Table 419
Units of Circular Measure 419
Books and Paper 420
Metric System of Weights and Measures .. 421–422*
Answers 423–408

University Arithmetic.

DEFINITIONS.

1. A UNIT is a single thing, or one.

2. A NUMBER is a unit, or a collection of units.

3. SCIENCE treats of the properties and relations of things: ART is the practical application of the principles of Science.

4. ARITHMETIC is the Science of Numbers, and also the Art of applying numbers to practical purposes.

5. A PROPOSITION is something to be done, or demonstrated.

6. AN ANALYSIS is an examination of the separate parts of a proposition.

7. AN OPERATION is the doing of something with numbers.

8. A RULE is the direction for performing an operation.

9. AN ANSWER is the result of a correct operation.

OPERATIONS OF ARITHMETIC.

10. There are, in Arithmetic, five fundamental operations: Notation and Numeration, Addition, Subtraction, Multiplication, and Division.

.
.
.

---

1. What is a Unit?—2. What is a Number?—3. Of what does Science treat? What is Art?—4. What is Arithmetic?—5. What is a Proposition?—6. What is an Analysis?—7. What is an Operation?—8. What is a Rule?—9. What is an Answer?—10. How many fundamental operations are there in Arithmetic? What are they?

EDWARD BROOKS

Edward Brooks (1831–1912) was one of the foremost mathematics educators of the second half of the nineteenth century. He was president of the Normal Department of the National Teachers' Association in 1876, became Philadelphia's superintendent of public schools in 1891, and was one of the Committee of Fifteen of the National Education Association. He began publishing mathematics texts in 1859, and his texts were still on the market in 1923. His *Philosophy of Arithmetic* (1880) is credited with being the first arithmetic methods book for elementary school teachers; his *Mental Science and Methods of Mental Culture* (1883) is recognized as one of five pre–John Dewey works dealing with educational psychology.[1]

The following passages are from these two books. In the selection from *Philosophy of Arithmetic,* Brooks explained that mathematical structure is basic to arithmetic. The first excerpts from *Mental Science,* essentially a text dealing with psychology rather than mathematics education, are included as background for the following passages, which expound implications of the psychological theory for mathematics teaching and explain why mathematics should be a major component of the curriculum. They were selected as a statement of the faculty theory and its relation to mathematics teaching.

---

1. Abraham Roback, *History of American Psychology* (New York: Library Publishers, 1952), p. 378.

THE

PHILOSOPHY OF ARITHMETIC

AS DEVELOPED FROM THE

THREE FUNDAMENTAL PROCESSES

OF

SYNTHESIS, ANALYSIS, AND COMPARISON

CONTAINING ALSO

A HISTORY OF ARITHMETIC

BY

EDWARD BROOKS, A. M., PH. D.,

SUPERINTENDENT OF PUBLIC SCHOOLS OF PHILADELPHIA,
PRINCIPAL OF PENNSYLVANIA STATE NORMAL SCHOOL, AND AUTHOR OF A
NORMAL SERIES OF MATHEMATICS.

"The highest Science is the greatest simplicity."

LANCASTER, PA.:
NORMAL PUBLISHING COMPANY.
1880.

TABLE OF CONTENTS.

INTRODUCTION.

	PAGE
Chapter I. Logical Outline of Arithmetic	9
" II. Origin and Development of Arithmetic	17
" III. Early Writers on Arithmetic	29
" IV. Origin of Arithmetical Processes	44

PART I.—The Nature of Number.

Section I.—*Number, the Subject-matter of Arithmetic* | 67

Chapter I. Definition of Number	72
" II. Classes of Numbers	76
" III. Numerical Ideas of the Ancients	81

Section II.—*Arithmetical Language.*

Chapter I. Numeration, or the Naming of Numbers	93
" II. Notation, or the Writing of Numbers	101
" III. Notation of Arithmetical Symbols, etc.	108
" IV. Origin of the Scale of Numeration	113
" V. The Scales of Numeration	121
" VI. Other Scales of Numeration	135
" VII. A Duodecimal Scale	141
" VIII. Roman Arithmetic	147
" VIII. Greek Arithmetic	
" IX. Palpable Arithmetic	165

Section III.—*Arithmetical Reasoning.*

Chapter I. There is Reasoning in Arithmetic	171
" II. Nature of Arithmetical Operations	177
" III. Reasoning in the Fundamental Operations	185
" IV. Arithmetical Analysis	193
" V. The Equation in Arithmetic	197
" VI. Induction in Arithmetic	

PART II.—Synthesis and Analysis.

Section I.—*Fundamental Operations.*

Chapter I. Addition	207
" II. Subtraction	213
" III. Multiplication	221
" IV. Division	227

Section II.—*Derivative Operations.*

Chapter I. Introduction to Derivative Operations	237
" II. Composition	240
" III. Factoring	244
" IV. Greatest Common Divisor	249
" V. Least Common Multiple	257
" VI. Involution	261
" VII. Evolution	267

(ix)

1*

---

x

CONTENTS.

PART III.—Comparison.

Section I.—*Ratio and Proportion.*

	PAGE
Chapter I. Introduction to Comparison	291
" II. Nature of Ratio	294
" III. Nature of Proportion	305
" IV. Application of Simple Proportion	310
" V. Compound Proportion	318
" VI. History of Proportion	326

Section II.—*The Progressions.*

Chapter I. Arithmetical Progression	341
" II. Geometrical Progression	345

Section III.—*Percentage.*

Chapter I. Nature of Percentage	355
" II. Nature of Interest	361

Section IV.—*The Theory of Numbers.*

Chapter I. Nature of the Subject	371
" II. Even and Odd Numbers	375
" III. Prime and Composite Numbers	378
" IV. Perfect, Imperfect, etc., Numbers	383
" V. Divisibility of Numbers	389
" VI. The Divisibility by Seven	397
" VII. Properties of the Number Nine	404

PART IV.—Fractions.

Section I.—*Common Fractions.*

Chapter I. Nature of Fractions	413
" II. Classes of Common Fractions	420
" III. Treatment of Common Fractions	426
" IV. Continued Fractions	434

Section II.—*Decimal Fractions.*

Chapter I. Origin of Decimals	443
" II. Treatment of Decimals	455
" III. Nature of Circulates	460
" IV. Treatment of Circulates	464
" V. Principles of Circulates	470
" VI. Complementary Repetends	476
" VII. A New Circulate Form	481

PART V.—Denominate Numbers.

Chapter I. Nature of Denominate Numbers	489
" II. Measures of Extension	497
" III. Measures of Weight	512
" IV. Measures of Value	531
" V. Measures of Time	541
" VI. The Metric System	565

PART I.—The Nature of Arithmetic.

Section III.—*Arithmetical Reasoning.*

CHAPTER I.

There Is Reasoning in Arithmetic.

All reasoning is a process of *comparison;* it consists in comparing one idea or object of thought with another. Comparison requires a standard, and this standard is the old, the axiomatic, the known. To these standards we bring the new, the theoretic, the unknown, and compare them that we may understand them. The law of correct reasoning, therefore, is to compare the new with the old, the theoretic with the axiomatic, the unknown with the known.

This process, simple as it seems, is the real process of all reasoning. We pass from idea to truth, and from lower truth to higher truth, in the endless chain of science, by the simple process of comparison. Thus the facts and phenomena of the material world are understood, the laws of nature interpreted, and the principles of science evolved. Thus we pass from the old to the new, from the simple to the complex, from the known to the unknown. Thus we discover the truths and principles of the world of matter and mind, and construct the various sciences. Comparison is the science-builder; it is the architect which erects the temples of truth, vast, symmetrical, and beautiful.

In mathematics this process is, perhaps, more clearly exhibited than in any other science. In geometry, the definitions and axioms are the standards of comparison; beginning in these, we trace our way from the simplest primary truth to the profoundest theorem. In arithmetic we have the same basis, and proceed by the same laws of logical evolution. Definitions, as a description of fundamental ideas, and axioms, as the statement of intuitive and necessary truths, are the foundation upon which we rear the superstructure of the science of numbers.

These views, though admitted in respect of geometry, have not always been fully recognized as true of arithmetic. The science, as presented in the old text-books, was simply a collection of rules for numerical operations. The pupil learned the rules and followed them, without any idea of the reason for the operation dictated. There was no thought, no deduction from principle; the pupil plodded on, like a beast of burden or an unthinking machine. There was, in fact, as the subject was presented, no science of arithmetic. We had a science of geometry, pure, exact, and beautiful, as it came from the hand of the great masters. Beginning with primary conceptions and intuitive truths, the pupil could rise step by step from the simplest axiom to the loftiest theorem; but when he turned his attention to numbers, he found no beautiful relations, no interesting logical processes, nothing but a collection of rules for adding, subtracting, calculating the cost of groceries, reckoning interest, etc. Indeed, so universal was this darkness, that the metaphysicians argued that there could be no reasoning in the science of numbers, that it is a science of intuition; and the poor pupil, not possessing the requisite intuitive power, was obliged to plod along in doubt, darkness, and disgust.

Thus things continued until the light of popular education began to spread over the land. Men of thought and genius began to teach the elements of arithmetic to young pupils; and the necessity of presenting the processes so that children could see the reason for them, began to work a change in the science of numbers. Then came the method of arithmetical analysis, in that little gem of a book by Warren Colburn. It touched the subject as with the wand of an enchantress, and it began to glow with interest and beauty. What before was dull routine, now became animated with the spirit of logic, and arithmetic was enabled to take its place beside its sister branch, geometry, in dignity as a science, and value as an educational agency.

Before entering into an explanation of the character of arithmetical reasoning, it may be interesting to notice the views of some metaphysicians who have touched upon this subject. It has been maintained, as already indicated, by some eminent logicians, that there is no reasoning in arithmetic. Mansel says, "There is no demonstration in pure arithmetic," and the same idea is held by quite a large number of metaphysicians. This opinion is drawn from a very superficial view of the subject of arithmetic,— a not uncommon fault of the metaphysician when he attempts to write upon mathematical science. The course of reasoning which led to this conclusion, is probably as follows:

First, addition and subtraction were considered the two fundamental processes of arithmetic; all other processes were regarded as the outgrowth of these, and as contained in them. Second, there is no reasoning in addition; that the sum of 2 and 3 is 5, says Whewell, is seen by intuition; hence subtraction, which is the reverse of addition, is pure intuition also; and therefore the whole science, which is contained in these two processes, is also intuitive, and involves no reasoning. This inference seems plausible, and by the metaphysicians and many others has been considered conclusive.

That this conclusion is not only incorrect but absurd, may be seen by a reference to the more difficult processes of the science. Surely, no one can maintain that there is no reasoning in the processes of *greatest common divisor, least common multiple, reduction* and *division* of fractions, *ratio* and *proportion*, etc. If these are intuitive with the logicians, it is very certain that they require a great deal of thinking on the part of the learner. These considerations are sufficient to disprove their conclusions, but do not answer their arguments; it becomes necessary, therefore, to examine the matter a little more closely.

Whether the uniting of two small numbers, as *three* and *two*, involves a process of reasoning, is a point upon which it is admitted there may be some difference of opinion. The difference of two numbers, however, may be obtained by an inference from the results of addition, and, as such, involves a process of reasoning. The elementary products of the multiplication table are not intuitive truths; they are, as will be shown in the next article, derived, as a logical inference, from the elementary sums of addition. The same is also true in the case of the elementary quotients in division. Even admitting, then, that there is no reasoning in addition or subtraction, it can clearly be shown that the derivation of the elementary results in multiplication and division does require a process of reasoning. Passing from small numbers, which may be treated independently of any notation, to large numbers expressed by the Arabic system, we see that we are required to reduce from one form to another, as from units to tens, etc., which can be done only by a comparison, and also that the methods are based upon, and derived from such general principles, as "the sum of two numbers is equal to the sum of all their parts," etc.

The great mistake, however, in their reasoning, is in assuming that all arithmetic is included in addition and subtraction. If it could be proved that addition and subtraction, and the processes growing immediately out of them, contain no reasoning, a large portion of the science remains which does not find its root in these primary processes. Several divisions of arithmetic have their origin in and grow out of comparison, and not out of addition or subtraction; and since comparison is reasoning, the divisions of arithmetic growing out of it, it is natural to suppose, involve reasoning processes. Ratio, the comparison of numbers; proportion, the comparison of ratios; the progressions, etc., certainly present pretty good examples of reasoning. These belong to the department of pure arithmetic. A proportion is essentially numerical, as is shown in another place, and belongs to arithmetic rather than to geometry. If, in geometry, the treatment of a proportion involves a reasoning process, as the logicians will surely admit, it must certainly do so when presented in arithmetic, where it really belongs. It must, therefore, be admitted that there is reasoning in pure arithmetic.

Again, if there is no reasoning in arithmetic there is no science, for science is the product of reasoning. If we admit that there is a science of numbers, there must be some reasoning in the science. And again, arithmetic and geometry are regarded as the two great co-ordinate branches of mathematics. Now it is admitted that there is reasoning in geometry, the science of extension; would it not be absurd, therefore, to suppose that there is no reasoning in arithmetic, the science of numbers?

Mansel, as already quoted, says: "Pure arithmetic contains no demonstrations." If by this he means—and I presume he does—that pure arithmetic contains no reasoning, he is answered by the previous discussion. If, however, he means that arithmetic cannot be developed in the demonstrative form of geometry—that is, by definition, axiom, proposition, and demonstration—he is also in error. Though arithmetic has never been developed in this way, it can be thus developed. The science of number will admit of as rigid and systematic a treatment as the science of extension. Some parts of the science are even now presented thus; the principles of ratio, proportion, etc., are examples. I propose, at some future time, to give a complete development of the subject, after the manner of geometry. The science, thus presented, would be a valuable addition to our academic or collegiate course, as a review of the principles of numbers. Assuming, then, that there is reasoning in arithmetic, in the next chapter I shall consider the nature of reasoning, as employed in the fundamental operations of arithmetic.

.
.
.

MENTAL SCIENCE

AND

METHODS OF MENTAL CULTURE,

DESIGNED FOR

THE USE OF NORMAL SCHOOLS, ACADEMIES, AND PRIVATE
STUDENTS PREPARING TO BE TEACHERS.

BY

EDWARD BROOKS, A. M., Ph. D.,

PRINCIPAL OF STATE NORMAL SCHOOL, MILLERSVILLE PENNSYLVANIA, AND AUTHOR
OF NORMAL METHODS OF TEACHING. A NORMAL SERIES OF MATHEMATICS, ETC.

*" Whatever that is which thinks, which understands, which wills, which acts,
it is something celestial and divine; and, upon that account, must necessarily
be eternal."*—CICERO.

LANCASTER, PA.:
NORMAL PUBLISHING COMPANY.
1883.

TABLE OF CONTENTS.

PAGE

INTRODUCTION. iii

CHAPTER I.

The Nature of the Subject, . . . 13

CHAPTER II.

The Sources of the Mind, . . . 23

CHAPTER III.

The Nature of the Mind, . . . 30

CHAPTER IV.

The Functions of the Mind, . . . 36

MENTAL ATTRIBUTES.

CHAPTER I.

The Nature and Occasions. 43
Definition and Nature 46
Objects of Consciousness 48
Presentative Mental Modification

CHAPTER II.

The Objects of Consciousness. . . 55
Knowledge 58
Development of Consciousness . . 61
Knowledge through Individual Con-

CHAPTER III.

The Nature of Attention 67
Limits of Attention . . . .
Description of Attention . . . . .

CHAPTER IV.

The Culture of Attention. 73
Importance of Habits of At-
tention 75
Methods of Cultivating Atten-
tion 79
Securing Attention of Pupils. . .

THE INTELLECT.

PERCEPTION.

CHAPTER I.

The Nature of Power 86
Definition and Nature 94
The Nervous Organism . . . . . .
The Perceptive Process 99
Remarks on the Process . . . . .
Perception by the Different
Senses 110
The Qualities of Bodies . . . . .

CHAPTER II.

The Culture of Perception. 110
Importance of Culture 115
The Culture of the Process . . . 117
Importance of Culture . . . . . .
Difference of Perceptive
Power 119
Time for Culture 130
Methods of Culture 131
Special Lessons 135

THE MEMORY.

CHAPTER I.

The Nature of Memory . . . .
Definition . . . .
Recollection . . . .
Association 136
Recognition . . . .

8 CONTENTS

PAGE

Laws of Memory 140
Nature of the Laws 140
Primary Laws of Memory 113
Secondary Laws of Memory . . . 149
The One Primary Law 153
Remarks on the Memory 155

CHAPTER II.

The Culture of the Memory . . . .
Nature of the Culture 157
Value of Culture 163
Application in Teaching 166

THE IMAGINATION.

CHAPTER I.

The Nature of the Imagination . .
Nature of the Imagination . . . .
Products of the Imagination . . . 169
Forms of the Imagination 171
Scale of the Imagination . . . . .
Limits and Spheres 178

CHAPTER II.

The Culture of the Imagination . . 188
Value of the Imagination . . . . .
Culture of the Imagination . . . 191

THE UNDERSTANDING.

CHAPTER I.

The Nature of the Powers 204

CHAPTER II.

The Nature of Conception,
or the Concept. 210
Conception and Concept 210
Formation of Concepts 211
Nature of the Concept 214
Qualities of Concepts 215
Unfolding Conceptions 221
The Value of General Ideas. . . 223
Existence of General Ideas 223
Classification 225

CHAPTER IV.

The Nature of the Judgment. . . . 228
Definition and Nature 228
Nature of Judgments 149
Verbal Statement . . . .
Correctness of Judgment . . . . .

CHAPTER V.

The Nature of Reasoning 237
Definition and Kinds 241
The Syllogism 249
Deductive Reasoning . . . .
Another Form of Deduction . . . 251
Inductive Reasoning . . . .
Criteria of Induction 256
By-paths of Casual Agency . . . 261
Analogy and Theory 268
Testing 269

CHAPTER VI.

The Culture of the Understanding . 274
Importance of Culture 275
Neglect of Culture 276
Time for Culture 277
Culture of Abstraction . . . . . .

CHAPTER VII.

The Culture of Conception 279
By Logical Analysis . . . .
By Logical Division 281
By Logical Definition 284
The Culture of Classification . . . 287
Importance of Classification . . .
Methods of Culture 288

CHAPTER VIII.

The Culture of the Judgment. . . . 291
Importance of the Judgment . . .
Culture of the Judgment 295

CHAPTER IX.

The Culture of Reasoning 210
The Culture of Deduction 210
Study of Mathematics 211
Study of Language 212
Study of Metaphysics 213
Avoid Fallacies 291
The Culture of Induction 309
Inductive Teaching 310
Study of Natural Science 311

CONTENTS 9

PAGE

Inductive Teaching 311
Avoid Fallacies 316

INTUITION.

CHAPTER I.

The Nature of Intuition . . . . . .
Definition and Nature 319
Relation to other Faculties . . . 321
Relation to the Senses 323
Primacy of Intuition 324
Proof of Primacy 325
Nature of Primary Truths 326
Classes of Primary Truths 327
Proof of Primary Truths 329
Primary Ideas . . . .

CHAPTER II.

Temperament of Intuition 334
Beauty 340

THE INTUITIONS OF THE BEAUTIFUL.

CHAPTER III.

The Intuitions of the Beautiful . . 345
Objective Theory . . . .
Subjective Theory . . . .
The Feelings . . . .
Nature of the Ludicrous . . . . .
On Power of Taste . . . .

CHAPTER IV.

The Intuitions of the Beautiful. . .
Nature of the Ideal . . . .
Nature of the True . . . .
Origin of the Right . . . .
Nature of Conscience . . . .

CHAPTER V.

The Culture of the Intuitions . . .

CHAPTER VI.

The Nature of the Intuitions . . . 359
Value of Duty . . . .
Culture of the Intuition . . . . .
Culture of the Beautiful. . . . . .

CHAPTER VII.

THE CULTURE OF THE RIGHT.

Nature of Intuition 405
Importance of Ethical Culture . .
Importance of Moral Culture . . 408
Culture of Natural Culture . . . 409
Culture of the Conscience 413
Personal Duties 417
Duties to Others 417
Duties to God 424

THE SENSIBILITIES.

CHAPTER I.

The Nature of the Sensibilities. . . 432
Objective Feelings 435
Emotions 438
Definition and Nature . . . .
Primitive Emotions . . . .
Rational Emotions . . . .
The Ideal Emotions . . . .

CHAPTER II.

The Abstract Emotions 449
The Desires 450
The Animal 450
The Rational Desires 451

THE WILL.

CHAPTER I.

The Nature of the Will. 475
Definition and Nature . . . . . .
Importance of the Will. 484

CHAPTER II.

The Culture of the Will. . . . . . .
Culture of the Sensibilities . . . 435
Culture of the Affections 493
Freedom of the Will 502
Human Spiritual Culture . . . . .

Introduction.

CHAPTER III.

The Faculties of the Mind.

The mind is that which thinks, feels, and wills. It is that immaterial principle which we call the soul, the spirit, or the intelligence. Of its essence or substance, nothing is known; we know it only by its activities and its operations. The different forms of activity which it presents, indicate different mental powers, which are called *Faculties* of the mind.

A Mental Faculty.—A Mental Faculty is a capacity for a distinct form of mental activity. It is the mind's power of doing something, of putting forth some energy, of manifesting itself in some particular manner. The mind possesses as many faculties as there are distinct forms of mental activity. In order, therefore, to ascertain the different faculties of the mind, we must notice carefully the various ways in which the mind acts.

General Classification.—The mind embraces three general classes of faculties; the *Intellect*, the *Sensibilities*, and the *Will*. Every capacity or power which the mind possesses falls under one of these three heads. Every mental act is an act of the Intellect, the Sensibilities, or the Will. Every product of the mind is either an *intellection*, a *feeling*, or a *volition*.

The Mind Triune.—The mind is thus a tri-unity,—one substance with a trinity of powers. The doctrine of the Trinity is as evident in the creature as in the Creator. Made in the image of God, the mind reflects the nature of the divine pattern after which it was fashioned. As in God we have the Father, the Son, and the Holy Spirit; so in man we have the Intellect, the Sensibilities, and the Will.

The Intellect.—The Intellect is the power by which we think and know. Its products are *ideas* and *thoughts*. An Idea is a mental product, which may be expressed in one or more words, not forming a proposition; as, a *man*, an *animal*, etc. A Thought is a mental product consisting of the combination of two or more ideas, which when expressed in words, gives us a proposition; as, *a man is an animal*. Our notions of the different figures of geometry, as *angles*, *triangles*, *squares*, etc., are *ideas;* while our conceptions of *axioms* and *theorems* are *thoughts*.

The Sensibilities.—The Sensibilities are the powers by which we feel. Their products are *emotions*, *affections*, and *desires*. An *emotion* is a simple feeling, as the emotion of joy, sorrow, etc. An *affection* is an emotion that goes out towards an object; as *love, hate, envy,* etc. A *desire* is an emotion that goes out to an object with the wish of possession; as the *desire* of *wealth, fame,* etc.

The Will.—The Will is the power of deciding or determining what to do and of putting forth volitions accordingly. It is the executive power of the mind, the power by which man becomes the conscious author of an intentional act. It is the motive power of the mind; by it we put the other faculties into activity and control their action. The products of the Will are *volitions* and *voluntary actions.* It is in the domain of the Will that man becomes a moral and responsible being.

The Intellect.—The Intellect embraces several distinct faculties; *Perception, Memory, Imagination, Understanding,* and *Intuition,* or the *Reason.* This classification of the Intellect is now almost universally accepted, though writers occasionally differ in the terms they use to name the different powers.

Perception.—Perception is the power by which we gain a knowledge of external objects through the senses. It is the faculty by which we gain a knowledge of objects and their qualities. Its products are ideas of external objects and of the qualities of objects. The products of perception are called *percepts.* The ideas which we possess of persons, places, things, etc., are mainly given by perception.

Memory.—Memory is the power by which we retain and recall knowledge. It enables us to hold fast to the knowledge we have acquired, and also to recall it when we wish to use it. These two offices of the Memory are distinguished as *Retention* and *Recollection.* By some writers these are regarded as separate faculties; and others again discard the element of retention. Besides these, the memory also gives us a *representation* of that which it recalls, and *recognizes* it as something of our past experience.

Imagination.—Imagination is the power by which we form ideal conceptions. It is the power of forming mental images by uniting different parts of objects given by perception, and also of creating ideals of objects different from anything we have perceived. Thus, I can conceive of a *flying horse* by uniting my ideas of wings and a horse; or I can imagine a landscape or a strain of music different from anything I have ever seen or heard. Imagination is thus *the power of ideal creation.*

Understanding.—The Understanding is the power by which we compare objects of thought and derive abstract and general ideas and truths. It is the elaborative power of the mind; it takes the materials furnished by the other faculties and works them up into new products. Its products are *abstract* and *general ideas, truths, laws, causes,* etc.

Intuition.—Intuition, or the Reason, is the power which gives us ideas and thoughts not furnished by the senses nor elaborated by the Understanding. Its products are called *primary ideas* and *primary truths*. The Primary Ideas are such as Space, Time, Cause, Identity, the True, the Beautiful, and the Good. The Primary Truths are all self-evident truths, as the axioms of mathematics and logic.

The Understanding.—The Understanding embraces several distinct faculties or forms of mental activity. These are *Abstraction, Conception, Judgment,* and *Reasoning.* This division is now almost universally adopted, and the same terms are employed by nearly all modern writers.

Abstraction.—Abstraction is the power of forming abstract ideas. It is the power by which the mind draws a quality away from its object, and makes of it a distinct object of thought. Its products are *abstract ideas,* such as *hardness, softness, color,* etc. The naming of abstract ideas gives us abstract terms. The term *Abstraction* is derived from *ab,* from, and *traho,* I draw, and signifies a drawing from.

Conception.—Conception is the power of forming general ideas. By it we take several particular ideas, and unite their common properties, and thus form a general idea which embraces them all. The products of Conception are *general ideas,* or ideas of *classes;* as *horse, bird, man,* etc. The naming of general ideas gives us *common terms.* This faculty is often called *Generalization;* but the term *Conception* is more appropriate, and is the one generally adopted by logicians. The term *Conception* is derived from *con,* together, and *capio,* I take, and signifies a taking together.

Judgment.—Judgment is the power of perceiving the agreement or disagreement of two objects of thought. It is the power of comparison. It compares one object directly with another, and gives us a *proposition.* A proposition is a judgment expressed in words. Thus, *a bird is an animal,* is a judgment expressed. The term Judgment is applied to both the mental faculty and its product.

Reasoning.—Reasoning is the power of comparing two ideas through their relation to a third. It is a process of indirect or mediate comparison. It deals with three objects of thought, and requires· three propositions. Thus, suppose I wish to compare A and B, and perceiving no relation between them, see that A equals C, and B equals C, and thus infer that A equals B; such an inference is an act of reasoning.

The Syllogism.—The form in which reasoning is expressed is called a *Syllogism.* A Syllogism consists of three propositions so related that one is an inference from the other two. Two of these propositions are called the *premises* and the third the *conclusion.* Thus, in the above example the two propositions, "A equals C" and "B equals C," are the premises; and "A equals B" is the conclusion.

Inductive Reasoning.—Reasoning is of two kinds; *Inductive Reasoning* and *Deductive Reasoning.* Inductive Reasoning is the process of deriving a general truth from particular truths. Thus, if I find that heat expands several metals, as zinc, iron, copper, etc., I may infer that heat will expand *all metals*. Such an inference of a general truth from the particular facts is called *Induction*. Inductive Reasoning proceeds upon the principle that *what is true of the many is true of the whole*.

Deductive Reasoning.—Deductive Reasoning is the process of deriving a particular truth from a general truth. Thus, from the general proposition that *heat expands all metals*, I may infer by Deduction that heat will expand any particular metal, as silver. Deduction proceeds upon the principle that *what is true of the whole is true of the parts*.

Other Forms of Activity.—Besides the faculties now named, two other forms of mental activity or mental states are usually described by writers on mental science; namely, *Consciousness* and *Attention*. These are not regarded as specific faculties of the mind, but as conditions or accompaniments of these faculties. A term very frequently used in mental philosophy also is that of *Conception*, which also requires a few words of explanation.

Consciousness.—Consciousness is the power or attribute of the mind by which it knows its own states and actions. The term is derived from *con*, with, and *scio*, I know, and means a knowing with the mental acts or states. It is a kind of inner light by which one knows what is going on within his mind; it is a revealer of the internal phenomena of thought, feeling, and will. Consciousness is regarded as an attribute of the mind, involved in the very idea of mind, and not as a distinct mental faculty.

Attention.—Attention is the power of directing the mind voluntarily to any object of thought to the exclusion of others. It is the power of selecting one of several objects, and concentrating the mental energies upon it. Attention is not a distinct form of mental activity, but is involved in and underlies the activity of all the faculties. The voluntary operation of any of the mental powers, as Perception, Memory, etc., carries with it an act of attention. The term is derived from *ad*, to, and *tendo*, I bend, which was probably suggested by the attitude of the body in listening attentively to a sound.

Conception.—The term *Conception* is often used in a general and popular sense, meaning that power which the mind has of making anything a distinct object of thought. In this sense it is intimately related to all the mental faculties. Thus I can conceive of a tree or a horse which I have seen, a landscape which I may not have seen, a proposition in geometry, a truth in natural philosophy, etc. Some writers have used the term in a more specific sense, as the power of forming an exact transcript of a past perception. In Logic the term is restricted to the power of forming general ideas, as we have previously defined it.

Hamilton's Classification.—Sir Wm. Hamilton, one of the most eminent philosophers of modern times, presents a classification of the intellect which has been much admired for its simplicity and the suggestive character of the terms used. He divides the Intellect into the Presentative, Conservative,

Reproductive, Representative, Elaborative, and Regulative powers.

The Presentative power is that which presents knowledge to the mind; it corresponds to Perception. The Conservative power is that which retains or preserves knowledge in the mind; it corresponds to the retentive element of the Memory. The Reproductive power is that which reproduces knowledge in the mind; it corresponds to the recalling element of the Memory. The Representative power is that which represents knowledge to the mind; it corresponds to the Imagination. The Elaborative power is that which works up or elaborates the knowledge attained by the other faculties; it corresponds to the Understanding. The Regulative power is that which regulates the activities of the other faculties; it corresponds to the Reason.

CHAPTER IV.

The Culture of the Mind.

The Science of Education treats of the developing of the powers of man and the furnishing of his mind with knowledge. The developing of the powers is called *culture,* and the furnishing of the mind with knowledge is called *instruction.* A formal treatment of the methods of cultivating the mind is called *Methods of Culture;* a formal treatment of the methods of instructing the mind is called *Methods of Instruction.*

Nature of Culture.—Methods of Culture treats of the nature of the powers of man and how to develop them. It includes several branches, such as Physical Culture, Intellectual Culture, Aesthetic Culture, Moral Culture, and Religious Culture. The present work treats of the nature of the mind and the methods of cultivating it, and is entitled Mental Science and Mental Culture. Our purpose, therefore, is not only to describe the different faculties of the mind, but also to discuss the methods of cultivating them. Having given an idea of the general nature of the mind, we now present a few principles relating to its culture. These may be called the fundamental principles of mental culture.

1. *The object of mental culture is the fullest development and highest activity of the faculties of the mind.* The mind is developed by culture. Its powers are strengthened and made to act with vigor and skill by judicious training. Without such training the mind may either remain comparatively inert, or its activities may conflict with the normal laws of mental development and fail to produce the best fruits of culture and knowledge. In this respect the mind is like a field, and mental culture like the culture of the soil. Left to itself, a farm may be overrun with weeds and briers, while if subjected to the careful culture of the husbandman, it will teem with golden harvests. So the mind, if left to itself, may waste its energies and acquire incorrect habits of activity; while if subjected to the guiding hand of culture, it may develop in normal strength and vigor, and bring forth rich harvests of precious knowledge.

2. *One of the primary conditions of mental culture is a well-organized and healthy brain.* The mind acts largely, if not entirely, through or by means of the brain. In its first activities of sensation, the brain and nervous system are an essential condition and medium of mental activity. Impressions made upon the nerves are transmitted to the brain, and there emerge

83

in conscious knowledge. Subsequently thought becomes abstract and seems to be independent of the brain; yet experience proves that the power of abstract thought depends for clearness and vigor upon the condition of the physical system. Indeed, it is not certain that genius and hereditary mental traits may not depend on some subtle organic peculiarity of the brain. It is, therefore, an established fact, that for the best results in mental culture we must endeavor to secure the best condition of the brain and nervous system. "A sound mind in a sound body" is a maxim not to be forgotten in mental culture.

3. *The mind is cultivated by the activity of its faculties.* The mind is a spiritual activity and grows by its own inherent energies. Mental exercise is thus the law of mental development. As a muscle grows strong by use, so any faculty of the mind is developed by its proper use and exercise. An inactive mind, like an unused muscle, becomes weak and unskillful. Hang the arm in a sling and the muscle becomes flabby and loses its vigor and skill; let the mind remain inactive, and it acquires a mental flabbiness, that unfits it for any severe or prolonged activity. An idle mind loses its tone and strength, like an unused muscle; the mental powers go to rust through idleness and inaction. To develop the faculties of the mind and secure their highest activity and efficiency there must be a constant and judicious exercise of these faculties. The object of culture is to stimulate and direct the activity of the mind.

4. *The activity of the mind requires objective realities for it to act upon.* The mind cannot act upon itself; there must be material for it to act upon. As a power to know, it demands an external world of knowledge to meet the wants of the internal knowing subject. There is such a world of knowledge suited to and correlating with every mental activity. The material world is seen to be an embodiment of thought, and the mind begins its activities with the objects of the material world. The mind itself has developed knowledge by its powers of thought, which is also adapted to give culture to each faculty and capacity. This adaptation is manifest, since knowledge, as the product of one mind, must be suited to the different capacities of all minds. The mind begins its activity with the knowledge thus furnished; it then passes to the creation of knowledge for itself, which affords it its highest and best activity. It is thus apparent that the culture of the mind requires objective realities, and that these realities are abundantly furnished.

5. *Each faculty of the mind requires a culture adapted to itself.* The mind possesses a variety of powers, and each one of these powers operates with different material, and has an activity peculiar to itself. Each power needs different materials for its activity; what would be best for one faculty would not be the appropriate material for some other faculty. We need concrete objects for perception, facts for the memory, abstract truth for the judgment and the power of reasoning, beauty for the imagination, moral

truth for the conscience, etc. Besides this difference of material, there is also a difference in the activity of the different faculties; the memory operates in one way, the understanding in another, etc. Both of these things, the material and the methods of activity, are to be taken into consideration in the culture of the mind. Each faculty, therefore, requires, for its training and development, a culture peculiar to itself.

6. *The culture of the mind should be adapted to the order of the development of its faculties.* The different faculties do not develop simultaneously. Though all are active from the earliest dawn of intelligence, yet they are active in different degrees at different periods. Some faculties are much more active in childhood, and others need the maturity of years for their mature and full development. The natural order of their development should be understood and followed in culture. To endeavor to force all the faculties to equal activity in childhood would be a mistake injurious to the mind and subversive of the best results of culture. The true order of development should be carefully studied and distinctly understood, and the work of culture adapted thereto.

7. *The culture of the mind should aim at a harmonious development of all the faculties.* Man possesses a multiplicity of capacities and powers, all of which contribute to his well-being and his dignity. These powers are so related that they may be unfolded in very nearly equal proportions, and harmoniously blend in the final results of culture. For the attainment of a true ideal of education such a development is required. A perfectly developed manhood or womanhood implies the complete development of every capacity and every gift. The training of the mind, therefore, should reach every power and unfold every capacity. The high aim of culture should be the full and harmonious development of all the faculties.

8. *The culture of the mind should be modified by the different tastes and talents of a pupil.* While all minds possess the same general powers, these powers are often possessed in different degrees. There is often an unusual gift of some one power or combination of powers which gives us what we call genius. Tastes or dispositions for different activities or pursuits also vary. Such differences are not to be overlooked in mental culture. While we should aim to give a general development to all the faculties, we should not forget these special gifts. Genius should be recognized, and an opportunity given for its highest development and achievements.

.
.
.

The Understanding.

CHAPTER IX.

The Culture of Reasoning.

Reasoning is the last and the highest operation of the Understanding. There are two distinct forms of reasoning: Deductive Reasoning and Inductive Reasoning. Each of these two forms of reasoning may be cultivated by appropriate exercise. We shall therefore discuss the culture of reasoning under the two distinct heads; the Culture of Deductive Reasoning, and the Culture of Inductive Reasoning.

I. The Culture of Deductive Reasoning.

Deductive Reasoning, as already defined, is the process of deriving a particular truth from a general truth. It is a form of mental activity which operates early in the mind of the child; and is to be trained by appropriate exercises. Many of the branches of the school course are especially adapted to give exercise and culture to this power. The teacher should understand the relation of these studies to the mind, that he may give this culture consciously and intelligently. Some of the exercises and studies particularly suited to the culture of deductive reasoning, will therefore be mentioned.

I. Study of Mathematics.—The study, *par excellence*, for the culture of deductive reasoning, is mathematics. The several branches of mathematics present the purest examples of deductive reasoning; they are therefore pre-eminently fitted to give training to the power of deductive thought. They are also adapted to every stage of intellectual development, since they range from the simplest processes of mental arithmetic to the profoundest generalizations of calculus. The pupil should, at an early age, begin the simple analyses of arithmetic; from this he should pass to the more concise and abstract reasoning of algebra, which, in its first steps, is similar to the reasoning of arithmetic. Following the elements of algebra, or in connection with it, he should take up the science of geometry, in which he will become acquainted with the more formal methods of syllogistic reasoning.

Mental Arithmetic.—Mental arithmetic is especially adapted to give culture to the reasoning power of the young mind. By mental arithmetic, we mean not the mere working of problems without slate or pencil, but that system of arithmetical analysis which is found developed in a good work on the subject. Mental arithmetic is a system of practical logic in its simplest form; every step is a judgment direct or indirect, and the entire subject is permeated with the spirit of logic. Its processes are purely analytic, and it thus trains the mind to the most rigid analysis. Every truth is bound to some other truth by the thread of related thought; and the mind of the pupil acquires the habit of following a chain of logically-connected judgments until it reaches a satisfactory conclusion. To give exercise to the reasoning powers of the child, mental arithmetic may be placed at the head of the list of studies of the primary school.

Sharpens the Mind.—Mental arithmetic sharpens and strengthens the powers of thought. The system of rigid analysis gives point and penetrating power to the mind, and enables it to pierce a subject to its core and discover its elements. In this respect, mental arithmetic is a sort of mental whetstone, which gives edge and keenness to the mind. Old Robert Recorde called his work on arithmetic the "Whetstone of Witte;" had he lived until the era of mental arithmetic, he would have seen the full meaning of his words, for the method of analysis found in mental arithmetic is indeed a whetstone of wit, a sharpener of the mental faculties. Mental arithmetic is a system of mental gymnastics; through it the mind grows strong and tough, taking hold of difficulties with a will, laughing at obstacles, and rejoicing in the investigation of the intricate and profound.

Study of Written Arithmetic.—The study of written arithmetic leads the mind to a higher plane of deductive thought. While the reasoning in mental arithmetic is purely analytic, the reasoning of written arithmetic is more synthetic and demonstrative in its nature. Thus many subjects which in mental arithmetic are treated by pure analysis, in written arithmetic are treated by demonstration. In mental arithmetic we treat all the various cases of Fractions by analysis; while in written arithmetic we may first establish a few general principles, and then derive all the rules for the several cases by deduction from these principles. Many subjects in written arithmetic are purely deductive and demonstrative in their nature, as Proportion, Progression, Evolution, etc. The study of written arithmetic thus lifts the mind up into a higher plane of deductive thought, and gives a culture adapted to the advancing maturity of the mind. When properly taught, not as a collection of rules for arbitrary results, but as a system of logical processes, it affords the mind a delightful and valuable exercise in deductive thought.

Study of Algebra.—Algebra is also a valuable study in training the power of deductive reasoning. In its elementary ideas and processes, it has its origin in arithmetic, and flows out of it; and its spirit and methods are essentially deductive. Its methods of calculation are analytic and demonstrative; and it rises into the sphere of generalization, which gives a breadth and reach of mind that we cannot acquire in arithmetic. This spirit of generalization lies at the basis of the science, and has given us the profound thinkers in astronomy and physics, such as Newton and La Place. The interpretation of these general formulas, as applied to particular cases, so valuable in the investigations of the physical sciences, is also an excellent exercise for the development of the thought-powers of the student.

Study of Geometry.—In giving discipline to the power of reasoning, geometry has been placed high in the list of thought studies. Geometry is purely a deductive science. It begins with definite ideas expressed in strictly logical definitions, has its fundamental truths or axioms given by intuition, and with these as a basis, proceeds by the logic of deduction to derive all the other truths of the science. It is regarded as the most perfect model of a deductive science, and is the type and model of all science.

Invaluable Discipline.—As a study for the discipline of the power of thought, geometry is invaluable. It is the perfection of logic, and excels in training the mind to logical habits of thinking. In this respect it is superior to the study of logic itself, for it is logic embodied in the science of tangible form. While logic makes us familiar with the principles of reasoning, geometry trains the mind to the habit of reasoning. No study is better adapted to make close and accurate thinkers. Euclid has done more to develop the logical faculty of the world than any book ever written. It has been the inspiring influence of scientific thought for ages, and is one of the corner-stones of modern civilization.

A Test of Power.—Geometry not only gives mental power, but is a test of mental power. The boy who cannot readily master his geometry will never attain to much in the domain of thought. He may have a fine poetic sense that will make a writer or an orator; but he can never reach any eminence in scientific thought or philosophic opinion. All the great geniuses in the realm of science, as far as known, had fine mathematical abilities. So valuable is geometry as a discipline that many lawyers and preachers review their geometry every year in order to keep the mind drilled to logical habits of thinking.

Subjects for Original Thought.—In these branches of mathematics, the student should have problems and theorems for original thought. Problems for solution are usually given in arithmetic and algebra; in geometry, however, the practice has been to present only theorems demonstrated in the text-book, but no undemonstrated theorems to train the student to reason independently of the text-book. This is regarded as a serious defect in the methods of teaching geometry. There should be a large number of theorems for original thought; and the student should be required to discover the demonstrations for himself. In this way he may be able not only, as Cyril said of the girl-students, to "hunt old trails," but also "to invent" processes of reasoning for himself. He will become an original thinker in the domain of quantity, and acquire that acuteness of insight and independence of thought that characterize the profound thinker.

.
.
.

II. Culture of Inductive Reasoning.

Inductive Reasoning is the process of deriving a general truth from particular truths. It is one of the earliest forms of thinking manifested by the young mind; and is developed by appropriate exercise and training. This exercise and training may be given in four different ways; by the inductive teaching of several of the elementary branches of study; by the formal study of the material sciences; by original investigations in these sciences; and by being careful to avoid the fallacies of induction.

I. Inductive Method of Teaching.—The power of inductive reasoning may be cultivated by the inductive method of teaching several of the elementary branches. The inductive method of teaching is that form of teaching which passes from particulars to generals. By it the pupil may be led from particular ideas to general ideas, or from particular truths to general truths. The former gives culture to generalization, which is in the spirit of inductive thought; the latter requires inductive reasoning on the part of the pupil, which gives direct culture to inductive thinking. The principal of the school branches for the inductive method, are Object Lessons, Geography, Grammar, and Arithmetic.

In Object Lessons.—Object Lessons deal with objects and their properties, and these constitute the foundation of the inductive sciences. A system of object lessons is especially adapted to train the power of observation, which lies at the basis of the development of the inductive sciences. An object lesson requires a pupil to analyze an object into its parts, to look at its details; and thus leads him to acquire the habit of close, accurate, and analytical perception. The pupil may also be led to classify objects, which is a stage of inductive science. He may also be led to inquire after the causes of certain facts and appearances of the objects, which is induction proper. A system of object lessons, in the hands of an intelligent teacher, may thus lead a pupil in the first steps of inductive thought and science.

In Teaching Geography.—Geography is a natural science and is developed inductively; and when properly taught, gives exercise in inductive thought. In this branch, a pupil should first see particular examples of the different divisions of land and water,—continents, capes, peninsulas, islands, oceans, gulfs, bays, etc.,—and from these be led up to the general notion of them and their definitions. So also the particular rivers and mountains should be first presented, and the pupil be led to unite them into river-systems and mountain-chains, thus proceeding from the particular to the general. So far as geography treats of causes and laws, they should follow the facts which depend upon them. Taught in this way, geography cultivates inductive thinking; taught, however, by the ordinary method of definition and description, very little thought is awakened, and what there is, is in the spirit of deduction rather than induction.

In Teaching Arithmetic.—Even arithmetic, which is a deductive science, may be so taught as to train the faculty of inductive thought. The earliest instruction in arithmetic should be presented concretely and inductively. The mind should proceed from objects to numbers, from ideas of processes to their formal statement, from the analysis of particular examples to the general rules, from the use of a principle in some special case that gives rise to it, to its formal announcement in a general proposition. Thus the pupil may be made familiar with the process of uniting and separating numbers before he learns to call it addition and subtraction; he may analyze special examples in the different cases of fractions, and then derive a rule from the steps of the analysis; and this is inductive in its character. So, in common divisor, common multiple, evolution, etc., the principle may be first presented in the special case of a problem being solved, from which the mind may be led to its formal statement. Subsequently, the principles may be demonstrated by deductive processes, and the rules derived from general principles.

In Teaching Algebra.—Some culture of inductive thought may be given, even in the study of algebra. We may pass from the particular solutions of arithmetic to the more general solutions with algebraic symbols. The transition from figures to letters, from numerical exponents to literal exponents, and the generalization of particular processes, are all in the spirit of inductive thought. Some of the methods of operation and general formulas may also be obtained by inductive methods of reasoning. Newton discovered his celebrated "binomial formula" by induction; he left no deductive demonstration of it and probably never discovered one. Fermat's formula for prime numbers, $2^m + 1$, when m is a term in the series 1, 2, 4, 8, etc., which Euler showed is incorrect when m equals 32, was derived by induction. The method of "mathematical induction," often used in algebra, is more deductive in its nature than inductive, and does not afford culture to inductive reasoning; and most of the reasoning of algebra trains to deductive rather than inductive thought.

In Teaching Grammar.—Grammar is largely a deductive science, but its elements may be taught inductively; and when thus taught, will give culture to inductive reasoning. Thus, we may first present individual examples of nouns, and then lead to the general idea of a noun and to its definition; and so with all the parts of speech. So also we may lead the pupil to discover the properties of number, case, etc., from language, and to derive the rules of inflection from individual cases of inflection. The rules of syntax may also be first presented in special cases, and the mind be led to grasp the general from the particular. Such teaching is in the spirit of induction, and trains to inductive habits of thought. Other school studies may be presented in a like manner, and when so taught do something for the culture of inductive reasoning.

.
.
.

The following three readings detail the early-grade arithmetic methods of the late nineteenth century. The first is from an 1885 prospectus for books of the popular Wentworth series. It describes the approach used in *First Steps in Number,* copyright 1884, which was still in print in 1921—well after the doctrine of incidental learning gained acceptance for early number work. The second selection expounds the Grube method with its Pestalozzian roots. Grube's *Leitfaden für das Rechnen in der Elementarschule* (1842) had been translated earlier, and its influence is noticeable in *First Steps in Number* as well as in various other elementary texts of this time. The third selection is from a "how to teach" book and is included as an example of a less specialized work.

Biographical information about Wentworth precedes these selections.

GEORGE ALBERT WENTWORTH

George Albert Wentworth (1835–1906) was educated at Exeter Academy and taught there for more than half his life.[1] His texts are credited with having the widest circulation of any used in the 1880s. Because of his forceful method of teaching he was known by his students as "Bull" Wentworth. After his death his son George (1868–1921), who also taught at Exeter, continued his father's tradition by coauthoring the extremely popular Wentworth-Smith Mathematical Series with David Eugene Smith.

Since G. A. Wentworth's name sometimes appeared on texts written mainly by others and his primary interest was in secondary school mathematics, we may surmise that *First Steps in Number* is largely the work of E. M. Reed, the coauthor. The popularity of this book continued well into the period when extensive early number work had lost support.

1. B. F. Finkel, "Biography of George Albert Wentworth," *School Science and Mathematics* 7 (June 1907): 485–88, and Harry Gwinner, "The Two Wentworths." *National Mathematics Magazine* 9 (March 1935): 165.

How to Teach Number.

AN OUTLINE OF THE METHOD EMBODIED IN

WENTWORTH & REED'S

First Steps in Number,

WITH

SPECIMEN PAGES AND A FULL DESCRIPTION OF

THIS AND THE OTHER BOOKS

IN

WENTWORTH'S MATHEMATICAL SERIES.

————o0⚬0o————

Copyright, 1885, by

GINN & COMPANY, PUBLISHERS,

Boston, New York, and Chicago.

How to Teach Number.

In the primary grades Number-work is chiefly constructive; the object is knowledge of numbers, and so the teacher should begin with a number, and take all processes with it.

The first thing to do is to find out what the children know of number. For this purpose the teacher may call them, half a dozen at a time, about a table on which are objects of various kinds, and holding up two objects, say:—

Edith, find so many blocks; Harry, find so many buttons; Walter, find so many wheels; Mabel, find so many spools.

Come and tell me how many you show me.

If all give the correct answer, she may continue the test by requiring each child to draw two marks on the board, to show two pegs, to show two different things, to name two different things in the room, two things seen on the street, two things at home, two days of the week.

If a child does not stand this test, the teacher should excuse him, and proceed with the rest until assured that they know *two* under all ordinary conditions. Then she may test for *three* in the same way. More children will have to be excused during this test. She should proceed in the same way with higher numbers, until the limit of the children's knowledge is reached.

The ability to count by ones is no proof of the perception of a number. The child may know the succession of numbers without knowing that four is different from one. As he repeats the numbers, each is only one to him. The fourth one is four, not the four ones taken together.

Two is usually the limit of the child's knowledge. About one-fourth of the children know three when they enter school. A few know four. So there will be three groups of beginners, namely, those whose knowledge of numbers is confined to two, those who know three, and those who know four. One group, therefore, begins with three, another with four, and the other with five.

Suppose that the number four is to be taught. Four is so many [things], not a sign which we call a figure; so to give an idea of four, the teacher must present things, not a sign. Four has an individuality of its own, and is worthy of introduction without the aid of its smaller sisters; so do not let the child arrive at four by counting.

There is no call at any time for any teaching of counting by ones. The pupil learns the right succession of numbers unconsciously as numbers are presented to him in a logical order. The teaching of each number may be considered under four heads:—

    1. The perception of the number.
    2. The analysis of the number.
    3. Drill to fix facts discovered by analysis.
    4. Comparison with smaller numbers.

To give the child an opportunity of getting this knowledge, the teacher must present the number under many conditions, or, in other words, cause it to be applied to various classes of objects. Objects most convenient for use are light wooden blocks, checkers, buttons, card-board disks, and rings of stiff paper, sticks, spools, paper money, geometric figures (cut from bright paper), artificial flowers, and paper patterns of familiar objects, horses, birds, dogs, cats, mice, fish, butterflies, bugs, pails, cups, spoons, knives, forks, brooms, dust-pans, spades, rakes, scissors, hats, caps, gloves, boots. These patterns can be easily cut out for one's self, and are specially recommended as being very suggestive in language work in number.

A table is almost indispensable in the objective work in number. It places the objects within convenient reach of all, and brings the children into the most favorable position for giving attention to the work in hand. By such an arrangement, too, the teacher's effort travels over the smallest possible amount of space, and is, therefore, utilized to its utmost.

Holding up four blocks, the teacher directs each child to show so many; saying, "I show you *four* blocks. How many buttons do you show me, Bessie, when you show me so many? How many knives, Henry? How many brooms, Katie? How many silver dollars, Mary?" She then directs each pupil to show four, mentioning the objects she wishes him to take. "Ella, show me four pails. Dolly, four birds. Harry, four beetles. Susie, four rings. Annie, four flowers." This is not difficult, and the number is almost always correctly shown the first time. She continues, "Make on the board four straight marks up and down, four from right to left. Four is four dots, four crosses, four rings. Show me four things unlike each other. Tell me how many things I show you," showing a flower, a stick, a pair of scissors, and a bird. "Tell me how many flowers I name: a violet, a daisy, a buttercup, and a dandelion. How many trees: an oak, a maple, an elm, and a chestnut tree. How many animals: a horse, an ox, a sheep, and a dog. You may name four things not in this room, four kinds of food, four things you can do, four things that you wear, four streets, four children."

Some important discoveries will be made here, namely, (1) That four large objects, as blocks, are known as four, when the same number of pegs cannot be told. (2) That four things of the same color are recognized, while four things of different colors are not. (3) That four things of a kind are recognized when four things of different kinds are not. (4) That four things can be selected when four cannot be created, as making four marks on the board. (5) That to carry the number in the mind while four different objects not visible are named, is quite a difficult feat, and equally difficult is it for the child to name four different things, no more, no less. The teaching of number should follow an order corresponding to these discoveries; therefore the pupil must not be considered ready for the next number until he has fully mastered these steps. It simply requires close observation, and if the pupil has not this power, he cannot advance in his study of a number. This is the test of his ability to take up the regular work of the school.

When a *perception* of the number has been gained, then comes the analysis of it. The teacher says: "We shall find some other number in four if we will look at it. Who sees it?" Three is the number usually found at this suggestion. Take it away, and see what number is left. Put back the three with the one, and tell what number you see. Who finds another number in four? Two is the number found this time. Take it away, and tell me what is left.

Put the two you took away with the two that is left; what number is formed? Take away the smallest number you see in four. How many are left? Put the one with three. What is formed? Take four away, and tell me what you see. Separate the one-blocks from one another. How many one-blocks do you find? Separate the twos from each other. How many twos do you find? Who will show me all by himself one thing we found out about four? Who will show me another? another?

The facts in the number having been found, namely, $3 + 1$, $4 - 1$, $4 - 3$, $2 + 2$, $4 - 2$, 2×2, $4 \div 2$, $4 - 4$, $4 \div 1$, 4×1, each fact must be repeated until it is fixed in the mind. Seeing the fact helps to fix it. Hearing about the fact helps to fix it. Giving for one's self problems whose conditions fit the fact helps to fix it: so all these ways must be employed until quick, bright, and accurate answers from each child are secured. Example making becomes easy when the child has before him the objects about which to talk. One tells of his horses, another of his tops, another of his tubs, another of her dolls. When the child's imagination suggests objects about which to talk, give him blocks and let him call them what he wishes. He calls them barrels, elephants, lions, tigers, torches, guns, banners, and tells his story to fit his subject. When the work with objects has been carried far enough, remove them and ask for a story.

In the presentation of any fact the first questions should relate to the objects before the children; the second to objects represented by blocks, and the final questions to objects without representation.

When *one* fact has been taught, the next fact in order should be taken and presented in a similar way. *One fact at a time and only one*, not a half dozen, nor even two, but just *one* new fact together with review at each lesson. This is the secret of success in teaching facts. It does not lie in the first presentation, however clear that may be; but the fact must be recalled until the memory can call it up at any time without effort. Then it is known.

The last point in teaching a single number is to compare it with smaller numbers for relative size. This comparison must not be made by division, but by placing the two numbers to be compared side by side, that a visual measurement may be taken to ascertain how many more in one than in the other.

Place four blocks in a row and below them three blocks. "In which row is there the more blocks? Howe many more?" This is one of the most difficult questions to answer. Children who have worked intelligently up to this point are puzzled by the "How many *more?*" It is not always necessary to help them out of their perplexity. Let them look and think, and they see it. When it is necessary to give help, let the teacher say: "You may take one from the three-row at the same time that I take one from the four-row until you have taken all of yours." The teacher, of course, has one left, and to the question "How many more in four than in three?" the child is now ready to answer. "One." Then problems relating to this fact must be given until sufficient repetition has been made to impress the truth. The comparison of four with two, with one, and with none is made in like manner.

All numbers to ten should be measured in the same way. No figures or signs of operations should be used in connection with the first numbers taught; only the written words one, two, three, four, etc., and the expression of facts in words. The children have their board work in number, but it is expressed in words instead of in figures. The teacher may arrange short lines or dots in groups on the board at the left of a long, vertical line, and let the children copy and put the result in one group at the right of the line.

Brown paper charts with groups of colored triangles, squares, or rings pasted on them can be used with great advantage for drill in quick recognition of groups of numbers, and for drill in making rapid combinations and separations. Thus: the teacher points to any group not larger than five, and requires instant recognition of the number, or points to two groups of numbers, as ○ ○ ○, ○ ○ ○ ○, and requires the answer, five, seven, at once. At almost every recitation there should be a similar exercise at the number table. Showing a number of blocks, ask, "How many?" or showing one number and adding another to it, say, "Read what I show you." Facts in subtraction, multiplication, and division are shown and read. It is wonderful what quickness of sight can be cultivated by this simple exercise. The teacher must never allow hesitation or counting by ones, and must treat a mistake as a serious thing, saying to the child, "You must sit here by me and look while the rest answer, for you do not see well." She must never expect mistakes in any part of the work, nor let the children. She must take great care to cultivate the closest attention when seeing, hearing, or doing, and thus prepare the child for good thinking.

In the second place, she must know just what each child is able to do, and suit her demands to his knowledge, so that he may always expect to *know* and not to guess, haphazard. He thus forms the habit of accuracy.

Guessing implies lack of thinking; it establishes a carelessness as to the right or wrong answer, and a wrong answer having been given, the impression that it is the right answer is just as liable to remain in the mind as the required correction of the wrong answer.

Of course children must be encouraged to *think* for themselves, and they cannot be expected to *know* everything, but they must be taught to distinguish between mere guessing and real knowledge. Lax intellectual habits lead to lax moral habits. A boy that is not sensible to the difference between error and truth in his arithmetic is very apt to be equally insensible to the difference between error and truth in his ordinary statements of fact. Where one evil prevails the other prevails also.

Teachers do much toward encouraging the habit of inaccuracy by not knowing what to demand. They expect the little child to reason about the combination $4 + 3$ when he is only just able to see the truth with the objects before him. They require him to reason through figures when the numbers for which the figures stand are not comprehended. In work with fractions there is much guess-work and mere memorizing without association unless we follow the new education loyally, for in this work all the figures are not used in performing an operation; for example, $\frac{1}{4} + \frac{2}{4}$ is not $\frac{3}{8}$, as the child who works with figures says, nor is $\frac{5}{6} - \frac{2}{6}$ equal to three. Let the fractions be shown as parts of some tangible wholes, and the process is readily understood.

The child should be taught to count by groups in getting the perception of a number larger than five. Suppose seven is presented. It will be seen as two, two, two, and one; or as three, three, and one; or, more unlikely, as three and four.

The teacher must never allow counting by ones, for the reason that it takes more time, does not require the child to observe, and does not call into exercise his knowledge of facts in number.

It is very important to make a distinction between *facts of a number that must be recognized instantly,* as, $4 + 3$, $9 - 4$, 4×2, $6 \div 3$, $\frac{1}{2}$ of 4, $\frac{1}{3}$ of 6, etc., and *facts that may be found by calculation,* as, $4 + 2 + 3 = 9$, $8 + 1 - 4 = 5$.

Teachers who do not make this distinction give as much energy to one set of facts as to the other, and the result is that owing to the endless combinations thus given few are fixed. The facts to be known are: (1) The combination of any two numbers, neither of which is greater than ten. (2) The separation of a number into any two numbers, neither of which is ten. (3) Products of entire numbers, neither number being greater than ten. (4) The value of one of the fractional parts of a number when the value is not more than ten. All others grow out of these, and can be readily found if these are known. Exercise in rapid calculation should be given, but not to the exclusion of fixing the facts just described. These are of the first importance. Give the others by way of simply testing the child's knowledge of these.

Board work should be mainly single combinations and separations, and not a string of them. Time will be gained and better results obtained by adhering to this rule.

Certain classes of facts need little or no repetition after the first presentation. Of this class are combinations with one, the subtraction of one, the doubling of numbers, and the halving of numbers; so we need not make the mistake of drilling upon them.

The question is often asked, How far shall the teaching of number be made objective? When a perception of a number is to be gained, objects are indispensable. When it is possible to arrive at a correct conclusion by reasoning from data already stored in the mind, require the child to reason out the result. Only be sure that the facts are there. We are apt to think the child has data from which to reason just because we have. The presentation of all facts from one to ten should be objective. The presentation of each number from one to twenty should be objective. Many processes with higher numbers should be objective. Elementary work in fractions should be objective.

For work above ten, arrange bundles of short splints, ten in each bundle. Have numbers shown with these bundles plus the ones required to make the number. These bundles are a necessity in teaching processes in which we deal with ones and tens separately; for example, in teaching to find the sum of 32, 24, and 63, or the difference of 75 and 38, the product of 37 by 5, or the quotient of 86 by 2.

The board work should be the simple expression of what has been done with objects.

It is not necessary that drill should be objective. When an image is in the mind, it needs only to be frequently recalled to fix it. This is often more effectively done without objects than with. And in every case, as soon as objects have done their work, remove them. Do not forget that as much depends upon drill and memorizing, after relations have been seen, as upon the clear seeing of relations.

.
.
.

99

GRUBÉ'S

METHOD OF TEACHING

ARITHMETIC.

Explained and Illustrated. Also the improvements upon the method made by the followers of Grubé in Germany.

BY

LEVI SEELEY, A.M., PH.D. *(Leipsic)*.

"THAT MAN WILL BE A BENEFACTOR OF HIS RACE WHO SHALL TEACH US HOW TO MANAGE RIGHTLY THE FIRST YEARS OF A CHILD'S EDUCATION."

Garfield.

NEW YORK AND CHICAGO:

E. L. KELLOGG & CO.

1888.

PREFACE.

There is a widespread feeling among American teachers that there is need of better methods of teaching Number, especially in the primary classes. During the last few years, the Grube System, having been introduced into a few schools and discussed at teachers' institutes and in educational journals, has attracted the attention of thoughtful educators in various parts of our land. Many of the later Arithmetics have devoted a few pages in outlining this system or in giving a few hints in regard to it. The excellent results apparent in those schools that have tried the system, the enthusiasm of its adherents, and the belief that it is based on sound philosophical principles, have created a desire to a better understanding of it. The design of this little book is to give a plain, concise exposition of the Grube theory, and, at the same time, to illustrate the method of teaching Number in accordance with it. It is intended to be a helpful book for the primary teacher.

This book is not simply a translation of Grube's treatise, nor is it the Grube system exclusively; it includes *all of that system, and in addition the latest and best ideas of the disciples of Grube in Germany,* whose works were studied and whose personal acquaintance was made by the author in their school-rooms and in their educational associations during a three years' study of the German schools.

In the preparation of this book I have examined with care the following works: Grube's "Leitfaden für das Rechnen in der Elementarschule" (the original exposition of Grube's system), German works on Arithmetic by Bräutigam, Göpfert, Lincke, Schellen, Berthelt und Petermann, Rein's "Theorie und Praxis," Soldan's "Grube's Method," Indianapolis School Manual of 1876, Quincy (Mass.) Course of Study of 1879, and other treatises.

LEVI SEELEY.

LAKE FOREST, ILL., 1888.

CONTENTS.

	PAGE
I. SKETCH OF GRUBE	9
II. INTRODUCTION OF GRUBE'S METHOD	11
III. ADVANTAGES OF GRUBE'S METHOD	13
IV. DIRECTIONS TO TEACHERS	17
V. THE FIRST YEAR	
First Step—The One	19
Second Step—The Two	22
Third Step—The Three	26
Fourth Step—The Four	30
Fifth Step—The Five	34
Sixth Step—The Six	37
Seventh Step—The Seven	41
Eighth Step—The Eight	44
Ninth Step—The Nine	50
Tenth Step—The Ten	54
VI. THE SECOND YEAR. OBSERVATIONS	55
Eleventh Step—The Eleven	58
Twelfth Step—The Twelve	62
Thirteenth Step—The Thirteen	63
Fourteenth Step—The Fourteen	64
Fifteenth Step—The Fifteen	66
Sixteenth Step—The Sixteen	68
Seventeenth Step—The Seventeen	70
Eighteenth Step—The Eighteen	71
Nineteenth Step—The Nineteen	73
Twentieth Step—The Twenty	

CONTENTS.

	PAGE
VI. THE SECOND YEAR. OBSERVATIONS.—Continued.	
Thirtieth Step—The Thirty	77
Fiftieth Step—The Fifty	80
Hundredth Step—The Hundred	82
VII. APPENDIX TO SECOND YEAR'S WORK	90
Section I.—First Unity	90
Second Unity	94
Section II.—Third Unity	96
Fourth Unity	98
Fifth Unity	99
Section III.—Tenth Unity	101
Eleventh Unity	104
Twelfth Unity	105
Thirteenth Unity	106
VIII. SECOND COURSE. THE THIRD YEAR	107
I. First Half of the Third Year	107
A. The Pure Number—First Step	108
Second Step	109
Third Step	111
Fourth Step	113
Fifth Step	115
Sixth Step	118
B. The Applied Number	122
II. Second Half of the Third Year	123
A. With Abstract Numbers—First Step: Numeration	123
Second Step: Addition	127
Third Step: Subtraction	130
Fourth Step: Multiplication	133
Method for School Work	136
Fifth Step—Division	140
Oral Method—A. Without Remainder	140
B. With Remainder	142
Written Method—A. Without Remainder	143
B. With Remainder	146
Concrete Numbers	150
IX. THIRD COURSE—FRACTIONS. THE FOURTH YEAR	155
I. First Half of the Fourth Year	155
First Step: Halves	156

CONTENTS.

	PAGE
IX. THIRD COURSE. THE FOURTH YEAR.—Continued.	
Second Step: Thirds	159
Third Step: Fourths	162
Fourth Step: Fifths	166
Fifth Step: Sixths	169
II. Second Half of the Fourth Year	170
1. Unity	171
2. Expansion and Reduction	172
3. Common Denominator	174
4. Number relations in fractional form	175

SKETCH OF GRUBE.

August Wilhelm Grube was born in Wernigerode at the foot of the Harz Mountains, Germany, on the 16th of December, 1816. His father was a tailor, and August was his only child. He commenced school when four years of age, and very early decided to devote himself to teaching. Grube often said in later years that it was his love for his teacher that awakened in him the wish to become a teacher.

When eight years of age he entered the Lyceum of his native city, where he remained till his fifteenth year, after which he entered the Teachers' Seminary at Weissenfels near Leipzig. In 1836, when twenty years of age, he completed his work here, and obtained a testimonial which stated that Grube was well fitted to teach in the best grade of schools. After teaching a short time in a public school, he took the position of family teacher (Hauslehrer) in the family of a count in the province of Posen. A like position in the family of a wealthy manufacturer near Bregenz occupied his time until he gave up teaching and devoted himself to authorship. He died January 27, 1884.

"Grube was one of the most fruitful and, at the same time, most important pedagogical authors of the present time; a man endowed with philosophical penetration and sound knowledge, great from inclination and character, likewise rich in the experiences of life and of the schoolroom. He has by means of his writings exercised an extensive, blessed influence upon the educators of our time."

His works cover all departments of pedagogics. From the many we name "Pedagogical Studies and Criticisms" (Pädagogische Studien und Kritiken), in one part of which he discusses "Darwinism and its Consequences," taking a stand against Darwin. Especially has Grube rendered great service to the young by his "Geographical Character-pictures" (Geographischen Charakterbilder), "Biographies from Natural Science" (Biographien aus der Naturkunde), "Character-pictures from History and Tradition" (Charakterbilder aus der Geschichte und Sage). Grube was the forerunner of new methods of teaching geography in Germany. He opposed the practice of making the study of geography a memorizing of numbers and facts, and arranged the material to be taught so that it could be used to advantage. He connected the teaching of geography with pictures of the landscape, with productions, temperature of the country, and would show how the customs, religion, government, history, and happiness of the people are related to and dependent upon the country.

But of particular interest to us in connection with this work is Grube's "Guide for Reckoning in the Elementary School, according to the Principles of an Inventive Method" (Leitfaden für das Rechnen in der Elementarschule, nach den Grundsätzen einer heuristischen Methode). This book marked an epoch in the teaching of Number in Germany and has exerted a wide influence on American teaching.

INTRODUCTION.

Pestalozzi was the pioneer who broke new ground in elementary instruction and led the way from mechanical, abstract methods to those which are more natural and psychological. He laid down the principle *that all mathematical knowledge is founded upon immediate observation, and therefore must proceed from the concrete to the general or abstract by means of innumerable examples.* This discovery was not only of vast importance to pupils in the schools, but it opened up to teachers the psychological principles of all pedagogics.

In 1842, only fifteen years after Pestalozzi's death, appeared Grube's "Leitfaden für das Rechnen in der Elementarschule." In this work Grube gives a thoroughly developed system of teaching number. Pestalozzi was unfortunately lacking in system. While he brought to light pedagogical principles, he developed no system of pedagogics. He taught the world that the proper way to teach the child is to go directly to Nature, let her operate on the mind and follow her harmonious development. Grube found the germ of his system in Pestalozzi's teachings, but went farther than his master in that he broke away from the idea of teaching the four processes, addition, subtraction, multiplication, and division, separately and in the order named. This is one of the great and most important features of the Grube system. Grube held that the four simple processes of arithmetic should go together in the small numbers, believing it to be the natural process of the mind.

By the use of objects the child is brought to see the relations of numbers until he is able to reproduce the relations without the objects. As the elementary work properly covers the period from the sixth to the tenth year, the period of observation, and as the method is purely elementary, Grube discusses only the first four years' work. His plan provides for three hours (full hours) per week. The end to be reached is a thorough knowledge of the fundamental rules and common fractions. His work is divided into three parts or courses:

I. Whole numbers from 1 to 100, employing the first two years.

II. Whole numbers above 100, employing the third school year.

III. Fractions, employing the fourth year.

He lays down the work definitely for each half-year, which we shall fully discuss later.

ADVANTAGES OF GRUBE'S METHOD.

I. It recognizes the psychological fact that nearly all the knowledge obtained by the child in its earlier years is by means of the senses.

By observation and not by reasoning does the child gain his first knowledge of number. In the earlier years the child's reasoning powers must be brought very little into play. He is not yet especially ready for reasoning, and Nature did not intend that he shall gain knowledge at this early period through the reason. He is eager for knowledge, but such knowledge as is obtainable by the senses. He learns mechanically. He comes to know all the combinations and manipulations taught him so as to give them with absolute accuracy and great rapidity without stopping to think.

II. As it makes the first year's work a study of the numbers 1 to 10 it lays a solid foundation.

The knowledge thus obtained becomes an acquirement which will be a methodical, substantial product. According to our usual crude methods this may seem but little work for an entire year, yet by this scientific study the first ten numbers will be found to furnish ample work. They are the foundation of the whole number system; all larger numbers are only a repetition, in a sense, of the first orders. The more thoroughly the numbers from one to ten are known, the surer and more rapid will be all later work in arithmetic. Let this foundation be well laid and the structure is well begun. Within these limits there is so much rich material for all-sided practical applications that the teacher will find plenty to do to accomplish the teaching of the first ten numbers in one year.

III. The Grube method progresses gradually and naturally according to the ability of the child.

It proceeds from the knowledge already gained to new knowledge by a very easy step. The knowledge possessed is utilized in mastering new knowledge. The child must not be subjected to mental over-exertion at any period. This is especially dangerous during the first years. The Grube method does not require too much, and yet it gives endless and suitable variety so that the child does not tire of number.

IV. It develops the mental powers evenly and in all directions.

One-sided teaching should always be avoided. All development should

106

be harmonious and natural. Grube considers each number by itself as an entirety and teaches all about it completely, thus building the mathematical structure step by step.

V. Elementary teaching of number should proceed from observation, or, better, it should proceed from things.

Grube's system calls for the use of things—balls, marbles, cubes, blocks. It uses objects repeatedly until the child is thorough master of the number and can make the combinations abstractly. After a time the simple remembrance of the objects used will always be sufficient to recall to the consciousness the number until no object is longer necessary and the pure relations of numbers are fixed. Then the child needs no object, or intermediate process, to help him to know the number, but he knows it instantly, and the simple, fundamental processes are mechanical. So we pass from the object to the symbol, from this to the comprehension of number, and lead in this way the interest from the empire of objects over to the empire of the number forms.

VI. The Grube method makes the teaching of number an excellent language-lesson.

The answers and statements are to be complete sentences; and as the subject is always kept within the ability of the child to comprehend, the number-lesson becomes one of the most valuable means of teaching language.

VII. The child acquires the habit of close observation.

As only that which is within the child's comprehension is brought before him, and as familiar objects are placed before him so frequently and so systematically, he acquires the habit of accurate and close observation. He learns to *see* what is brought to his notice, and to see all about it. This is one of the most important features of the Grube method, in that it is thoroughly psychological.

VIII. It develops and trains the attention.

As the child can understand the matter, it interests him, and interest is the first factor of attention. Because of its harmonious, all-sided development it cultivates the power of attention and leads the child to the habit of commanding and fixing the attention at will.

IX. It forms the habit of thoroughness in the child.

Mastering each number in all its details and possible combinations, it becomes, like a habit, a part of the very being of the child, until he is able to use it exactly as he uses the eye or the hand, without conscious thought. Beginning thus early in his school life to gain a thorough mastery of each step, he is led to desire mastery in other departments of learning and of practical life.

X. The Grube method gives pleasure and awakens a love for the study of number.

If the pleasure of work is not found in the work itself, all incentives and threatenings will be in vain. The desire to know a thing must be produced in the child himself. The impulse can begin in the young mind only when there is the consciousness of continual unity in the development of his powers, and then he will be driven by this impulse to further development by his self-activity. This method contains such unity and thus awakens in the child a love for the subject.

XI. It makes the child self-active in a proper manner.

Becoming complete master of a number, he is able to combine and operate with it by making original examples. Thus number becomes to him from the first a living, practical reality.

XII. The Grube method is a logical one.

It proceeds systematically and according to an order of sequence; it is psychological in that it teaches the use of the senses, in that it proceeds from the simple to the more difficult, and in that it goes out from the known to unknown and makes constant use of the known; it is practical because it gives a sure foundation for all future work in arithmetic, and because it brings the child immediately to measure and compare numbers and to make use of the relations of the same.

DIRECTIONS TO TEACHERS.

The first course includes whole numbers 1 to 100. Two years are required for this work, the first year being spent on 1 to 10 and the second on the rest, 10 to 100.

It must not be forgotten that the number-lesson must at the same time be a language-lesson. It is of the highest importance that the child give his answers in complete sentences, plainly spoken, with clear accent. Great importance must be attached to the explanation of every example from the outset. So long as the child is not master of the language necessary to express the operations performed with the number, he is not master of the representation or idea of the number itself, he does not know the number.

An example is not finished when the answer is found, but when it has been analyzed. The language may be taken as a safe test that a pupil has completely mastered a step.

So far as possible the pupil must be led to speak for himself and not to depend upon half the answer being put into his mouth by the teacher. Concert and individual answers must interchange in order that the interest of the class be maintained.

The uniform objects to be used are the fingers and blocks; for blackboard or slate use simple straight lines. Too many kinds of objects must not be used. The child has only a certain amount of strength and mental power which he can apply, and his interest must not be divided.

The mental comprehension of number is disturbed if things which awaken other ideas or desires are employed. The mind is capable of only a certain amount of interest, and when this interest is wholly or partly withdrawn but little can be expected for the particular thing at hand. For this reason, while teaching the abstract number, there should be but few things shown the child, and these should be simple and uniformly the same. The best things are blocks, which awaken little interest in themselves, and these must be the chief objects used throughout. Other objects should be referred to after the child has a number well fixed, by way of application, but should seldom be shown him, at least during the study of the first numbers. Thus apples, nuts, etc., which awaken desire, stimulate the appetite, and thus divide the attention, must not be used as objects in teaching number. All the interest which the child gives to the color, taste, etc., of objects is just so much lost to number.

The operations in any step consist simply of comparing and measuring what has been gained in the preceding steps with that which is new. The child proceeds from the known to the unknown, from the easy to the difficult; hence the method must follow a psychological law. The *pure* number is first learned, and then it is applied to *things* in order to fix it and make its practical use apparent.

The work of teaching a number is not complete until the child has been taught to make neatly and with dispatch the figure which stands for the number. This makes excellent employment for the children at their seats, and is a good preparation for written arithmetic, for which the foundation is being laid.

Go slowly—do not measure the ability of the child by your ability; bring yourself down to the level of the child's mind; be patient; repeat everything many times; review daily; use many examples and lead the children to make original problems.

Lastly, do not expect too much of the children; give them the kind and quantity of food that they can digest, remembering that real, sound, intellectual growth is slow, especially at the beginning.

THE FIRST YEAR: 1–10.

The work of the first year embraces a study of the numbers, 1, 2, 3, 4, 5, 6, 7, 8, 9, 10. Each number is taken by itself, measured by those that precede it, compared and studied in all its possible operations.

FIRST STEP.

THE ONE.[1]

The one can only be measured by itself. The child has only to learn the idea of unity.

.
.
.

---

1. Many insist that the child already knows the *one,* and that it is folly to spend time in teaching it. But it must not be forgotten that the child when he enters school must begin the study of number, must begin to form habits of correct speaking and thinking, must learn to observe carefully what is done, to tell what he sees done, and to answer in complete sentences. Then, too, the Grube system builds step by step, always making use of the knowledge possessed. The *one* is the first step. For these reasons and for these purposes a short time can be profitably spent with the *one.* It may be further added that the fact of the child's knowing the *one* will make it especially valuable in getting him to feel confidence in himself, an important matter for the child when he begins school.

HOW TO ORGANIZE, CLASSIFY

AND

TEACH A COUNTRY SCHOOL,

BY

W. M. WELCH, A.M.,

COUNTY SUPERINTENDENT OF JACKSON COUNTY, IOWA.

*Author of Classification Register and Course of Study for Country Schools,
Institute Record, Reporting Sheets, Memory Gems, etc.*

CHICAGO, ILL.,
DONOHUE & HENNEBERRY.

MAQUOKETA, IA.,
W. M. WELCH,
1889.

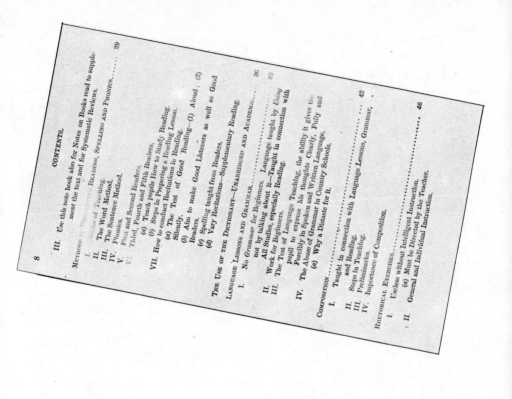

CONTENTS.

PREFACE 3
INTRODUCTION 5
PRELIMINARIES 11
  I. Securing a Country School.
  II. Getting Acquainted—"First Day."
  III. Preparation for the First Day.
  IV. Working Out an Attendance.

CLASSIFYING AND ORGANIZING THE SCHOOL 14
  Temporary, then Permanent Classifications.
  I. Temporary, then Permanent Proper Studies.
  II. Pupil should pursue the ... Record and Course of
  III. How pupils proceed with ... Classifications.
  IV. The importance of a Study for rural Schools.
  V. How a School may be Classified in such a record. 24

GENERAL SUGGESTIONS ...... Cooperate with the County Superintendent.
  Necessary Apparatus—Cooperate with the County Superintendent.
  I. Apparatus to be procured—
    contain to have an intelligent use of Apparatus.
    (a) Preservation and intelligent use of Apparatus.
    (b) Have School board provide Shelves or Case for it.
    (c) Preparation to use Apparatus intelligently.
  II. Care of Desks, Fairides and Vestibules.
  III. Care of pupils in the Open Air—Ventilation at
    Ventilation, Fairies and Vestibules.
  IV. Bare Desks.

  VI. Programs.—Arrange them for a Purpose. 28
    (a) Study Programs.
    (b) Sample of Program for Study and Recitation.

THE TEACHER'S SPECIAL OR DAILY PREPARATION.
    Study each Lesson before assigning it.
  I. Study each Lesson before assigning it.
  II. Systematize each lesson in a Blank Book for use at Recitations.

7

8

CONTENTS.

  III. Use this note book also for Notes on Books read to supplement the text and for Systematic Reviews.

METHODS OF TEACHING READING, SPELLING AND PHONICS...... 29
  I. Methods of Teaching.
  II. The Word Method.
  III. The Sentence Method.
  IV. Phonics.
  V. First and Second Readers.
  VI. Third, Fourth and Fifth Readers.
    (a) Teach pupils How to Study Reading.
  VII. How to conduct Recitations in Reading.
    (a) Steps in Preparing a Reading Lesson.
    (b) The Test of Good Reading in Reading.
      Silently.
    (c) Aim to make Good Listeners as well as Good
      Readers.
    (d) Spelling taught from Readers.
    (e) Vary Recitations—Supplementary Reading.

THE USE OF THE DICTIONARY—UNABRIDGED AND ACADEMIC...... 36

LANGUAGE LESSONS AND GRAMMAR. 37
  I. No Grammar for Beginners. Language taught by Using
    not by talking about it.
  II. All Studies, especially Reading.
  III. Work for Beginners.—Taught in connection with
    The Test of Language Teaching, the ability it gives the
    pupil to express his thoughts Clearly, Fully and
    Forcibly in Spoken and Written Language.
  IV. The Abuse of Grammar in Country Schools.
    (a) Why a Distaste for it.

COMPOSITION 42
  I. Taught in connection with Language Lessons, Grammar,
    and Reading.
  II. Steps in Teaching.
  III. Preliminaries.
  IV. Importance of Composition.

RHETORICAL EXERCISES. 46
  I. Useless without Intelligent Instruction.
  II. General and Individual Instruction.
    (a) Must be Directed by the Teacher.

CONTENTS.

THOUGHTS ON MENTAL PHILOSOPHY.
  I. Why teachers should study it.
  II. What portion the teacher should study.
  III. Chart of the Human Mind.
  IV. Hints on the Practical Application of this study to teaching. 68

THE TEACHER'S PERSONAL INFLUENCE 74

MISCELLANEOUS.
  I. Visit Patrons.
  II. Direct the course of Pupils' Home Reading.
  III. Take part in Pupils' Home Amusements.
  IV. Have Graduating and Closing Exercises.
  V. Have a care for Pupils' Personal Appearance and Manners.
  VI. Character Building. 77

GOVERNMENT. 82
  I. Important Elements.
  II. Have a Plan in Closing School.
  III. Correction, the Last Element Considered.

POINTS OF SCHOOL LAW WITH WHICH TEACHERS SHOULD BE FAMILIAR. 88

CONTENTS.

WRITING 47
  I. No Good Work with Poor Tools.
  II. Necessary Provisions for—Material Provided at Public Expense.
  III. The Three Essential Elements of Penmanship. 50

ARITHMETIC 54
  I. Aim.
  II. Primary Work—Numbers.
  III. Advanced Work.
  IV. Important Points.

PHYSIOLOGY 56
  I. Oral Lessons.
  II. Specimens and Illustrations in Class.

GEOGRAPHY
  I. Introductory Lessons.
    (a) Steps.
    (b) Teach Topically—In a Connected Whole.
    (c) Not to draw Nice Maps, but to form Accurate Mental Pictures.
  II. Map Drawing. 61
    (a) ...
    (b) But Little Time consumed in Map Drawing.

UNITED STATES HISTORY 63
  I. Begin Orally.
  II. What to take up the Text Book.
  III. How to Recite it.
  IV. Outlining Lessons in Advance for pupils.
  V. Generalization to get a Comprehensive View.

BUSY WORK 64

GENERAL EXERCISES
  I. Opening and Closing School.
    (a) Music—Singing.
    (b) Memory Gems.
  II. News of the day—New facts, etc.
  III. Civil Government.
  IV. General Lessons.
    (a) General Information.
    (b) The Sciences.

BOOKS ON TEACHING 68
  I. The Importance of.
  II. Some Books mentioned.

ARITHMETIC.

AIM.—To develop the reasoning powers; to cause pupils to *think; to think clearly; to think accurately; to think quickly;* TO THINK THINGS THROUGH.

NUMBERS.

1. Counting should begin by counting objects—not *abstractly;* use numeral frame, pieces of chalk, grains of corn, books—any objects. Add them, subtract them, multiply them, divide them, take parts of each, etc. Spend a little time at first teaching number language, as "one dog," "two boys," "three hats," etc.; then using objects, as blocks, pegs, toothpicks, etc., add, subtract, multiply (in groups), divide, etc. By cutting out pictures of birds, pigs, dogs, etc., from magazines and journals, the teacher can furnish First Grade pupils with material for "number stories." Pupils can easily be led to talk of these things in number language, to group them, portion them, etc. Tables can be made with *pegs,* as $I + I + I + I = IIII$; $II + II = IIII$, etc., the pegs being laid on plates instead of writing marks. Then numbers of objects may be represented by figures. Use objects until the child can grasp the thought without the aid of them. They have a *place* in primary work, but there is a *limit* to their usefulness.

Take five minutes each day in lower Grades for *rapid work* in addition, subtraction, multiplication and division and their combinations. It is surprising with what facility pupils will handle numbers if drilled in *rapid work* daily.

On this subject read Anna Johnson's little book "Education by Doing," published by E. L. Kellogg & Company, New York, N. Y. It costs but thirty or forty cents.

2. Associate this idea of numbers and figures with the objects counted. Give small groups of *objects* to be represented by figures on slates; add both objects and figures. Do not allow pupils to count by rote, but always associate the numbers with the objects; also begin at other numbers than unity, as 20, 35, etc., and count upwards.

3. Add single columns written on the board. Addition and subtraction should be taken up together; in fact, the four fundamental principles of Arithmetic, and also the rudiments of fractions, may be taught together. Teachers who cannot do this successfully should study the "Grube method," also the "Quincy method."

115

Any teacher can do this work successfully by following the plan outlined in Piper's "Seat Work." Write Prof. J. Piper, 149 Wabash avenue, Chicago, Ills., and get a sample copy for five or six cents, or Hailman's "Primary Helps" (price 75 cents).

4. In beginning notation and numeration, the names of the first three or four periods should be taught until pupils can call each period readily telling its name from its position. Mark three or four spaces on the board large enough for three figures each. Let pupils call spaces by names, *i. e.,* first space, units; second, thousands; third, millions, etc. Then write the required numbers in each space, etc.

5. In teaching multiplication, each step should be mastered thoroughly. Various exercises may be adopted both on the board and orally. In subtraction, "borrowing" may be illustrated by dollars and cents, etc.

6. In Mental Arithmetic, answers should be simple and concise; avoid long analysis with repetitions.

ADVANCED WORK.

Mental Arithmetic should precede and accompany written Arithmetic. Exercises in rapid calculation should be frequent. When the divisor is less than 13, long divisions should not be permitted. In beginning Fractions, *great pains should be taken to lay the basis thoroughly.* Comprehension of illustrations and readiness to perform operations should precede rules. The relations of Decimals, Common Fractions and Percentage should be illustrated. Notation and numeration of Decimals may be taken up with that of whole numbers. Decimals should precede Common Fractions. Where the text-book places Common Fractions first, they may be passed over until decimals are finished.

After canvassing any subject as laid down in the book, the teacher should furnish supplementary work to make pupils clearly understand the principles canvassed before passing on to the next subject. The importance of this work to supplement the text-book, and make pupils think for themselves, can hardly be sufficiently emphasized. Pupils are usually "at sea" when given work outside the book and not under a certain "case."

7. Exercises for drill in rapid calculation should be given almost daily. In this work let *accuracy* and *rapidity* be the two goals to be reached. The *form* of work is frequently neglected. Teachers should insist on having the work in good form, whether on board, or paper, slates, etc. It will take time at first, but will be a great saving of time and labor in the long run. To this end the pupils should be drilled in—

   I. The arrangement of work on the board.

  II. The making of good, plain figures.

 III. Care in using the proper signs when necessary.

The work should be so plain that it can be read like a sentence. Pupils should learn that there is a mathematical language; that figures, signs, and symbols largely compose it, and that these should not be omitted any more than the words of a sentence.

The *habit* of doing work *plainly,* clearly and systematically is of great *practical importance.* The *habit* formed during school life goes with the pupil into business and is not easily changed.

THE PRINCIPLES

OF

PSYCHOLOGY

BY

WILLIAM JAMES

PROFESSOR OF PSYCHOLOGY IN HARVARD UNIVERSITY

IN TWO VOLUMES

VOL II.

NEW YORK
HENRY HOLT AND COMPANY

CONTENTS.

CHAPTER XVII

SENSATION, ... PAGE 1

Its distinction from perception, 1. Its cognitive function— No pure sensations, 3. No distinction with qualities, 3. The law of acquaintance with knowledge, 9. The 'relativity' of knowledge, 9. The physiological theories days of it, 13. The psychological theories of it, 17. Hering's experiments, 20. The oceantric projection contrast, 18. of sensations, 31.

CHAPTER XVIII

IMAGINATION, ... 44

Our images are usually vague, 45. Vague images not necessarily general notions, 46. Individuals differ in imagination; 'audile' type, 58. The 'visible' type. Galton's researches, 50. The 'motile' type, 61. Tactile images 65. The neural type, 60. The 'motile' type, 61. Its relations to that of sensation, 72. process of imagination.

CHAPTER XIX

THE PERCEPTION OF 'THINGS,' 76

Perception and sensation, 76. Perception is of definite and probable things, 82. Illusions, 85—of first type, 86.—of Perception in perception, 103. The neural process in perception? the second type, 95. Is perception an unconscious inference? Apperception, 107. Is perception a neural process in hallucination, 111. Hallucinations, 114. The neural process, 131. Binet's theory, 129. 'Perception-time.'

CHAPTER XX

THE PERCEPTION OF SPACE, ... 134

The feeling of crude extensity, 134. The perception of spatial order, 145. The meaning of 'real' space, 148. The perception of localization, 166. Space 'relation,' 148. The construction of 'Local signs,' 155. The sensation The subdivision of the original sense-spaces, 167.

of motion over surfaces, 171. The measurement of the sense-spaces by each other, 177. Their summation, movement in joints, 177. Their summation, 189. Feelings of muscular contraction, 181. Feelings of Visual space, 211. 302. How the blind perceive space, 203. The theory of Helmholtz and Reid on the test of a sensation, 224. Ambiguity of identical points, 222. The theory of projection, we ignore, 240. Sensations which seem suppressed, 243. Discussion of Wundt's and Helmholtz's reasons for denying that retinal sensations are of extension, 246. Summary, 268. Historical remarks, 270.

CHAPTER XXI

THE PERCEPTION OF REALITY, ... 283

Belief and its opposites, 283. The various orders of reality, 'Practical' realities, 298. The sense of our own bodily existence is the nucleus of all reality, 297. The paramount reality of sensations, 299. The influence of emotion and active impulse on belief, 307. Belief in theories, 311. Doubt, 318. Relations of belief and will, 320.

CHAPTER XXII

REASONING, ... 323

'Recepts,' 327. In reasoning, we pick out essential qualities, 329. What is meant by a mode of conceiving, 332. What is involved in the existence of general propositions, 332. Sagacity, 340. The intellectual part played by association by similarity, 345. The two factors of reasoning, 340. The intellectual contrast between brute and man: association by similarity the fundamental human distinction, 348. Different orders of human genius, 360.

CHAPTER XXIII

THE PRODUCTION OF MOVEMENT, . . . 373

The diffusive wave, 373. Every sensation produces reflex effects on the whole organism, 374.

CHAPTER XXIV

INSTINCT, ... 383

Its definition, 383. Instincts not always blind or invariable, Two principles of non-uniformity in instincts: 1) Their inhibition by habits, 394; 2) Their transitoriness, 398. Man has

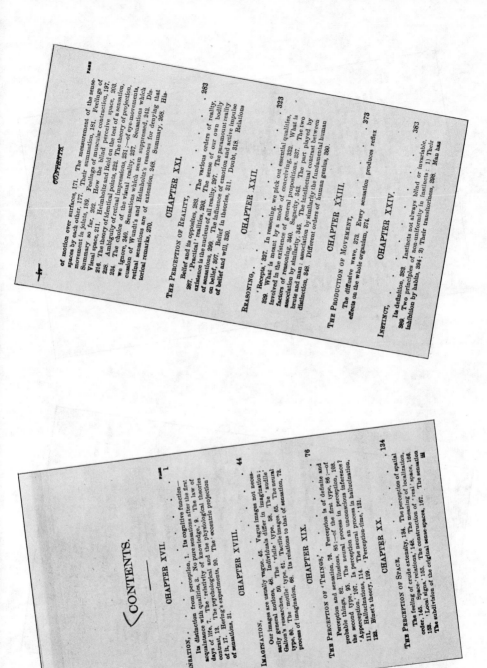

CHAPTER XXVIII.

NECESSARY TRUTHS AND THE EFFECTS OF EXPERIENCE, . 617

Programme of the chapter, 617. Elementary feelings are innate, 618. The question refers to their combinations, 619. What is meant by 'experience,' 620. Two ways in which new cerebral structure arises: the 'back-door' and the 'front-door' way, 625. The genesis of the natural elementary mental categories, 631. The genesis of the more complex objects of thought, 633. Scientific conceptions arise: as accidental variations, 636. The genesis of the pure sciences, 641. Series of evenly increasing terms, 644. That of skipped intermediaries, 646. The principle of mediate comparison, 645. Predication, 647. Classification, 652. Arithmetic, 653. Geometry, 656. Mathematical propositions, 659. Formal logic, 658. Our doctrine is the same as Locke's, 661. Relations of ideas e. couplings of things, 663. The natural sciences are inward ideal schemes with which the order of nature proves congruent, 666. Æsthetic and moral principles are properly only postulates, 669. Metanature, 672. Summary of what precedes, 673. The origin of instinct, 678. Insufficiency of proof for the transmission to the next generation of acquired habits, 681. Weismann's views, 683. Conclusion, 688.

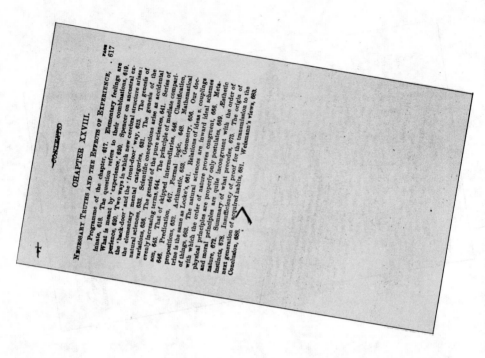

more instinctes than any other mammal, 403. Reflex impulses, 403. Imitation, 408. Emulation, 409. Pugnacity, 409. Sympathy, 410. The hunting instinct, 411. Fear, 415. Acquisitiveness, 422. Constructiveness, 426. Play, 432. Curiosity, 429. ness, 422. Constructiveness, 430. Secretiveness, 432. Cleanliness, 434. Shame, 435. Love, 437. Maternal love, 439. Sociability and shyness, 431.

CHAPTER XXV.

THE EMOTIONS, ... 442

Instinctive reaction and emotional expression shade imperceptibly into each other, 442. The expression of grief, 443; of fear, 446, of bodily expression discussed, 456. Emotion is a consequence of feeling this view, 454. Objections to it for emotion, 472. The various cause, of the various 463. No special brain-centres, 474. The genesis of the various ferences between individuals, 477.

CHAPTER XXVI.

WILL, ... 486

Voluntary movements: they presuppose a memory of involuntary movements, 487. Kinæsthetic impressions, 488. No need of muscular feelings of innervation, 503. The 'mental cue' for a movement may be the image of its visual or auditory action, 522. The feelings of muscular effects as to assume may be the way it feels, 518. Ideo motor action, 531. The extreme effort may be the way it feels, 518. Five types of decision, 528. well as an image of the act, 528. Five types of will: 1) The reasonable type, 531. 2) The obstructed type, 540. Pleasure and Action after deliberation. Unhealthiness type, 546. All consciousness is feeling type, 587; 2) springs of action, 549 what idea dominates pleasure not the only spur, will depends on what idea dominates from the impulse active, 551. What idea's outward effects follow naturally in our mind, 559. The essential feature of willing, 568. The cerebral important idea is the effort of attention to a naturally repugnant controversy, 571. Psychology, be true, 578. The educational determinism, even if free-will be true, 578. The free-will determinism, even if free-will be true, 582. postulate of the Will, 579. Hypothetical brain-schemes, 582.

CHAPTER XXVII.

HYPNOTISM, ... 594-616

Theories about

Modes of operating and susceptibility, 594. The symptoms of the trance, 601.

CHAPTER XXVIII.

NECESSARY TRUTHS AND THE EFFECTS OF EXPERIENCE.

MATHEMATICAL RELATIONS.

So much for the *a priori* necessities called systematic classification and logical inference. The other couplings of data which pass for *a priori* necessities of thought are the *mathematical* judgments, and certain metaphysical propositions. These latter‚we shall consider farther on. As regards the mathematical judgments, they are all 'rational propositions' in the sense defined on p. 644, for they express results of comparison and nothing more. The mathematical sciences deal with similarities and equalities exclusively, and not with coexistences and sequences. Hence they have, in the first instance, no connection with the order of experience. The comparisons of mathematics are between numbers and extensive magnitudes, giving rise to arithmetic and geometry respectively.

Number seems to signify primarily the strokes of our attention in discriminating things. These strokes remain in the memory in groups, large or small, and the groups can be compared. The discrimination is, as we know, psychologically facilitated by the mobility of the thing as a total. But within each thing we discriminate parts; so that the number of things which any one given phenomenon may be depends in the last instance on our way of taking it. A globe is one, if undivided; two, if composed of hemispheres. A sand-heap is one thing, or twenty thousand things, as we may choose to count it. We amuse ourselves by the counting of *mere* strokes, to form rhythms, and these we compare and name. Little by little in our minds the number-series is formed. This, like all lists of terms in which there is a direction of serial increase, carries with it the sense of those mediate relations between its terms which we expressed by the axiom "the more than the more is more than the less." That axiom seems, in fact, only a way of

121

stating that the terms do form an increasing series. But, in addition to this, we are aware of certain other relations among our strokes of counting. We may interrupt them where we like, and go on again. All the while we feel that the interruption does not alter the strokes themselves. We may count 12 straight through; or count 7 and pause, and then count 5, but still the strokes will be the same. We thus distinguish between our acts of counting and those of interrupting or grouping, as between an unchanged matter and an operation of mere shuffling performed on it. The matter is the original units or strokes; which all modes of grouping or combining simply give us back unchanged. In short, *combinations of numbers are combinations of their units,* which is the fundamental axiom of arithmetic,[1] leading to such consequences as that $7 + 5 = 8 + 4$ because both $= 12$. The general axiom of mediate equality, that equals of equals are equal, comes in here.[2] The principle of constancy in our meanings, when applied to strokes of counting, also gives rise to the axiom that the same number, operated on (interrupted, grouped) in the same way will always give the same result or be the same. How shouldn't it? Nothing is supposed changed.

Arithmetic and its fundamental principles are thus independent of our experiences or of the order of the world. The matter of arithmetic is *mental matter;* its principles flow from the fact that the matter forms a series, which can be cut into by us wherever we like without the matter changing. The empiricist school has strangely tried to interpret the truths of number as results of coexistences among outward things. John Mill calls number a physical property of things. 'One,' according to Mill, means one sort of passive sensation which we receive, 'two' another, 'three' a third. The same things, however, can give us different number-sensations. Three things arranged thus, o o o , for example, impress us differently from three things arranged thus,   o o o . But experience tells us that every real object-group which can be arranged in one of these ways can always be arranged in the other also, and that $2 + 1$ and 3 are thus modes of numbering things which 'coexist' invariably with each other. The indefeasibility of our belief in their 'coexistence' (which is Mill's word for their equivalence) is due solely to the enormous amount of experience we have of it. For all things, whatever other sensations they may give us, give us at any rate number-sensations. Those number-sensations which the same thing may be successively made to arouse are the numbers which we deem equal to each other; those which the same thing refuses to arouse are those which we deem unequal.

1. Said to be expressed by Grassman in the fundamental Axiom of Arithmetic $(a + b) + 1 = a + (b + 1)$.

2. Compare Helmholtz's more technically expressed Essay 'Zählen u. Messen, in the Philosophische Aufsätze, Ed. Zeller gewidmet (Leipzig, 1887), p. 17.

This is as clear a restatement as I can make of Mill's doctrine.[3] And its failure is written upon its front. Woe to arithmetic, were such the only grounds for its validity! The same real things are countable in numberless ways, and pass from one numerical form, not only to its equivalent (as Mill implies), but to its other, as the sport of physical accidents or of our mode of attending may decide. How could our notion that one and one are eternally and necessarily two ever maintain itself in a world where every time we add one drop of water to another we get not two but one again? in a world where every time we add a drop to a crumb of quicklime we get a dozen or more?—had it no better warrant than such experiences? At most we could then say that one and one are *usually* two. Our arithmetical propositions would never have the confident tone which they now possess. That confident tone is due to the fact that they deal with abstract and ideal numbers exclusively. *What we mean* by one plus one *is* two; we *make* two out of it; and it would mean two still even in a world where *physically* (according to a conceit of Mill's) a third thing was engendered every time one thing came together with another. We are masters of our meanings, and discriminate between the things we mean and our ways of taking them, between our strokes of numeration themselves, and our bundlings and separatings thereof.

Mill ought not only to have said, "All things are numbered." He ought, in order to prove his point, to have shown that they are *unequivocally* numbered, which they notoriously are not. Only the abstract numbers themselves are unequivocal, only those which we create mentally and hold fast to as ideal objects always the same. A concrete natural thing can always be numbered in a great variety of ways. "We need only conceive a thing divided into four equal parts (and all things may be conceived as so divided)," as Mill is himself compelled to say, to find the number four in it, and so on.

The relation of numbers to experience is just like that of 'kinds' in logic. So long as an experience will keep its kind we can handle it by logic. So long as it will keep its number we can deal with it by arithmetic. *Sensibly,* however, things are constantly changing their numbers, just as they are changing their kinds. They are forever breaking apart and fusing. Compounds and their elements are never numerically identical, for the elements are sensibly many and the compounds sensibly one. Unless our arithmetic is to remain without application to life, we must somehow *make* more numerical continuity than we spontaneously find. Accordingly Lavoisier discovers his weight-units which remain the same in compounds and elements, though volume-units and quality-units all have changed. A great discovery! And modern science outdoes it by denying that compounds exist at all.

3. For the original statements, cf. J. S. Mill's Logic, bk. II. chap VI. §§ 2, 3; and bk. III. chap. XXIV. § 5.

There is no such thing as 'water' for 'science;' that is only a handy name for H_2 and O when they have got into the position H-O-H, and then affect our senses in a novel way. The modern theories of atoms, of heat, and of gases are, in fact, only intensely artificial devices for gaining that constancy in the numbers of things which sensible experience will not show. "Sensible things are not the things for me," says Science, "because in their changes they will not keep their numbers the same. Sensible qualities are not the qualities for me, because they can with difficulty be numbered at all. These hypothetic atoms, however, are the things, these hypothetic masses and velocities are the qualities for me; they will stay numbered all the time."

By such elaborate inventions, and at such a cost to the imagination, do men succeed in making for themselves a world in which real things shall be coerced *per fas aut nefas* under arithmetical law.

The other branch of mathematics is *geometry*. Its objects are also ideal creations. Whether nature contain circles or not, I can know what I mean by a circle and can stick to my meaning; and when I mean two circles I mean two things of an identical kind. The axiom of constant results holds in geometry. The same forms, treated in the same way (added, subtracted, or compared), give the same results—how shouldn't they? The axioms of mediate comparison, of logic, and of number all apply to the forms which we imagine in space, inasmuch as these resemble or differ from each other, form kinds, and are numerable things. But in addition to these general principles, which are true of space-forms only as they are of other mental conceptions, there are certain axioms relative to space-forms exclusively, which we must briefly consider.

Three of them give marks of identity among straight lines, planes, and parallels. Straight lines which have two points, planes which have three points, parallels to a given line which have one point, in common, coalesce throughout. Some say that the certainty of our belief in these axioms is due to repeated experiences of their truth; others that it is due to an intuitive acquaintance with the properties of space. It is neither. We experience lines enough which pass through two points only to separate again, only we won't call them straight. Similarly of planes and parallels. We have a definite idea of what we mean by each of these words; and when something different is offered us, we see the difference. Straight lines, planes, and parallels, as they figure in geometry, are mere inventions of our faculty for apprehending serial increase. The farther continuations of these forms, we say, *shall* bear the same relation to their last visible parts which these did to still earlier parts. It thus follows (from that axiom of skipped intermediaries which obtains in all regular series) that parts of these figures separated by other parts must agree in direction, just as contiguous parts do. This uniformity of direction throughout is, in fact, all that makes us care for these forms, gives them their beauty, and stamps them into fixed conceptions in our mind. But obviously if two lines, or two planes, with a common segment, were to part company beyond the segment, it could only be because the direction of at least one of them had changed. Parting company in lines and planes *means* changing direction, means assuming a new relation to the parts that pre-exist; and assuming a new relation means ceasing to be straight or plane. If we mean by a parallel a line that will never meet a second line; and if we have one such line drawn through a point, any new line drawn through that point which does not coalesce with the first must be inclined to it, and if inclined to it must approach the second, i.e., cease to be parallel with it. No properties of outlying space need come in here: only a definite conception of uniform direction, and constancy in sticking to one's point.

The other two axioms peculiar to geometry are that figures can be moved in space without change, and that no variation in the way of subdividing a given amount of space alters its total quantity.[4] This last axiom is similar to what we found to obtain in numbers. 'The whole is equal to its parts' is an abridged way of expressing it. A man is not the same biological whole if we cut him in two at the neck as if we divide him at the ankles; but geometrically he is the same whole, no matter in which place we cut him. The axiom about figures being movable in space is rather a postulate than an axiom. *So far as they are* so movable, then certain fixed equalities and differences obtain between forms, *no matter where placed*. But if translation through space warped or magnified forms, then the relations of equality, etc., would always have to be expressed with a position-qualification added. A geometry as absolutely certain as ours could be invented on the supposition of such a space, if the laws of its warping and deformation were fixed. It would, however, be much more complicated than our geometry, which makes the simplest possible supposition; and finds, luckily enough, that it is a supposition with which the space of our experience seems to agree.

By means of these principles, all playing into each other's hands, the mutual equivalences of an immense number of forms can be traced, even of such as at first sight bear hardly any resemblance to each other. We move and turn them mentally, and find that parts of them will superpose. We add imaginary lines which subdivide or enlarge them, and find that the new figures resemble each other in ways which show us that the old ones are equivalent too. We thus end by expressing all sorts of forms in terms of other forms, enlarging our knowledge of the kinds of things which certain other kinds of things are, or to which they are equivalent.

---

4. The subdivision itself consumes none of the space. In all practical experience our subdivisions do consume space. They consume it in our geometrical figures. But for simplicity's sake, in geometry we postulate subdivisions which violate experience and consume none of it.

The result is a new system of mental objects which can be treated as identical for certain purposes, a new series of *is*'s almost indefinitely prolonged, just like the series of equivalencies among numbers, part of which the multiplication-table expresses. And all this is in the first instance regardless of the coexistences and sequences of nature, and regardless of whether the figures we speak of have ever been outwardly experienced or not.

PART TWO: 1891–1919

Emergence of National Organizations as a Force in Mathematics Education

During the period from 1891 through 1919, national and international organizations began to study the mathematics curriculum and to make recommendations for reform. Initial examples in the 1890s are the reports of the National Education Association's Committee of Ten on Secondary School Studies and Committee of Fifteen on Elementary Education. These reports and later ones by other organizations offer a more comprehensive view of the mathematics taught and the general direction of change than do the writings of individuals.

The mathematics subcommittee of the Committee of Ten offered specific reforms, one of which was the introduction of concrete geometry and algebra into the arithmetic program. This committee, as well as others of the period, was dominated by college professors and school administrators. Only later were secondary teachers invited to participate in committee work, notably in the case of the National Committee on Mathematical Requirements, which reported in 1923.

The report of the Committee on College Entrance Requirements of the National Education Association in 1899 marked the beginning of concerted efforts to stabilize the secondary school curriculum for college entrance. The College Entrance Examination Board, which has had great influence in curriculum reform, was founded in 1900. The extensive report of the Committee of the Chicago Section of the American Mathematical Society is of special interest because its chairman was J. W. A. Young, one of the early professional mathematics educators in the modern sense of the term. The reports, in 1911, of the International Commission on the Teaching of Mathematics offer a clear picture of the school practices of the period. We find in them the basic outline of many current curriculum practices.

Of main concern near the turn of the century was the utility of mathematics. Although mental discipline was still not totally discredited, reformers increasingly advocated pruning obsolete material, including difficult hypothetical problems that were originally introduced for the purpose of mental exercise. In keeping with the trend toward practicality was John Perry's reform platform of integrating science and mathematics and of using the laboratory method. Also consistent with the move toward utility were the pragmatic philosophy and functional psychology expounded by William James and John Dewey.

An earmark of the arithmetic at the turn of the century was the popularity of teaching "methods" in the narrow sense of limited key approaches on which the remainder of the subject was to be made dependent. Besides the subsiding Grube method, the ratio (or Speer) method and the measurement method that can be associated with the pragmatism of James A. McLellan and John Dewey gained prominence.[1] By 1910, however, this emphasis on methods had lost support, as is evident in the selections on arithmetic from David Eugene Smith and the reports of the International Commission.

Two items receiving brief consideration in the International Commission reports are worthy of note as indicating movements that gained prominence in later years. The scientific comparison of teaching methods made at Columbia University foreshadowed the development of research in mathematics education; the habituation extreme of the habituation-rationalization continuum was an augury of the influence of connectionistic psychology, which is detailed in the readings of Part Three.

---

1. Ratio was also given play by McLellan and Dewey. but not to the same extent nor in the same spirit as by Speer. The degree to which the various methods were bound to a single theme varied considerably. Later critics tended to overemphasize the one-sidedness of these methods.

[*Whole Number 205*

UNITED STATES BUREAU OF EDUCATION.

REPORT

OF THE

COMMITTEE ON SECONDARY SCHOOL STUDIES

APPOINTED AT THE MEETING OF THE

National Educational Association

July 9, 1892,

WITH THE

REPORTS OF THE CONFERENCES

arranged by this Committee and held December 28–30, 1892.

WASHINGTON:
GOVERNMENT PRINTING OFFICE.
1893.

MATHEMATICS.

March, 1893.

To President Charles W. Eliot, Chairman Committee of Ten, National Council of Education : —

Sir, — The undersigned, having been appointed by your Committee to hold a Conference on the subject of secondary instruction in Mathematics, have the honor to report that such Conference was held on the 28th, 29th, and 30th of December, 1892, in Cambridge, Mass.

On mapping out its work, the Conference found that the general subject of secondary mathematics might be conveniently considered under four different heads. It is deemed advisable to preface the separate reports on each of these heads with a general statement of the conclusions reached by the Conference. The following five reports are therefore submitted :

   I. General statement of conclusions.

   II. Special report on the teaching of arithmetic.

   III. Special report on the teaching of concrete geometry.

   IV. Special report on the teaching of algebra.

   V. Special report on the teaching of formal geometry.

Very respectfully,

SIMON NEWCOMB, *Professor, Johns Hopkins University, Baltimore, Md.,* Chairman.

WILLIAM E. BYERLY, *Professor, Harvard University, Cambridge, Mass.,* Vice Chairman.

ARTHUR H. CUTLER, *Principal of a Private School for Boys, 20 East 50th Street, New York City,* Secretary.

FLORIAN CAJORI, *Professor, Colorado College, Colorado Springs, Colo.*

HENRY B. FINE, *Professor, College of New Jersey, Princeton, N. J.*

W. A. GREESON, *Principal of the High School, Grand Rapids, Mich.*

ANDREW INGRAHAM, *Swain Free School, New Bedford, Mass.*

GEORGE D. OLDS, *Professor, Amherst College, Amherst, Mass.*

JAMES L. PATTERSON, *Lawrenceville School, Lawrenceville, N. J.*

T. H. SAFFORD, *Professor, Williams College, Williamstown. Mass.*

I. GENERAL STATEMENT OF CONCLUSIONS.

The Conference was, from the beginning of its deliberations, unanimously of opinion that a radical change in the teaching of arithmetic was necessary. Referring to the special report on that subject for a statement of the reasons on which its conclusion is based, the conference recommends that the course in arithmetic be at the same time abridged and enriched; abridged by omitting entirely those subjects which perplex and exhaust the pupil without affording any really valuable mental discipline, and enriched by a greater number of exercises in simple calculation and in the solution of concrete problems.

Among the subjects which should be curtailed, or entirely omitted, are compound proportion, cube root, abstract mensuration, obsolete denominate quantities, and the greater part of commercial arithmetic. Percentage should be rigidly reduced to the needs of actual life. In such subjects as profit and loss, bank discount, and simple and compound interest, examples not easily made intelligible to the pupil should be omitted. Such complications as result from fractional periods of time in compound interest are useless and undesirable. The metric system should be taught in applications to actual measurements to be executed by the pupil himself; the measures and weights being actually shown to, and handled by, the pupil. This system finds its proper application in the course which the Conference recommends in concrete geometry.

The method of teaching should be throughout objective, and such as to call into exercise the pupil's mental activity. The text-books should be subordinate to the living teacher. The illustrations and problems should, so far as possible, be drawn from familiar objects; and the scholar himself should be encouraged to devise as many as he can. So far as possible, rules should be derived inductively, instead of being stated dogmatically. On this system the rules will come at the end, rather than at the beginning, of a subject.

The Conference at the same time insists upon the importance of practice in quick and accurate reckoning. The scholar should be thoroughly trained in performing correctly and rapidly the four fundamental operations with integers, vulgar fractions and decimals.

The course in arithmetic thus mapped out should begin about the age of

---

[The entire mathematics report is included. This was one of many reports on secondary school subjects contained in the report of the Committee of Ten.]

six years, and be completed at the end of the grammar school course, say about the thirteenth year of age. The conference does not feel competent to decide how many hours a week should be devoted to it, and therefore leaves this question to teachers and other school authorities.

The second recommendation of the Conference is that a course of instruction in concrete geometry, with numerous exercises, be introduced into the grammar school. The object of this course would be to familiarize the pupil with the facts of plane and solid geometry, and with those geometrical conceptions to be subsequently employed in abstract reasoning. During the early years the instruction might be given informally, in connection with drawing, and without a separate appointment in the school calendar; after the age of ten years, one hour per week should be devoted to it.

While the systematic study of algebra should not begin until the completion of the course in arithmetic, the Conference deems its necessary that some familiarity with algebraic expressions and symbols, including the methods of solving simple equations, should be acquired in connection with the course in arithmetic. From the age of fourteen, systematic algebra should be commenced, and should be studied for five hours a week during the first year, and for about two hours and a half a week during the two years next succeeding.

The Conference is of opinion that the subject of reckoning in algebra should receive more attention than it actually does, and that the same skill and accuracy should be required in dealing with literal as with numerical coefficients and exponents. It strongly urges that when, as must sometimes be the case, the scholar has occasion to learn and use propositions before he is prepared to understand their rigorous demonstration, he should be convinced of their truth by abundant concrete illustrations and examples, instead of being allowed to accept them as empirical conclusions, or to found them on demonstrations that lack rigor.

The Conference believes that the study of demonstrative geometry should begin at the end of the first year's study of algebra, and be carried on by the side of algebra for the next two years, occupying about two hours and a half a week. It believes that if the introductory course in geometry has been well taught, both plane and solid geometry can be mastered at this time.

Exercises in constructing demonstrations of theorems in plane geometry will naturally occupy much of the attention of teacher and pupil. The Conference deems it very important that great stress be laid by the teacher upon accuracy of statement and elegance of form in such demonstrations, as well as on clear and rigorous reasoning. Special attention should be given to the oral statement of demonstrations.

It is very desirable that colleges should supplement their written admission examinations in geometry by oral ones; and a substantial part of the examination, whether written or oral, should be devoted to testing the ability of the candidate to construct original demonstrations.

Finally, the Conference is of opinion that up to the completion of the first year's work in algebra, the course should be the same, whether the pupils are preparing for college, for scientific schools, or intend their systematic education to end with the high school. In the case of those who do not intend to go to college, but to pursue a business career, the remainder of the term which has been allotted to algebra might well be devoted to book-keeping, and the technical parts of commercial arithmetic. Boys going to a scientific school might profitably spend a year on trigonometry and some of the higher parts of algebra, after completing the regular course in algebra and geometry.

II. SPECIAL REPORT ON ARITHMETIC.

Among the branches of this subject which it is proposed to omit, are some which have survived from an epoch when more advanced mathematics was scarcely known in our schools, so that the course in arithmetic was expected to include all that the pupil would ever know of mathematics. Examples of these subjects are cube root, duo decimals, and compound proportion. Their teaching serves no useful purpose at the present time. So far as any useful principles are embodied in them, they belong to algebra, and can be taught by algebraic methods with such facility that there is no longer any sound reason for their retention in the arithmetical course.

The case is different with commercial arithmetic. The subjects taught under this head have been greatly multiplied and enlarged in recent years, in consequence of the popular demand for a system of education which should be more practical and better suited to the demands of modern commercial and business life, than the old one was supposed to be. It may be well that those pupils of our business colleges who are mature enough to understand such subjects as banking, insurance, discount, partial payments, equation of payments, and the other branches commonly included under the term commercial arithmetic, and who have no expectation of taking any other mathematical course than this, should study these subjects exhaustively. But the case is different with pupils who are going through the courses of our regular graded schools. For them the subjects in question have no practical value, for the reason that they are too young and inexperienced to understand the principles on which business is conducted, and therefore waste valuable mental energy in fruitless struggles with problems which they cannot comprehend. In the text-books we find the subjects in question prefaced by very excellent definitions. The pupil who masters them will be able to state on examination that "the market value of stock is what the stock brings per share when sold for cash"; that "stock is at a discount when

133

its market value is less than its par value"; that "its par value is that named in the certificate"; that "the payee of a bill of exchange is the person to whom the money is ordered to be paid"; in fine, to state in brief sentences the first principles of commercial law. He may also, after much conjecturing, be able to solve many questions in banking, exchange, insurance, and custom-house business. But until he is brought into actual contact with the business itself, he can᾽ form no clear conception of what it all means, or what are the uses or applications of the problems he is solving. On the other hand, when he is once brought face to face with business as an actuality; when for the first time he becomes a depositor in a savings bank, or a purchaser of shares in a corporation, he will find all the arithmetic necessary for his purposes to be interest, discount, and percentage. The conceptions which he vainly endeavored to master by recitations from a text-book take their places in his mind with hardly the necessity of an effort on his part.

The opinion is widely prevalent that even if the subjects are totally forgotten, a valuable mental discipline is acquired by the efforts made to master them. While the Conference admits that, considered in itself, this discipline has a certain value, it feels that such a discipline is greatly inferior to that which may be gained by a different class of exercises, and bears the same relation to a really improving discipline that lifting exercises in an ill-ventilated room bear to games in the open air. The movements of a race horse afford a better model of improving exercise than those of the ox in a tread-mill. The pupil who solves a difficult problem in brokerage may have the pleasant consciousness of having overcome a difficulty, but he cannot feel that he is mentally improved by the efforts he has made. To attain this end he must feel at every step that he has a new command of principles to be applied to future problems. This end can be best gained by comparatively easy problems, involving interesting combinations of ideas.

Most of the improvements which the Conference has to suggest in teaching can be summed up under the two heads of giving the teaching a more concrete form, and paying more attention to facility and correctness in work. The relations of magnitudes should, so far as possible, be represented to the eye. The fundamental operations of arithmetic should not only be performed symbolically by numbers, but practically, by joining lines together, dividing them into parts, and combining the parts in such a way as to illustrate the fundamental rules for multiplication and division of fractions. A pupil can learn to divide a line into parts more easily than he can master definitions; and when this is done he has a conception of fractions which he cannot gain in any other way. The visible figures by which principles are illustrated should, so far as possible, have no accessories. They should be magnitudes pure and simple, so that the thought of the pupil may not be distracted and that he may know what feature of the thing represented he is to pay atten-

tion to. The elementary theorems of arithmetic should be enforced and illustrated in the same way, without an attempt at formal demonstration, the
generalization being reached inductively. Thus, when the pupil comprehends
clearly, by means of dots arranged in a rectangle, that three fives contain
the same number of units as five threes, that is, when he sees that the commutative law is true, then it may be expressed to him in the general form,
$a \times b = b \times a$.

The concrete system should not be confined to principles, but be extended
to practical applications in mensuration and physics. Measurements of the
room, the house, and the yard; the calculation of the weights of visible objects, or of the number of articles that a given receptacle will hold; the computation of distances and areas in the town, by measures on a map of known
scale, of the number of cubic feet in a room, and of the weight of the air
which fills the room, are examples of problems which can be extended by
the teacher indefinitely. The simple operations of arithmetic can be better
exemplified by problems set on the spur of the moment, and springing
naturally from the environment of teacher and pupil, than by those given in
a printed book; and have the inestimable advantage of exciting the interest
of the pupil.

When such a system of teaching is once introduced, the teacher will
probably be surprised to find to what seemingly abstruse problems the simplest principles of arithmetic can be applied. The problem of computing the
quantity of coal which would have to be burned in order to heat the air of
a room from the freezing point to 70° would probably be beyond the powers
of all our college graduates, except those who have made physics one of their
specialties. Yet there is nothing in its elements above the powers of a boy
of twelve. At this age the child could, by a few very simple experiments, gain
the idea of a quantity of heat much more easily than the idea of stock in a
corporation. Having gained this, the elements which enter into the problem
in question could be measured one by one.

III. SPECIAL REPORT ON CONCRETE GEOMETRY.

The Conference recommends that the child's geometrical education should
begin as early as possible; in the kindergarten, if he attends a kindergarten,
or if not, in the primary school. He should at first gain familiarity through
the senses with simple geometrical figures and forms, plane and solid; should
handle, draw, measure, and model them; and should gradually learn some of
their simpler properties and relations. It is the opinion of the Conference
that in the early years of the primary school this work could be done in
connection with the regular courses in drawing and modelling without requiring any important modification of the school curriculum.

At about the age of ten for the average child, systematic instruction in concrete or experimental geometry should begin, and should occupy about one school hour per week for at least three years. During this period the main facts of plane and solid geometry should be taught, not as an exercise in logical deduction and exact demonstration, but in as concrete and objective a form as possible. For example, the simple properties of similar plane figures and similar solids should not be proved, but should be illustrated and confirmed by cutting up and re-arranging drawings or models.

This course should include among other things the careful construction of plane figures, both by the unaided eye and by the aid of ruler, compasses and protractor; the indirect measurement of heights and distances by the aid of figures carefully drawn to scale; and elementary mensuration, plane and solid.

The child should learn to estimate by the eye and to measure with some degree of accuracy the lengths of lines, the magnitudes of angles, and the areas of simple plane figures; to make accurate plans and maps from his own actual measurements and estimates; and to make models of simple geometrical solids in pasteboard and in clay.

Of. course, while no attempt should be made to build up a complete logical system of geometry, the child should be thoroughly convinced of the correctness of his constructions and the truth of his propositions by abundant concrete illustrations and by frequent experimental tests; and from the beginning of the systematic work he should be encouraged to draw easy inferences, and to follow short chains of reasoning.

From the outset the pupil should be required to express himself verbally as well as by drawing and modelling, and the language employed should be, as far as possible, the language of the science, and not a temporary phraseology to be unlearned later.

It is the belief of the Conference that the course here suggested, if skilfully taught, will not only be of great educational value to all children, but will also be a most desirable preparation for later mathematical work.

Then, too, while it will on one side supplement and aid the work in arithmetic, it will on the other side fit in with and help the elementary instruction in physics, if such instruction is to be given.

IV. SPECIAL REPORT ON ALGEBRA.

It is desirable, during the study of arithmetic, to familiarize the pupil with the use of literal expressions and of algebraic language in general. The teacher may advantageously introduce the simple equation in the study of proportion, of the more difficult problems in analysis, and of percentage and its applications. The designation of positive integral powers by exponents may also be taught.

Avoiding the introduction of negative numbers, the pupil should be drilled in easy problems like the following:

If one stone weighs p pounds and another weighs q pounds, what is the weight of both together?

If a square table is a feet long, what is its area?

If a yards of cloth cost b dollars, what will c yards cost?

Such exercises should grow out of similar ones involving numerical data.

The average pupil should be prepared to undertake the study of formal algebra at the beginning of the fourteenth year. For students preparing to enter college, the time assigned to this study in the high school should be about the equivalent of five hours per week during the first year, and an average of two hours and a half per week during the two following years. This affords ample time for the thorough mastery of algebra through quadratic equations and equations of quadratic form. The course should include radicals, but exclude the progressions, series, and logarithms, although a familiarity with logarithmic tables is desirable for those who expect to take a technical course in any department.

There are certain propositions in algebra the rigorous demonstration of which is unintelligible to pupils at the time when these propositions are first encountered. Such is usually the case with the rule of signs in multiplication and with the binomial formula. In cases of this kind the proof should be at first omitted, but always introduced at a later period in school or college. When such omissions are made, the pupil must be convinced of the truth of the propositions by illustration or induction. In many of our text-books the proofs of the theorems above referred to are not rigorous. The truth of the binomial formula for fractional or negative exponents had best be reserved for the more advanced courses in college or the scientific school. In case of positive integral exponents the pupil should arrive at the mode of expansion through the examination of products obtained by actual multiplication.

Oral exercises in algebra, similar to those in what is called "mental arithmetic," are recommended. Such exercises are particularly helpful in conducting brief and rapid reviews. Quickness and accuracy in both oral and written work should be rigidly enforced. The same facility should be attained in dealing with expressions containing coefficients and exponents that are literal as with expressions in which they are numerical. Radicals and fractional and negative exponents need more attention than they commonly receive. Especial emphasis should be laid upon the fundamental nature of the equation. The distinction should be clearly and repeatedly drawn between the ordinary algebraic equation and the identities with which the pupil has grown familiar in his study of arithmetic. He should also be given drill in the solution of an ordinary equation with reference to any letter that it may contain.

V. SPECIAL REPORT ON DEMONSTRATIVE GEOMETRY.

In regard to the teaching of formal geometry the Conference invites attention to the following considerations:

1. A course of study in demonstrative geometry properly begins with a careful and exhaustive enumeration of those properties of space which do not admit of being deduced from still simpler properties; that space is continuous and of three dimensions; that figures may be moved about in it without change of size or shape; that straight lines and planes may exist in space, determined by two and three points respectively; that of two intersecting straight lines but one can be parallel to a given straight line—the so-called geometric axioms.

It is of the first importance that the role which these axioms—or better, postulates—play in the demonstrative geometry be correctly understood: together they constitute a *definition of space,* from which—with certain formal definitions of figures—it is the business of demonstrative geometry to deduce all other facts regarding space with which it may concern itself.

2. The function of the construction postulates also, by which the elementary geometry is restricted in its constructions to the use of the compasses and ungraduated straight-edge, merits careful exposition, inasmuch as these postulates define the province of the elementary as distinguished from higher geometry. That it is not always understood is obvious from conceptions which are current as to what is and what is not allowable in the elementary geometry.

3. There are two methods employed in geometry for dealing with size-relations among the geometric magnitudes, the methods of immediate comparison of the magnitudes, and of comparison by means of their numerical measure. Thus the theorem, "the square on the sum of two lines is equal to the sum of the squares on those lines plus twice their rectangle," is demonstrated after the first method by showing that the square on the sum may be actually divided into these four parts; after the second, by deducing it from the algebraic theorem that the square of the sum of two quantities is equal to the sum of the squares of those quantities plus twice their product.

The first method is purely geometrical. None of its notions are arithmetical. Magnitudes are defined as equal when they can be made to coincide, they are added and substracted geometrically—by juxtaposition and separation—and their ratios are not expressed numerically but, like the magnitudes themselves, compared directly. The second method, on the other hand, is essentially arithmetical. Replacing the magnitudes by their measures, it at the same time replaces geometric equality, addition and substraction by the equality, addition and substraction of irrational numbers.

Opinions differ as to what the relative prominence of these two methods should be in elementary geometry. But, the first method being pure and thoroughly elementary and involving no abstraction, is surely better suited to the beginner. Indeed the student is most likely to become a sound geometer who is not introduced to the notion of numerical measures until he has learned that geometry can be developed independently of it altogether. For this notion is subtle, and highly artificial from a purely geometrical point of view and its rigorous treatment is difficult. The student generally only half comprehends it, so that for him demonstrations lose more in rigor as well as in vividness and objectivity by its use than they gain in apparent simplicity. Moreover the constant association of number with the geometric magnitudes as one of their properties tends to obscure the fundamental characteristic of these magnitudes—their continuity.

The numerical method is of course to be taught—with due attention to its rigorous presentation—for its own sake and for the sake of the mensuration to which it leads; but serious harm is done by allowing it to entirely supplant the pure method at as early a period as is customary.

4. Many students who can reason logically cannot present a geometrical demonstration orally with due elegance of form. Their statement of the argument is incomplete or illogical, or they express themselves in an awkward and inexact manner. This is a fault which may render the recitation of the proofs of geometry practically valueless, inasmuch as it prevents the discipline for which this exercise is chiefly prized, and cultivates instead the vicious habit of slovenly expression. It is due in part to the willingness of certain teachers to accept in lieu of the demonstration of a proposition any kind of evidence that the pupil understands it, in part to the widespread practice of substituting written for oral demonstration. The remedy is obvious: abundance of oral recitation—for which there is no proper substitute—and the rejection of all proofs which are not formally perfect.

5. The elementary ideas of logic may be introduced early in the course in demonstrative geometry with great advantage. One need only explain that if a class of things be represented by a symbol, say A, all things not belonging to this class may also be thought of as constituting a class, represented by the symbol *not A;* and that the proposition A *is* B is not a declaration of the equivalence of A and B, but that every individual of the class A belongs to the class B — to make it easily understood why the converse proposition B *is* A is not a necessary consequence of A *is* B and under what conditions it becomes such a consequence; and why, on the other hand, the "contrapositive" *not B is not A* is the logical equivalent of A *is* B and the "obverse" *not A is not B* of B *is* A.

Yet this little knowledge would add materially to the student's equipment for geometry. The contrapositive of a proposition is oftentimes more readily demonstrated than the proposition itself, its obverse than its converse; and when it has been proven that A *is* B it is often easier to show that there is but one B (when such is the case) than to show directly that B *is* A.

This knowledge, furthermore, is seriously needed to dispel existing confusion. For many students have a strong, though of course unformulated conviction — with apparently a good deal to justify it — that the logic of algebra is quite distinct from the logic of geometry, and both from the logic of ordinary correct thinking. Without a knowledge of the conditions under which the truth of the converse of a demonstrated proposition may be immediately inferred, for instance, it is difficult to see how the student is to reconcile the need of demonstrating converses in geometry with the practice which is common in algebra of establishing a proposition by proving its converse — as in proving the truth of an algebraic relation by showing that it leads to an identity.

Finally the very fact that demonstrative geometry is the most elaborate illustration of the mechanism of formal logic in the entire curriculum of the student, makes the consideration of these elementary principles of logic more interesting and profitable in this connection than in any other.

6. As soon as the student has acquired the art of rigorous demonstration, his work should cease to be merely receptive. He should begin to devise constructions and demonstrations for himself.

Geometry cannot be mastered by reading the demonstrations of a text book; and while there is no branch of the elementary mathematics in which purely receptive work, if continued too long, may lose its interest more completely, there is also none in which independent work can be made more attractive and stimulating. It possesses remarkable qualifications for quickening and developing creative talent. Its materials are a few simple, concrete, and easily apprehended notions which admit of numberless interesting and valuable combinations, some very simple, some very complex. The lack of general methods is the weakness of elementary geometry as a science. Each theorem must be demonstrated for itself by a process differing in some respect from that followed in the case of every other. But the invention of these processes — unimportant as they may be individually — is an intellectual exercise as much higher than the mechanical illustration of some powerful and general method—which is all that the ordinary exercises of elementary algebra involve — as it is lower than the discovery of a new truth by aid of such a method.

At the same time this characteristic of the elementary geometry makes the acquisition of any considerable degree of skill in independent geometrical work difficult. It requires abundant practice in exercises which have been carefully graduated and adapted to the abilities of the individual student. In particular it is important that the student should comprehend that, notwithstanding the rigorously synthetic form of its demonstrations, the method of investigation in elementary geometry, as in all science, is essentially analytic — that the clue to a demonstration or construction is most likely to be found by assuming it accomplished and tracing its consequences until results previously established have been deduced from it.

By wise instruction after this method, the inferior student can at least be freed from slavish dependence on his text book, while the able student will gain power enough in large part to construct his own geometry. But whatever the training may accomplish for him geometrically, there is no student whom it will not brighten and strengthen intellectually as few other exercises can.

7. It is desirable, if feasible, that solid as well as plane geometry be studied in preparation for college.

A place should also be found either in the school or college course for at least the elements of the modern synthetic or projective geometry. It is astonishing that this subject should be so generally ignored, for mathematics offers nothing more attractive. It possesses the concreteness of the ancient geometry without the tedious particularity, and the power of analytical geometry without the reckoning, and by the beauty of its ideas and methods illustrates the esthetic quality which is the charm of the higher mathematics, but which the elementary mathematics in general lacks.

REPORT OF THE COMMITTEE OF FIFTEEN ON ELEMENTARY EDUCATION ✒ WITH THE REPORTS OF THE SUB-COMMITTEES: ON THE TRAINING OF TEACHERS; ON THE CORRELATION OF STUDIES IN ELEMENTARY EDUCATION; ON THE ORGANIZATION OF CITY SCHOOL SYSTEMS

PUBLISHED FOR THE NATIONAL EDUCATIONAL ASSOCIATION BY THE AMERICAN BOOK COMPANY ✦ NEW YORK, CINCINNATI, CHICAGO

M D CCC XC V

CONTENTS

PAGE

INTRODUCTION 7

REPORTS OF SUB-COMMITTEES ON
    I. The Training of Teachers 19
    II. The Correlation of Studies in Elementary Education 40
    III. The Organization of City School Systems 114

APPENDICES: OPINIONS SUBMITTED TO SUB-COMMITTEES ON
    I. The Training of Teachers 135
    II. The Correlation of Studies in Elementary Education 157
    III. The Organization of City School Systems 198

INDEX 227

INTRODUCTION

To THE DEPARTMENT OF SUPERINTENDENCE
OF THE NATIONAL EDUCATIONAL ASSOCIATION:

THE undersigned, chairman of the Committee of Fifteen, appointed at the meeting of the Department of Superintendence held in Boston, Mass., in February, 1893, would respectfully report:

On February 22, 1893, the following resolution was adopted by the Department of Superintendence, on motion of Superintendent Maxwell, of Brooklyn, N. Y.:

Resolved, That a Committee of Ten be appointed by the Committee on Nominations, to investigate the organization of school systems, the coördination of studies in primary and grammar schools, and the training of teachers, with power to organize subconferences on such subdivisions of these subjects as may seem appropriate, and to report the results of their investigations and deliberations at the next meeting of the Department of Superintendence.

Resolved, That the officers of the Department of Superintendence be, and hereby are, directed to make application to the Board of Directors of the National Educational Association for an appropriation of twenty-five hundred dollars to defray the expenses of the Committee of Ten and of the conferences which that committee is empowered to appoint.

On February 23 the Committee on Nominations appointed the following Committee of Ten:

Superintendent William H. Maxwell, of Brooklyn, N. Y., chairman; Dr. William T. Harris, United States Commissioner of Education; Superintendent T. M. Balliet, of Springfield, Mass.; Superintendent N. C. Dougherty, of Peoria, Ill.; Superintendent W. B. Powell, of Washington, D. C.; Superintendent H. S. Tarbell, of Providence, R. I.; Superintendent L. H. Jones, of Indianapolis, Ind.; Superintendent J. M. Greenwood, of Kansas City, Mo.; State Superintendent A. B. Poland, of New Jersey; Superintendent Edward Brooks, of Philadelphia.

On motion of Superintendent Maxwell, the members of the Committee on Nominations were added to the Committee of Ten, so that the committee became one of fifteen. The names thus added to the committee were the following: President Andrew S. Draper, of the University of Illinois; Superintendent E. P. Seaver, of Boston, Mass.; Superintendent A. G. Lane, of Chicago, Ill.; Superintendent Charles B. Gilbert, of St. Paul, Minn.; Superintendent Oscar H. Cooper, of Galveston, Tex.

.
.
.

APPENDICES: OPINIONS SUBMITTED TO SUB-COMMITTEES ON

.
.
.

II. THE CORRELATION OF STUDIES IN ELEMENTARY EDUCATION

.
.

B. ARITHMETIC.

[*The entire section on arithmetic is given here.*]

Side by side with language study is the study of mathematics in the schools, claiming the second place in importance of all studies. It has been pointed out that mathematics concerns the laws of time and space—their structural form, so to speak—and hence that it formulates the logical conditions of all matter both in rest and in motion. Be this as it may, the high position of mathematics as the science of all quantity is universally acknowledged. The elementary branch of mathematics is arithmetic, and this is studied in the primary and grammar schools from six to eight years, or even longer. The relation of arithmetic to the whole field of mathematics has been stated (by Comte, Howison, and others) to be that of the final step in a process of calculation in which results are stated numerically. There are branches that develop or derive quantitative functions: say geometry for spatial forms, and mechanics for movement and rest and the forces producing them. Other branches transform these quantitative functions into such forms as may be calculated in actual numbers; namely, algebra in its common or lower form, and in its higher form as the differential and integral calculus, and the calculus of variations. Arithmetic evaluates or finds the numerical value for the functions thus deduced and transformed. The educational value of arithmetic is thus indicated both as concerns its psychological side and its objective practical uses in correlating man with the world of nature. In this latter respect as furnishing the key to the outer world in so far as the objects of the latter are a matter of direct enumeration, —capable of being counted,—it is the first great step in the conquest of nature. It is the first tool of thought that man invents in the work of emancipating himself from thraldom to external forces. For by the command of number he learns to divide and conquer. He can proportion one force to another, and concentrate against an obstacle precisely what is needed to overcome it. Number also makes possible all the other sciences of nature which depend on exact measurement and exact record of phenomena as to the following items: order of succession, date, duration, locality, environment, extent of sphere of influence, number of manifestations, number of cases of intermittence. All these can be defined accurately only by means of number. The educational value of a branch of study that furnishes the indispensable first step toward all science of nature is obvious. But psychologically its importance further appears in this, that it begins with an important step in analysis; namely, the detachment of the idea of quantity from the concrete whole which includes quality as well as quantity. To count, one drops the qualitative and considers only the quantitative aspect. So long as the individual differences (which are qualitative in so far as they distinguish one object from another) are considered, the objects cannot be counted together. When counted, the distinctions are dropped out of sight as indifferent. As counting is the fundamental operation of arithmetic, and all other arithmetical operations are simply devices for speed by using remembered countings instead of going through the detailed work again each time, the hint is furnished the teacher for the first lessons in arithmetic. This hint has been generally followed out and the child set at work at first upon the counting of objects so much alike that the qualitative difference is not suggested to him. He constructs gradually his tables of addition, subtraction, and multiplication, and fixes them in his memory. Then he takes his next higher step, namely the apprehension of the fraction. This is an expressed ratio of two numbers, and therefore a much more complex thought than he has met with in dealing with the simple numbers. In thinking five-sixths he first thinks five and then six, and holding these two in mind thinks the result of the first modified by the second. Here are three steps instead of one, and the result is not a simple number but an inference resting on an unperformed operation. This psychological analysis shows the reason for the embarrassment of the child on his entrance upon the study of fractions and the other operations that imply ratio. The teacher finds all his resources in the way of method drawn upon to invent steps and half steps, to aid the pupil to make continuous progress here. All these devices of method consist in steps by which the pupil descends to the simple number and returns to the complex. He turns one of the terms into a qualitative unit and thus is enabled to use the other as a simple number. The pupil takes the denominator, for example, and makes clear his conception of one-sixth as his qualitative unit, then five-sixths is as clear to him as five oxen. But he has to repeat this return from ratio to simple numbers in each of the elementary operations—addition, subtraction, multiplication, and division, and in the reduction of fractions—and finds the road long and tedious at best. In the case of decimal fractions the psychological process is more complex still; for the pupil has given him one of the terms, the numerator, from which he must mentally deduce the denominator from the position of the decimal point. This doubles the work of reading and recognizing the fractional number. But it makes addition and subtraction of fractions nearly as easy as that of simple numbers and assists also in multiplication of fractions. But division of decimals is a much more complex operation than that of common fractions.

The want of a psychological analysis of these processes has led many good teachers to attempt decimal fractions with their pupils before taking up common fractions. In the end they have been forced to make introductory steps to aid the pupil and in these steps to introduce the theory of the common fraction. They have by this refuted their own theory.

Besides (*a*) simple numbers and the four operations with them, (*b*) fractions common and decimal, there is (*c*) a third step in number, namely the theory of powers and roots. It is a further step in ratio, namely the relation of a simple number to itself as power and root. The mass of material which fills the arithmetic used in the elementary school consists of two kinds of examples, first, those wherein there is a direct application of simple numbers, fractions, and powers, and secondly the class of examples involving operations in reaching numerical solutions through indirect data and consequently involving more or less transformation of functions. Of this character is most of the so-called higher arithmetic and such problems in the text-book used in the elementary schools as have, not inappropriately, been called (by General Francis A. Walker in his criticism on common-school arithmetic) numerical "conundrums." Their difficulty is not found in the strictly arithmetical part of the process of the solution (the third phase above described), but rather in the transformation of the quantitative function given into the function that can readily be calculated numerically. The transformation of functions belongs strictly to algebra. Teachers who love arithmetic, and who have themselves success in working out the so-called numerical conundrums, defend with much earnestness the current practice which uses so much time for arithmetic. They see in it a valuable training for ingenuity and logical analysis, and believe that the industry which discovers arithmetical ways of transforming the functions given in such problems into plain numerical operations of adding, subtracting, multiplying, or dividing is well bestowed. On the other hand the critics of this practice contend that there should be no merely formal drill in school for its own sake, and that there should be, always, a substantial content to be gained. They contend that the work of the pupil in transforming quantitative functions by arithmetical methods is wasted, because the pupil needs a more adequate expression than number for this purpose; that this has been discovered in algebra, which enables him to perform with ease such quantitative transformations as puzzle the pupil in arithmetic. They hold, therefore, that arithmetic pure and simple should be abridged and elementary algebra introduced after the numerical opera-

147

tions in powers, fractions, and simple numbers have been mastered, together with their applications to the tables of weights and measures and to percentage and interest. In the seventh year of the elementary course there would be taught equations of the first degree and the solution of arithmetical problems that fall under proportion or the so-called "rule of three," together with other problems containing complicated conditions—those in partnership for example. In the eighth year quadratic equations could be learned, and other problems of higher arithmetic solved in a more satisfactory manner than by numerical methods. It is contended that this earlier introduction of algebra, with a sparing use of letters for known quantities, would secure far more mathematical progress than is obtained at present on the part of all pupils, and that it would enable many pupils to go on into secondary and higher education who are now kept back on the plea of lack of preparation in arithmetic, the real difficulty in many cases being a lack of ability to solve algebraic problems by an inferior method.

Your Committee would report that the practice of teaching two lessons daily in arithmetic, one styled "mental" or "intellectual" and the other "written" arithmetic (because its exercises are written out with pencil or pen) is still continued in many schools. By this device the pupil is made to give twice as much time to arithmetic as to any other branch. It is contended by the opponents of this practice, with some show of reason, that two lessons a day in the study of quantity have a tendency to give the mind a bent or set in the direction of thinking quantitatively with a corresponding neglect of the power to observe, and to reflect upon, qualitative and causal aspects. For mathematics does not take account of causes, but only of equality and difference in magnitude. It is further objected that the attempt to secure what is called thoroughness in the branches taught in the elementary schools is often carried too far, in fact, to such an extent as to produce arrested development (a sort of mental paralysis) in the mechanical and formal stages of growth. The mind in that case loses its appetite for higher methods and wider generalizations. The law of apperception, we are told, proves that temporary methods of solving problems should not be so thoroughly mastered as to be used involuntarily or as a matter of unconscious habit, for the reason that a higher and a more adequate method of solution will then be found more difficult to acquire. The more thoroughly a method is learned, the more it becomes part of the mind and the greater the repugnance of the mind toward a new method. For this reason parents and teachers discourage young children from the practice of counting on the fingers, believing that it will cause much trouble later to root out this vicious habit and replace it by purely mental processes. Teachers should be careful, especially with precocious children, not to continue too long in the use of a process that is becoming mechanical; for it is already growing into a second nature, and becoming a part of the unconscious apperceptive process by which the mind reacts against the environment, recognizes its presence, and explains it to itself. The child that has been overtrained in arithmetic reacts apperceptively against his environment chiefly by noticing its numerical relations—he counts and adds; his other apperceptive reactions being feeble, he neglects qualities and causal relations. Another child who has been drilled in recognizing colors apperceives the shades of color to the neglect of all else. A third child, excessively trained in form studies by the constant use of geometric solids and much practice in looking for the fundamental geometric forms lying at the basis of the multifarious objects that exist in the world, will as a matter of course apperceive geometric forms, ignoring the other phases of objects.

It is, certainly, an advance on immediate sense-perception to be able to separate or analyze the concrete, whole impression, and consider the quantity apart by itself. But if arrested mental growth takes place here the result is deplorable. That such arrest may be caused by too exclusive training in recognizing numerical relations is beyond a doubt.

Your Committee believes that, with the right methods, and a wise use of time in preparing the arithmetic lesson in and out of school, five years are sufficient for the study of mere arithmetic—the five years beginning with the second school year and ending with the close of the sixth year; and that the seventh and eighth years should be given to the algebraic method of dealing with those problems that involve difficulties in the transformation of quantitative indirect functions into numerical or direct quantitative data.

Your Committee, however, does not wish to be understood as recommending the transfer of algebra, as it is understood and taught in most secondary schools, to the seventh year or even to the eighth year of the elementary school. The algebra course in the secondary school, as taught to pupils in their fifteenth year of age, very properly begins with severe exercises with a view to discipline the pupil in analyzing complex literate expressions at sight and to make him able to recognize at once the factors that are contained in such combinations of quantities. The proposed seventh-grade algebra must use letters for the unknown quantities and retain the numerical form of the known quantities, using letters for these very rarely, except to exhibit the general form of solution or what, if stated in words, becomes a so-called "rule" in arithmetic. This species of algebra has the character of an introduction or transitional step to algebra proper. The latter should be taught thoroughly in the secondary school. Formerly it was a common practice to teach elementary algebra of this sort in the preparatory schools and reserve for the college a study of algebra proper. But in this case there was often a neglect of sufficient practice in factoring literate quantities, and as a consequence the pupil suffered embarrassment in his more advanced mathematics, for example in analytical geometry, the differential calculus, and mechanics. The proposition of your Committee is intended to remedy the two evils already named: first to aid the pupils in the elementary school to solve, by a higher method, the more difficult problems that now find place in advanced arithmetic; and secondly, to prepare the pupil for a thorough course in pure algebra in the secondary school.

Your Committee is of the opinion that the so-called mental arithmetic should be made to alternate with written arithmetic for two years and that there should not be two daily lessons in this subject.

JAMES A. McLELLAN

James A. McLellan (1832–1907) was a Canadian high school inspector, principal of the Ontario School of Pedagogy, and president of the Ontario Association of Teachers of Mathematics and Physics. He had a formative influence on Canadian mathematics education in the nineteenth century. He believed in the value of mental arithmetic, a segment of mathematics given great credit for its value as mental discipline. Among other texts, he published *Mental Arithmetic, Fundamental Rules, Fractions, Analysis* (1878).

Later, in 1895, McLellan coauthored with John Dewey a classic in mathematics education, *The Psychology of Number and Its Application to Methods of Teaching Arithmetic,* a chapter of which is included here. He also coauthored, with A. F. Ames, a three-book arithmetic series applying the theory expounded in *The Psychology of Number.* These arithmetics are an interesting union of nineteenth-century approaches to arithmetic and new, reform-inspired ideas. As the first pages of the grammar-grades text included here indicate, the idea of the practicality of measurement permeates the series. However, the old structure is evident in that (1) this text begins with a section of definitions and (2) one of the other books of the series was a separate mental arithmetic, though the inclusion of mental arithmetic had already become uncommon.

INTERNATIONAL EDUCATION SERIES

THE

PSYCHOLOGY OF NUMBER

AND ITS APPLICATIONS TO
METHODS OF TEACHING ARITHMETIC

BY

JAMES A. McLELLAN, A. M., LL. D.
PRINCIPAL OF THE ONTARIO SCHOOL OF PEDAGOGY, TORONTO

AND

JOHN DEWEY, PH. D.
HEAD PROFESSOR OF PHILOSOPHY IN THE UNIVERSITY OF CHICAGO

"The art of measuring brings the world into subjection to man ; the art of writing prevents his knowledge from perishing along with himself : together they make man—what Nature has not made him—all-powerful and eternal."—MOMMSEN.

NEW YORK
D. APPLETON AND COMPANY
1895

CONTENTS.

	PAGE
EDITOR'S PREFACE	v
AUTHOR'S PREFACE	xi

CHAPTER

I.—WHAT PSYCHOLOGY CAN DO FOR THE TEACHER . .	1
II.—THE PSYCHICAL NATURE OF NUMBER	23
III.—THE ORIGIN OF NUMBER : DEPENDENCE OF NUMBER ON MEASUREMENT, AND OF MEASUREMENT ON ADJUSTMENT OF ACTIVITY	35
IV.—THE ORIGIN OF NUMBER : SUMMARY AND APPLICATIONS	52
V.—THE DEFINITION, ASPECTS, AND FACTORS OF NUMERICAL IDEAS	68
VI.—THE DEVELOPMENT OF NUMBER ; OR, THE ARITHMETICAL OPERATIONS	93
VII.—NUMERICAL OPERATIONS AS EXTERNAL AND AS INTRINSIC TO NUMBER	119
VIII.—ON PRIMARY NUMBER TEACHING	144
IX.—ON PRIMARY NUMBER TEACHING	166
X.—NOTATION, ADDITION, SUBTRACTION . . .	190
XI.—MULTIPLICATION AND DIVISION	207
XII.—MEASURES AND MULTIPLES	227
XIII.—FRACTIONS	241
XIV.—DECIMALS	261
XV.—PERCENTAGE AND ITS APPLICATIONS . . .	279
XVI.—EVOLUTION	297

2

CHAPTER IV.

The Origin of Number: Summary and Applications.

SUMMARY: *Complete Activity and Subordinate Acts.*—Through the foregoing illustrations—which are illustrations of one and the same principle regarded from different points of view—we are now prepared for the statement which sums up this preliminary examination of quantity. *That which fixes the magnitude or quantity which, in any given case, needs to be measured is some activity or movement, internally continuous, but externally limited. That which measures this whole is some minor or partial activity into which the original continuous activity may be broken up (analysis), and which repeated a certain number of times gives the same result (synthesis) as the original continuous activity.*

This formula, embodying the idea that number is to be traced to measurement, and measurement back to adjustment of activity, is the key to the entire treatment of number as presented in these pages, and the reader should be sure he understands its meaning before going further. In order to test his comprehension of it he may ask himself such questions as these: The year is some unified activity—what activity does it represent? At first sight simply the apparent return of the sun to the same point in the heavens —an external change; yet the only reason for attaching so much importance to this rather than to any other cyclical change, as to make it the unit of time measurement, is that the movement of the sun controls the cycle of human activities—from seedtime to seedtime, from harvest to harvest. This is illustrated historically in the fact that until men reached the agricultural stage, or else a condition of nomadic life in which their movements were controlled by the movement of the sun, they did not take the sun's movement as a measure of time. So, again, the day represents not simply an external change, a recurrent movement in Nature, but a rhythmic cycle of human action. Again, what activity is represented by the pound, by the bushel, by the foot? [1] What is the connection between the decimal system and the ten fingers of the hands? What activity does the dollar stand for? If the dollar did not represent certain possible activities which it places at

1. The historical origin of these measures will throw light upon the psychological point.

our control, would it be a measure of value? Why may a child value a bright penny higher than a dull dollar? And so on.

Illustrations: Stages of Measurement.—Suppose we wish to find the quantity of land in a certain field. The eye runs down the length and along the breadth of the field; there is the sense of a certain amount of movement. This activity, limited by the boundaries of the field, constitutes the original vague muchness—the quantity to be measured—and therefore determines all succeeding processes. Then analysis comes in, the breaking up of this original continuous activity into a series of minor, discrete acts. The eye runs down the side of the field and fixes upon a point which appears to mark half the length; this process is repeated with each half and with each quarter, and thus the length is divided roughly into eight parts, each roughly estimated at twenty paces. The breadth of the field is treated in the same way. The eye moves along till it has measured, as nearly as we can judge, just as much space as equals one of the smallest divisions on the other side.

The process is repeated, and we estimate that the breadth contains six of these divisions. Through these interrupted or discrete movements of the eye we are able to form a crude idea of the length and breadth of the field, and thus make a rough estimate of its area. The separate eye movements constitute the analysis which gives the unit of measurement, and the counting of these separate movements (units) is the synthesis giving the total numerical value.

But the breaking up of the original continuous movement into minor units of activity is obviously crude and defective, and hence the resulting synthesis is imperfect and inadequate. The only thing we are certain of is the number of times the minor act has been performed; it is pure assumption that the minor act measures an equal length every time, and a mere guess that each of the lengths is twenty yards. In order, therefore, to make a closer estimate of the content of the field, we may mark off the length and breadth by pacing, and find that it is a hundred and seventy paces in length and a hundred and thirty paces in breadth. This is probably a more correct estimate, because (*a*) we can be much more certain that the various paces are practically equivalent to one another than that the eye movements are equal, and (*b*) since the pace is a more definite and controlled movement, we have a much clearer idea of how much the pace or unit of measurement really is.

But it is still an assumption that the various paces are equal to one another. In other words, this unit of measure is not itself a constant and measured thing, and the required measurement is therefore still imperfect. Hence the substitution for the pace of some measuring unit, say the chain, which is itself defined; the chain is applied, laid down and taken up, a certain number of times to both the length and the breadth of the field. Now the minor act is uniform; it is controlled by the measuring instrument, and hence marks off exactly the same *space* every *time*.[2] The partial activity being defined, the resulting numerical value—say, eight chains by six chains—is equally definite. Besides, the chain itself may be measured off into a certain number of equal portions; we may apply a minor unit of measure— e.g., the link—until we have determined how many links make up the chain. By means of this analysis into still smaller acts, the meaning of the unit is brought more definitely home to consciousness.[3]

But this mathematical measurement, this analysis-synthesis, is still insufficient for complete adjustment of activity. What, after all, is the value of this measured quality? What is it good for? Until this question is answered there can not be perfect adjustment of activities. To answer this brings us to the third and final stage of number measurement. This field will produce, say, only so many bushels of corn at a given price per bushel; it is, therefore, not worth so much as a smaller field which will produce as much wheat at a larger price per bushel. Or, in addition to the mere size of the field, it may be necessary to take into account not only the value of the crop it will raise, but also the cost of tilling it. Here there must be a much more complete adjustment of activities. The analysis concerns not only so many square rods; it includes also the money value of the crop and the cost of its production. The synthesis compares the result of this complex measurement with the results of other possible distributions of energy. Analytically the conditions are completely defined; synthetically there can be a complete and economical adjustment of the conditions to secure the best possible results.

The measured quantity representing the unified (or continuous) activity is the whole or unity; the measuring parts, representing the minor or partial activities, are the components or units, which make up the unified whole. In all measurement each of these measuring parts in itself is a whole act— as a pace, a day's journey, etc. But in its function of measuring unit it is at once reduced to a mere means of constructing the more comprehensive act. The end or whole is *one,* and yet made up of *many* parts.

SUMMARY.—All numerical concepts and processes arise in the process of fitting together a number of minor acts in such a way as to constitute a complete and more comprehensive act.

1. This fitting together, or adjusting, or balancing, will be accurate and economical just in the degree in which the minor acts are the same *in kind* as the major. If, for example, one is going to build a stone wall, the use of

2. Note how the two factors of *space* and *time* appear in all measurement, *space* representing concrete value, *time* the abstract number, and both, the measured magnitude.

3. If it be noted that all we have done here is to make the original activity of running the eye along length and breadth first continuously and then in an interrupted series of minor movements, more controlled and hence more precise, the meaning of the proposition (page 52) regarding the origin of measurement in the adjustment of minor acts to constitute a comprehensive activity will be apparent once more.

the means—the minor activities—will not be accurate until one can find a common measure for both the means, the use of the particular stones, and the end, the wall. Size, or amount of space occupied, is this common element. Hence, to define the process in terms of just so many cubic feet required is economical; to describe it in terms of so many stones would be impossible unless one had first found the volumes of the stones. Hence, once more, the abstraction and the generalization involved in all numerical processes—the special qualities of the stone are neglected, and the only thing considered is the number of cubic feet in the stone—abstraction. But through this factor of so much size the stone is referred at once to its place in the whole wall and to the other stones—generalization.

2. An end, or whole of a certain *quality*, furnishes the *limit* within which the magnitude lies. Quantity is limited quality, *and there is no quantity save where there is a certain qualitative whole or limitation.*

3. *Number* arises through the use of means, or minor units of activity, to construct an activity equal in value to the given magnitude. This process of constructing an equivalent value is *numbering*—evaluation. Hence, there are no *numerical distinctions* (psychologically) except in the process of measuring some qualitative whole.[4]

4. This measuring or valuation (defining the original vague qualitative whole) will transform the vague quantity into precise *numerical value;* it will accomplish this successfully in just the degree in which the minor activity or unity of construction is itself measured, or is also a numerical value. Unless it is itself a numerical quantity, a unity measured by being counted out into so many parts, the minor and the comprehensive activity can not be made precisely of the same kind. (Principle 1.)

5. Hence the purely correlative character of much and many, of measured whole and measuring part, of value and number, of unity and units, of end and means.

EDUCATIONAL APPLICATIONS.

We have now to apply the principle concerning the psychological origin of quantity and number to education. We have seen (*a*) the need in life, the demand in actual experience of the race and the individual, which brings the numerical operations; the process of measuring, into existence. We have seen (*b*) what forms number is required to assume in order to meet the need, fulfill the demand. We have now to inquire how far these ideas and principles have a practical application in educational processes.

The school and its operations must be either a natural or an artificial thing. Every one will admit that if it is artificial, if it abandons or distorts the normal processes of gaining and using experience, it is false to its aim

---

4. The pedagogical consequences of neglecting this principle will be seen in discussing the Grube method, or use of the *fixed* unit.

157

and inefficient in its method. The development of number in the schools should therefore follow the principle of its normal psychological development in life. If this normal origin and growth have been correctly described, we have a means for determining the true place of number as a means of education. It will require further development of the idea of number to show the educational principles corresponding to the growth of numerical concepts and operations in themselves, but we already have the principle for deciding how number is to be treated as regards other phases of experience.

THE TWO METHODS: THINGS; SYMBOLS.—The principle corresponding with the psychological law—the translation of the psychological theory into educational practice—may be most clearly brought out by contrasting it with two methods of teaching, opposed to each other, and yet both at variance with normal psychological growth. These two methods consist, the one in teaching number merely as a *set of symbols;* the other in treating it as a *direct property of objects.* The former method, that of symbols, is illustrated in the old-fashioned ways—not yet quite obsolete—of teaching addition, subtraction, etc., as something to be done with "figures," and giving elaborate rules which might guide the *doer* to certain results called "answers."

It is little more than a blind manipulation of number symbols. The child simply takes, for example, the figures 3 and 12, and performs certain "operations" with them, which are dignified by the names addition, subtraction, multiplication, etc.; he knows very little of what the figures signify, and less of the meaning of the operations. The second method, the simple perception or observation method, depends almost wholly upon physical operations with things. Objects of various kinds—beans, shoe-pegs, splints, chairs, blocks—are separated and combined in various ways, and true ideas of number and of numerical operations are supposed necessarily to arise.

Both of these methods are vitiated by the same fundamental psychological error; they do not take account of the fact that number arises in and through *the activity of mind in dealing with objects.* The first method leaves out the objects entirely, or at least makes no reflective and systematic use of them; it lays the emphasis on symbols, never showing clearly what they symbolize, but leaving it to the chances of future experience to put some meaning into empty abstractions. The second method brings in the objects, but so far as it emphasizes the objects to the neglect of the mental activity which uses them, it also makes number meaningless; it subordinates thought (i. e., mathematical abstraction) to things. Practically it may be considered an improvement on the first method, because it is not possible to suppress entirely the activity which uses the things for the realization of some end; but whenever this activity is made incidental and not important, the method comes far short of the intelligence and skill that should be had from instruction based on psychological principles.

While *the method of symbols* is still far too widely used in practice, no educationist defends it; all condemn it. It is not, then, necessary to dwell upon it longer than to point out in the light of the previous discussion *why* it should be condemned. It treats number as an independent entity—as something apart from the mental activity which produces it; the natural genesis and use of number are ignored, and, as a result, the method is mechanical and artificial. It subordinates sense to symbol.

The *method of things*—of observing objects and taking vague percepts for definite numerical concepts—treats number as if it were an inherent property of things in themselves, simply waiting for the mind to grasp it, to "abstract" it from the things. But we have seen that number is in reality a *mode of measuring value,* and that it does not belong to things in themselves, but arises in the economical adaptation of things to some use or purpose. *Number* is not (psychologically) got *from* things, it is put *into* them.

It is then almost equally absurd to attempt to teach numerical ideas and process *without* things, and to teach them simply *by* things. Numerical ideas can be normally acquired, and numerical operations fully mastered only by arrangements of things—that is, by certain acts of mental construction, which are aided, of course, by acts of physical construction; it is not the mere perception of the things which gives us the idea, but the *employing of the things in a constructive way.*

The method of symbols supposes that number arises wholly as a matter of abstract reasoning; the method of objects supposes that it arises from mere observation by the senses—that it is a property of things, an external energy just waiting for a chance to seize upon consciousness. In reality, it arises from *constructive* (psychical) activity, from the actual use of certain things in reaching a certain end. This method of constructive use unites in itself the principles of both abstract reasoning and of definite sense observation.

If, to help the mental process, small cubical blocks are used to build a large cube with, there is necessarily continual and close observation of the various things in their quantitative aspects; if splints are used to inclose a surface with, the particular splints must be noted. Indeed, this observation is likely to be closer and more accurate than that in which the mere observation is an end in itself. In the latter case there is no interest, no purpose, and attention is laboured and wandering; there is no aim to guide and direct the observation. The observation which goes with constructive activity is a part of the activity; it has all the intensity, the depth of excitation of the activity; it shares in the interest of and is directed by the activity. In the case where the observation is made the whole thing, distinctions have to be *separately* noted and *separately memorized.* There is nothing intrinsic by which to carry the facts noted; that the two blocks here and the two there make four is an *external* fact to be carried by itself in memory. But when the two sets are so used as to construct a whole of a certain value, the fact is *internal;* it is part of the mind's way of acting, of seeing a definite whole through seeing its definite parts. Repetition in one case means simply learning by rote; in the other case, it means repetition of activity and formation of an intelligent habit.

The rational factor is found in the fact that the constructive activity proceeds upon a principle; the construction follows a certain regular or orderly method. The method of action, the way of combining the means to reach the end, the parts to make the whole, is *relation;* acting according to this relation is rational, and prepares for the definite recognition of reason, for consciously grasping the nature of the operations. Rational action will pass over of itself when the time is ripe into abstract reasoning. The habit of abstracting and generalizing of analysis and synthesis grows into definite control of thinking.

THE FACTORS IN RATIONAL METHOD.—In more detail, dealing with number by itself, as represented by symbols, introduces the child at an early stage to abstractions without showing how they arise, or what they stand for; and makes clear no reason, no necessity, for the various operations performed, which are all reducible to (*a*) synthesis—addition, multiplication, involution; and (*b*) analysis—subtraction, division, evolution. The object or observation method shows the relation of number to things, but does not make evident why it has this relation; does not bring out its value or measuring use, and leaves the operations performed purely external manipulations of number, or rather with things which may be numbered, not internal developments of its measuring power. The method which develops numerical ideas in connection with the construction of some definite thing, brings out clearly (*a*) the natural unity, the limit (the magnitude) to which all number refers; (*b*) the unit of measurement (the particular thing) which helps to construct the whole; and (*c*) the process of measuring, by which the second of these factors is used to make up or define the first—thus determining its numerical value.

(*a*) Only this method presents naturally the idea of a magnitude from which to set out. The end to be reached, the object to be measured, supplies this idea of a given quantity, and thus gives a natural basis for the development and use of ideas of number. In numbers simply as objects, or in things *simply* as observed things, there is no principle of unity, no basis for natural generalization. Only using the various things for a certain end brings them together into one; we count and measure some quantitative *whole.*

(*b*) While every object is a whole in itself, a unity in so far as it represents one single act, no object simply as an observed object is a *unit.* Objects which *we* recognise as three in number may be before the child's senses, and yet there may be no consciousness of them as three different units, or of the sum three. Some writers tell us that each object is one, and so gives the natural basis for the evolution of number; that the starting point is *one* object, to which another object is "added," then a third, etc. But this overlooks the fact that each object is one, not a *unit* but one *whole*, differing from and exclusive of every other whole. That is, to take it as an *observed* object is to centre attention wholly upon the thing itself; attention would discriminate and unify the qualities which make the thing what it is—a *qualitative* whole; but there would be little room for the abstracting and relating action involved in all number. A numerical unit is not merely a whole, a unity in itself, but is, as we have seen, a unity employed as a means for constructing or measuring some larger whole. *Only this use, then, transforms the object from a qualitative unity into a numerical unit.* The sequence therefore is: first the vague unity or whole, then discriminated parts, then the recognition of these parts as measuring the whole, which is *now* a *defined* unity—a sum. Or, briefly, the undefined whole; the parts; the *related* parts (*now* units); the *sum*.

(c) Beginning with the numbers in themselves, as represented by mere symbols, or with perceived objects in themselves, there is no intrinsic reason, *no reason in the mind itself*, for performing the operations of putting together parts to make a whole (using the unit to measure the magnitude), or of breaking up a whole into units—discovering the standard of reference for measuring a given unity. These operations,[5] from either of these standpoints, are purely arbitrary; we may, if we wish, do something with number, or rather with number symbols: the operations are not something that we *must* do from the very nature of number itself. From the point of view of the constructive (or psychical) use of objects, this is reversed. These processes are simply phases of the *act of construction*. Moreover, the operations of addition, multiplication, division, etc., in the method of perceived objects, have to be regarded as *physical* heaping up, *physical* increase, *physical* partition; while in that of number by itself they are purely mental and abstract. From the standpoint of the psychological use of the things, these processes are not performed upon physical things, but with reference to establishing definite values;[6] while each process is itself concrete and actual. It is not something to be grasped by abstract thought, it is something done.

Finally, to teach symbols instead of number as the instrument of measurement is to cut across all the existing activities, whether impulsive or

5. It will be shown in a later chapter that all numerical operations grow out of this fundamental process.

6. The complications introduced in schools—e. g., that you can not multiply by a fraction, nor increase a number by division, etc., because multiplication means increase, etc.—result from conceiving the operations as physical aggregation or separation instead of synthesis and analysis of values—mental processes. To multiply $10 by one third is absurd if multiplication means a physical increase; if it means a measurement of value, taking a numerical value of $10 (a measured quantity) in a certain way to find the resulting numerical value, it is perfectly rational.

habitual. To teach number as a property of observed things is to cut it off from all other activities. To teach it through the close adjustment of things to a given end is to re-enforce it by all the deepest activities.

All the deepest instinctive and acquired tendencies are towards the constant use of means to realize ends; this is the law of all action. All that the teaching of number has to do, when based upon the principle of rationally using things, is to make this tendency more definite and accurate. It simply directs and adjusts this process, so that we notice its various factors and measure them in their relation to one another. Moreover, it relies constantly upon the principle of rhythm, the regular breaking up and putting together of minor activities into a whole; a natural principle, and the basis of all easy, graceful, and satisfactory activity.

The following extract, giving the first three pages of an upper-grade text by McLellan and Ames, illustrates the emphasis on measurement of the Dewey-McLellan approach to arithmetic. The appearance of definitions as the first order of business is also of interest, especially when compared with the corresponding first pages of the texts of Slocomb and Davies included in Part One. The more extensive list of definitions given by Davies illustrates the greater concern of his era with mathematical structure. After 1900 the use of such definitions became less common. With the emergence of connectionistic psychology as a basis for arithmetic teaching, they disappeared almost entirely from texts after 1920.

THE
PUBLIC SCHOOL ARITHMETIC

FOR GRAMMAR GRADES

BASED ON McLELLAN AND DEWEY'S

"PSYCHOLOGY OF NUMBER"

BY

J. A. McLELLAN, A.M., LL.D.

PRESIDENT OF THE ONTARIO NORMAL COLLEGE; AUTHOR (WITH DR. DEWEY)
OF "THE PSYCHOLOGY OF NUMBER," "APPLIED PSYCHOLOGY,"
"THE TEACHER'S HANDBOOK OF ALGEBRA," ETC.

AND

A. F. AMES, A.B.

HONOR GRADUATE IN MATHEMATICS; FORMERLY MATHEMATICAL MASTER
ST. THOMAS COLLEGIATE INSTITUTE, ETC.; SUPERINTENDENT
OF SCHOOLS, RIVERSIDE, ILL.

New York
THE MACMILLAN COMPANY
LONDON: MACMILLAN & CO., LTD.
1902

CONTENTS

PAGE

CHAPTER I
Definitions and Review 1

CHAPTER II
Review 14

CHAPTER III
Numeration and Notation 28

CHAPTER IV
Addition 35

CHAPTER V
Subtraction 50

CHAPTER VI
Multiplication 66

CHAPTER VII
Division 84

CHAPTER VIII
Comparison of Numbers 103

CHAPTER IX
Square Root 106

CHAPTER X
Greatest Common Measure and Least Common Multiple . 117

xi

---

xii   CONTENTS

PAGE

CHAPTER XI
Fractions 124

CHAPTER XII
Decimals 171

CHAPTER XIII
Compound Quantities 193

CHAPTER XIV
Percentage 234

CHAPTER XV
Interest 272

CHAPTER XVI
Ratio and Proportion 287

CHAPTER XVII
Square Root 296

CHAPTER XVIII
Mensuration 298

CHAPTER XIX
Metric System 320

CHAPTER XX
Miscellaneous Exercise 328

CHAPTER XXI
Appendix 349

CHAPTER I

Definitions and Review

1. A unit is a quantity used to measure quantity of the same kind.

Thus, 1 mi. is a unit used to measure distance, 1 A. to measure the size of a farm, and 1 doz. eggs to measure the quantity of eggs. If a lady wants to know into how many hair ribbons, each 1 ft. 6 in. long, she can cut a piece of ribbon 2 yd. 1 ft. 6 in. long, she must use 1 ft. 6 in. as a unit with which to measure the length 2 yd. 1 ft. 6 in. Cut a piece of string 2 yd. 1 ft. 6 in. long and divide it into parts each 1 ft. 6 in. long. How many?

2. As a person measures a quantity he counts the **Number** of units in the quantity. The *number* and the *unit* measure the *quantity*.

Draw a line 7½ in. long and measure it with a unit 2½ in. How many 2½-in. units in 7½ in.? Measure the same quantity with a unit 1½ in. How many 1½-in. units in 7½ in.?

3. The number is the **Ratio** of the quantity to the unit.

A line 15 in. long is measured 5 times by the unit 3 in., hence 5 is the ratio of 15 in. to 3 in. What is the ratio of 6 in. to 2 in.? 12 qt. to 3 qt.? 1 hr. to 10 min.? 1 ft. 6 in. to 6 in.?

Exercise 1

1. Mark two points on the blackboard 6 yd. apart. Cut a string 2 ft. long, and by measuring find how often 2 ft. is contained in 6 yd.

2. Find, without actually measuring, how often 2 ft. is contained in 6 yd. How many widths of carpet 2 ft. wide are needed to carpet a room 6 yd. wide?

3. Draw an oblong 12 in. long and 8 in. wide. Cut out of paper an oblong 4 in. long and 3 in. wide. Using this as a unit of measure, find how often it is contained in the larger oblong.

4. Find, without actually measuring, how many oblongs 4 in. by 3 in. can be cut from an oblong 12 in. by 8 in.

5. A piece of cardboard 18 in. by 12 in. is cut into cards 6 in. long and 4 in. wide. How many are there?

6. Put 2 gal. 1 qt. of water into a pail and measure it with a pint measure. 2 gal. 1 qt. = ? pt.

7. Find, without actually measuring, how many pints are equal to 2 gal. 1 qt.

8. How many pint jars can be filled with 4 gal. 2 qt. of maple syrup?

9. Cut out a piece of cardboard 4 in. long. Measure a distance equal to 8 of these units. Measure this distance again with a foot rule. 8 times 4 in. = ? ft. ? in.

166

10. Find, without actually measuring, how many feet and inches a string is that can be cut into 8 pieces each 4 in. long.

11. In the following examples what number expresses the measurement of the quantity by the unit?

Quantity	Unit	Quantity	Unit
2 ft. 6 in.	3 in.	3 bu.	12 qt.
11 qt. 2 pt.	6 pt.	$4.50	1 dime
3 wk. 4 da.	5 da.	24 sq. in.	oblong 3 in. × 2 in.
1 hr. 30 min.	18 min.	30¢	3¢ + 2¢

How do you find the number of units in a given quantity?

12. In the preceding example what is the ratio of each quantity to its own unit? What is the ratio of the unit to the quantity?

13. In the following examples find the quantities measured by the numbers and the units:

Number	Unit	Number	Unit
8	2 qt.	6	3 for 10¢
2½	6¢	9	2 pk.
3	35 mi.	40	5 da.
2 doz.	2¢ apiece	6	3 mi. + 4 mi.

14. How do you find the quantity containing a given number of units?

Exercise 2

1. A boy saves $4 a month. In how many months will he save the price of a bicycle worth $32?

2. A man earns $18 a week and spends $15. In how many weeks will he save enough to pay a debt of $24?

3. A family uses 2½ qt. of milk at 6¢ a quart daily. What does their milk cost per day?

What do they pay for milk in a month of 30 da.?

4. A family uses 1 qt. 1 pt. of milk at 6¢ a quart daily. What is their milk bill for the month of April? May?

5. A family uses 2 qt. 1 pt. of milk at 6¢ a quart daily. What do they pay for milk in the month of March, if they get 8 qt. extra?

6. A boy riding on a bicycle gains 3 mi. an hour on a man who is driving. In how many hours after passing him will he be 15 mi. ahead?

7. Two boats travel down a river at the rate of 14 and 9 mi. an hour respectively. If they start together, when will the faster be 20 mi. ahead?

8. Two trains travel, one east and the other west, at the respective rates of 35 and 23 mi. an hour. How far apart will they be in 3 hr.?

THE RATIO METHOD

The approach to arithmetic learning advocated by William W. Speer and embodied in the texts he wrote was a radical departure from the norm—the most radical of any of the approaches to gain even modest acclaim between the time of Colburn and the present (including the changes of today's ''new'' mathematics).

His texts, written from 1896 through 1899, completely abandoned the structure of arithmetic as it was then understood and relied instead on an activity-centered approach based on comparison of quantities. The books lacked not only the old topics such as notation and numeration, definitions, and analysis but also such familiar framework as sections entitled ''Division'' and ''Multiplication of Fractions.'' Immediately after the 1895 recommendation of the Committee of Ten to discard all but incidental arithmetic in the first year of school, Speer suggested a method that put even more stress on carefully sequenced primary school experiences than did earlier approaches. But whereas earlier methods such as that of Grube concentrated on the number of small collections, Speer made direct comparison of quantities (ratio, as Speer used the term) fundamental. The ratio concept was to be understood without physically or mentally subdividing either of the two quantities compared. The ability to make the comparisons required was to be developed by extensive and continued physical contact with the things compared: by seeing, hearing, touching, building, finding, cutting, and drawing. Speer's primary support for basing number in comparison was Herbert Spencer, who made comparison basic to thought. The selection here includes Speer's sequence from the beginning lesson involving identification and large-small comparison to his comparison-based introduction of equality.

PRIMARY

ARITHMETIC

FIRST YEAR

FOR THE USE OF TEACHERS

BY

WILLIAM W. SPEER

Assistant Superintendent of Schools, Chicago

Boston, U.S.A., and London

GINN & COMPANY, PUBLISHERS

The Athenæum Press

1897

PREFACE.

This book is one of a series soon to be issued. The point of view from which it is written is indicated in the introduction.

The essence of the theory of teaching arithmetic can be expressed in a few sentences. The fundamental thing is to induce judgments of relative magnitude. The presentation regards the fact that it is the *relation* of things that makes them what they are. The *one* of mathematics is not an individual, separated from all else, but the union of two like impressions: the *relation* of two equal magnitudes. A child does not perceive this *one* until he sees the *equality* of two magnitudes. He will not become sensitive to relations of equality by handling equal units with the attention directed to something else, as the color, the texture, or the how many; nor by one or two experiences in comparing magnitudes.

To aid the learner in seeing a 1 as the *relation* of two equal units, a 2 as the *relation* of a unit to another one half as large, a ½ as the *relation* of a unit to another twice as large, we must induce the repeated acts of comparing which bring these relations vividly before the mind. With this purpose the child is not required to build out of parts a whole which he has never seen, nor expected to discover a relation in the absence of one of the related terms. He does not begin with elements. He is not prevented from seeing things as they are by pushing elements into the foreground. The mind grasps something vaguely as a whole, moves from this to the parts, and gradually advances to a clearer and fuller idea of the whole. Whether the object of study be a flower, a picture, a cubic foot, or a six, the process of learning is the same. If we promote progress in the discovery of relations of magnitude, we will make it possible for the compared wholes to be pictured in their full extent, thus affording opportunity for comparing, for activity in judging. There is no such opportunity when a child who has no idea of a thing constructs it mechanically from given parts. Creation, in any subject, requires a basis in elementary ideas.

It is not to be forgotten that there is a wide difference between seeing that the relation of two particular things is 8, and realizing 8 as a relation, realizing it in such a way that it can be freely used without misapplying it.

There is no real progress unless the mind is gradually gaining power to think of things not present to sense, and to think of a relation apart from a particular thing. But there is no way to promote this progress except by securing continued activity of sense and mind. The child grows into the idea 8, slowly and unconsciously but surely, under right conditions. A cube does not become known by counting surfaces, edges, etc., again and again, but by observing other forms and many different cubes. Through repeated acts of dissociating and relating, what is particular sinks out of sight and the common trait stands out. This principle is of general application.

There should be constant calls for reperception, for judging and verifying. Only by multiplying experiences in the concrete, by noting the same relation in many different things and in many different conditions, does the child come to know a relation as it is.

The slow development of the power to form perfectly quantitative judgments is considered. Hence the earlier work makes no demand for close analysis. It provides for a gradual advance toward exactness. The exercises are only suggestive. The condition of the child determines what he should do. But in any case, the work in the beginning should be so simple that it can be done easily; it should look to the free action of both body and mind.

The child interested in finding colors and forms wishes to move about, to touch and handle things. Out of school he combines thinking and acting. Why should he not do so in the school? Interest will lead the child to control himself, but repression from without induces dullness, indifference, and antagonism. Force a child to preserve a regulation attitude, to keep his nerves tense, and you destroy the foundation of healthful mental activity. In the transition from home to school life, careful provision should be made for the *whole* child to express himself.

Attention is asked to the remarks upon over-direction, premature questioning, demands for analysis beyond the inclination and power of the pupil and for outward forms which are not the genuine expression of the child.

Great importance is attached to that order of work which puts things before the pupil and leaves him free to see and to tell all he can before interfering with his action by questioning or direction. Questions have their uses. They serve to arouse attention, to aid in testing the pupil's view, and may lead to the correct use of new forms of expression. But there are effects of questioning which are too often overlooked. Questions do for the child what he should do for himself; they conceal his attitude toward the work and prevent your seeing what he would do unaided. They call attention to details for which the mind may not be prepared, and present a partial, fragmentary view. The questioning may be logical, but the learner connects only that which he himself relates. Questions cause the teacher to suppose that the child grasps what is not appreciable by him, and so prevent the adaptation of the work. To attempt to force through questions what *you* see in a poem, picture, or problem, instead of leaving the pupil to discover what *he* is prepared to see, is to ignore the true basis of advance, to disregard the law that the mind passes from vague ideas to those fuller and more exact, only through its own acts of analysis and synthesis. Free work reveals the pupil and makes it possible to meet his needs.

171

This view furnishes no excuse for random, desultory work. The teacher must carefully select the means, whether the ideas into which he wishes to lead the child are mathematical, biological, or historical.

In conclusion it is urged that any success is dangerous which lessens the susceptibility of the mind to new impressions. We may be so successful in training the child to reproduce as to destroy his power to produce. Progress is impossible without growing power to do unconsciously what was at first done consciously; but accuracy is not to be desired at the expense of growth. The purpose of automatic action in education is not to restrict, but to set force free. When the work of the school is mechanical it weakens the relating power, the power to act in new circumstances, and thus lowers the child in the scale of being.

As insight into the subject and contact with the child enable us to open right channels for free action, there will be little occasion for drills. The fresh, vigorous effort of involuntary attention carries the child forward with surprising rapidity. Out of *self*-activity comes the self-control which gives strength to persist.

FIRST STEPS. — SENSE TRAINING.

[This section follows 36 pages devoted to preliminary material for teachers.]

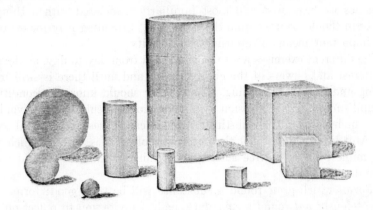

Finding solids.—Place spheres, cubes, cylinders, and other forms of various sizes in different parts of the room where the children can find them.

Show a sphere to the pupils. Ask:

1. What is this?

Find other balls or spheres.

Find a larger sphere than this. Find smaller ones.

2. Name objects like a sphere. Example: An orange is like a sphere.

3. What is the largest sphere that you have seen?

What is one of the smallest spheres that you have seen?

4. To-morrow tell me the names of spheres that you see when going from school and at home.

Ask, to-morrow, for the names of the objects and where they were seen.

5. What is the largest sphere you found? What is the smallest?

Review and work in a similar way with other solids.

"He should at first gain familiarity through the senses with simple geometrical figures and forms, plane and solid; should handle, draw, measure, and model them; and should gradually learn some of their simpler properties and relations."—Committee of Ten.

Children recognize objects similar in form, color, etc., before they desire or have the ability to express what they see.

Until a child can readily select a form he is not ready to make a statement of what he has found. Let the approach to telling be through doing; through the activity of the pupil in discriminating and relating.

The teacher, and such pupils as are able, should use the proper terms, so that pupils who have not heard the terms may learn to apply them. Children can discover likenesses and differences—relations—but not the terms in which they are expressed. They should learn the terms unconsciously by living in an atmosphere where they are used. Since we think most easily in the names we have first and most familiarly associated with a thing, the right term should be used from the beginning. Providing fitly for expressing is an important means of arousing self-activity.

The different exercises are to be continued from day to day, as the growing interest and powers of the child suggest, and until there is skill in performing and ease in expressing. The teacher should know the condition of the pupil's mind. His expression is the index to his mental state. Avoid anything which will tend to substitute mechanical expression for real expression. Any form which is not the outgrowth of what is within, which is not the genuine product of free activity, will mislead the teacher and weaken the child.

"Forms which *grow* round a substance will be true, good; forms which are consciously *put* round a substance, bad. I invite you to reflect on this." —Carlyle.

Finding colors.—Tests in color should be given before the more formal work suggested below. For example: Group cards of the same color and threads of worsted.[1]

Provide ribbons, worsted, cards, etc., of different colors, to be found by pupils when looking for a particular color.

Pin or paste squares of standard red and orange where they can be seen. Pin the red above the orange.

1. Find things in the room of the same color as the red square. What things can you recall that are red?

2. Look at the orange square. Find the same color elsewhere in the room. Recall objects that have this color.

3. Close the eyes, and picture or image the red square. Now the orange square.

4. Which square is above? Which below? Name the two colors.

---

1. These exercises are not to teach color, but are to train pupils to visualize, to attend, to compare, and to secure greater freedom in expressing through noting different relations. All pupils need such work before beginning the usual studies of the primary school. They lack needful elementary ideas, which must be obtained through the senses. The range of the perceptions needs to be widened.

5. To-morrow bring something that is red and something that is orange. Also tell the names of orange or red objects that you see in going to and from school.

Pin or paste a square of yellow below the orange.

1. Look at the yellow. Find the same color in the room. Recall objects having this color.

2. Look at the red, then the orange, then the yellow. Close the eyes and picture the colors one after another in the same order.

Cover the squares.

3. Which color is at the top? At the bottom? In the middle?

4. Name the three, beginning at the top. Name from the bottom.

5. Which color is third from the top? Second from the top? Third from the bottom?

6. To-morrow bring something that is yellow and tell me the names of things that you have seen that are yellow.

Add a square of green.

1. Find green. Recall objects that are green.

2. Try to see the green square with the eyes closed.

3. Look at the four colors.

4. Think of the four, one after another, with the eyes closed.

Cover the squares.

5. Think the colors slowly from the top down. From the bottom up.

6. Name the colors from the top down. From the bottom up. Which is second from the top? Third from the bottom? Second from the bottom?

7. Which color do you like best?

Add a square of blue and work in the same manner with the five as with the four.

Add a square of purple.

Work for a few minutes each day until the colors can easily be seen mentally in the order given.

Show a standard color. Have pupils find tints and shades of this color, and tell whether they are lighter or darker than the standard.

Have pupils bring things that are shades or tints of standard colors.

Using colored crayon or water-colors, have pupils combine primary colors and tell whether the result is darker or lighter than the standard secondary color. Example: Mix red and yellow. Is the result darker or lighter than the standard orange?

Why is it one of the first duties of the schools to test the senses and to devise means for their development?

Handling solids.—Cover the eyes.

Have a pupil handle a solid. Take it away.
Uncover the eyes. Pupil finds a solid like the one handled.
Cover the eyes.
Give a pupil a solid. Take it away. Give him another.
Are the solids alike?
Which is the larger? Which is the heavier?
Repeat the exercise from day to day.

Judgment and memory should be carefully cultivated through the sense of touch as well as through the sense of sight. Touch and motion give ideas of form, distance, direction, and situation of bodies. "All handicrafts, and after them the higher processes of production, have grown out of that manual dexterity in which the elaboration of the motor faculty terminates."

Similar solids.—Have a pupil select a solid and think of some object like it. Have other pupils guess the name of the object.

Ex.: I am thinking of something like a sphere.
Is it an orange?
No, it is not an orange.
Is it a ball of yarn?
It is not.

Relative magnitudes.—Place a number of solids on the table.

1. Find the largest solid. Find the smallest solid.

2. Find solids that are larger than other solids.

Ex.: This solid is larger than that one.

Find solids that are smaller.

3. Name objects in the room larger than other objects.

Ex.: That eraser is larger than this piece of chalk.

Name objects less than other objects.

4. Give names of objects at home that are smaller than other objects.

Ex.: A cup is smaller than a bowl.

5. Recall objects that are larger than other objects.

Ex.: An orange is larger than a peach. Some beetles are larger than bees.

6. What animals are larger than other animals?

7. Recall objects that are smaller than other objects.

Ex.: A base ball is smaller than a croquet ball.

8. Find the largest pupil in the class. The smallest.

9. To-morrow tell me the names of objects that are larger than other objects and the names of others that are smaller.

1. Find things that are higher than other things in the room.

Ex.: The door is higher than that table.

2. Find the tallest pupil. The shortest.

Compare heights of pupils.

Ex.: Mary is taller than Harry.

Compare the heights of other objects.

3. Recall objects that are longer than other objects.

4. What leaves are longer than they are wide? What leaves are wider than they are long?

5. To-morrow tell me the names of other leaves that are longer than they are wide.

Cutting.—Let the pupils at first cut and draw what they choose. After a number of daily exercises, when they have gained some command of the muscles, let them try to cut in outline objects which you place before them or which they have seen. Let the work be simple.

The drawing and cutting should be done freely, without the restraint of definiteness. If you ask more than the pupil can easily represent, the strained, unnatural tension interferes with free muscular action. In the slow and painful effort to represent perfectly, the mind is absorbed in the parts and is prevented from seeing the whole. A *premature* demand for definite action is a fundamental error, in that it separates thought from expression.

"The imperative demand for finish is ruinous because it refuses better things than finish."—Ruskin.

"Of course one cannot understand a child's picture-speech at once, any more than one can his other utterances. We must study and learn it."—H. Courthope Bowen.

Building.—Have pupils build prisms equal to other prisms.

Teacher shows a prism and the pupils build.

Hold the attention to the relative size. This is the mathematical element.

Avoid the analysis of solids until the habit of recognizing them as wholes is formed. Do not ask for number of surfaces, lines, corners, etc. Such questions, if introduced *prematurely*, tend to destroy self-activity, to interfere with judgments of relative size and with the power to see relations.

"Analysis is dangerous if it overrules the synthetic faculty. Decomposition becomes deadly when it surpasses in strength the combining and constructive energies of life, and the *separate* action of the powers of the soul tends to mere disintegration and destruction as soon as it becomes impossible to bring them to bear as *one* undivided force."—Amiel.

Ear training.—Have pupils listen and tell what they hear.

Have pupils note sounds when various objects are struck.

Pupils close eyes. Teacher strike one of the objects. Pupils tell which was struck.

Teacher strike two or more objects.

Pupils tell by the sound the order in which they were struck.

Train pupils to recognize one another by their voices and by the sounds made in walking.

Pupils close eyes and listen.

Drop a ball or marble two feet, then three.

Pupils tell which time it fell the farther.

"There are two ways, and can be only two, of seeking and finding truth. . . . These two ways both begin from sense and particulars; but their discrepancy is immense. The one merely skims over experience and particulars in a cursory transit; the other deals with them in a due and orderly manner."—Bacon.

"It appears to me that by far the most extraordinary parts of Bacon's works are those in which, with extreme earnestness, he insists upon a *graduated* and *successive* induction as opposed to a hasty transit from special facts to the highest generalizations."—Whewell.

Touch and sight training.—Pupils handle solids:

1. Find one of the largest surfaces of each solid.

Ex.: This is one of the largest surfaces of this solid.

2. Find one of the smallest surfaces.

3. Find surfaces that are larger than other surfaces.

Ex.: This surface is larger than that one.

4. Find surfaces that are smaller than other surfaces.

5. Compare the size of other surfaces in the room.

6. Find the largest surface or one of the largest surfaces in the room.

7. Close the eyes, handle solids, and find largest and smallest surfaces.

8. Cover the eyes; handle and tell names of blocks and of other objects.

The exercises for mental training are only suggestive of many others which teachers should devise. Be sure that the exercises are suited to the learner's mind, and to his physical condition.

Visualizing.—Place on the table three objects, for example: A box, a book, and an ink-bottle.

1. What can you tell about the box? About the book? About the ink-bottle? Which is the heaviest? Which is the lightest? Which is the largest?

2. Look at the three objects carefully, one after another.

3. Close your eyes and picture one after another.
Cover the objects.

4. Think the objects from right to left. From left to right.

5. Name the objects from right to left. From left to right.

6. Which is the third from the right? The second from the left?

"Our bookish and wordy education tends to repress this valuable gift of nature,—visualizing. A faculty that is of importance in all technical and artistic occupations, that gives accuracy to our perceptions and justness to our generalizations, is starved by lazy disuse, instead of being cultivated judiciously in such a way as will, on the whole, bring the best return. I believe that a serious study of the best method of developing and utilising this faculty without prejudice to the practice of abstract thought in symbols is one of the many pressing desiderata in the yet unformed science of education."—Francis Galton.

When the position of every object in the group can easily be given from memory, place another object at the left or right. Add not more than one object in an exercise unless the work is very easy for the pupils.

When a row of five is pictured and readily named in any order, begin with another group of five. Each day review the groups learned, so as to keep them vividly in the mind.

Questions or directions similar to the following will test whether the groups are distinctly seen:

Picture each group from the right. Name objects in each from the right.

In the third group, what is the second object from the left?

What is the middle object in each group? What is the largest object in each group?

When four or five groups can be distinctly imaged, this exercise might give place to some other.

Finding circles.—Show pupils the base of a cup, a cylinder, or a cone, and tell them that it is a circle.

Conduct the exercises so that the doing will call forth variety of expression in telling what is done.

The correct use of the pronouns, verbs, etc., will thus be secured without waste of the pupils' energy. What the pupils see and do should lead to statements similar to the following:

That circle is larger than this one. I have found a circle that is larger than that one. Helen has found a circle larger than that one. He has found a circle smaller than this one. They have found circles larger than this one.

1. Find circles.

2. Find circles that are larger than others. Find circles that are smaller.

3. Find the largest circle in the room.

4. Find one of the smallest.

5. Find circles in going to and from school and at home, and tell me to-morrow where you saw them.

Finding forms of the same general shape as those taken as types is of the highest importance. Unless this is done pupils are not learning to pass from the particular to the general. They are not taught to see many things through the one, and the impression they gain is that the particular forms observed are the only forms of this kind. Unless that which the pupil observes aids him in interpreting something else, it is of no value to him. Teaching is leading pupils to discover the unity of things.

Finding rectangles.—Show pupils rectangles (faces of solids), and tell them that such faces are *rectangles*.

1. Find other rectangles in the room.

Ex.: This blackboard is a rectangle.

2. Find larger and smaller rectangles than this one.

3. Find square rectangles. Find oblong rectangles.

Finding triangles.—Show the pupils the base of a triangular prism or pyramid.

The base of this solid is a triangle.

1. Find triangles in the room.

2. Find triangles that are larger and smaller than other triangles.

Finding edges or lines.—Place solids where they can be handled.

1. Show edges of different solids.

Show one of the longest[2] edges of the largest solid.

2. Look for the longest edges in each of the solids.

3. Show the longer edges of other objects in the room.

Ex.: This and that are the longer edges of the blackboard.

4. Show the shorter edges of different objects.

5. Find edges of different solids and tell whether they are longer or shorter than other edges.

Ex.: This edge of this solid is shorter than that edge of that one.

6. Find edges of objects in the room and tell whether they are longer or shorter than other edges.

Ex.: This edge of the table is longer than that edge of the desk.

7. Make sentences like this: This edge is longer than that one and shorter than this one.

"Vision and manipulation,—these, in their countless indirect and transfigured forms, are the two coöperating factors in all intellectual progress." —John Fiske.

Relative length.—Scatter sticks of different lengths on a table.

Use one as a standard. Pupils select longer and shorter, and state what they have selected.

---

2. The form of the solid will, of course, determine the adjective to use. Every lesson should help to familiarize the child with correct forms of speech.

After pupil selects a stick and expresses his opinion, let him compare the sticks by placing them together. This will aid him in forming his next judgment.

Select sticks that are a *little* longer or a *little* shorter. This exercise will demand finer discrimination than an exercise where there is no restriction as to comparative lengths.

Direction and position.—Pupils and teacher point:

1. Teacher: That is the ceiling. This is the floor. That is the back wall. This is the front wall. This is the right wall. That is the left wall. This is the north wall. That is the south wall. This is the east wall. That is the west wall.

2. A pupil points and teacher tells to what he is pointing. A pupil points and the pupils tell to what he is pointing.

3. Tell the position of objects in the room.

Ex.: There is a picture of a little girl on the north wall. There are three windows in the west wall.

Place groups of solids on three or four desks in different parts of the room, thus:

1. Tell the position of each.

Ex.: The cylinder is at the left at the back. The cube is at the right in front.

2. Without looking tell where the objects are.

Tell where different pupils sit.

Ex.: Mary sits on the second seat in the fourth row from the right.

Place a number of objects on a table.

Let pupils look not longer than ten seconds. Cover the objects. Have pupils tell what they saw. Practise until pupils learn to recognize objects quickly.

Have a pupil from another class walk through the room. Ask pupils to tell what they observed.

Such exercises as the following, if not carried to the point of fatigue, cultivate alertness of mind, concentration, and power to respond quickly to calls for action.

Teacher occupy a pupil's seat, give directions slowly, then place hand where she wishes the pupils to place theirs.

1. Place hand on the front of your desk. On the back. In the middle. At the middle of the right edge. At the middle of the left edge. On the right corner in front. On the left corner at the back. On the left corner in front. On the right corner at the back.

2. Pupil place hand and teacher or other pupil tell whère it is.

3. Pupil place an object in different positions on the desk. Pupils tell where it is.

Give each pupil a cube. Teacher use rectangular solid and follow her own directions.

4. Place finger on upper base. On the lower base. On the right face. On the left face. On the front face. On the back face.

5. Pupils place finger and teacher tell where it is placed.

6. Pupils place finger and tell where they have placed it.

Place solids where they can be observed.

"We overlook phenomena whose existence would be patent to us all, had we only grown up to hear it familiarly recognized in speech."—William James.

1. Tell the names of as many as you can.

2. What is the name of the first at the left? Give name if none of the pupils know it. Of the second? Of the third? Of the first, second, and third? Of the fourth? Of the first, second, third, fourth? Of the fifth? Of the five?

3. Look at the solids. Then think of them without looking. Cover the solids.

4. Give names in order from left to right. From right to left.

5. Tell position.

Ex.: The square prism is the second solid from the left.

Building.—Give pupils a number of cubic inches.

1. Build a prism equal to this one (show prism only for an instant).

Build a prism equal to *this* one.

Build a cube equal to this one.

Give other similar exercises from day to day.

Cutting.—1. Cut a slip. Cut a longer slip.

2. Cut a slip. Cut a shorter slip.

Give each pupil a square two inches long.

3. Cut larger squares than the square two inches long. What did I ask you to cut?

4. Cut smaller squares than the square two inches long. What did I ask you to cut?

5. Cut a square that is neither larger nor smaller than the square two inches long.

Give other exercises.

"Almost invariably children show a strong tendency to cut out things in paper, to make, to build,—a propensity which, if duly encouraged and directed, will not only prepare the way for scientific conceptions, but will develop those powers of manipulation in which most people are most deficient."—Herbert Spencer.

Drawing.—1. Draw a square. Draw a smaller square.

2. Draw a large square, a small square, and one larger than the small square and smaller than the large square.

3. Draw two equal squares.

4. Draw a line. Draw a longer line.

5. Draw a line. Draw a shorter line.

6. Draw a line. Draw another neither longer nor shorter than this line. Draw other equal lines.

Do not push demands in advance of the child's growing power to do.

Through the child's attempts to do that which it wishes, comes the fitting of the muscles for more definite and more complex movements. Above all things let the earlier movements be pleasurable, that an impulse to renewed exertion may be given. The desire to create is the truest stimulus to that action which gives muscular control. Our exactions may make the doing so disagreeable as to destroy the desire to produce.

Relative magnitude.—Place solids where they can be handled.

1. Find solids that are a little larger than other solids.

2. Find solids that are a little smaller.

3. Find objects that are a little larger or a little smaller than other objects.

Ex.: That desk is a little larger than this.

4. Find surfaces of the solids that are a little larger or a little smaller than other surfaces.

5. Find edges of the solids that are a little longer or a little shorter than other edges.

6. Find edges of other objects that are a little longer and those that are a little shorter than other edges.

Cutting.—1. Cut a slip of paper. Cut another a *little* longer. Another a *little* shorter. Measure. Practise.

2. Cut a square. Cut another a *little* larger. Another a *little* smaller. Measure. Practise.

Drawing.—1. Draw a line. Draw another a *little* longer. Another a *little* shorter. Measure. Practise.

2. Draw a square. Draw another a *little* longer. Another a *little* smaller. Measure. Practise.

Cutting.—1. Cut a slip of paper. Try to cut another equal in length to the first. Look at them. Which is the longer? Place them together to see if they are equal. Practise cutting and comparing. Give each pupil paper and an oblong rectangle.

2. Cut a rectangle as large as, or equal to, the rectangle I have given you. What are you to cut? Is the rectangle you cut as long as the rectangle I gave you? Is it as wide? Does the one you cut exactly cover the one I gave you? Are the two rectangles equal? Practise trying to cut a rectangle exactly the same size as or equal to the one I gave you.

Equality.—"The intuition underlying all quantitative reasoning is that of the equality of two magnitudes."—Herbert Spencer.

1. Find solids and other objects that are equal.

2. Find solids in which the surfaces are all equal.

3. Find solids that have surfaces of only two sizes.

4. Find solids that have surfaces of three sizes.

5. Find solids in which the edges are all equal.

6. Find solids that have edges of two different lengths.

7. Find solids that have edges of three different lengths.

8. Find a solid that has four equal surfaces. How many other equal surfaces has it?

9. Find a solid that has two equal large surfaces.

10. Find a solid that has two equal small surfaces.

11. Find a solid that has four equal long edges.

12. Show me an edge of one solid equal to an edge of another.

13. Show me two edges of a solid which, if put together, will equal one edge of another.

14. Find objects in the room that are equal, or of the same size.

Ex.: Those two windows are equal. Those two erasers are equal.

Give each pupil a square.

1. Cut a square equal to the one I have given you. Compare. Is the square you have cut equal to the one I gave you? Practise cutting and comparing.

Give each pupil a triangle.

2. Cut a triangle equal to the one I have given you? Compare. Are they equal? Which is the larger?

1. Draw a line. Draw another equal to the first. Measure. Are the lines equal?

Give each pupil a square.

2. Draw a square equal to the one I have given you. Do the squares look exactly alike? Measure. Are they equal?

3. Draw a triangle. Draw an equal triangle. Do the triangles look exactly alike? Are they equal?

1. Show me equal surfaces in the room. Equal edges.

2. Show me the equal long edges of the blackboard. How many equal long edges has the blackboard? How many short? Show me the two equal long edges and the two equal short edges of other surfaces.

3. Show me the two largest surfaces of this box.

4. A chalk-box has surfaces of how many sizes?

Show a real brick or a paper model.

5. How many equal large surfaces has a brick? How many equal small surfaces? How many other equal surfaces?

6. Show me a surface in one solid equal to a surface in another.

7. Show me two surfaces which, if put together, will equal one surface that you see.

8. Show me one of the longest edges of this box. One of the shortest. One of the other edges.

9. How many equal long edges has the box? How many equal short edges? How many other equal edges?

10. How many rows of desks do you see?

11. Show me two equal rows.

Pupil observe objects. Cover his eyes. Let another pupil substitute an object for one of those observed. Uncover eyes. Pupil tell what was taken away and what was put in its place.

Secure sets of squares and of other rectangles of different dimensions.

Scatter sets over the table.[3]

Train pupils to select those that are equal.

Ex.: That square rectangle equals this one, or that oblong rectangle equals this one, or James found a square equal to this one.

Secure variety of statement.

Cutting.—1. Look at a cube 2 in. long and cut a square equal to one of its surfaces, or look at a square rectangle 2 in. long and cut an equal one. What did I ask you to cut?

Let pupils criticise their own work. Do not tell them that the square rectangle they cut is too large or too small; let them compare and tell you. The work will be good, no matter how crude or imperfect, if it is the best the pupil can do. Growth is possible only from the basis of genuine, natural expression.

2. Practise cutting and comparing.

3. Cut a square rectangle two inches long without observing model.

4. Cut a rectangle whose length and width are the same. Measure. Are they equal? What is the name of this figure? Practise.

To-morrow, have pupils cut the square rectangle again.

Have them tell what they cut, in order to learn to associate the language with the thing.

Give pupils square rectangles four inches long and train them to cut, first when observing, then from memory.

Give pupils rectangles 4 in. by 2 in., and tell them to cut rectangles 4 in. by 2 in.

5. What did I tell you to cut? After cutting, compare and measure.

6. What are the names of the three forms that you have cut?

7. What is the width of the square 2 in. long? Of the square 4 in. long?

Why are a child's ideas *necessarily* crude rather than complete? What, then, should be true of his outward representations?

Why is it impossible to secure perfect forms from young children without interfering with mental and moral development?

"We shall not *begin* with a pedantic and tiresome insistence on accuracy (which is not a characteristic of the young mind), but endeavor steadily to lead up to it—to *grow* it—producing at the same time an ever-increasing appreciation of its value."—H. Courthope Bowen.

3. Length of squares,—2 in., 2½ in., 3 in., 3½ in.. 4 in. Dimensions of oblong rectangles, —1 × 2, 2 × 2, 3 × 2, 4 × 2, 5 × 2, and others 1 × 3, 2 × 3, 3 × 3, 4 × 3, 5 × 3, 6 × 3.

As before urged, let the work be done freely. Unnatural restraint in expressing results in lack of feeling. It lessens desire to see and to do. The use of things in which mathematical relations are conspicuous furnishes no excuse for disregarding the truth that progress in the power to represent either within or without is ever from the less to the more definite. The child is not troubled by a complexity or a definiteness which it does not see. Teaching in harmony with nature will permit the child to see freely and express freely.

Exercise in judging will gradually increase the power of definite thinking; and exercise in doing the power of definite action.

.
.
.

NATIONAL EDUCATIONAL ASSOCIATION

JOURNAL

OF

PROCEEDINGS AND ADDRESSES

OF THE

THIRTY-EIGHTH ANNUAL MEETING

HELD AT

LOS ANGELES, CALIFORNIA

JULY 11–14, 1899

1899

Published by the Association

CONTENTS

PAGE

Constitution, - - - - - - - 1

By-Laws, - - - - - - - - 4

Act of Incorporation, - - - - - 5

Calendar of Meetings, - - - - - 6

Officers for 1898–99, - - - - - - 8

Officers for 1899–1900, - - - - 12

Treasurer's Report, - - - - - - 16

Report of Board of Trustees, - - - - 20

Journal of Proceedings — General Sessions, - - - 23

Minutes of Proceedings — Board of Directors (1898–99), - - - 34

Minutes of Proceedings — Board of Directors (1899–1900), - - 38

General Sessions — Addresses and Discussions, - - - 47

   Report of Committee on Necrology, - - - - 232

Department of Superintendence (Columbus Meeting), - - 251

The National Council of Education, - - - - 380

   Special Report of Committee on Public Libraries, - - 452

Department of Kindergarten Education, - - - - 530

Department of Elementary Education, - - - 575

Department of Secondary Education, - - - - 601

   Special Report of Committee on College-Entrance Requirements, - 632

Department of Higher Education, - - - - - 818

Department of Normal Schools, - - - - 835

   Special Report of Committee on Normal Schools, - - - 836

Department of Manual Training, - - - - - 904

Department of Art Education, - - - - - 932

Department of Music Education, - - - - 970

Department of Business Education, - - - - 998

Department of Child Study, - - - - - 1031

Department of Physical Education, - - - - 1064

Department of Natural Science Instruction, - - - 1097

Department of School Administration, - - - - 1118

Library Department, - - - - - - 1135

Department of Education of Deaf, Dumb, and Feeble-Minded, - - 1156

List of Active Members, - - - - - 1179

List of Corresponding Members, - - - - 1237

Index to List of Active Members, - - - - 1238

Statistical Table of Membership for 1899, - - - 1247

Statistical Table of Membership since 1884, - - - 1248

Inventory and Price List of Publications, - - - 1249

General Index, - - - - - - 1250

iii

A. F. NIGHTINGALE, *Chairman*,

> Superintendent of High Schools, Chicago, Ill.

W. H. SMILEY, *Secretary*,

> Principal of High School, District No. 1, Denver, Colo.

GEORGE B. AITON,

> State Inspector of High Schools, Minneapolis, Minn.

J. REMSEN BISHOP,

> Principal, Walnut Hills High School, Cincinnati, O.

JOHN T. BUCHANAN,

> Principal of Boys' High School, New York, N. Y.

HENRY B. FINE,

> Professor of Mathematics, Princeton University, Princeton, N. J.

PAUL H. HANUS,

> Professor of the Science and Art of Education, Harvard University, Cambridge, Mass.

BURKE A. HINSDALE,

> Professor of the Science and Art of Education, University of Michigan, Ann Arbor, Mich.

RAY GREENE HULING,

> Principal of the English High School, Cambridge, Mass.

EDMUND J. JAMES,

> Professor of Public Administration, University of Chicago, Chicago, Ill.

WILLIAM CAREY JONES,

> Professor of Jurisprudence, University of California, Berkeley, Cal.

JAMES E. RUSSELL,

> Dean of the Teachers' College, Columbia University New York, N. Y.

- CHARLES H. THURBER,

> Associate Professor of Pedagogy, University of Chicago, Chicago, Ill.

[*Members of the Committee on College-entrance Requirements were listed in the journal as shown above.*]

MATHEMATICS

The committee begs to submit the following report on mathematics. It will be found that our recommendations are in the main in agreement with those of the mathematical conference of the Committee of Ten and with those contained in the appended report of the committee appointed by the Chicago Section of the American Mathematical Society. These reports contain many suggestions relative to the teaching of mathematics in which we heartily concur, but which we have not thought it necessary to repeat.

I. We recommend that the course in arithmetic required of all students be limited, roughly speaking, to the following topics: the four fundamental operations for integers, and common and decimal fractions; the most important weights and measures; percentage and its application to simple interest; and that it be completed in the sixth grade. An admirable statement of the reasons for this recommendation is to be found in the report of the mathematical conference of the Committee of Ten, and they need not be repeated here. The recommendation involves the omission of commercial arithmetic from the prescribed course in mathematics. If it be deemed necessary, an elective course in this subject may be offered at some convenient time during the high-school period, and in connection with it a course in bookkeeping.

We concur with both committees in urging that the instruction in arithmetic be enlivened by numerous applications to problems which are of immediate interest to the pupil, or can be made so by simple explanations—notably problems of elementary mensuration and physics.

The most important practical end to be secured by the study of arithmetic is skill in accurate reckoning with integers and common and decimal fractions. That the pupil may not lose this skill, after having once acquired it, we deem it indispensable that he be given frequent practice in numerical reckoning thruout the school course. Algebra, metrical geometry, and the physical sciences afford abundant opportunities.

II. We suggest the following arrangement of the course in mathematics

---

The complete section on mathematics is included. The report of the Chicago section, which appeared later, follows immediately here.

from the seventh to the twelfth grades inclusive, assuming the length of the recitation period to be at least forty-five minutes:

Seventh grade—Concrete geometry and introductory algebra   -   4 periods
Eighth grade—Introductory demonstrative geometry and algebra - 4   "
Ninth and tenth grades—Algebra and plane geometry   -   -   4   "
Eleventh grade—Solid geometry and plane trigonometry   -   -   4   "
Twelfth grade—Advanced algebra and mathematical reviews   -   4   "

1. The algebra of the seventh and eighth grades should, at the outset, be mere literal arithmetic. But we are of the opinion that, by limiting the working material to very simple polynomials and fractional expressions, and to equations of the first degree with numerical coefficients, the four fundamental operations for rational algebraic expressions, simple factoring, and the solution of equations of the first degree in one and two unknown quantities may be taught effectively in the course of these two grades.

Young students enjoy reckoning, and elementary algebraic reckoning will interest them far more than the complexities of commercial arithmetic. The principles of the subject must, of course, be presented concretely, and unnecessary generalizations should be carefully avoided. Simple problems which can be solved by aid of equations of the first degree should be introduced as early as possible. The sooner the pupil appreciates the power of algebraic methods, the sooner will the subject attract him.

2. Concrete geometry may be taught with advantage earlier than the seventh grade. But even in that case we deem it wise to devote half the time given to mathematics in the seventh grade to this subject.

3. The amount of demonstrative geometry which should be given in the eighth grade will depend somewhat upon the knowledge of concrete geometry which the pupil has by that time acquired. In any event, we should question the wisdom of undertaking any systematic study of a text-book of demonstrative geometry in this grade. An important object of the instruction should be to awaken an interest in the demonstrative process, and that may be best accomplished by confining the pupil's attention to the propositions which his concrete work has taught him to appreciate, and which admit of easy demonstration. The theorems which relate to the congruence of triangles, parallel lines, the angle-sum of the triangle, parallelograms, and some of the simpler and more useful properties of the circle, and many of the problems of construction, belong to this category; the propositions which necessitate the consideration of incommensurables do not.

4. We recommend that the time allotted to mathematics in the ninth and tenth grades be divided equally between algebra and plane geometry; and that the course in algebra include: (*a*) a more systematic and comprehensive study of the topics treated in the introductory course of the seventh and eighth grades, with a thoro drill in factoring, highest common factor, least common multiple, and complex fractions; (*b*) radicals and fractional

193

exponents, and quadratic equations in one and two unknown quantities; (c) ratio and proportion, the progressions, the elementary treatment of permutations and combinations, the binomial theorem for positive integral exponents, and the use of logarithms.

There is time enough in this course for the topics (c), and they seem to us to belong here rather than in the advanced algebra of the twelfth grade, because of their elementary character and general interest. The acquisition, thus early, of a practical acquaintance with logarithms in particular would be of great advantage to the pupil in his work in metrical geometry and physical science. The slight theoretical knowledge of logarithms which it requires is easily within his reach; for the theorems relating to the logarithm of a product, a quotient, a power, and a root are mere restatements of theorems regarding exponents with which he is already familiar, and it is certain to interest him, for it appeals, as few other topics in algebra can, to the utilitarian instinct which is so strong in young students.

5. By "advanced algebra" we mean the remaining topics which are to be found in an ordinary text-book of "college algebra," viz.: the elementary treatment of infinite series, undetermined coefficients, the binomial theorem for fractional and negative exponents, the theory of logarithms, determinants, and the elements of the theory of equations.

III. In solid geometry, plane trigonometry, and advanced algebra the schools should insist upon the same amount of work and aim at the same standard of scholarship as the best American colleges require in their courses in these subjects.

IV. When a student who is preparing for college does not intend to offer advanced algebra, he should defer some or all of the mathematics of the eleventh grade until the last year of his school course, or be given opportunity for mathematical reviews in that year.

V. We recommend that the several mathematical subjects count toward satisfying the requirements for admission to college, as follows:

(a) Elementary algebra, as defined in II, 4   -   -   -   -   - $1\frac{1}{2}$ units
(b) Advanced algebra   -   -   -   -   -   -   -   -   -   - $\frac{1}{2}$ unit
(c) Plane geometry -   -   -   -   -   -   -   -   -   -   -   -1   "
(d) Solid geometry   -   -   -   -   -   -   -   -   -   - $\frac{1}{2}$ "
(e) Plane trigonometry -   -   -   -   -   -   -   -   - $\frac{1}{2}$ "

REPORT OF THE COMMITTEE OF THE CHICAGO SECTION
OF THE AMERICAN MATHEMATICAL SOCIETY

Dr. A. F. Nightingale, Chairman.

SIR: In compliance with a request from you, the Chicago Section of the American Mathematical Society, at its session in December, 1898, appointed a committee to co-operate with the committee of the National Educational Association of which you are chairman, by preparing for the use of the latter committee a report "on the scope, aim, and place of these studies (mathematics) in the secondary schools and in preparation for college, with model courses in algebra, geometry (plane and solid), and trigonometry, with methods to be used, time to be consumed, etc., etc." This action was afterward approved by the Council of the society.

In order that the various phases of instruction in mathematics might be more fully represented, it was decided to associate with the members of the American Mathematical Society upon the committee several persons not members of the society, these persons to have equal voice and vote with the members of the society in the proceedings of the committee, but to be designated as associate members of the committee. The associate members are Messrs. Lyon and Schobinger.

The committee held several sessions in December, at which the various problems presenting themselves were discussed, and a subcommittee was appointed to prepare a draft of a report. This was done, and a copy sent to each member of the committee. These drafts were returned with criticisms and amendments, upon the basis of which a second draft was prepared by the subcommittee and a copy sent to each member of the committee. The comments hereupon were discussed by those members of the committee present at the meeting of the Chicago Section of the American Mathematical Society at Evanston, April 1, 1899, and the subcommittee was directed to prepare a third and final draft, which is submitted herewith. Since the report is submitted to you directly, and not to the society; the individuals concurring in the report are alone responsible for its contents.

Very respectfully,

J. W. A. YOUNG,

Chairman.

PRELIMINARY REMARKS

1. *Terms used.*—The term "secondary school" is used to designate, generically, all schools which have courses fitting for college. The term includes high schools, academies, and private college-preparatory schools. The course of study in the secondary school proper is assumed to cover four years.

The term "the grades" is used to designate the work prior to the secondary school. It is assumed to cover eight years. The work of each of these years is sometimes alluded to as a "grade," the grades being numbered in order from one to eight. The child is assumed to enter the first grade at the age of six years.

2. *Scope of report.*—In determining the phases of topics to be discussed

195

and the nature of its detailed suggestions, the committee has been governed by the condition of instruction today, rather than the absolute importance in themselves of the topics selected for remark. It was found impracticable to discuss the work in mathematics in the secondary school without giving quite a little consideration to the closely related antecedent work in the grades.

3. *Scope of mathematical work.*—At its sessions in December the following resolutions were adopted by the committee:

(*a*) That before the pupils reach the secondary school the work in mathematics should be the same for all.

(*b*) That in the secondary school the standard course in mathematics should be sufficient to admit to college; that this course should be required of all pupils, and that the instruction in this course should be the same for all pupils.

(*c*) That the main emphasis should be given to such topics as are useful in later work.

(*d*) That the best place for a topic in the course of study is where it is most closely related to other topics; that there should be applications of algebra, geometry, and arithmetic to each other, and to various sciences and the practical affairs of life.

CONCERNING METHODS

Various methods of teaching mathematics are in vogue. The good teacher will not tie himself to any one method, but, on occasion, will make use of the good features of every one. The committee recommends no single method above all others, but whatever method may be used, the aim should always be to cultivate independent thinking on the part of the pupil. A method which encourages, or even permits, rote work, or mechanical manipulations, is radically wrong. The value of the study of mathematics cannot be realized, not one of its objects attained, unless the student himself thinks, produces. *Not to learn proofs, but to prove,* must be his task. This idea should dominate the instruction from the very beginning. The independent work should not be left to the close; not to the closing years, nor to the close of the subject in hand, nor to the close of the chapter, nor even to the close of the first lesson in arithmetic.

GENERAL METHODIC SUGGESTIONS

1. *Steps.*—The importance of distinguishing the various steps of a process, and of taking them *one at a time,* can hardly be overemphasized. This is sometimes irksome to the pupil, and the consequent attempts to take several steps at once are responsible for much of some pupils' lack of success in mathematics.

2. *Oral work.*—In all the subjects of mathematics much stress should be

laid on oral solution of *many easy* and carefully graded exercises. Principles are just as effectually applied in these as in more complicated exercises, and the application is more readily seen.

3. *Testing results.*—The pupil should be taught to test the accuracy of his results by applying a check whenever this is possible, and before completing any topic he should have acquired sufficient facility in checking his work against errors, to rely with confidence upon the correctness of his own results, independently of corroboration by the teacher or a printed answer. Often a rough estimate of the probable character of the result will enable the pupil to detect a glaring error, without the use of a more detailed check. Written exercises should by no means all have results of a simple form, since pupils are very apt to fall into the habit of thinking that the result *must* be simple to be correct.

4. *Translation.*—Mathematics has a language of its own. The teacher must be unwearying in his endeavors to teach his pupils to speak the sentences of the mathematical language with intelligence, and he must be ever on the alert to check the tendency to use them as meaningless jargon. Here, as in other languages, one who has made some progress shows that he has intelligent control of the language by uttering consistent sentences conveying ideas. Ability to think *in* the language is one of the ends aimed at, but in the language of mathematics this can be attained only by much translating; the beginner must assure himself that he understands the mathematical sentence, by giving its equivalent in ordinary English; and, what is more difficult, must be able to clothe in mathematical symbols thoughts expressed in English.

5. *Different presentations.*—In the fundamentals and in the beginning of any subject the committee is decidedly of opinion that one set of definitions and style of presentation should be strictly adhered to. After a time (and still adhering to the one style of treatment adopted) the presentation by the pupils of other proofs which they may have found for the same proposition, or of different methods of attaining the result of some exercise, and the discussion of these in class, is of great value. More may often be gained by proving one proposition in three different ways than by proving three propositions in the same way. This practice should, however, be introduced gradually, great care being taken to avoid confusion; and its use should be much increased as the pupils gain a firm grasp of the subject.

Definitions, tho developed in class as needed, should not be left in an inaccurate form, nor inconsistent with the analogous definitions of later mathematics. Tho in higher mathematics the definitions of the elementary subjects may be generalized, it should not be necessary to overturn them. (E.g., the circle should be defined as a curve, not as a portion of a plane.)

6. *Neatness and accuracy.*—Papers written in a slovenly manner, slip-

197

shod work, half-guessing at results, and artificial juggling with the quantities involved, are far too frequently found. The difficulty can be met only by persistent training, from the very beginning of mathematical instruction, in neatness and accuracy. In particular, the committee suggests the use of numerous short written exercises, in which the pupil is not hurried for time by the amount assigned, and in which the requirement is made that what he hands in must be accurate and neatly arranged.

7. *Synopses.*—At the close of each chapter or topic a synopsis in schematic form of its definitions, methods, and results should be made. The object of this is to correlate the material and to secure that view of the topic as a whole which is too likely to be obscured by the details of the first study and the working of exercises. This will serve also to bring clearly before the pupils that the solution of exercises is not an end in itself, but is a means of impressing a connected theory.

8. *Correlation of work.*—The subjects arithmetic, geometry, algebra should be treated as branches of one whole—mathematics—and each of these subjects freely applied in illustrating and broadening the others.

9. *Independent thinking.*—Whatever specific method or methods may be used in conducting the instruction, the controlling principle must be that the pupil is to be kept thinking for himself. The learning of proofs, even tho it be done understandingly, is not sufficient. *Not learning proofs, but proving,* should be the pupil's principal activity in the study of mathematics.

ARITHMETIC

The instruction in arithmetic, except as it would properly come up in connection with geometry, algebra, and trigonometry, thus adding to their interest and usefulness, should be confined to the following topics:

1. The four fundamental processes with integers, all the computations being tested.

2. Factorization of all numbers up to 100, and some above 100, exponents being used. The results not to be derived by rule, but from the multiplication table.

3. Easy work by short rule in L. C. M. and H. C. D.; to be tested by seeing whether the quotients obtained by dividing L. C. M. by the numbers are relatively prime, and whether the numbers divided by the H. C. D. also give relatively prime results.

4. Simple work in denominate numbers, only the measures generally in vogue being used.

5. Simple operations in fractions, geometric, i.e., graphic illustrations being given, and fractions with large terms being, as a rule, avoided. Application of simple fractions to making rough estimates.

Much stress on cancellation; actual multiplication or division being performed by cancellation wherever possible.

6. United States money. The commoner measures of the metric system; the measures being actually constructed, and measurements performed with them. There should also be rough comparison with our own measures.

7. Decimals: the four rules, with especial attention to the correct placing of the decimal point.

8. Simple problems in percentage; the fact being emphasized that "per cent." means hundredths, or a fraction with 100 for denominator. The pupil should be trained always first to ask himself of what the per cent. is to be taken. This (the determination of the base) is largely a matter of use of language. Making use of "aliquot parts" (where the per cent. can easily be converted into such) connects per cent. with fractions and helps to prevent rote methods.

9. Examples in simple interest where the time and rate are given.

10. The use of the "method of analysis" for the solution of problems in simple and compound proportion, and in interest, without ever introducing the terminology and machinery usual in proportion.[1]

11. The concrete exemplification of the simpler geometric notions and facts should begin with the beginning of the arithmetic and be carried on in connection with this subject and with drawing during the first six years. By the close of this time the leading facts and theorems of geometry, plane and solid, should have become familiar by means of concrete illustrations and computations (mensuration). The pupil will now, perhaps, himself begin to feel the need of *proof* rather than illustrations (or will be led to feel it by the teacher), and at the beginning of the seventh year this transition may be made, and the developing of proofs begun carefully, gradually, and as informally as possible. In the seventh year the work in arithmetic may per-

---

1. As sufficient exemplification of the method we give the following: If 48 men can do a piece of work in 12 days, working 10 hours a day, in how many days of 8 hours each would 40 men accomplish the same work?

Arrangement:	Men	Days	Hours
	48	12	10
	40	?	8

Oral explanation: We seek days, so we begin with days. If 48 men accomplish the work in 12 days, 1 man would have to work 48 times as many days as 48 men, and 40 men $\frac{1}{40}$ as many as 1 man. That is, working 10 hours per day. To accomplish it by working 1 hour per day, it would take ten times as many days as when working 10 hours per day, and to do it by working 8 hours per day, $\frac{1}{8}$ as many days as when working 1 hour per day. We have now considered all the data, and, performing the multiplication, we obtain the result.

The written work is by cancellation. Nothing is written down except the arrangement and the following equation:

$$12 \cdot 48 \cdot \tfrac{1}{40} \cdot 10 \cdot \tfrac{1}{8} = 18.$$

This method makes compound proportion correspondingly easy, and dispenses entirely with the confusing verbiage of the subject. The work is precisely the same, no matter which of the quantities is unknown.

mit the informal beginning (as abbreviations) of literal arithmetic. The committee recommends that all topics not mentioned be omitted from the instruction in arithmetic as such—in some cases to be taken up later (in algebra, geometry, or trigonometry), in others to be omitted altogether.

In all the instruction in arithmetic there should be insistence upon neatness and upon accuracy; much oral work (object: correct thinking) and frequent short oral drills (object: quickness and accuracy); the testing of computations, both by rough estimates and exact tests; avoidance of technical terms and formal rules, save where absolutely necessary and when the need is felt by the pupil; ideas before definitions or rules.

ALGEBRA

While not recommending any radical alterations in the subject-matter of algebra, as usually presented in our best schools,[2] the committee desires to emphasize the following points:

1. *The arithmetical side of algebra.*—Computations with numbers should be constantly introduced, problems with literal quantities being worked out

2. The report of 1896–97 of the Commissioner of Education contains (pp. 457–613) a collocation of the entrance requirements of 432 institutions having a course leading to the degree of A.B. Of these institutions, 346 specify arithmetic as an entrance requirement, the others probably regard it as implied in the requirement of algebra. Algebra is required in 412 institutions to the following amounts:

To quadratics - - - - - -	37 institutions
Including quadratics - - - -	74 "
Amount not specified - - - -	201 "
	312 "

The other requirements are as follows:

Plane geometry in - - - - -	294 institutions
Solid geometry in - - - - - -	93 "
Trigonometry in - - - - - - -	4 "
Conic sections in - - - - - -	2 "

Upon looking over the detailed statement of the requirements for each institution, it appears that the better institutions require arithmetic (explicitly or tacitly), algebra including quadratics, and plane geometry.

Solid geometry is required by many institutions of high rank, and not required by others of equally high rank. The territorial distribution of the institutions requiring solid geometry is interesting.

Division	Total number of institutions	Number requiring solid geometry
North Atlantic - - - -	76 - - -	5 6.6 per cent.
South Atlantic - - - -	61 - - - -	4 6.6 "
North Central - - - -	183 - - -	68 37.1 "
South Central - - - - -	75 - - -	8 10.7 "
Western - - - - -	37 - - -	8 21.6 "
Total - - - -	432 - - - -	93 21.5 per cent.

200

or verified with numerical data also. The processes of arithmetic, both oral and written, should not be allowed to fall into disuse, but facility therein should rather be increased. At the same time, the pupil should understand the value of algebra in abridging or simplifying computation with numbers, or in proving the correctness of rules of computation, and should understand clearly that the devices of mathematics (especially algebra) have the purpose of enabling us *not* to compute; and that actual computations are usually not to be made so long as they can be avoided; that cancellation is to be resorted to wherever possible; and that to obtain an expression in factored form, or in any form in which operations are *indicated,* is a distinct advantage, not to be surrendered by needlessly performing the operations. Some of the topics omitted from arithmetic should be taken up at appropriate places in the work of algebra.

2. *The equational side of algebra.*—The equation should be made from the very beginning. Very simple problems in words leading to equations can be given at the outset.

3. *Algebraic translation.*—What has been said as to the value and necessity of translation in general applies with special force to algebra. Here the danger of mechanical, or even haphazard, manipulation of symbols is perhaps the greatest, and it must be especially guarded against by care that the meaning of the symbols, and the reason for the operations, be always clear in the pupil's mind. This can be done to a large extent by requiring the pupil to give readily and clearly in words the meaning of the formulæ and equations. On the other hand, the danger is exaggerated by the use of complicated and long examples, which seem to emphasize operative skill merely, and make that appear as the main object sought. Better many short examples with the principles always clearly apprehended than a few complicated ones with the principle obscured.

(Skill in manipulating long and intricate algebraic expressions should also be attained, and for this purpose the use of long and hard examples, after the principles and methods of a topic are clearly understood, is indispensable.)

4. *Topics to be emphasized.*—The following topics require especially careful treatment:

The meaning and use of exponents, positive, negative, and fractional; the handling of the simpler surds; the distinction between identical equations and equations of condition; the character of the roots of the quadratic equation as determined by inspection; the connection between the roots and the coefficients of the quadratic; the solution of equations by factoring; and the making of the algebraic statements for problems given in words.

5. *Secondary-school algebra and college algebra.*—It should be the aim of the secondary school to avoid taking up any of the topics which are customarily treated in college algebra, but rather to secure as thoro a mastery

as possible of those topics which the college presupposes. It is recommended that schools which have hitherto taken up topics anticipatory of college algebra devote the time gained by omitting them to a more thoro study of the topics of the previous head.

The progressions, arithmetical and geometric (with applications to interest, simple and compound), and the theory and use of logarithms, might well, so far as the nature and difficulties of the subject are concerned, be included in the secondary-school course, but as they are required for entrance by very few colleges, and are accordingly taken up in connection with college algebra, the committee recommends that they be omitted from the secondary-school course, in the interests of economy of energy, and to avoid duplication of work; until such time at least as, by action on the part of the colleges, these topics (or any of them) are relinquished as parts of college algebra, and made parts of the entrance requirements.

These remarks relate solely to the work in algebra *required of all pupils* in the secondary school. It is not meant to discourage the offering of more advanced courses in algebra ("college algebra") or in trigonometry to such pupils as may wish to take them. As these pupils will often desire that these advanced courses in the secondary school should be accepted by some college as the equivalent of college work, the scope and character of the work will usually be determined by the requirements of the college in question.

DEMONSTRATIVE GEOMETRY

The instruction in demonstrative geometry should not begin with a mass of definitions and axioms. All definitions should be introduced when needed, and not earlier; and, as a rule, only after the teacher has, by suitable examples and problems, familiarized the pupil to some extent with the notion in question, and the pupil himself feels the need of some convenient term by which to designate it, or the need of a precise agreement as to the meaning to be given to a term already used vaguely in common parlance.

Care should be taken to select for the early instruction such propositions as are less difficult to understand because less nearly self-evident; those that are more nearly self-evident being reserved for a later stage. Such propositions as, "All straight angles are equal," "All right angles are equal," should be omitted altogether.

Oral proofs (i.e., proofs in which nothing but the figure is placed upon the board) may well be used in geometry. Later even the figure may often be omitted. After the pupil has had some practice of this sort with familiar proofs, he will be able to work out the proofs of simple new propositions, with the figures only before him, and even if no figure, carrying the whole proof in the mind.

Frequent drills in seeing relations in a given figure (angles equal, supplementary; lines parallel, perpendicular; triangles equal, similar; etc., etc.) as a general exercise, without having any specific theorem proposed for proof, are also helpful. The teacher should prepare the figure, at first simple and anticipating coming propositions; later more complicated and unlike any of the figures of the text.

As to subject-matter, the propositions taken up may be divided into two classes: *fundamental* propositions and *exercises*. The fundamental propositions together constitute the nucleus or skeleton of the subject, being that minimum which all pupils alike should know. They should be reduced to as small a compass as possible. All other propositions constitute the class we have called *exercises*. The proofs of the exercises are to be based upon the fundamental propositions. Every course in geometry should invariably include all the fundamental propositions and a large number of exercises; the selection of the latter may vary from year to year. It is not at all implied here that the proofs of the fundamental propositions may not also be obtained as original exercises.

What has been said applies to both plane and solid geometry. A word may be added as to the use of models in solid geometry. While not wishing to undervalue models which are presented to the pupils ready-made, the committee believes that, as a rule, the pupils gain more by constructing their own models, and that this can be done very easily in a sufficient number of theorems. Some pieces of cardboard, darning needles, and thread constitute apparatus sufficient for making models of a large class of propositions. Another large class of models can be cut out of potatoes. A broomstick furnishes all the models needed for the cylinder. An orange will do fairly well for the sphere, but a small slated globe in the hand of each pupil is better.

The attempt has been successfully made to teach geometry by interweaving solid and plane geometry from the outset. While the committee is not prepared to commend this, there are advantages to be gained by beginning solid geometry before plane geometry is completed. In the opinion of the committee, the restriction of the study of geometry in many secondary schools to plane geometry is unfortunate, and it is desirable that the school course and the college-entrance requirement in geometry should cover both plane and solid geometry.

The notions and results of modern geometry may be used with advantage, but only so far as they actually simplify or make clearer the topic in hand.

The work in demonstrative geometry should be accompanied by construction and measurement. E.g., in connection with similar triangles, pupils may measure distance of some inaccessible object, simply measuring base line and two angles, and then drawing to scale. Of course, the work is crude, but this form of exercise opens a new window in the child's mind.

In the work in geometry, arithmetic, and also algebra (so far as this subject has been developed), should be frequently applied.

TRIGONOMETRY

Trigonometry is at present usually not required in the school curriculum; to prepare pupils for admission to certain technical schools and colleges, it is sometimes taught in the schools. When thus taught, the subject-matter taken up is determined by the requirements of the institutions in preparation for which it is taught.

There is, however, no intrinsic reason why the elements of plane trigonometry should not be an integral part of the school course in mathematics; it can be developed well in continuation of algebra and plane geometry, and is a fitting sequel to them. The matter should be restricted to that needed for the solution of plane triangles—numerous, but simple applications to the determination of heights and distances should be made.

To avoid duplication of work, the introduction of plane trigonometry into the school course (like that of certain portions of algebra mentioned above) should be an action of school and college jointly.

The trigonometric functions should be defined as ratios, and the whole treatment should be based upon the ratio definitions exclusively.

Before logarithmic tables are introduced, sufficient training should have been given in the solution of problems by means of the natural functions to make the pupils regard these as the real functions; log sin., log cos., etc., appearing merely as tools.

The object of a logarithmic table is to abridge computations. Those tables are accordingly to be preferred which furnish such aids to interpolation that the value sought may be read off quickly with the desired degree of accuracy and without side computations.

DISTRIBUTION

I. IN THE GRADES

The committee believes that the work in arithmetic outlined by it can be completed in the seventh grade, and that in this grade half the time can be given to demonstrative geometry. In all the preceding grades concrete geometry should be interwoven with arithmetic and with drawing. The transition to demonstrative geometry will thus not be abrupt, but will find the pupil prepared for it. The introduction of demonstrations into the concrete work should be gradual and informal; there should be much demonstration before the machinery and technical terminology of demonstrations are introduced. In the eighth grade demonstrative geometry would continue to occupy half the time, and the other half would be devoted to the beginning of algebra. This should be a natural growth of the arithmetic; the use of letters to stand for numbers may be introduced even earlier in formulating rules; as, "The area of a rectangle is equal to the length times the breadth,"

$A = LB$. The equation with one unknown quantity may also be introduced informally as occasion may arise. Under favorable circumstances the following ground could perhaps be covered in the grammar grades:

Geometry.—Lines, angles, triangles, parallelograms, elements of the circle.

Algebra.—The four fundamental operations with positive and negative numbers; simple cases of factoring under multiplication; simple equations with one unknown, and problems leading to such equations.

In the work in these subjects and in their further development in the secondary school, numerical applications of the results should be made continually. These applications should lead to computations sufficiently difficult to keep in practice the facility in computation gained in arithmetic, and to increase it. Stress should be laid on the simplifications in computations which may often be made by the literal notation of algebra.

In suggesting this course of study for the grammar grade, the committee realizes that in many places it would be impracticable to adopt the suggestions at once as a whole. In fact, under some circumstances the committee would not encourage, but would actually discourage, the immediate and complete adoption of its suggestions. On the other hand, in cases where some (perhaps a large part) of the suggestions of the committee are already in force, and where the corps of teachers is prepared to adapt its work to the new plan, there would be no obstacle, but indeed a distinct gain, in putting the committee's suggestions as a whole into immediate operation. The committee believes that the suggestions made (followed, if need be, gradually) are generally feasible.

The study of demonstrative geometry should in all cases be begun before that of algebra. Geometry is less abstract, less artificial, lends itself less readily to mere mechanical manipulations, and is more easily illustrated by concrete and familiar examples than algebra.

II. IN THE SECONDARY SCHOOL

The great desideratum for the distribution of mathematics in the secondary school is that it should be studied thruout each of the four years of the course. It is not meant by this that more time should be given to mathematics, but that this time should be distributed over the entire secondary-school course. The committee recommends no specific distribution over the four years of the hours now given to mathematics, but simply the general rule that there be work in mathematics required of all thruout the course, and that in no year less than two hours weekly be given to mathematics during the whole year.

If in any school it is altogether impracticable to take up mathematics in each of the four years, the state of affairs is to be deplored. If a year *must* be left free from mathematics, the committee recommends that it be the second or the first year.

The distribution of the subject-matter over the various years will be influenced by the distribution of the hours. The same general principles would, however, govern in all cases; of these are:

1. The study of geometry should be begun before that of algebra. Reasons for this have already been indicated.

2. When algebra has been begun, the two subjects should be carried on simultaneously in each year of the remainder of the four years. By simultaneously is meant simply in the same year. It is not necessary that the hours of instruction be given to each alternately. The division may even be the first half-year to one (geometry) and the second half-year to the other (algebra), but this arrangement is not to be preferred.

3. The work of the fourth year should include a review of all of the previous work of the course, with the aim to extend, broaden, deepen, and correlate what has already been done.

4. The instruction in mathematics of each class or section of a class should be, as far as practicable, in the hands of the same instructor for at least two years. It is still more important that, instead of trying to plan the assignment of work so that certain teachers do "first-year work," others "second-year work," etc., year after year, the aim should be to plan the assignment so that each teacher habitually teaches all the mathematical subjects, tho not necessarily all in one year.

5. Under no circumstances should an instructor who has not qualified himself especially to teach mathematics be intrusted with a class in mathematics simply because he may have a vacant hour which must be filled up.

Thruout the course (and especially in the last year) the more the subjects can be interwoven, and made to illustrate and support each other, the better. The teacher should not hesitate to introduce a geometric illustration or a geometric truth into algebra, nor to avail himself in algebra of apt occasions for recalling previous geometric theorems, or developing and discussing new ones. Quite similarly, algebraic proofs and methods should be freely used in geometry, and, as need arises, new algebraic results established. It is quite wrong to teach geometry and algebra (and arithmetic) in the high school as subjects so essentially different that the purity of the one would be impaired by the use of the methods and results of the other.

PREPARATION OF TEACHERS

The preparation of teachers for high-school work should include a good college course, with special attention to mathematics, either by electives during the course or by some graduate study. The minimum attainment in mathematics should include analytic geometry, a first course in the calculus, and the elements of the theory of equations (including determinants).

The committee regards it as desirable that the teacher should have paid some attention, under guidance, to the pedagogy of mathematics (problems, means, and methods of instruction; if practicable, seeing actual teaching and discussing it afterward), before beginning his own teaching. Still more important is it that his first teaching should be under the careful supervision of an experienced teacher of mathematics. If possible, his first year or two of service should be explicitly and actually under the direction and guidance of older teachers. Perhaps each beginner may be assigned by his principal to some specific teacher of experience and tact, for supervision and counsel. The relation will be more or less formal, under varying circumstances; but it should always be actual and effective, never merely nominal; it should involve personal consultation, mutual class-room visits, friendly, careful advice.

Much can be accomplished in this way. At present young teachers of no experience, having no pedagogic preparation, are often put into full charge of classes, and receive no assistance, no advice, no encouragement from their more experienced colleagues. They have as model only some recollections of their impressions (as pupils) of the teaching which they received. They profit as best they can by their own experience, and learn from their own mistakes. Some never appreciate their shortcomings or how to remedy them; even for the best it is a devious and painful path to excellence, which might be shortened and eased by the judicious counsel of one who had traversed the path himself.

In institutions where there are several teachers of mathematics it would be well for them to meet statedly for the discussion of questions of local administration, of pedagogy, of mathematical topics; perhaps the systematic study together of some mathematical subject could be undertaken. (Among the suitable subjects for such study are the following: modern synthetic geometry, analytic geometry, the differential and integral calculus, determinants, the theory of equations, analytic mechanics, the history of mathematics.)

It is very desirable that the teacher be making year by year new acquisitions of mathematical knowledge.

CORRELATION OF WORK

Mathematics is unique in the extent to which it builds on previous work. Hence secondary-school work should be correlated as closely as possible both with grade work and with college work. The division of the work in mathematics into three portions, carried on in different institutions (grades, secondary-school, college) differing in management, methods, and aims, and with teachers differing radically in type of preparation, causes a great waste of teaching energy. Much can be done to diminish this waste by close relations between the teachers of the three divisions, and the comparison of results and adaptation of work to mutual needs. The relationship may be official or unofficial, formal supervision or friendly suggestion; it should, however, never be a mere form, but a cordial co-operation for strengthening and unifying the work in mathematics in grades, secondary schools, and colleges.

LIBRARY

Every secondary school should have for the use of the pupils, and especially of the teachers, a carefully selected library of reference-books in mathematics (standard elementary texts, histories, tables, books of problems and recreations, and advanced mathematical works suited to the needs of the teachers). Measuring instruments should also be provided.

SUMMARY OF PRINCIPAL CONCLUSIONS

The most important of the conclusions which were reached by the committee are the following:

1. To the close of the secondary-school course the required work in mathematics should be the same for all pupils.

2. The formal instruction in arithmetic as such should terminate with the close of the seventh grade.

3. Concrete geometry should be a part of the work in arithmetic and drawing in the first six grades.

4. One-half of the time allotted to mathematics in the seventh grade should be given to the beginning of demonstrative geometry.

5. In the eighth grade the time allotted to mathematics should be divided equally between demonstrative geometry and the beginning of algebra.

6. In the secondary school, work in mathematics should be required of all pupils thruout each of the four years of the course.

7. Wherever, from local conditions, it is necessary to defer the beginning of geometry and algebra to the secondary school, here, likewise, geometry should be begun before algebra.

8. When once begun, the subjects of geometry and algebra should be developed simultaneously, in so far, at least, that both geometry and algebra should be studied in each of the four years of the secondary-school course.

9. The unity of the work in mathematics is emphasized, and the correlation and interapplication of its different parts recommended.

10. The instruction should have as its chief aim the cultivation of inde-

pendent and correct thinking on the part of the pupil.

11. The importance of thoro preparation for teachers, both in mathematical attainments and in the art of teaching, is emphasized.

J. W. A. YOUNG, *Chairman,*
> Assistant Professor of Mathematical Pedagogy in the University of Chicago.

J. J. SCHOBINGER, *Secretary,*
> Principal of the Harvard School, Chicago.

ELLERY W. DAVIS,
> Professor of Mathematics in the University of Nebraska.

THOMAS F. HOLGATE,
> Professor of Applied Mathematics in Northwestern University.

L. S. HULBURT,
> Collegiate Professor of Mathematics in Johns Hopkins University.

C. W. LYON, JR.,
> Principal of Grammar School No. 78 (formerly Professor of Mathematics in the Boys' High School), Brooklyn, N. Y.

H. B. NEWSON,
> Associate Professor of Mathematics in Kansas State University.

W. F. OSGOOD,
> Assistant Professor of Mathematics in Harvard University.

JAMES BYRNIE SHAW,
> Department of Mathematics in Michigan Military Academy.

B. M. WALKER,
> Professor of Mathematics in the Mississippi Agricultural and Mechanical College.

DAVID EUGENE SMITH

David Eugene Smith (1860–1944) was born and raised in Cortland, New York.[1] He was educated at Cortland State Normal School and at Syracuse University. After his graduation from Syracuse in 1881 he practiced law with his father until 1884, when he began teaching mathematics at Cortland State Normal School. He received his Ph.D. from Syracuse in 1887 and continued his life in teaching. He held the professorship of mathematics at Michigan State Normal College at Ypsilanti from 1891 to 1898, was principal at Brockport State Normal School from 1898 to 1901, and in 1901 became a professor at Teachers College, Columbia University, where he remained until his retirement in 1926.

Smith, along with J. W. A. Young, was one of the early mathematics educators in the modern sense of the term. In addition to his work as a historian of mathematics, he was vice-president of the International Commission on the Teaching of Mathematics, a member of the Committee of Fifteen on the Geometry Syllabus, and president of the Mathematical Association of America.

The first of the two selections from Smith's writings included here is from *The Teaching of Elementary Mathematics* (1900), which is credited with being the first American textbook on the teaching of mathematics. The extract illustrates Smith's use of historical perspective in discussing the purposes and content of school algebra. Also worthy of note in this selection is the identification of the function concept as a unifying idea.

In the second selection, from *The Teaching of Arithmetic* (1909), Smith attacked "teaching methods" and justified the middle-of-the-road approach that helped keep his textbooks among the most popular on the market for the following twenty years. In accordance with the chronological method of presentation, this selection appears later in Part Two.

---

1. E. R. Breslich, "David Eugene Smith, 1860–1944," *School Science and Mathematics* 44 (December 1944): 838–89.

THE TEACHING

OF

ELEMENTARY MATHEMATICS

BY

DAVID EUGENE SMITH

PROFESSOR OF MATHEMATICS IN TEACHERS' COLLEGE, COLUMBIA
UNIVERSITY, NEW YORK.

New York

THE MACMILLAN COMPANY

LONDON: MACMILLAN & CO., LTD.

1904

CONTENTS

CHAPTER I

HISTORICAL REASONS FOR TEACHING ARITHMETIC.—Importance of the question. The evolution of reasons. The culture-beginning utilitarian. The culture-beginning utilitarian. Early correlation. Tradition and examinations. As a mere show of trading peoples. As a remunerative trade. As a quickener of the future value. As an amusement. As a quickener of knowledge. Scientific investigation of reasons . . . 1-18

CHAPTER II

WHY ARITHMETIC IS TAUGHT AT PRESENT. — Two general reasons. The utility of arithmetic overrated. The culture value. Teachers generally fail here. Recognition of the culture value. What chapters bring out the value of culture and utility . . . 19-41

CHAPTER III

HOW ARITHMETIC HAS DEVELOPED. — Reasons for studying the subject. Extent of the subject. The first step — counting. The second step — notation. The next great step in arithmetic. The twofold nature of ancient arithmetic. Arithmetic of the middle ages. The period of the Renaissance. Arithmetic since the Renaissance. The present status of school arithmetic . . . 42-70

xiii

xiv

CONTENTS

CHAPTER IV

HOW ARITHMETIC HAS BEEN TAUGHT. — The value of the investigation. The departure from object teaching. Rhyming arithmetics. Form instead of substance. Instruction in method. Pestalozzi, Tillich. Reaction against Pestalozzi, Grube. Recent writers . . . 71-97

CHAPTER V

THE PRESENT TEACHING OF ARITHMETIC. — Objects aimed at. The number concept. The great question of method. The writing of numbers. The work of the first year. The time for beginning the study. Oral arithmetic. Treating the processes simultaneously. The spiral method. Common or decimal fractions. Improvements in algorism. The formal solution. Longitude and time. Ratio and proportion. Square root. The metric system. The applied problems. Mensuration. Text-books. Explanations. Approximations. Reviews . . . 98-144

CHAPTER VI

THE GROWTH OF ALGEBRA. — Egyptian algebra. Greek algebra. Oriental algebra. Sixteenth century algebra. Growth of symbolism. Number systems. Higher equations . . . 145-160

CHAPTER VII

ALGEBRA, WHAT AND WHY TAUGHT. — Algebra defined. The function. Why studied. Training in logic. Ethical value. When studied. Arrangement of text-books . 161-174

CHAPTER VIII

TYPICAL PARTS OF ALGEBRA. — Outline. Definitions. The awakening of interest. Stating a problem. Signs of aggregation. The negative number. Checks. Factoring. The

CONTENTS

xv

remainder theorem. The quadratic equation. Equivalent equations. Extraneous roots. Simultaneous equations and graphs. Methods of elimination. Complex numbers. The applied problems. The interpretation of solutions . . . 175-223

CHAPTER IX

THE GROWTH OF GEOMETRY. — Its historical position. The dawn of geometry. Geometry in Egypt; in Greece. Recent geometry. Non-Euclidean geometry . . . 224-233

CHAPTER X

WHAT IS GEOMETRY? GENERAL SUGGESTIONS FOR TEACHING. — Geometry defined. Limits of plane geometry. The reasons for studying. Geometry in the lower grades. Intermediate grades. Demonstrative geometry. The use of text-books . . . 234-256

CHAPTER XI

THE BASES OF GEOMETRY. — The bases. The definitions. Axioms and postulates . . . 257-270

CHAPTER XII

TYPICAL PARTS OF GEOMETRY. — The introduction to demonstrative geometry. Symbols. Reciprocal theorems. The converse theorems. Generalization of figures. Methods of attack. Generalization of figures. Ratio and proportion. Loci of points. Solid geometry. The impossible in geometry. . . 271-296

CHAPTER XIII

THE TEACHER'S BOOK-SHELF. — Arithmetic. Algebra. Geometry. History and general method . . . 297-305

INDEX . . . 307-312

CHAPTER VII

Algebra,—What and Why Taught

Algebra defined—In Chapter VI the growth of algebra was considered in a general way, assuming that its nature was fairly well known. Nor is it without good reason that this order was taken, for the definition of the subject is best understood when considered historically. But before proceeding to discuss the teaching of the subject it is necessary to examine more carefully into its nature.

It is manifestly impossible to draw a definite line between the various related sciences, as between botany and zoölogy, between physics and astronomy, between algebra and arithmetic, and so on. The child who meets the expression $2 \times (?) = 8$, in the first grade, has touched the elements of algebra. The student of algebra who is called upon to simplify

$$(2 + \sqrt{3})/(2 - \sqrt{3})$$

is facing merely a problem of arithmetic. In fact, a considerable number of topics which are properly parts of algebra, as the treatment of proportion, found lodgment in arithmetic before its sister science became generally known; while much of arithmetic, like the theory of irrational (including complex) numbers, has found place in algebra simply because it was not much needed in practical arithmetic.[1]

Recognizing this laxness of distinction between the two sciences, Comte[2] proposed to define algebra "as having for its object the resolution of equations; taking this expression in its full logical meaning, which signifies the transformation of implicit functions into equivalent explicit ones.[3] In the same way arithmetic may be defined as destined to the determination of the

---

1. Teachers who care to examine one of the best elementary works upon arithmetic in the strict sense of the term, should read Tannery, Jules, Leçons d'Arithmétique théorique et pratique, Paris, 1894.

2. The Philosophy of Mathematics, translated from the Cours de Philosophie positive, by W. M. Gillespie, New York, 1851, p. 55.

3. *I.e.*, in $x^2 + px + q = 0$ we have an implicit function of x equated to zero; this equation may be so transformed as to give the explicit function

$$x = -\frac{p}{2} \pm \tfrac{1}{2} \sqrt{p^2 - 4q,}$$

and this transformation belongs to the domain of algebra.

values of functions. Henceforth, therefore, we will briefly say that *Algebra is the Calculus of Functions,* and *Arithmetic the Calculus of Values.*"[4]

Of course this must not be taken as a definition universally accepted. As a prominent writer upon "methodology" says: "It is very difficult to give a good definition of algebra. We say that it is merely a generalized or universal arithmetic, or rather that 'it is the science of calculating magnitudes considered generally' (D'Alembert). But as Poinsot has well observed, this is to consider it under a point of view altogether too limited, for algebra has two distinct parts. The first part may be called universal arithmetic. . . . The other part rests on the theory of combinations and arrangement. . . . We may give the following definition. . . . Algebra has for its object the generalizing of the solutions of problems relating to the computation of magnitudes, and of studying the composition and transformations of formulæ to which this generalization leads."[5] The best of recent English and French elementary algebras make no attempt at defining the subject.[6]

The function—Taking Comte's definition as a point of departure, it is evident that one of the first steps in the scientific teaching of algebra is the fixing of the idea of *function.* How necessary this is, apart from all question of definition, is realized by all advanced teachers. "I found," says Professor Chrystal, "when I first tried to teach university students coördinate geometry, that I had to go back and teach them algebra over again. The fundamental idea of an integral function of a certain degree, having a certain form and so many coefficients, was to them as much an unknown quantity as the proverbial x."[7]

Happily this is not only pedagogically one of the first steps, but practically it is a very easy one because of the abundance of familiar illustrations. "Two general circumstances strike the mind; one, that all that we see is subjected to continual transformation, and the other that these changes are mutually interdependent."[8] Among the best elementary illustrations are those involving time; a stone falls, and the distance varies as the time, and *vice versa;* we call the distance a function of the time, and the time a function of the distance. We take a railway journey; the distance again varies as the time, and again time and distance are functions of each other. Similarly, the interest on a note is a function of the time, and also of the rate and the principal.

This notion of function is not necessarily foreign to the common way of

---

4. Laisant begins his chapter L'Algèbre (La Mathématique, p. 46) by reference to this definition, and makes it the foundation of his discussion of the science.
5. Dauge, Félix, Cours de Méthodologie Mathématique, 2. éd., Gand et Paris, 1896. p. 103.
6. Chrystal, G., 2 vols. 2 ed., Edinburgh, 1889. Bourlet, C., Leçons d'Algèbre élémentaire, Paris, 1896.
7. Presidential address, 1885.

presenting algebra, except that here the idea is emphasized and the name is made prominent. Teachers always give to beginners problems of this nature: Evaluate $x^2 + 2x + 1$ for $x = 2$, 3, etc., which is nothing else than finding the value of a function for various values of the variable. Similarly, to find the value of $a^3 + 3a^2b + 3ab^2 + b^3$ for $a = 1$, $b = 2$, is merely to evaluate a certain function of a and b, or, as the mathematician would say, $f(a, b)$, for special values of the variables. It is thus seen that the emphasizing of the nature of the function and the introduction of the name and the symbol are not at all difficult for beginners, and they constitute a natural point of departure. The introduction to algebra should therefore include the giving of values to the quantities which enter into a function, and thus the evaluation of the function itself.

Having now defined algebra as the study of certain functions,[9] which includes as a large portion the solution of equations, the question arises as to its value in the curriculum.

Why studied—Why should one study this theory of certain simple functions, or seek to solve the quadratic equation, or concern himself with the highest common factor of two functions? It is the same question which meets all branches of learning,—*cui bono?* Why should we study theology, biology, geology—God, life, earth? What doth it profit to know music, to appreciate Pheidias, to stand before the façade at Rheims, or to wonder at the magic of Titian's coloring? As Malesherbes remarked on Bachet's commentary on Diophantus, "It won't lessen the price of bread;"[10] or as D'Alembert retorts from the mathematical side, *à propos* of the Iphigénie of Racine, "What does this prove?"

Professor Hudson has made answer: "To pursue an intellectual study because it 'pays' indicates a sordid spirit, of the same nature as that of Simon, who wanted to purchase with money the power of an apostle. The real reason for learning, as it is for teaching algebra, is, that it is a part of Truth, the knowledge of which is its own reward.

"Such an answer is rarely satisfactory to the questioner. He or she considers it too vague and too wide, as it may be used to justify the teaching and the learning of any and every branch of truth; and so, indeed, it does. A true education should seek to give a knowledge of every branch of truth, slight perhaps, but sound as far as it goes, and sufficient to enable the possessor to sympathize in some degree with those whose privilege it is to acquire, for themselves at least, and it may be for the world at large, a fuller

---

8. Laisant, p. 46.

9. *Certain* functions, for functions are classified into algebraic and transcendental, and with the latter elementary algebra concerns itself but little. *E. g.*, algebra solves the algebraic equation $x^a = b$, but with the transcendental equation $a^x = b$ it does not directly concern itself.

10. "Le commentaire de Bachet sur Diophante ne fera pas diminuer le prix du pain."

and deeper knowledge. A person who is wholly ignorant of any great subject of knowledge is like one who is born without a limb, and is thereby cut off from many of the pleasures and interests of life.

"I maintain, therefore, that algebra is not to be taught on account of its utility, not to be learnt on account of any benefit which may be supposed to be got from it; but because it is a part of mathematical truth, and no one ought to be wholly alien from that important department of human knowledge."[11]

The sentiments expressed by Professor Hudson will meet the approval of all true teachers. Algebra is taught but slightly for its utilities to the average citizen. Useful it is, and that to a great degree, in all subsequent mathematical work; but for the merchant, the lawyer, the mechanic, it is of slight practical value.

Training in logic—But Professor Hudson states, in the above extract, only a part of the reason for teaching the subject—that we need to know of it as a branch of human knowledge. This might permit, and sometimes seems to give rise to, very poor teaching. We need it also as an exercise in logic, and this gives character to the teacher's work, raising it from the tedious, barren, mechanical humdrum of rule-imparting to the plane of true education. Professor Hudson expresses this idea later in his paper when he says, "Rules are always mischievous so long as they are necessary: it is only when they are superfluous that they are useful."

Thus to be able to extract the fourth root of $x^4 + 4x^3 + 6x^2 + 4x + 1$ is a matter of very little moment. The pupil cannot use the result, nor will he be liable to use the process in his subsequent work in algebra. But that he should have power to grasp the logic involved in extracting this root is very important, for it is this very mental power, with its attendant habit of concentration, with its antagonism to wool-gathering, that we should seek to foster. To have a rule for finding the highest common factor of three functions is likewise a matter of little importance, since the rule will soon fade from the memory, and in case of necessity a text-book can easily be found to supply it; but to follow the logic of the process, to keep the mind intent upon the operation while performing it, herein lies much of the value of the subject,—here is to be sought its chief *raison d'être*.

Hence the teacher who fails to emphasize the idea of algebraic function fails to reach the pith of the science. The one who seeks merely the answers to a set of unreal problems, usually so manufactured as to give rational results alone, instead of seeking to give that power which is the chief reason for algebra's being, will fail of success. It is of little value in itself that the necessary and sufficient condition for $x^3 - x = 0$ is that $x = 0$, $x = 1$,

11. Hudson, W. H. H., On the Teaching of Elementary Algebra, paper before the Educational Society (London), Nov. 29, 1886.

$x = -1$; but it is of great value to see *why* this is such condition.

Practical value—Although for most people algebra is valuable only for the culture which it brings, at the same time it has never failed to appeal to the common sense of practical men as valuable for other reasons. All subsequent mathematics, the theory of astronomy, of physics, and of mechanics, the fashioning of guns, the computations of ship building, of bridge building, and of engineering in general, these rest upon the operations of elementary algebra. Napoleon, who was not a man to overrate the impractical, thus gave a statesman's estimate of the science of which algebra is a cornerstone: "The advancement, the perfecting of mathematics, are bound up with the prosperity of the State."[12]

Ethical value—There are those who make great claims for algebra, as for other mathematical disciplines, as a means of cultivating the love for truth, thus giving to the subject a high ethical value. Far be it from teachers of the science to gainsay all this, or to antagonize those who follow Herbart in bending all education to bear upon the moral building-up of the child. But we do well not to be extreme in our claims for mathematics. Cauchy, one of the greatest of the French mathematicians of the nineteenth century, has left us some advice along this line: "There are other truths than the truths of algebra, other realities than those of sensible objects. Let us cultivate with zeal the mathematical sciences, without seeking to extend them beyond their own limits; and let us not imagine that we can attack history by formulæ, or employ the theorems of algebra and the integral calculus in the study of ethics." For illustration, one has but to read Herbart's Psychology to see how absurd the extremes to which even a great thinker can carry the applications of mathematics.

Of course algebra has its ethical value, as has every subject whose aim is the search for truth. But the direct application of the study to the life we live is very slight. When we find ourselves making great claims of this kind for algebra, it is well to recall the words of Mme. de Staël, paying her respects to those who, in her day, were especially clamorous to mathematicize all life: "Nothing is less applicable to life than mathematical resoning. A proposition in mathematics is decidedly false or true; everywhere else the true is mixed in with the false."

When studied—Having framed a tentative definition of algebra, and having considered the reason for studying the science, we are led to the question as to the place of algebra in the curriculum.

At the present time, in America, it is generally taken up in the ninth school year, after arithmetic and before demonstrative geometry. Since most teachers are tied to a particular local school system, as to matters of cur-

---

12. L'avancement, le perfectionnement des mathématiques sont liés à la prospérité de l'État.

riculum, the question is not to them a very practical one. But as a problem of education it has such interest as to deserve attention.

Quoting again from Professor Hudson: "The beginnings of all the great divisions of knowledge should find their place in a perfect curriculum of education; at first something of everything, in order later to learn everything of something. But it is needless to say all subjects cannot be taught at once, all cannot be learnt at once; there is an order to be observed, a certain sequence is necessary, and it may well be that one sequence is more beneficial than another. My opinion is that, of this ladder of learning, Algebra should form one of the lowest rungs; and I find that in the *Nineteenth Century* for October, 1886, the Bishop of Carlisle, Dr. Harvey Goodwin, quotes Comte, the Positivist Philosopher, with approval, to the same effect.

"The reason is this: Algebra is a certain science, it proceeds from unimpeachable axioms, and its conclusions are logically developed from them; it has its own special difficulties, but they are not those of weighing in the balance conflicting probable evidence which requires the stronger powers of a maturer mind. It is possible for the student to plant each step firmly before proceeding to the next, nothing is left hazy or in doubt; thus it strengthens the mind and enables it better to master studies of a different nature that are presented to it later. Mathematics give power, vigor, strength, to the mind; this is commonly given as the reason for studying them. I give it as the reason for studying Algebra early, that is to say, for beginning to study it early; it is not necessary, it is not even possible, to finish the study of Algebra before commencing another. On the other hand, it is not necessary to be always teaching Algebra; what we have to do, as elementary teachers, is to guide our pupils to learn enough to leave the door open for further progress; we take them over the threshold, but not into the innermost sanctuary.

"The age at which the study of Algebra should begin differs in each individual case. . . . It must be rare that a child younger than nine years of age is fit to begin; and although the subject, like most others, may be taken up at any age, there is no superior limit; my own opinion is, that it would be seldom advisable to defer the commencement to later than twelve years."

This opinion has been quoted not for indorsement, but rather as that of a teacher and a mathematician of such prominence as to command respect. The idea is quite at variance with the American custom of beginning at about the age of fourteen or fifteen, or even later, and it raises a serious question as to the wisdom of our course. Indeed, not only is the question of age involved, but also that of general sequence. Are we wise in teaching arithmetic for eight years, dropping it and taking up algebra, dropping that and taking up geometry, with possibly a brief review of all three later, at the close of the high school course?

Fully recognizing the folly of a dogmatic statement of what is the best course, and hence desiring to avoid any such statement, the author does not

218

hesitate to express his personal conviction that the present plan is not a wisely considered one. He feels that with elementary arithmetic should go, as already set forth in Chapter V, the simple equation,[13] and also metrical geometry with the models in hand; that algebra and arithmetic should run side by side during the eighth and ninth years, and that demonstrative geometry should run side by side with the latter part of algebra. One of the best of recent series of text-books, Holzmüller's,[14] follows this general plan, and the arrangement has abundant justification in most of the Continental programmes. It is so scientifically sound that it must soon find larger acceptance in English and American schools.

Arrangement of text-books—As related to the subject just discussed, a word is in place concerning the arrangement of our text-books. It is probable that we shall long continue our present general plan of having a book on arithmetic, another on algebra, and still another on geometry, thus creating a mechanical barrier between these sciences. We shall also, doubtless, combine in each book the theory and the exercises for practice, because this is the English and American custom, giving in our algebras a few pages of theory followed by a large number of exercises. The Continental plan, however, inclines decidedly toward the separation of the book of exercises from the book on the theory, thus allowing frequent changes of the former. It is doubtful, however, if the plan will find any favor in America, its advantages being outweighed by certain undesirable features.[15] There is, perhaps, more chance for the adoption of the plan of incorporating the necessary arithmetic, algebra, and geometry for two or three grades into a single book, a plan followed by Holzmüller with much success.

13. There is a good article upon this by Oberlehrer Dr. M. Schuster, Die Gleichung in der Schule, in Hoffmann's Zeitschrift. XXIX. Jahrg. (1898), p. 81.
14. Leipzig, B. G. Teubner.
15. An interesting set of statistics with respect to German text-books is given by J. W. A. Young in Hoffmann's Zeitschrift, XXIX. Jahrg. (1898), p. 410. under the title, Zur mathematischen Lehrbücherfrage.

BRITISH ASSOCIATION

MEETING AT GLASGOW, 1901

DISCUSSION ON THE

TEACHING OF MATHEMATICS

Which took place on September 14th, at a Joint Meeting
of two Sections.

Section A.—Mathematics and Physics
Section L.—Education

CHAIRMAN OF THE JOINT MEETING
THE RIGHT HON. SIR JOHN E. GORST, K.C., M.P.
President of Section L

EDITED BY PROFESSOR PERRY

To which is now added the Report of the British Association
Committee drawn up by the Chairman
Professor FORSYTH

London
MACMILLAN AND CO., LIMITED
NEW YORK: THE MACMILLAN COMPANY

1902

THE TEACHING OF MATHEMATICS

By Professor John Perry, M.E., D.Sc., LL.D., F.R.S.

For many years mathematicians have occasionally denounced our methods of teaching mathematics from their own point of view. I might quote Professor Sylvester, Professor De Morgan, and many others. Some of my friends who are interested in the education of possible mathematicians, and others like myself who are more interested in the education of the average citizen, feel that we ought not to wait longer in obtaining from such an audience as is here present an authoritative statement on this subject.

I beg to present to you a specimen syllabus which I have recently prepared for training colleges; any syllabus following more orthodox lines may be adopted by any training college, but as a member of a departmental committee which has recently been sitting, I have recommended this one.

It is to be remembered that courses of instruction adopted in training colleges are very likely to be adopted in primary schools, in continuation schools, and in many secondary schools. I have been allowed by the Science and Art Department to introduce this method of mathematical teaching in many evening science-schools and technical colleges. In some technical schools the usual pure mathematics syllabus has already been discarded altogether in favour of the new one. It is obvious, therefore, that what I am doing may have far-reaching consequences, and I beg, gentlemen, that you who represent so well every kind of authority on this subject will give me the benefit of your severest criticism and advice.

This is not to be a mere academic discussion. Anybody who thinks that I am making a mistake, or who sees how my method may be improved and who holds his tongue, is doing a real harm to the country. In a few years this new system will have become to some extent crystallised, and it will not then be so easy as it is now to get changes made in it; it will be a very difficult thing indeed to get it discarded altogether. I have shown that I recognise the greatness of my responsibility, but I hope that you will see that you have a duty to perform.

I have taught mathematics and applied science or engineering to almost every kind of boy or man. I have had my present notions almost as far back as thirty years ago. When I was young I felt diffident: now I have lost most of that feeling, because all my experience has confirmed my opinions and has shown me that many other teachers have the same views as myself.

I am about to say again to you what I said in 1880, in a paper read before the Society of Arts, and what I have said many times since then. If I could think that you had read the book containing some of my papers, of which I have sent a copy to almost all of you, it would not be necessary for me to say much now.

In presenting the syllabus, I want it to be clearly understood that I recommend this method, not only for classes of engineer apprentices, not only for children in Board schools, not only for the average British boy, but for the boys of very acute intellect who form less than one per cent. of the higher-class population, as well as for the few boys—say one in ten millions —who are likely to become great mathematicians.

I have said that it is usefulness which must determine what subjects ought to be taught to children and in what ways, and as I have been blamed for this, I should like to say something about the *utility* of the study of mathematics.

Although we can understand the old "mark-time" philosophers, who loved to plough the sand for the thousandth time and never reaped any harvest, saying with Seneca, "Invention of useful things is drudgery for the lowest slaves," surely it can only be affectation in a mathematician of the twentieth century to echo, "It is an affront to geometry to say that it led to the principle of the arch," or "the sole function of astronomy is to assist in raising the mind to the contemplation of things which are to be perceived by the pure intellect alone." In truth, the pure mathematician is just like the rest of us. People outside any study are apt to think the student foolish if his results are not useful to outsiders. The student, irritated that an ignorant outsider should apply a stupid standard to his work, is tempted to say that in so far as he is useful to outsiders he is hateful to himself. But this is temporary irritation. The pure mathematician is pleased when his discoveries are of use to the physicist. The physicist is pleased when his discoveries are of use to the engineer. And, whether they like it or not, it is true that the engineer does often suggest new departures in physics and the physicist does often suggest new departures to the pure mathematician.

What an affectation it is for a student to say that his study is *useless!* The pursuit of pure knowledge for its own sake is one of the noblest occupations. But why? Surely because of its many-sided usefulness, one side being its development of the mental power and soul, and indeed one may say the emotions of the student. And because a worker in some quite different branch of science greatly ignorant of the first branch gets from a discovery in the first branch an idea which helps him in his own work, surely, surely

" Nothing is here for tears, nothing to wail
 Or knock the breast. . . ."

222

Let not, then, the pure mathematician be angry with me if I, an outsider, hold the view that my study is nobler than his. Let him keep to his ideals; but to me the pure mathematician is great because he has helped me so much in which I consider important things. The politician has his ideals, and so has the financier; but to me their value consists in what they have done to help forward what seem to me important things. What we want is a great Toleration Act which will allow us all to pursue our own ideals, taking each from the other what he can in the way of mental help. We do not want to interfere with the students of pure mathematics, men whose peculiar mental processes are suited to these studies, men whose labours cannot be spared from the world's service. We believe that, the more they hold themselves in their studies as a race of demigods apart, the better it may be for the world. They are pursuing a branch of science for its own sake, and doing it all the better for the belief they hold that pure mathematics ought to be studied with no view to its application. But all the same I hold that the study began because it was useful, it continues because it is useful, and it is valuable to the world because of the usefulness of its results. The pure mathematician must allow me to go on thinking that, if his discoveries were not being utilised continually, his study would long ago have degenerated into something like what the Aristotelian dialectic became in the fourteenth century.

I belong to a great body of men who apply the principles of mathematics in physical science and engineering; I belong to the very much greater body of men who may be called persons of average intelligence. In each of these capacities I need mental training and also mathematical knowledge. The mathematician says that he wants to have nothing to do with us; but it is too late to say this sort of thing. It is he who has fixed how his subject shall be taught to us in schools, and he provides us with teachers of it. We pay these teachers to give us something that will be useful in our education and useful to us in life, useful to us in understanding our position in the universe. Surely we have a right to ask the mathematicians to look at this matter from our point of view, and to ask if it is not possible to help us without hurting themselves and their study. Without the help of the mathematicians I feel that it is almost impossible to get the teachers of mathematics to give us instruction of a useful kind.

I have hurriedly put together what strike me as obvious forms of usefulness in the study of mathematics.

(1) In producing the higher emotions and giving mental pleasure. Hitherto neglected in teaching almost all boys.

(2) *a* In brain development. *b*. In producing logical ways of thinking. Hitherto neglected in teaching most boys.

(3) In the aid given by mathematical weapons in the study of physical science. Hitherto neglected in teaching almost all boys.

(4) In passing examinations. The only form that has not been neglected. The only form really recognised by teachers.

(5) In giving men mental tools as easy to use as their legs or arms; enabling them to go on with their education (development of their souls and brains) throughout their lives, utilising for this purpose all their experience. This is exactly analogous with the power to educate one's self through the fondness for reading.

(6) Perhaps included in (5): in teaching a man the importance of thinking things out for himself and so delivering him from the present dreadful yoke of authority, and convincing him that, whether he obeys or commands others, he is one of the highest of beings. This is usually left to other than mathematical studies.

(7) In making men in any profession of applied science feel that they know the principles on which it is founded and according to which it is being developed.

(8) In giving to acute philosophical minds a logical counsel of perfection altogether charming and satisfying, and so preventing their attempting to develop any philosophical subject from the purely abstract point of view, because the absurdity of such an attempt has become obvious.

I believe that all these functions would be performed well under the new system which is suggested. At present, with the exception of (4), which is not particularly nice, in the performance of these functions mathematics affects less than one per cent. of the boys who are supposed to study it. I am aware that it is the taunt of some mathematical teachers that they are the caretakers of a useless and worshipful holy of holies, but I would have them consider if they have ever themselves been anywhere but in the outer courts of the temple where the shrines are tawdry and the traffic in sacrificial animals is nauseous. With the great leaders of mathematical thought here present I thought I could have no quarrel. I hope that they will agree with me when they understand my scheme. I know that I have the sympathy of many of them, and that they will forgive what might seem to some people my impudence in speaking about mathematics before them. The very severe remarks of the President of Section A have been reported at full length in the newspapers. I am sorry to think that I have had so little success in explaining my proposed reform. I am inclined to think that, when I have explained it, he will really approve of what he seems now to condemn. He used a very happy illustration of the delights of the specialist in pure mathematics—that waterfall in Labrador, finer than Niagara, which had only been seen by nine white men; and I thought there was more than a little selfishness in his taking that view of matters. Using the illustration in explaining my reform, may I say that by building a railway in Labrador, by making bridges and paths, and hanging wire ropes, and cutting steps, I hope to throw that beautiful scene of which he spoke open to the gaze of many thousands of people. Surely he will see that it was not created for the enjoyment of nine men, however white. And I am afraid, very much afraid, that, in spite of him, engineers will proceed to utilise the power of that waterfall.

Fifty years ago it was thought right to teach physics and chemistry to all men in the same way; as if all men were to be physicists or chemists. The great growth of these subjects made a change necessary, and the newness of the studies made a change possible. For the same reasons I would teach mathematics, at all events advanced mathematics, in quite different ways to different students. In any case, I feel sure that our system of teaching boys elementary mathematics as if they were all going to be pure mathematicians must be altered. Perhaps the mathematicians will forgive my impertinence in saying that even for the boy who is likely to become a great mathematician I advocate improved methods of teaching: I say that the old Alexandrian method is bad. It is immensely important that if any one method of elementary teaching be generally adopted it shall not be hurtful to the one boy in a thousand who is fond of abstract reasoning, but it is just as important that the average boy shall not be hurt. In the heroic times every traveller was asked an enigma; if he did not answer he was killed with torments; if he answered, he was declared a demigod and given to rule over nations. In those times it was thought good to sacrifice myriads of people for the purpose of finding the one demigod.

So now we teach all boys what is called mathematical philosophy, that we may catch in our net the one demigod, the one pure mathematician, and we do our best to ruin all the others. It is Nature's way with fishes: 10,000 herrings spawned for one survivor; 10,000 salmon eggs for one marketable fish; 10,000 Toms, Dicks, and Harrys mentally destroyed for the sake of producing one man fit to be a mathematical master of a second-rate public school; 10 million destroyed for the sake of producing one great mathematician.

But I would like to point out that ours is an altogether foolish way of producing the mathematical master also. To the age of twenty-four one may say that the very brightest mathematical minds of the world are being trained on problems about which there is nothing new, in the study of which there is absolutely no chance of a new discovery. The apparatus of this gymnasium of ours differs very little now from what it was thirty or fifty or eighty years ago. One cannot help referring to the similar state of things in regard to the scholastic philosophy. Roscelin, Anselm, Abelard, Peter Lombard, Albertus Magnus, Thomas Aquinas, Duns Scotus, Ockham, were the mental giants of their own time; they were men of the most acute and profound understanding. And the pupils of all their followers traversed the Aristotelian ground in exactly the same way, one generation after another. No advance made by a master was utilised in teaching his pupil. John of Salisbury observed of the Paris dialecticians of his own time that after several years' absence he found them not a step advanced and still employed in urging and parrying the same arguments. Bring up students to the age of twenty-four in such a system, and how few of them will show that they can get out of it ever after. Let a young mathematician know that all his difficulties were solved long ago; that almost no old mathematical man he meets ever makes a new discovery, nor wants to make one, and you give him the mental attitude of the Schoolmen.

Consider the really clever mathematical men whose academic education is completed in any particular year. Shall we say that one of them becomes a mathematician? that is, a man who extends the boundary of mathematical knowledge. And what of the others, of those whose education has ceased? I think you must admit that if they do not utilise their mathematical knowledge in the study of physical science, their mathematical horizon gets smaller and smaller. From the mathematical point of view they become vegetables. They are not even like the Greek scholars of Constantinople during the dry-rot 1000 years period, when the world was handed over to the scholastic devil for 1000 years. The students in Constantinople really read and copied manuscripts and took an interest in learning, but the ordinary mathematical man, as he vegetates, seems to take no interest in mathematics, and never opens a mathematical book except to keep him right when he is drilling the young recruit. Observe that I say nothing about him as a citizen, as an authority on the training of the mind, as a centre of intellectual light for the people among whom he dwells; I speak of him as a mathematician merely.

Now in my experience there is hardly any man who may not become a discoverer, an advancer of knowledge, and the earlier the age at which you give him chances of exercising his individuality the better. Put him in command of all [1] existing knowledge as quickly as possible, and while doing it let him know that he also has the marshal's *baton* in his knapsack. Let him know that he is expected to be making discoveries all the time; not merely that the best established law is not complete, but that in the very simplest things it is not so much what he is told by a teacher, but what he discovers for himself, that is of real value to him, that becomes permanently part of his mental machinery. Educate through the experience already possessed by a boy; look at things from his point of view—that is, lead him to educate himself. I feel that throughout one's whole mathematical course it is important to teach a student through his own experiments, through concrete examples worked out by him. Even good mathematical teachers hate to see their students "wasting time," as they call it, in actually plotting lines of force or stream lines after the algebraic academic answer has been arrived at. They would probably call it waste of time to caulk the joints of plates in a ship. Without this kind of illustration I feel sure that the whole study

1. In a corrected proof this word *all* would have been altered to *much essential.*

is useless except for one man in a thousand. I am here speaking of advanced work. But even in elementary work a student ought to be induced to apply his mathematics to problems in his own experience.

When I was an apprentice I knew some trigonometry, much more algebra, and I was an adept in geometry. I wanted to know engineering theory, and the only two books available contained unknown mathematical symbols. Other boys might sigh for other luxuries, but to me the one thing wanting was a knowledge of

$$\frac{dx}{dy} \text{ and } \int .$$

Looking back, I seem to have panted for a knowledge of the use of these symbols for years. There was nobody to give me advice: I knew many clever engineers, but they could not help me. At length I had an opportunity of getting this knowledge. Now I was as well prepared as my fellow students, and yet somehow I lagged behind in exercise work. They dashed easily through twenty examples at the end of a chapter; to me every example was a labour, an interesting labour; but truly a difficult job. And all through that college session I was filled with a sense of my stupidity; satisfied with my progress in itself, but utterly dissatisfied when I compared myself with the others.

Now I know wherein the difference consisted. I was really using the idea of the calculus in all sorts of problems outside the academic ones; making them part of my mental machinery. They had the knack (their previous training had all been in the direction of giving them this knack) of rapidly picking up just such instruction as enabled them to do the examples, and for them there was nothing else.

If I had time I could illustrate my meaning in many ways. From my observation of men and boys I am inclined to think that my way of taking up a study is the common way, the natural way, and that the schoolmasters destroy it and replace it by something that conduces to mere learning.

In this connection it is worth remarking that if a student has been learning and not discovering, when at length as a man he is so exceptional as not to have become *stale* and he does make a discovery, he thinks too much of this child of his old age; he squabbles in the most vulgar manner for priority of discovery. If he had been discovering things all his life he would let anybody claim priority who cared to do so. The fame of having made a discovery would be no great reward for a man from whom an inward glow of pioneering satisfaction had never been absent since he began his studies.

I do not care here to dwell on the fact that, if a student has been increasing his learning all his life, he will make too much of the importance of mere learning.

The unpractical character of mathematical teaching causes mathematical men to leave common-sense out of all teaching. Good illustrations of this come from Germany, France, and Switzerland. An engineer needs a knowledge of graphical statics. A good practical course of a few weeks will give him such a thorough grasp of the general principle as will enable him—depending on his own common-sense—to do almost anything. It is quite usual in some polytechnics to give an elaborate course of many months, sometimes of a year; every problem ever worked by anybody must be done by every student. Every solution of nearly every problem has got tacked on to it the name of the professor who did it. It is the same with descriptive geometry and other branches of graphical mathematics. The average student properly taught during a few weeks is really a master of each of these subjects, whereas the student who has had an elaborate course retains no initiative and can attack no new problem. If time allowed I could state some amusing illustrations of this.

It is this want of common-sense which makes the usual school and polytechnic and university courses in applied science so elaborate. I have here an advertisement, covering the last large page of a daily paper, of all the courses in a certain foreign polytechnic. To prepare to enter, I may say that a boy must work very hard indeed till he is nineteen years of age. It is not at all unusual to find that at eighteen a boy has to stop working for a year because his health has broken down. I know that it is usual to find these boys ignorant of anything even slightly outside their school course.

A spiritless boy of nineteen, with rounded shoulders, tells you that he has done much science, and *all* algebra, and *all* trigonometry, and you feel proud that English boys stolidly refuse, in spite of all punishment, in spite of being called dunces, to become such products of academic machinery.

This polytechnic syllabus is well worth study. It begins with the stupefied boy of nineteen, and it gives him four years of pure and applied mathematics of all kinds, and after a practical course he is a finished civil, or mechanical, or electrical, or some other kind of engineer or architect.

Now I am an advocate of technical education as it is given in a few places in England, and as I hope that it will be given in many places when boys come to be properly prepared from school; but I solemnly affirm that an English boy with the usual ignorance of mathematics and physical science when leaving school, pitchforked into a workshop where nobody thinks it his duty to give him instruction; ignorant of theory all his life, getting no scientific education whatsoever, cannot be a much worse engineer than the product of such a polytechnic as this.[2] Can these students

2. I have taught and examined every kind of boy and man; I have worked with men in the shops as one of themselves; I have been a manager of works and an employer of labour; I have had long experience of the ways of all kinds of manufacturers and engineers. In spite of enormous loss continually going on through the ignorance of English-speaking engineers (I know of most dreadful examples), the great majority of

ever get back their birthright that they have fooled away? Workshop experience, contact with workmen and nature, must give them some common-sense, but it is difficult to see how they can ever get to think for themselves, to act without explicit orders. Can they ever invent? Can they ever become free men? I have seen them trying to become men by sedulously neglecting, forgetting, and contemning all the learning of their polytechnic.

On a very much smaller scale one may see the same thing in English Naval, and Artillery, and Royal Engineer officers. Every one of them will tell you that in general intelligence he must have greatly benefited by his mathematical training, although he may be unable to do any mathematical work, having forgotten everything that he ever learnt. He has the sort of respect for science that a famous ruffian of Charles the Second's time had for religion, who stated that he always saluted a church by uncovering his head to it.

All advocates of orthodox methods (keeping the examination form in the background) seem willing to sacrifice every form of usefulness of mathematics to one form, the emotional or soul-preserving mind-training inherent in a perfect logical system; a huge complex deduced logically from simple fundamental truths. It would take me too long if I were to dilate upon the fact that it is time to cease talking of certain things as being fundamental truths, and that all logical deductions from them must be correct. Unless I gave my reasons at considerable length, I might earn a character for flippancy, for sneering at one of the most wonderful and soundest structures built up by human beings out of mental chaos. But I have the right to exclaim against a worship of the structure which prevents its being preserved, enlarged, embellished, and made use of.

As soon as we give up the idea of absolute correctness we see that a perfectly new departure may be made in the study of mathematics. The ancients devoted a lifetime to the study of arithmetic; it required days to extract a square root or to multiply two numbers together. Is there any great harm in skipping all that, in letting a schoolboy learn multiplication sums, and in starting his more abstract reasoning at a more advanced point? Where would be the harm in letting a boy assume the truth of many propo-

---

English-speaking employers of engineers believe the unscientific English engineer to be preferable to the finished polytechnic engineer. As an employer I myself used to feel very undecided. Now, if there is even an approach to equality of value, see what a serious reproach there is upon the new system. Imagine polytechnic authority insisting on the learning of every detail of an elaborate life-course of study when not the smallest part of it is known to English engineers of practically the same actual value. I know by actual trial that with a quarter of the German fag we can give to the average young Englishman such a knowledge of scientific principles that they become part of his mental machinery, and he can no more forget them, or how to apply them, than he can forget how to read or write. Surely I may be forgiven if I urge strongly the enormous importance of the reform which I advocate.

sitions of the first four books of Euclid, letting him accept their truth partly by faith, partly by trial? Giving him the whole fifth book of Euclid by simple algebra? Letting him assume the sixth book to be axiomatic? Letting him, in fact, begin his severer studies where he is now in the habit of leaving off? We do much less orthodox things. Every here and there in one's mathematical studies one makes exceedingly large assumptions, because the methodical study would be ridiculous even in the eyes of the most pedantic of teachers. I can imagine a whole year devoted to the philosophical study of many things that a student now takes in his stride without trouble. The present method of training the mind of a mathematical teacher causes it to strain at gnats and to swallow camels. Such gnats are most of the propositions of the sixth book of Euclid; propositions generally about incommensurables; the use of arithmetic in geometry; the parallelogram of forces, &c.; decimals. The camels I do not care to mention, because I am in favour of their being swallowed, and indeed I should like to see them greatly increased in number: they exist in the simplest arithmetic, and geometry, and algebra. Why not put aside ever so much more, so as to let a young boy get quickly to the solution of partial differential equations and other useful parts of mathematics that only a few men now ever reach? I have no right to dictate in these matters to the pure mathematicians. They may see more clearly than I do the necessity for a great mathematician going through the whole grind in the orthodox way; but, if so, I hardly see their position in regard to arithmetic and other things in the study of which they do allow skipping. I should have thought that the advantage of knowing how to use spherical harmonics or Bessel functions at the age of seventeen, so as to be able to start in mathematics at Cambridge just about the place where some of the best mathematical men now end their studies for ever, of starting at this high level with youthful enthusiasm, and individuality, and inventiveness, would more than compensate for the evils of skipping.

I might have put all this in the following briefer form. Great fields of thought are now open which were unknown to the Alexandrian philosophers. If we begin our study as the Alexandrian philosophers did, with their simplest ideas in arithmetic and geometry, we shall get stale before we know much more than they did. If we begin assuming more complex things to be true (although I do not like to assume that in truth any idea is more complex than another), as we have done in arithmetic, as we ought to do in other parts of mathematics, without becoming stale we may know of all the modern discoveries. We shall thus get the same intellectual training with more knowledge.

I have been speaking of the training of the mathematician, and I may be wrong; but, as to the educational training of the man who is to use his mathematics in the study of pure and applied physical science, I have no

230

doubt whatever of the importance of skipping greatly in all early mathematical work.

In these days all men ought to study Natural Science. Such study is practically impossible without a knowledge of higher mathematical methods than that of the mere housekeeper. It must be more than what is called "knowledge"; it must be mental dexterity, and it must be kept in constant practice if it is not to become rusty, and if men are to remain unafraid of mathematics. As examples of methods necessary even in the most elementary study of nature I may mention:—the use of logarithms in computation; knowledge of and power to manipulate algebraic formulæ; the use of squared paper; the methods of the calculus. Dexterity in all these is easily learnt by all young boys. In such practice their brain power develops quite rapidly, and they learn with pleasure. I feel sure that such dexterity cannot hinder, and can only further the mathematical study of the exceptionally clever student.

For an advanced study of natural phenomena we need the results of the best study of the greatest mathematicians.[3] To me, mathematics is a power-

3. I believe that the useful methods of mathematics are easily to be learnt by quite young persons, just as languages are easily learnt in youth. What a wondrous philosophy and history underlie the use of almost every word in every language—yet a child learns to use the word unconsciously. No doubt when such a word was first invented it was studied over and lectured upon, just as one might lecture now upon the idea of a rate, or the use of Cartesian co-ordinates, and we may depend upon it that children of the future will use the idea of the calculus, and use squared paper as readily as they now cipher. As I said at the Society of Arts, in 1880:—"When Egyptian and Chaldean philosophers spent years in difficult calculations, which would now be thought easy by young children, doubtless they had the same notions of the depth of their knowledge that Sir Wm. Thomson might now have of his. How is it, then, that Thomson has gained his immense knowledge in the time taken by a Chaldean philosopher to acquire a simple knowledge of arithmetic? The reason is plain. Thomson, when a child, was taught in a few years more than all that was known three thousand years ago of the properties of numbers. When it is found essential to a boy's future that machinery should be given to his brain, it is given to him; he is taught to use it, and his bright memory makes the use of it a second nature to him; but it is not till after-life that he makes a close investigation of what there actually is in his brain which has enabled him to do so much. It is taken in because a child has much faith. In after years he will accept nothing without careful consideration. The machinery given to the brains of children is getting more and more complicated as time goes on; but there is really no reason why it should not be taken in as early, and used as readily, as were the axioms of childish education in ancient Chaldea. A watch is a complicated piece of mechanism, which it has taken the thought of all the ages to elaborate, but the smallest boy can make it useful to himself. In a recent number of *Macmillan's Magazine* there is a paper by the late Professor Clifford, on 'Boundaries.' It directs attention to some of the simplest mathematical ideas. I felt, when reading it, that nobody could take a greater interest in it than a mathematician who had long used those ideas. The notion of a boundary had long been simple to him, and useful, like his watch to a boy; but one day he looks into its mechanism, and without it becoming less useful, he finds that it opens up for him a world of thought." It is interesting to notice from this old paper

ful weapon with which to unlock the mysteries of Nature. If a man knows how to use the weapon, that is enough. Let him leave to others, the men who delight in that, the forging of the weapon, the complete study of it. If I can use the weapon, let my study be of another kind—I think, perhaps, of a higher kind—to study the secrets which even an unskilful use of the weapon will reveal to me. Fain would I know more about how the weapon was made and how to forge it for myself; but if I have no delight or skill in making weapons, and if I have enormous delight in using them, then will I use them if I can, and practise using them till I become skilful, for I know that the weapon-maker is not likely to be skilful in its use.

I have the belief that the study of physical science, and therefore the study of mathematics, by everybody, however poor or however rich, is of the utmost importance to our country, not merely for the knowledge it gives, but for producing the scientific habit of thought, giving to every unit of the population a power to think for itself, and so producing the greatest happiness, and giving the greatest strength of all kinds to the nation.

I believe that men who teach demonstrative geometry and orthodox mathematics generally are not only destroying what power to think already exists, but are producing a dislike, a hatred, for all kinds of computation, and therefore for all scientific study of nature, and are doing incalculable harm.

What I say is especially important for the great and increasing number of men whose occupations are with applied science. I am particularly interested in engineering, and have a particular knowledge of the wants of engineers. It must be remembered that the engineer is becoming a very important person. What is going to affect the rule of nations over one another more and more is that for which Napoleon gibed at us—manufacture, the development of all natural resources which help in manufacture, and the distribution of things manufactured. To perform this well requires character and power to think in every one who has to do with it, whether managers or

---

of 1880 how clearly we saw, even then, the necessity for the reform that I now advocate. I venture to give one more quotation:—"In pointing out that, as time goes on, we must begin from more and more comprehensive data—in fact, that pupils must commence their studies farther and farther from the real beginning of the subject—I point to a fact of which every teacher of physics gets good evidence even in the history of twenty years. Teachers of mathematics have not this evidence; but the teaching of natural science is obeying natural laws as yet, not being fettered by crystallised rules and vested interests. Instead of teaching pupils, . . . and giving them lectures on virtual velocities, and the like, as was common ten years ago, we begin with a great generalisation, the law of conservation of energy. And yet, after this generalisation was known to men of science, how long it was before teachers ventured to prune away excrescences from the text-books; how long it was before they ventured to say, 'It is not necessary to teach as we ourselves were taught; we can do better; we can give in a few words, and illustrate by a few experiments, a general law which it required years for us to understand.' "

foremen or workmen. It is becoming more and more evident that the engineer requires a scientific technical training, and we are face to face with the ghastly fact that our engineers young and old are unfitted by their school education to undergo this necessary training. Furthermore, although he feels his needs, bitterly, deeply, he scorns the idea that mathematics will help him in any way, for he has already done at school what was called mathematics. Such mathematics as he was taught is indeed a very useless thing to him. He wants to be able to use such very simple mental tools as the ideas of the calculus; he needs them in one way or another in every kind of engineering; he needs to be so familiar with them that he can use them in every kind of new problem that comes before him. There is no part of engineering of which the theory does not need the use of these simple tools. And we tell him that he cannot learn to use these tools until he has worked for many years on the studies of the Alexandrian philosophers and their followers. What I know for certain is that the average man cannot learn the use of these tools except when young. We have some excellent technical colleges at our universities and elsewhere, but the students who enter them are prepared to enter only the older kind of technical college which prepared clergymen and literary men and lawyers and legislators for their professions; they are in no way prepared to enter science colleges. And so, many of these science colleges are merely marking time, or doing what is much worse, giving to their students an education in mere formulæ which they do not really understand, the power to think being utterly lost, so that the students of these colleges become the laughing-stock of the average engineer.

It is curious how early mathematical training, by inducing a belief in what looks like mathematical reasoning, prevents men from testing the value of the engineering "laws" that they read or listen to. Rules that are approximately true in only certain cases are supposed to be absolutely true in all cases. In some of our colleges the engineering professor begins by trying to undo the evils of early mathematical training, cultivating the common-sense of his pupils, letting them see the real value of mathematics, and in such colleges very good work is being done. I may say, however, that it is really too late in the life of the average boy to begin such training after he enters college.

One sometimes finds a good mathematician taking to engineering problems. But he is usually "stale" and unwilling to go so thoroughly into these practical matters, and what he publishes is particularly harmful because it has such an honest appearance. When we do get, once in thirty years, a fairly good mathematician who has common-sense notions about the things that engineers deal with, or a fairly good engineer who has a common-sense command of mathematics, we have men who receive the greatest admiration from the engineering profession, and yet it seems to me that quite half of all the students leaving our technical colleges ought to be able to exercise these combined powers if mathematics were sensibly taught in school and college.

Perhaps the worst fault of our teaching is that the pupil is taught as if he were going to be a teacher himself. A man who teaches a subject is kept constantly in mind of a hundred rules. A man who does not teach but who is able to utilise his knowledge remembers only a very few rules—he knows these so well by constant use of them that he can apply them to every possible case that arises.

Take pure or applied mathematics, for example. In any ordinary treatise at the end of every chapter there are, say, twenty examples, all to be done by the labour-saving rule or rules taught in the chapter. But a clever man who is not a teacher can do every kind of problem—possibly in a clumsy way, but he can do it—by the use of perhaps one or two general principles which he never forgets. The average man not having to teach, who has gone through treatises and passed examinations, forgets these hundreds of rules; he remembers his hard study, gets disheartened at the notion of re-studying what he has forgotten, and indeed gets to loathe the idea of it. He was not taught to look at things from a really practical common-sense point of view; to practise the use of one general principle in all sorts of quite different-looking problems. I repeat—the average young engineer may be made to possess a power of using the methods of mathematics which will be as easy to him as reading or writing or using any hand tool, a power which never grows rusty because he exercises it every day of his life. His present intense hatred of mathematics and all theory of engineering requiring a knowledge of mathematics is very dreadful and is leading towards disaster. It seems greatest in men who have been to good schools; it is noticeable in many men who have attended science classes in colleges; it is very noticeable in electrical engineers whose whole profession is based on mathematical computation. Engineers some of whom are Fellows of the Royal Society are quite outspoken in their condemnation of all theory, all computation more complex than that of the housekeeper, and they themselves are unable to distinguish between work and power; between coulombs and ampères. I do not now speak merely of the older men.

For the boy of brilliant intellect, of whose education mathematics forms a small part, to whom Euclidean reasoning is a logical counsel of perfection, even the shortest study of it is altogether good. For such intellectual training as he requires I feel sure that my improved method of study would be ever so much better. I admit, however, that this sort of boy gets no great harm under the present system. It is the average boy who is to be pitied, because he is stupefied in being forced to study things that have no meaning to him whatsoever. And even the fairly clever mathematical man who becomes a teacher in other subjects is led by his mathematical study to be much too apt in teaching anything to begin with the abstract philosophy of the new study.

In beginning to teach a boy to play whist, or to swim, or to write, or to count, or to play billiards, he would philosophise so much and introduce difficulties so unnecessarily that the boy would find it practically impossible ever to learn. He never gets to know that the proper method of teaching any subject is through some kind of experimental work. He is the sort of man who makes children begin to learn a foreign language by its grammar.

I find that a quite common way of beginning the subject of practical geometry is to give lectures on the philosophy of representing a distance *to scale*. That the distance of three feet may be represented to scale by a distance of one inch really needs no philosophic introduction. I find that no boy meets with any difficulty in comprehending what one means by the scale of a map or any drawing; but it is easy to create in him much mental confusion if we proceed to point out what difficulties he *ought* to experience. And if the philosophy of such a simple scale as this is difficult, think what it must be when one represents on squared paper a quantity such as "the price of silk per pound," or "the height of the barometer in inches" by a distance of one inch. Think of how one could reduce not only the minds of all our students, but the mind of one's self, to imbecility by philosophising on this subject. I find that if you tell a boy to represent any quantity whatsoever to scale, showing him in ten seconds what you mean, he does it, he understands you, and it is only as a much older man that he begins to see how occult he ought to have found the subject.

Like almost every subject of human interest, this one is just as easy or as difficult as we choose to make it. A lifetime may be spent by a philosopher in discussing the truth of the simplest axiom. The simplest facts as to our existence may fill us with such wonder that our minds will remain overwhelmed with wonder all the time. A Scotch ploughman makes a working religion out of a system which appals a mental philosopher. Some boys of ten years of age study the methods of the differential calculus; other much cleverer boys working at mathematics to the age of nineteen have a difficulty in comprehending the fundamental ideas of the calculus. I wasted much precious time of my life on [the subject of] the fifth book of Euclid, and most people approach the sixth book through years of worry over the earlier geometry, but indeed almost all the propositions of the sixth book may be taken as axiomatic. I know men who seem as if they wanted to revert to the Greek method of dealing with arithmetic. I know teachers who complicate practical geometry work by extracting square roots and performing other simple arithmetical operations, and set such problems in examination papers as: Find

$$2 \sqrt{3} + \sqrt{2}.$$

They might be forgiven if they did not happen to be utterly wrong from the philosophic point of view which they fancy they occupy.

In most of what I have said I have been considering those boys who take readily to abstract reasoning. I wish to refer more particularly now to the average boy, who represents 99 per cent. of all boys, the boys who dislike abstract reasoning.

If a method of study is disliked by a pupil, a certain kind of knowledge may be given and the power to pass examinations; in this aspect there may be an advantage to the pupil; but there is no training of the mind except in the direction of dulness and stupidity.

A healthy English boy by resorting to excessive athletics and by sheer obstinacy resists the evil, and even when everybody has called him stupid so often that he is quite convinced of his own stupidity, it has no great effect on his conduct. And all the time his teacher, who when young took kindly to abstract reasoning, cannot see that the average boy has quite a different way from his own of looking at things, and is really not at all stupid. He is sharp enough outside the mathematical class-room; he shows no stupidity afterwards in business, as a legislator, as an engineer.

In the whole history of the world there was never a race with less liking for abstract reasoning than the Anglo-Saxon. Every other race has perfected abstract schemes of government. No other race has such an illogical law as our Toleration Act; and yet what a good law it is. Common-sense and compromise are believed in, logical deductions from philosophical principles are looked upon with suspicion, not only by legislators, but by all our most learned professional men.

When English visitors like Colet were privileged to meet Lorenzo and his friends in the Rucellai gardens, they also enthused over fresh finds of Greek manuscripts and over the philosophy of Plato, but it was then remarked that what they really brought back to England was just such knowledge as could be made of practical use. Always England has been less abstract than other countries. She has possessed mental philosophers, but the average Englishman tries to make use of his knowledge.

In this connection it is interesting to note that the complacent admiration of English engineers for the absence of mathematical theory from their profession is somewhat like that of English lawyers for the absence of all logic and philosophical principles from their technical and subtle system. Scientific men and psychologists hate to look into what they call our disgraceful engineering manuals and digests of the law. If English engineers had the same power over their trade as the lawyers have over theirs, no mathematics or physical science would ever be necessary for them.

No words of any English play are ever so enthusiastically applauded as Sir Peter Teazle's "Damn your principles, sir." No words have such an instantaneous effect in bringing the sympathy of an audience as "I am a practical man, gentlemen." If, then, our Tom Browns and Tom Tullivers really represent 99 per cent. of Anglo-Saxon boys, is it not a pity that educational systems should refuse to recognise the fact?

I should like to put my views as to the two kinds of English boy in the following two parallel statements:—

The average English boy takes unkindly to abstract reasoning, and if compelled to such study when unwilling is hurt mentally for life; loses his self-respect first, then his respect for all philosophy; gets to hate mathematics.

Even for exceptional young boys demonstrative geometry is bad educationally because they reason about geometrical magnitudes before they know what these magnitudes really are; they apply the same reasoning to more complex ideas of which they have the same ignorance; they become vain of their specious knowledge; they get to hate all applications of mathematics.

Philosophy was never intended as a study for children, and even exceptional children do not really learn the Alexandrian philosophy; they only get expert in solving puzzles. It needs age and also a knowledge from experience of the ideas to which the philosophy is applied.

Whether or not all men ought to attempt philosophical studies is a question I need not answer. The old Greek answer is that only a very few are capable. But I do say that, both for those who are dull and for those who are quick, it is important not to begin such study too soon.

It is not in my present brief to say whether the boy who takes kindly to abstract reasoning is really the mental superior of other boys. We are all agreed, I suppose, that if such a boy has also other mental qualities he may be intellectually great. It is, however, well to remember that the easier understanding of, say, Euclid I. 4 or 5 may imply not greater, but really less mental power, and that the early and seemingly simple proofs in Euclid are really difficult of comprehension to a mind of great natural power. A boy with good reasoning powers suspects a trick, thinks there must be some hidden meaning which he fails to grasp, and it may be that he could deal much more easily with much more involved reasoning than that of the early propositions of Euclid.[4]

When I am told that mathematics can only be learnt through a lifetime, and must remain unknown to the average boy to whom it might be useful, I

---

4. Nov. 13th, 1901.—I have stated elsewhere my own experience in trying to give mathematical ideas to some exceptionally clever boys. Mr. X. is my favourite modern writer. His dialogues are almost too clever. His intellect is exceptionally great. I am told to-day by my friend Y. that he used to make attempts to give ·X. an idea of an angle, of angular magnitude, and he utterly failed. I also should fail if I tried to make the ordinary mathematical teacher comprehend this psychological fact.

think of the time when men were able to do all their daily work without reading, writing, or ciphering; these were then the learned studies of lifetimes. But as soon as these were needed in people's daily work they were taught quite readily to children without unnecessary philosophy. And now, a child learns to compute long before it philosophises on number. Even Max Müller learned to speak and write long before he was taught grammar or philosophised on philology. M. Jourdain pronounced French very well before he was taught anything of the science of language. Even a poor training-college pupil has done some thinking for herself, and has had emotions, before she is compelled to begin courses on (save the mark) psychology and ethics.

Higher mathematics has got to be a very useful thing; what I argue is that, as in the case of all other generally useful things, the complete study of its philosophy in the orthodox manner is not a necessary part of a school or college curriculum.

My engineering friends think that I have an exaggerated notion of the importance to all men of possessing a love for mathematics. But they have not had my experience; they have not seen, as I have seen, that this affection can be produced in the average boy if he can be subjected to a delightful training when quite young; they have not seen its usefulness all through a man's life as I have seen it. I know of only one other thing that seems to be of equal importance in a man's education all through his life, and this is that he shall have got fond of reading all manner of books when quite young. Take almost any child who hates books, place it in a household where everybody is fond of reading, and it also gets fond of reading in a very short time.

Let me know that a boy possesses these two kinds of affection at the age of ten, and I know that, later, he will possess two great powers: that of being able to use mathematics and that of being able to use books. I have no time to describe what I mean by these two powers; I mean much more than might appear to a man who may have received only the orthodox scientific and literary training.

Such a boy's education will be a constant delight to his teachers if they will only refrain from prosing and the setting of tasks; if they merely make timely suggestions and answer his questions, and leave him to find out things for himself.

Gentlemen, I think the present method of so-called education all over the world to be utterly unscientific. I dare not venture to express my feelings as to the effect which might be produced on the whole world by a reform in the teaching of mathematics, because I wish to appear to you a nonvisionary, practical person who needs your votes. There can be no harm in saying that, as there is no real study of natural science which is not quantitative, it must be through mathematics. A man in the twentieth century, whose eyes are not educated through the principles of natural science, can take no proper lessons from history or literature. His imagination is dwarfed. He is a bad citizen because he is at the mercy of quacks of all kinds.

I maintain that the safety of a country is founded on the good education, the complete mental and physical development, not merely of a few, but of all its inhabitants. I can imagine a real education going on from childhood to old age. I can imagine citizens worthy of further developing and utilising the wondrous scientific discoveries of the world, of utilising the results of the labours of historians and philosophers; citizens enjoying poetry and all kinds of literature. Without the individuality of thought and inventiveness produced by true education in all people, one or two great races of the world may become more powerful than the Assyrians, or Persians, or Greeks, or Romans; but, as in those older races, each citizen will become a manufactured unideaed article, the creature of a system which must fall to pieces some time; and when this takes place the ruin will be so terrible, and the chaos will last so long, that our own past dark ages will seem to be insignificant in comparison.

A Course of Elementary Mathematics.

A course of study recommended for training colleges and for boys and girls. Preferably taken as part of the science course; that is, mixed with it.[1]

Arithmetic.—Decimals to be used from the beginning; the fallacy of retaining more figures than are justifiable in calculations involving numbers which represent observed or measured quantities. Contracted and approximate methods of multiplying and dividing numbers whereby all unnecessary figures may be omitted. Using rough checks in arithmetical work, especially with regard to the position of the decimal point.

The use of $5\cdot204 \times 10^5$ for 520400 and of $5\cdot204 \times 10^{-3}$ for $\cdot005204$. The meaning of a common logarithm: the use of logarithms in making calculations involving multiplication, division, involution, and evolution.[2] Calculation of numerical values from all sorts of formulæ however complex.

The principle underlying the construction and method of using a common slide rule; the use of a slide rule in making calculations. Conversion of common logarithms into Napierian logarithms. The calculation of square roots by the ordinary arithmetical method. Using algebraic formulæ in

1. Students of this Syllabus will do well to consult *A Summary of Lectures on Practical Mathematics*, published by the Board of Education, 1889.
2. I should like to say that, since the Science and Art Department has distributed its tables of four-figure logarithms and functions of angles over the country as cheaply as grocers' advertisements, there has been a wonderful development in knowledge and use of such tables.

working questions on ratio and variation. Simplification of fractions. Calculation of percentages. Expressing shillings and pence as decimals of a pound; quarters and pounds as decimals of a hundredweight or ton, &c., so that all problems in Practice, Interest, Discount, &c., become mere commonsense applications of the simple rules.

Algebra.—To understand any formula so as to be able to use it if numerical values are given for the various quantities. Rules of Indices.

Being told in words how to deal arithmetically with a quantity, to be able to state the matter algebraically. All this has already been stated under the head of Arithmetic. Problems leading to easy equations in one or two unknowns. Easy transformations and simplifications of formulæ and in easy cases finding any one of several quantities in a formula when the others are given. Practice in algebraic manipulation generally.

The determination of the numerical values of constants in equations of known form, when particular values of the variables are given. The meaning of the expression "A varies as B."

Factors of such expressions as $x^2 - a^2$, $x^2 + 11x + 30$, $x^2 - 5x - 66$.

Mensuration.—Testing experimentally the rule for the length of the circumference of a circle, using strings round cylinders, or by rolling a disc or a sphere. Inventing methods of measuring the lengths of curves. Testing the rules for the areas of a triangle, rectangle, parallelogram, circle, ellipse, surface of cylinder, surface of cone, &c., using scales and squared paper. Propositions in Euclid relating to areas tested by squared paper; also by arithmetical work on actual line and angle measurements. The determination of the areas of an irregular plane figure (1) by using the planimeter; (2) by using Simpson's or other well-known rules for the case where a number of equidistant ordinates or widths are given; (3) by the use of squared paper when equidistant ordinates are not given; finding such ordinates; (4) weighing a piece of cardboard and comparing with the weight of a square; (5) counting squares on squared paper to verify rules. Rules for surfaces of spheres and rings. Rules for volumes of prisms, cylinders, cones, spheres, and rings, verified by actual experiment; for example, by filling vessels with water or by weighing objects of these shapes made of material of known density, or by allowing such objects to cause water to overflow from a vessel.

The determination of the volume of an irregular solid by each of the three methods for an irregular area, the process being first to obtain an irregular plane figure in which the varying ordinates or widths represent the varying cross sections of the solid. Determination of weights from volumes when densities are given.

Stating a mensuration rule as an algebraic formula. In such a formula any one of the quantities may be the unknown one, the others being known. Numerical exercises in mensuration.

The experimental work in this subject ought to be taken up in connec-

240

tion with practice in weighing and measuring generally; finding specific gravities, illustrations of the principle of Archimedes, the displacements of floating bodies, and other elementary scientific work. A good teacher will not overdo this experimental work; he will preserve a proper balance between experimental work, didactic teaching, and numerical exercise work.[3]

Use of Squared Paper.—The use of squared paper by merchants and others to show at a glance the rise and fall of prices, of temperature, of the tide, &c. The use of squared paper should be illustrated by the working of many kinds of exercises, but it should be pointed out that there is a general idea underlying them all. The following may be mentioned:—

Plotting of statistics of any kind whatsoever, of general or special interest. What such curves teach. Rates of increase.

Interpolation, or the finding of probable intermediate values. Probable errors of observation. Forming complete price lists by manufacturers. The calculation of a table of logarithms. Finding an average value. Areas and volumes, as explained above. The method of fixing the position of a point in a plane; the x and y and also the r and θ, co-ordinates of a point. Plotting of functions, such as $y = ax^n$, $y = ae^{bx}$, where a, b, n may have all sorts of values. The straight line. Meaning of its *slope;* slope of a curve at any point in it. Rates of increase, illustrated by the speed of a body. Easy exercises on rates of increase of y with regard to x in the case of $y = ax^n$, with illustrations from mechanics and physics.

Determination of maximum and minimum values. The solution of equations; very clear notions of what we mean by the roots of equations may be obtained by the use of squared paper. Determination of laws which exist between observed quantities, especially of linear laws. Corrections for errors of observation when the plotted quantities are the results of experiment.

In all the work on squared paper a student should be made to understand that an exercise is not completed until the scales and the names of the plotted quantities are clearly indicated on the paper. Also that those scales should be avoided which are obviously inconvenient. Finally, the scale should be chosen so that the plotted figure shall occupy the greater part of the sheet of paper; at any rate, the figure should not be crowded into one corner of the paper.

Geometry.—Dividing lines into parts in given proportions, and other ex-

---

3. I may also hope that a good teacher will educate the hands and eyes of his pupils, so that they may become expert in guessing the weights of objects, and small and large distances. Absurd questions ought not to be set, because they teach a boy not to exercise his common-sense. There is the well-known university case of a man who was calculating how many postage stamps would be required to cover the walls of a large room, and his answer was 1'203. . . .; I am told that he had more than twenty decimal places. This kind of exhibition, not of faith in mathematics, but of mere stupidity, is very common in young engineers who have never made experiments.

perimental illustrations of the sixth book of Euclid. Measurement of angles in degrees and radians. The definitions of the sine, cosine, and tangent of an angle; determination of their values by graphical methods; setting out of angles by means of a protractor when they are given in degrees or radians, also when the value of the sine, cosine, or tangent is given. Use of tables of sines, cosines, and tangents. The solution of a right-angled triangle by calculation, and by drawing to scale. The construction of any triangle from given data; determination of the area of a triangle. The more important propositions of Euclid may be illustrated by actual drawing; if the proposition is about angles, these may be measured by means of a protractor; or if it refers to the equality of lines, areas, or ratios, lengths may be measured by a scale, and the necessary calculations made arithmetically. This combination of drawing and arithmetical calculation may be freely used to illustrate the truth of a proposition. A good teacher will occasionally introduce demonstrative proof as well as mere measurement.

The method of representing the position of a point in space by its distances from three co-ordinate planes. How the angles are measured between (1) a line and plane; (2) two planes. The angle between two lines has a meaning, whether they do or do not meet. What is meant by the projection of a line or a plane figure on a plane. Plan and elevation of a line which is inclined at given angles to the co-ordinate planes. The meaning of the terms "trace of a line," "trace of a plane."

The distinction between a scalar quantity and a vector quantity. Addition and subtraction of vectors. Experimental illustrations.

In setting out the above Syllabus, the items have been arranged under the various branches of the subject.

It will be obvious that it is not intended that these should be studied in the order in which they appear; the teacher will arrange a mixed course such as seems to him best for the class of students with whom he has to deal. A good teacher must understand that no examination made by any one other than himself can be framed which will properly test the result of his teaching. He must endeavour to give knowledge which becomes part of his pupil's mental machinery, so that the pupil is certain to apply it in all sorts of practical problems, and will no more allow it to become rusty than his power to read or write or walk.

Advanced Course.

The instruction includes greater elaboration of the work specified in the elementary course, that is, much more practice in such computation from more complex formulæ. Demonstrative Geometry based upon Euclid.

The use of approximate formulæ such as

$$(1 + a)^n = 1 + na \text{ when } a \text{ is small compared with 1.}$$

Rules in Arithmetic (as of compound interest, &c.) and in Mensuration, stated as algebraic formulæ. Any one of the quantities in a formula may be the unknown one.

Practice in the simplification of algebraical expressions. Solution of equations and problems leading to equations. Resolution of a fraction into partial fractions.

TRIGONOMETRY.—Some knowledge of such limits as sin $\theta \div \theta$. How to find the values of the sine, cosine, and tangent for angles greater than 90°; complementary and supplementary angles.

Fundamental relations such as $\sin^2 \theta + \cos^2 \theta = 1$.

Calculating the values of sin x, cos x, e^x and log x using series.

The fundamental formulæ for the sine and cosine of the sum or difference of two angles, that is

$$\sin (A + B) = \sin A \cos B + \cos A \sin B.$$

and the others. Formulæ derived from the above, such as those for the sum and difference of two sines or cosines, and those which connect an angle and the double angle.

The sine rule, or $\dfrac{\sin A}{\sin B} = \dfrac{a}{b}$ in triangles. Also the rule

$$c^2 = a^2 - 2ab \cos C + b^2.$$

The expression for the area of a triangle, having given two sides and the included angle, $\frac{1}{2} ab \sin C$.

The truth of such formulæ ought to be illustrated numerically and graphically by taking numerical values of the quantities.

MENSURATION.—Guldinus' Theorems relating to areas and volumes of surfaces and solids of revolution. Exercises on the area of a segment and sector of a circle, the area of the surface of a sphere between any two parallel planes; approximate rules for length of a circular arc.

Finding centres of gravity using squared paper.

Use of the calculus to find areas and volumes.

USE OF SQUARED PAPER.—The plotting of functions including such as

$$y = ax^n; \; y = ae^{bx}; \; y = a \sin (cx + d); \; y = ae^{bx} \sin (cx + d).$$

Having given observed values of two varying quantities which are known to follow one or other of laws like $pv^n = c$, $y = a + bx^2$, $axy = bx + cy$, to find the probable values of the constants.

When two varying quantities are known to follow a given but somewhat complex law, to determine a simple law which between certain limits will give values approximating to the correct ones.

Solving equations by the use of squared paper.

Maximum and minimum problems.

RATES AND SUMS.—Rate of increase of one quantity relatively to that of another; approximate method of calculating a rate of increase, as, for example, in the case where simultaneous values of two varying quantities have been observed experimentally, or by finding the *slope* of the curve obtained by plotting such values.

The term "differential coefficient" as applied to a rate of increase; and the symbol for it, namely $\dfrac{dy}{dx}$, where y and x represent the two varying quantities.

Rules for finding the differential coefficient of y with respect to x, that is, $\dfrac{dy}{dx}$, when y and x are related in the following ways:—

$$y = ax; \; y = ae^{bx}; \; y = \sin x; \; y = \cos x; \; y = a \sin (bx + c);$$
$$y = A \log (x + a).$$

The study of these functions.

Proof and use of the rules for differentiating a product of two functions or the function of a function. Successive and partial differentiation. Integrating by parts and by substitution and other simple devices.

Calculation of maximum and minimum values.

Integration regarded as the inverse of differentiation, or as a process of summation; the symbols

$$\int y \, dx \text{ and } \int_a^b y \, dx;$$ rough methods of finding an approximation to $\int_a^b y \, dx$

when numerical values of y and x are known. Integration of y when tabulated for equal increments in x.

The expressions for the following integrals:—

$$\int ax^n \, dx; \int ae^{bx} \, dx; \int \frac{A}{x + a} \, dx;$$
$$\int A \sin (ax + b) \, dx; \int A \cos (ax + b) \, dx.$$

The solution of simple differential equations.

In following the syllabus, to make students take an interest in the work, constant use ought to be made of illustrations from Mensuration, Mechanics, and Physics.

GEOMETRY.—How the position of a point in space is defined by its rectangular co-ordinates x, y, z, or by its polar co-ordinates r, θ, ϕ; the relations between x, y, z and r, θ, ϕ.

Determination of the three angles α, β, γ which a given line makes with the three co-ordinate axes; the relation

$$\cos^2\alpha + \cos^2\beta + \cos^2\gamma = 1.$$

Determination of the angles between a given line and each of the co-ordinate planes.

When a plane is given by its traces, to determine its inclination to each of the three co-ordinate axes and planes.

The above may be treated analytically or graphically.

Representation by its projections on the three co-ordinate planes of a line whose position and real length are given.

Determination of the angle between two given lines; the angle between two planes whose traces are given. Represent by its projections the line of intersection of two planes whose traces are given.

VECTORS.—The scalar product and vector product of two given vectors, with illustrations. Easy Vector Algebra.

[*Following this presentation in the book are several statements criticizing Perry's views. Each of the statements is followed by a rebuttal by Perry.*]

On the Foundations of Mathematics

By Eliakim Hastings Moore

A VISION

An Invitation.—The pure mathematicians are invited to determine how mathematics is regarded by the world at large, including their colleges of other science departments and the students of elementary mathematics, and to ask themselves whether by modification of method and attitude they may not win for it the very high position in general esteem and appreciative interest which it assuredly deserves.

This general invitation and the preceding summary view invoke this vision of the future of elementary mathematics in this country.

The Pedagogy of Elementary Mathematics.—We survey the pedagogy of elementary mathematics in the primary schools, in the secondary schools and in the junior colleges (the lower collegiate years.) It is, however, understood that there is a movement for the enlargement of the strong secondary schools, by the addition of the two years of junior college work and by the absorption of the last two or three grades of the primary schools, into institutions more of the type of the German gymnasia and the French lycée;[1] in favor of this movement there are strong arguments, and among them this, that in such institutions, especially if closely related to strong colleges or universities, the mathematical reforms may the more easily be carried out.

The fundamental problem is that of *the unification of pure and applied mathematics.* If we recognize the branching implied by the very terms 'pure,' 'applied,' we have to do with a special case of *the correlation of dif-*

---

1. As to the mathematics of these institutions, one may consult the book on 'The Teaching of Mathematics in the Higher School of Prussia' (New York, Longmans, Green & Co., 1900) by Professor Young, and the article (*Bulletin Amer. Math. Soc.* (2), vol. 6, p. 225) by Professor Pierpont.

This is a portion of Moore's presidential address before the American Mathematical Society at its ninth annual meeting, 29 December 1902. The address was printed first in *Science* n.s. 17 (March 1903). It was reprinted in the First Yearbook of the National Council of Teachers of Mathematics, 1926, and also in the April 1967 issue of the *Mathematics Teacher*.

In the opening section, entitled "A View," Moore discussed the state of abstract and applied mathematics. He particularly stressed the work of Perry and his speech of 1901.

ferent subjects of the curriculum, a central problem in the domain of pedagogy from the time of Herbart on. In this case, however, the fundamental solution is to be found rather by way of indirection—by arranging the curriculum so that throughout the domain of elementary mathematics the branching be not recognized.

The Primary Schools.—Would it not be possible for the children in the grades to be trained in power of observation and experiment and reflection and deduction so that always their mathematics should be directly connected with matters of thoroughly concrete character? The response is immediate that this is being done to-day in the kindergartens and in the better elementary schools. I understand that serious difficulties arise with children of from nine to twelve years of age, who are no longer contented with the simple, concrete methods of earlier years and who, nevertheless, are unable to appreciate the more abstract methods of the later years. These difficulties, some say, are to be met by allowing the mathematics to enter only implicitly in connection with the other subjects of the curriculum. But rather the material and methods of the mathematics should be enriched and vitalized. In particular, the grade teachers must make wiser use of the foundations furnished by the kindergarten. The drawing and the paper folding must lead on directly to systematic study of intuitional geometry,[2] including the construction of models and the elements of mechanical drawing, with simple exercises in geometrical reasoning. The geometry must be closely connected with the numerical and literal arithmetic. The cross-grooved tables of the kindergarten furnish an especially important type of connection, viz., a conventional graphical depiction of any phenomenon in which one magnitude depends upon another. These tables and the similar cross-section blackboards and paper must enter largely into all the mathematics of the grades. The children are to be taught to represent, according to the usual conventions, various familiar and interesting phenomena and to study the properties of the phenomena in the pictures: to know, for example, what concrete meaning attaches to the fact that a graph curve at a certain point is going down or going up or is horizontal. Thus the problems of percentage—interest, etc. —have their depiction in straight or broken line graphs.

The Secondary Schools.—Pending the reform of the primary schools, the secondary schools must advance independently. In these schools at present, according to one type of arrangement, we find algebra in the first year, plane geometry in the second, physics in the third, and the more difficult parts of algebra and solid geometry, with review of all the mathematics in the fourth.

2. Here I refer to the very suggestive paper of Benchara Branford, entitled 'Measurement and Simple Surveying. An Experiment in the Teaching of Elementary Geometry' to a small class of beginners of about ten years of age (*Journal of Education*, London, the first part appearing in the number for August, 1899.)

Engineers[3] tell us that in the schools algebra is taught in one water-tight compartment, geometry in another, and physics in another, and that the student learns to appreciate (if ever) only very late the absolutely close connection between these different subjects, and then, if he credits the fraternity of teachers with knowing the closeness of this relation, he blames them most heartily for their unaccountably stupid way of teaching him. If we contrast this state of affairs with the state of affairs in the solid four years' course in Latin, I think we are forced to the conclusion that the organization of instruction in Latin is much more perfect than that of the instruction in mathematics.

The following question arises: *Would it not be possible to organize the algebra, geometry and physics of the secondary school into a thoroughly coherent four years' course,* comparable in strength and closeness of structure with the four years' course in Latin? (Here under physics I include astronomy, and the more mathematical and physical parts of physiography.) It would seem desirable that, just as the systematic development of theoretical mathematics is deferred to a later period, likewise much of theoretical physics might well be deferred. Let the physics also be made thoroughly practical. At any rate, so far as the instruction of boys is concerned, the course should certainly have its character largely determined by the conditions which would be imposed by engineers. What kind of two or three years' course in mathematics and physics would a thoroughly trained engineer give to boys in the secondary school? Let this body of material postulated by the engineer serve as the basis of the four years' course. Let the instruction in the course, however, be given by men who have received expert training in mathematics and physics as well as in engineering and let the instruction be so organized that with the development of the boy, in appreciation of the practical relations, shall come simultaneously his development in the direction of theoretical physics and theoretical mathematics.

Perry is quite right in insisting that it is scientifically legitimate in the pedagogy of elementary mathematics to take a large body of basal principles

---

3. Why is it that one of the sanest and best-informed scientific men living, a man not himself an engineer, can charge mathematicians with killing off every engineering school on which they can lay hands? Why do engineers so strongly urge that the mathematical courses in engineering schools be given by practical engineers?

And why can a reviewer of 'Some Recent Books of Mechanics' write with truth: "The students' previous training in algebra, geometry, trigonometry, analytic geometry and calculus as it is generally taught has been necessarily quite formal. These mighty algorithms of formal mathematics must be learned so that they can be applied with readiness and precision. But with mechanics comes the application of these algorithms, and formal, do-by-rote methods, though often possible, yield no results of permanent value. How to elicit and cultivate thought is now of primary importance"? (E. B. Wilson, *Bulletin Amer. Math. Soc.,* October, 1902.) But is it conceivable that in any part of the education of the student the problem of eliciting and cultivating thought should not be of primary importance?

instead of a small body and to build the edifice upon the larger body for the earlier years, reserving for the later years the philosophic criticism of the basis itself and the reduction of the basal system.

To consider the subject of geometry in all briefness: with the understanding that proper emphasis is laid upon all the concrete sides of the subject, and that furthermore from the beginning exercises in informal deduction[4] are introduced increasingly frequently, when it comes to the beginning of the more formal deductive geometry why should not the students be directed each for himself to set forth a body of geometric fundamental principles, on which he would proceed to erect his geometric edifice? This method would be thoroughly practical and at the same time thoroughly scientific. The various students would have different systems of axioms, and the discussions thus arising naturally would make clearer in the minds of all precisely what are the functions of the axioms in the theory of geometry. The students would omit very many of the axioms, which to them would go without saying. The teacher would do well not to undertake to make the system of axioms thoroughly complete in the abstract sense. "Sufficient unto the day is the precision thereof." The student would very probably wish to take for granted all the ordinary properties of measurement and of motion, and would be ready at once to accept the geometrical implications of coordinate geometry. He could then be brought with extreme ease to the consideration of fundamental notions of the calculus as treated concretely, and he would find those notions delightfully real and powerful, whether in the domain of mathematics or of physics or of chemistry.

To be sure, as Study has well insisted, for a thorough comprehension of even the elementary parts of Euclidean geometry the non-Euclidean geometries are absolutely essential. But the teacher is teaching the subject for the benefit of the students, and it must be admitted that beginners in the study of demonstrative geometry can not appreciate the very delicate considerations involved in the thoroughly abstract science. Indeed, one may conjecture that, had it not been for the brilliant success of Euclid in his effort to organize into a formally deductive system the geometric treasures of his times, the advent of the reign of science in the modern sense might not have been so long deferred. Shall we then hold that in the schools the teaching of demonstrative geometry should be reformed in such a way as to take account of all the wonderful discoveries which have been made—many even recently—in the domain of abstract geometry? And should similar reforms be made in the treatment of arithmetic and algebra? To make reforms of

---

4. In an article shortly to appear in the *Educational Review*, on 'The Psychological and the Logical in the Teaching of Geometry,' Professor John Dewey, calling attention to the evolutionary character of the education of an individual, insists that there should be no abrupt transition from the introductory, intuitional geometry to the systematic, demonstrative geometry.

this kind, would it not be to repeat more gloriously the error of those followers of Euclid who fixed his 'Elements' as a textbook for elementary instruction in geometry for over two thousand years? Every one agrees that professional mathematicians should certainly take account of these great developments in the technical foundations of mathematics, and that ample provision should be made for instruction in these matters; and on reflection, every one agrees further that this provision should be reserved for the later collegiate and university years.

The Laboratory Method.—This program of reform calls for the development of a thoroughgoing laboratory system of instruction in mathematics and physics, a principal purpose being as far as possible to develop on the part of every student the true spirit of research, and an appreciation, practical as well as theoretic, of the fundamental methods of science.

In connection with what has already been said, the general suggestions I now add will, I hope, be found of use when one enters upon the questions of detail involved in the organization of the course.

As the world of phenomena receives attention by the individual, the phenomena are described both graphically and in terms of number and measure; the number and measure relations of the phenomena enter fundamentally into the graphical depiction, and furthermore the graphical depiction of the phenomena serves powerfully to illuminate the relations of number and measure. This is the fundamental scientific point of view. Here under the term graphical depiction I include representation by models.

To provide for the needs of laboratory instruction, there should be regularly assigned to the subject two periods, counting as one period in the curriculum.

As to the possibility of effecting this unification of mathematics and physics in the secondary schools, objection will be made by some teachers that it is impossible to do well more than one thing at a time. This pedagogic principle of concentration is undoubtedly sound. One must, however, learn how to apply it wisely. For instance, in the physical laboratory it is undesirable to introduce experiments which teach the use of the calipers or of the vernier or of the slide rule. Instead of such uninteresting experiments of limited purpose, the students should be directed to extremely interesting problems which involve the use of these instruments, and thus be led to learn to use the instruments as a matter of course, and not as a matter of difficulty. Just so the smaller elements of mathematical routine can be made to attach themselves to laboratory problems, arousing and retaining the interest of the students. Again, everything exists in its relations to other things, and in teaching the one thing the teacher must illuminate these relations.

Every result of importance should be obtained by at least two distinct methods, and every result of especial importance by two essentially distinct methods. This is possible in mathematics and the physical sciences, and thus the student is made thoroughly independent of all authority.

All results should be checked, if only qualitatively or if only 'to the first significant figure.' In setting problems in practical mathematics (arithmetical computation or geometrical construction) the teacher should indicate the amount or percentage of error permitted in the final result. If this amount of percentage is chosen conveniently in the different examples, the student will be led to the general notion of closer and closer approximation to a perfectly definite result, and thus in a practical way to the fundamental notions of the theory of limits and of irrational numbers. Thus, for instance, uniformity of convergence can be taught beautifully in connection with the concrete notion of area under a monotonic curve between two ordinates, by a figure due to Newton, while the interest will be still greater if in the diagram area stands for work done by an engine.

The teacher should lead up to an important theorem gradually in such a way that the precise meaning of the statement in question, and further, the practical, *i. e.*, computational or graphical or experimental—truth of the theorem is fully appreciated; and, furthermore, the importance of the theorem is understood, and, indeed, the desire for the formal proof of the proposition is awakened, before the formal proof itself is developed. Indeed, in most cases, much of the proof should be secured by the research work of the students themselves.

Some hold that absolutely individual instruction is the ideal, and a laboratory method has sometimes been used for the purpose of attaining this ideal. The laboratory method has as one of its elements of great value the flexibility which permits students to be handled as individuals or in groups. The instructor utilizes all the experience and insight of the whole body of students. He arranges it so that the students consider that they are studying the subject itself, and not the words, either printed or oral, of any authority on the subject. And in this study they should be in the closest cooperation with one another and with their instructor, who is in a desirable sense one of them and their leader. Instructors may fear that the brighter students will suffer if encouraged to spend time in cooperation with those not so bright. But experience shows that just as every teacher learns by teaching, so even the brightest students will find themselves much the gainers for this cooperation with their colleagues.

In agreement with Perry, it would seem possible that the student might be brought into vital relation with the fundamental elements of trigonometry, analytic geometry and the calculus, on condition that the whole treatment in its origin is and in its development remains closely associated with thoroughly concrete phenomena. With the momentum of such practical education in the methods of research in the secondary school, the college students would be ready to proceed rapidly and deeply in any direction in which their personal interests might lead them. In particular, for instance, one might expect to find effective interest on the part of college students in the most formal abstract mathematics.

For all students who are intending to take a full secondary school course in preparation for colleges or technological schools, I am convinced that the laboratory method of instruction in mathematics and physics, which has been briefly suggested, is the best method of instruction—for students in general, and for students expecting to specialize in pure mathematics, in pure physics, in mathematical physics or astronomy, or in any branch of engineering.

Evolution, not Revolution.—In contemplating this reform of secondary school instruction we must be careful to remember that it is to be accomplished as an evolution from the present system, and not as a revolution of that system. Even under the present organization of the curriculum the teachers will find that much improvement can be made by closer cooperation one with another; by the introduction, so far as possible, of the laboratory two-period plan; and in any event by the introduction of laboratory methods; laboratory record books, cross-section paper, computational and graphical methods in general, including the use of colored inks and chalks; the cooperation of students; and by laying emphasis upon the comprehension of propositions rather than upon the exhibition of comprehension.

The Junior Colleges.—Just as secondary schools should begin to reform without waiting for the improvement of the primary schools, so the elementary collegiate courses should be modified at once without waiting for the reform of the secondary schools. And naturally, in the initial period of reform, the education in each higher domain will involve many elements which later on will be transferred to a lower domain.

Further, by the introduction into the junior colleges of the laboratory method of instruction it will be possible for the colleges and universities to take up a duty which for the most part has been neglected in this country. For, although we have normal schools and other training schools for those who expect to teach in the grades, little attention has as yet been given to the training of those who will become secondary school teachers. The better secondary schools of to-day are securing the services of college graduates who have devoted special attention to the subjects which they intend to teach, and as time goes on the positions in these schools will as a rule be filled (as in France and Germany) by those who have supplemented their college course by several years of university work. Here these college and university graduates proceed at once to their work in the secondary schools. Now in the laboratory courses of the junior college, let those students of the senior college and graduate school who are to go into the teaching career be given training in the pedagogy of mathematics according to the laboratory system; for such a student the laboratory would be a laboratory in the pedagogy of mathematics; that is, he would be a colleague-assistant of the instructor. By this arrangement, the laboratory instruction of the colleges would be strengthened at the same time that well equipped teachers would be prepared for work in the secondary schools.

The Freedom of the Secondary Schools.—The secondary schools are everywhere preparing students for colleges and technological schools, and whether the requirements of those institutions are expressed by way of examination of students or by way of the conditions for the accrediting of schools or teachers, the requirements must be met by the secondary schools. The stronger secondary school teachers too often find themselves shackled by the specific requirements imposed by local or college authorities. Teaching must become more of a profession. And this implies not only that the teacher must be better trained for his career, but also in his career he be given with greater freedom greater responsibility. To this end closer relations should be established between the teachers of the colleges and those of the secondary schools; standing provisions should be made for conferences as to improvement of the secondary school curricula and in the collegiate admission requirements; and the leading secondary school teachers should be steadily encouraged to devise and try out plans looking in any way toward improvement.

Thus the proposed four years' laboratory course in mathematics and physics will come into existence by way of evolution. In a large secondary school, the strongest teachers, finding the project desirable and feasible, will establish such a course alongside the present series of disconnected courses—and as time goes on their success will in the first place stimulate their colleagues to radical improvements of method under the present organization and finally to a complete reorganization of the courses in mathematics and physics.

The American Mathematical Society.—Do you not feel with me that the American Mathematical Society, as the organic representative of the highest interests of mathematics in this country, should be directly related with the movement of reform? And, to this end, that the society, enlarging its membership by the introduction of a large body of the strongest teachers of mathematics in the secondary schools, should give continuous attention to the question of improvement of education in mathematics, in institutions of all grades? That there is need for the careful consideration of such questions by the united body of experts, there is no doubt whatever, whether or not the general suggestions which we have been considering this afternoon turn out to be desirable and practicable. In case the question of pedagogy does come to be an active one, the society might readily hold its meetings in two divisions—a division of research and a division of pedagogy.

Furthermore, there is evident need of a national organization having its center of gravity in the whole body of science instructors in the secondary schools; and those of us interested in these questions will naturally relate ourselves also to this organization. It is possible that the newly formed Central Association of Physics Teachers may be the nucleus of such an organization.

CONCLUSION

The successful execution of the reforms proposed would seem to be of fundamental importance to the development of mathematics in this country. I urge that individuals and organizations proceed to the consideration of the general question of reform with all the related questions of detail. Undoubtedly in many parts of the country improvements in organization and methods of instruction in mathematics have been made these last years. All persons who are, or may become, actively interested in this movement of reform should in some way unite themselves, in order that the plans and the experience, whether of success or failure, of one may be immediately made available in the guidance of his colleagues.

I may refer to the centers of activity with which I am acquainted. Miss Edith Long, in charge of the Department of Mathematics in the Lincoln (Neb.) High School, reports upon the experience of several years in the correlation of algebra, geometry and physics, in the October, 1902, number of the *Educational Review*. In the Lewis Institute of Chicago, Professor P. B. Woodworth, of the Department of Electrical Engineering, has organized courses in engineering principles and electrical engineering in which are developed the fundamentals of practical mathematics. The general question came up at the first meeting [5] (Chicago, November, 1902) of the Central Association of Physics Teachers, and it is to be expected that this association will enlarge its functions in such a way as to include teachers of mathematics and of all sciences, and that the question will be considered in its various bearings by the enlarged association. At this meeting informal reports were made from the Bradley Polytechnic Institute of Peoria, the Armour Institute of Technology of Chicago, and the University of Chicago. The question is evoking much interest in the neighborhood of Chicago.

I might explain how I came to be attracted to this question of pedagogy of elementary mathematics. I wish, however, merely to express my gratitude to many mathematical and scientific friends, in particular, to my Chicago colleagues, Mr. A. C. Lunn and Professor C. R. Mann, for their cooperation with me in the consideration of these matters, and further to express the hope that we may secure the active cooperation of many colleagues in the domains of science and of administration, so that the first

---

5. Subsequent to the meeting of organization in the spring of 1902. Mr. Chas. H. Smith of the Hyde Park High School, Chicago, is president of the Association. Reports of the meetings are given in *School Science* (Ravenswood, Chicago.)

carefully chosen steps of a really important advance movement may be taken in the near future.

I close by repeating the questions which have been engaging our attention this afternoon.

In the development of the individual in his relations to the world, there is no initial separation of science into constituent parts, while there is ultimately a branching into the many distinct sciences. The troublesome problem of the closer relation of pure mathematics to its applications: can it not be solved by indirection, in that through the whole course of elementary mathematics, including the introduction to the calculus, there be recognized in the organization of the curriculum no distinction between the various branches of pure mathematics, and likewise no distinction between pure mathematics and its principal applications? Further, from the standpoint of pure mathematics: will not the twentieth century find it possible to give to young students during their impressionable years, in thoroughly concrete and captivating form, the wonderful new notions of the seventeenth century?

By way of suggestion these questions have been answered in the affirmative, on condition that there be established a thoroughgoing laboratory system of instruction in primary schools, secondary schools and junior colleges —a laboratory system involving a synthesis and development of the best pedagogic methods at present in use in mathematics and the physical sciences.

American Teachers Series

The Teaching of Mathematics in the Elementary and the Secondary School

BY

J. W. A. YOUNG, Ph.D.

ASSOCIATE PROFESSOR OF THE PEDAGOGY OF MATHEMATICS IN
THE UNIVERSITY OF CHICAGO

NEW EDITION
NEW IMPRESSION

LONGMANS, GREEN AND CO.
FOURTH AVENUE & 30TH STREET, NEW YORK
39 PATERNOSTER ROW, LONDON
BOMBAY, CALCUTTA, AND MADRAS
1920

Contents

CHAPTER   PAGES

I. THE STUDY OF THE PEDAGOGY OF MATHEMATICS . . . 1-8
  Bibliography . . . 2
  The study needed . . . 2
  The study of interest in general pedagogy . . . 3
  The growth of interest . . . 3-5
  The pedagogic unrest . . . 5
  The pedagogy of mathematics . . . 5
  German tendencies . . . 6
  English tendencies . . . 6
  American tendencies . . . 7
  The outcome . . . 8
  The published results . . . 8
  The pedagogy of mathematics to other subjects . . . 8
  Relation of the study of pedagogy . . . 9-13
  Dangers of the study of pedagogy . . .
  Learn to teach by teaching . . .
  How the teaching of mathematics may be studied . . .

II. THE PURPOSE AND VALUE OF THE STUDY OF MATHE-
  MATICS IN PRIMARY AND SECONDARY SCHOOLS . . . 10-13
  Bibliography . . . 11
  The question . . . 12
  Need of considering the question . . . 13-17
  What is education? . . . 13
  The attitude of the pupil . . . 14
  The practical value of mathematics . . . 14
  The facts of mathematics practical value . . . 15
  The contingent value . . . 16-17
  The informational value . . . 17
  Mathematics in nature . . . 17
  Pedagogic bearing . . . 18
  Mathematics as a mode of thought . . . 19-22
  The chief value of the study of mathematics . . . 20
  The chief value situation . . . 21
  Grasping logic bearing . . . 21
  Pedagogic conclusions . . .
  Drawing conclusions . . .
  Certainty . . .
  Simplicity . . .
  Applicability . . .

viii

CHAPTER   PAGES

  What is mathematics? . . . 22
  Necessary conclusions from the logical point of view . . . 23-25
  A mathematical inference in every conclusion . . . 25
  Necessary conclusions from the point of view of
    everyday assumptions . . . 26
  Mathematical methods outside of mathematics . . . 27-30
  Contingent conclusions in mathematics . . . 30
  Summary . . . 30
    An objection considered . . . 31-34
  "No head for mathematics" . . . 34
    A warning to teachers . . . 34
    The reasons advanced . . . 35-37
    Pedagogic bearing . . . 37
  Memoriting . . . 38
  Sir William Hamilton on the study of mathematics . . . 38
  Observation in mathematics . . . 38-40
  A practical objection . . . 40
  Other functions of mathematics . . . 41-46
  Generalising conceptions; combining results . . . 41
  In formation and use of a symbolic language . . . 42
  As a type of complete scientific treatment . . . 42
  Early discoveries . . . 43
  As knowledge for its own sake . . . 43
  As cultivating reverence for truth . . . 44
  As cultivating the habit of self scrutiny . . . 44
  Æsthetic value . . . 45
  In the development of the imagination . . . 45
  In cultivating the power of attention . . . 46
  In fostering habits of neatness and accuracy . . . 46
  Summary of the chief values in the study of mathematics . . . 47-49
  Official statement of aims in mathematics . . . 49-53
  Time and scope of the study of mathematics . . . 53-68

III. METHODS AND MODES . . . 53
  Methods in mathematics . . . 53-62
  Methods and modes defined . . . 53
  The analytic and the synthetic method . . . 54-56
  The function of these methods . . . 55
  The synthetic method in the class-room . . . 56
  Geometric analysis . . . 56-58
  The deductive and the inductive method . . . 57
  Mathematical discovery inductive . . . 57
  Induction in the class-room . . . 58-61
  The Socratic method . . . 61
  Its value . . . 61

CHAPTER   PAGES

  The heuristic method . . . 61
  The laboratory method . . . 62
  Modes in mathematics . . . 62
  The examination mode . . . 62-68
  The recitation mode . . . 63
  The lecture mode . . . 63
  The genetic mode . . . 64
  The heuristic mode . . . 65
  The individual mode . . . 66
  The laboratory mode . . . 66
  No one mode to be used always . . . 66
  The test of the best mode . . . 66

IV. THE HEURISTIC METHOD . . . 66
  Bibliography . . . 67
  The heuristic method defined . . . 69-80
  The value of the method . . . 69
  The mode of instruction . . . 69-72
  Dangers and disadvantages . . . 71
  The verdict of experience . . . 72
  How to find proofs . . . 77
  How to introduce the heuristic method . . . 77-77

V. THE INDIVIDUAL MODE . . . 77
  Bibliography . . . 78
  The need of individual teaching . . . 79
  The need especially great in mathematics . . . 80-86
  Advantages and disadvantages of the individual mode . . . 81
  The outcome . . . 81

VI. THE PERRY MOVEMENT; THE LABORATORY METHOD . . . 87-121
  Bibliography . . . 87-90
  The movements . . . 90
  The keynote—interest . . . 91-96
  The dominating thought . . . 93
  The method of nature . . . 93
  The child's standard of interest . . . 94
  The real objection to the abstract . . . 95
  What arouses interest . . . 96
  The correlation of subjects . . . 97-103
  The mathematical with subjects among themselves . . . 99
  What is sound in these proposals? . . . 101
  Mathematical weakness in physics . . . 102
  Material for correlation . . . 103

CONTENTS

CHAPTER — PAGES

From concrete to abstract 103–109
  Mathematical origin of mathematics 103
  Experimental origin of mathematics 104–106
  Experiment abstracts his own mathematics . . 107
  Pupil abstracts his own mathematics 108
  Warrant study of mathematical processes needed . . 109–116
  Pupil is the concrete? 109
  Separate changes urged 110
  Some other changes urged 110
  Work with large body of axioms 110
  Various modes of proof to be admitted 110
  Proofs based on measurement 110–116
  Free use of motion 111–116
  Teach through the eye 112–114
  Graphs 114
  Geometric construction 116
  Graphic computation 116
  Uses of squared paper 116
  When to use graphs 116–119
  No daily allotment of teacher and pupils . . . 117
  Relations between teacher and pupils 118
  The laboratory and its equipment 119
  The term "laboratory" 119
  The laboratory of the physical laboratory . . 119
  Limitations better in mathematics 111
  The situation 121
  A mode proposed in Germany and France . . . 122–151
  Similar tendencies in Germany and France . . 122

VII. MISCELLANEOUS POINTS OF METHOD AND MODE . . 123–125
  Bibliography 123–125
  Rigor 125
  Extension of proofs 125–127
  Generalization on insufficient data 126
  How a proof may be extended 127
  An example 128–130
  Truths re. convention of mathematics 129
  The simple step a time 130
  One step at too long delay on same topic . . . 130
  Danger to be avoided 131
  Complexity as a language 131
  Mathematics problems 131–134
  Character of 132
  Home work 132
  Its purpose 133
  What should be assigned 133
  How treated afterwards 133
  The teacher's record 134

CONTENTS

CHAPTER — PAGES

Syllabus 134
Explanations at blackboard 134
"Chalk and talk" 134
The rôle of memory in mathematics 135–136
This ability, how attained 135
Remember; not memorize 137
Marking system 138
Avoid waste 138–140
Single pupil mode 139
Passive attitude of pupils to be avoided . . . 139
Teacher or pupil at board 140
Special assignments 140
The blackboard mode 140
Extemporizing problems 140
Making problems 141
Reviews 142
Direct and incidental reviews 142
Teaching through the eye 143
Neatness and orderly arrangement 143
Squared paper 143
Use of colors 143
Scientific analyses 143
Free questioning 144
The use of a text 144–146
Why a text should be used 144
How to use the text 145
Varying from the text 145
Notebooks 146
Chief uses of the notebook 146
Written exercises 147–149
Exercise books 147
Marking of exercises 148
Grading 148
Examinations 149–151
Two sorts of examinations 149
What the examination is not 149
What the examination is 150
VIII. PREPARATION OF TEACHERS; MATHEMATICAL CLUBS . 152–169
  Bibliography 152
  The preparation of teachers 152–163
  Command of subject matter taught 152
  This command, how attained 153
  Minimum equipment 153
  College graduation required 154

CONTENTS

CHAPTER — PAGES

For teachers already in the ranks 154
Advance in scientific knowledge needed . . . 155
English books for teachers' reading 155
Foreign books for teachers' reading 155–157
Elementary foreign texts 157
General addresses 158
The teacher's addresses 158
Pedagogic preparation 159
The teacher's heuristic spirit 159
Why facilities have been lacking 160
Theory and practice, hand in hand 161–163
What can be done in the secondary school . . 161
What has been done in Prussia 161
Daily preparation 162
Mathematical clubs 162
Nature of the organizations 163
Topics for teachers 163–169
Topics for pupils 163
Historical topics 164
Topics of subject matter 165–168
Models and instruments 165
Life and work of mathematicians 166
Mathematical recreations 167
Social features 168
Clubs for teachers 168

IX. THE MATERIAL EQUIPMENT 170–177
  The library 170–176
  On the selection of books 170
  Lists of books 171–175
  History 171
  Pedagogic, philosophical, general 172
  Geometry 173
  Collections of problems 173
  Mathematical recreations 173
  Quotations 174
  Journals 174
  The teacher's needs 175
  The other material equipment 176

X. THE CURRICULUM IN MATHEMATICS 178–188
  Bibliography 178
  What mathematics should be studied 178–180
  Desiderata for subject matter 178
  Close connection with modern life needed . . 179

CONTENTS

CHAPTER   PAGES

In the grades 180
In the secondary school 180
Current tendencies 180–182
  In England 180
  In France 181
  In Germany 181
  In America 181
Simultaneous teaching of algebra and geometry . 183–186
  Why this order is better 183
  What to do 184
  By single schools possible 184
Action 185
  Co-ordination of mathematics with physics . 185
  An example of readjustment 186
  An extent treatment of topics 187
Co-readjustment involving physics 188
A readjustment the same for all pupils? . . . 189
Should the work in mathematics be the same for all pupils? . 189–201

XI. DEFINITIONS AND AXIOMS 190
Bibliography 190
Definitions 190
  What is a definition? 190
  Classification of definitions 191
    Elementary notions 192
    General terms 192
    Other terms 193
  Redundant definitions 193–195
  Definitions not lend themselves to generalization . 195–197
  Definitions should be 195–198
Axioms 198–199
  Three views as to axioms 200
  The researches of recent decades 200
  Veblen's axioms 200
  Desiderata for a system of axioms 203
  Effect on elementary teaching 203
The term "axiom" in the secondary school . . 204
The treatment of axioms 204

XII. THE TEACHING OF ARITHMETIC 204–209
Bibliography 204
The aim in teaching arithmetic 205
Arithmetic as a type of thought 205
Arithmetic processes of arithmetic 207
Types of thought in arithmetic 207–209
The child's power to reason
Abstract arithmetic difficult
Planning work

CHAPTER   PAGES

Arithmetic and nature 209–214
The quantitative side of nature 209
Sources of material 210–213
  Local problems 210
  Arithmetical excursions 212
  Experiments in physics 213
Processes themselves must be studied . . . 214
Computation 214–216
  Degree of skill needed 214
  Accuracy and speed 215
  Drill problems 215
Practical applications 216–218
  Arithmetic and business 216–218
  Preparation for later mathematics 218
Simplifications 219–223
  What simplifications are needed 219
  Omissions proposed 220–223
Methods 223–231
  Three methods of teaching arithmetic . . 223
  The heuristic method 224
  The spiral method 225
  Definitions in arithmetic 226–228
  Rules in arithmetic 228
  Character of proofs in arithmetic 229
  Varying forms of solution 230
  Oral arithmetic 230
The subject matter of arithmetic 231–242
  The number concept 231
  Counting vs. measuring 331
  The four fundamental operations 333–336
    Addition 334
    Subtraction 335
    Division and partition 236
  Fractions 236–239
    Decimal fractions 237
  Proportion 239
  Square root and cube root 240
  The metric system 240–241
  Teaching the metric system 241
The algebraic side of arithmetic 243–246
  The use of letters 243
  The equation 244
  Technic of literal arithmetic 244
  Negative number not needed 245

CHAPTER   PAGES

The geometric side of arithmetic 246–249
  How to be treated 246
  Extent of the work 246
  What proofs are available 247
  The algebraic and geometric work, integral parts of arithmetic . 247
Miscellaneous Points 248
False accuracy 249–254
  Estimates 249
  Checks 249
  Memory in arithmetic 250
  Labelling steps 250
  Indicating work 251
  Very small numbers in new topics 251
  Pupils make problems 252
Characteristics of a good text 252
The teacher 252
  Qualifications 253
  General preparation 253
  Daily preparation 254–256
  Improvement needed and coming 254
  Adding local interest 355

XIII. THE TEACHING OF GEOMETRY 355
Bibliography 355
Special aim of the teaching of geometry . . . 356
The mode of instruction 357–391
  The analytic method 357–359
  An example of geometric analysis 359
  The transition from concrete to demonstrative geometry . 259–263
  When begin demonstrative geometry . . . 260–263
  Euclid as a text and as model 263
  The formal side of geometry 264
  Taking propositions for granted 264
  Methods of attack 264
  Books on methods of attack 265
  Definitions in geometry 266
Modern geometry 267
  Modern geometry in the class-room . . . 268
  The parallel axiom and the non-Euclidean geometries . 268–270, 270–275
  The use of motion and signed magnitudes . 775
Algebra in geometry 273–276
Experimental work in geometry 276–278
Relation to demonstrative geometry 279–280, 281

CONTENTS

CHAPTER
  Geometry and drawing . . . 281
  Models and apparatus . . . 283–284
  Models in solid geometry . . . 283
  Materials for models . . . 283
  Apparatus for models . . . 284–286
  Apparatus and plane geometry . . . 286
  Solid geometry for simultaneous treatment . . . 287
  Reasons for the course in geometry . . . 287–291
  The close of the trigonometry . . . 287
  The teaching of trigonometry . . . 288
  Trigonometry not really a separate subject . . . 288
  The separable parts of trigonometry . . . 290
  The practical interest of trigonometry . . . 290
  A simple course in trigonometry . . . 292

XIV. THE TEACHING OF ALGEBRA . . . 293–302
  Bibliography . . . 293
  The character, scope, and relations of elementary algebra . . . 293
  The definition of algebra . . . 293
  The oral purpose of the teaching of algebra . . . 294–297
  General purpose of the teaching of algebra . . . 294
  Special to be taken up in algebra . . . 296
  Topics to be taken up in algebra . . . 296
  Report of Committee . . . 297–299
  Tendencies of the day . . . 299
  The relation of algebra of algebra . . . 300
  The numerical side of algebra . . . 301
  Numerical interpretation of algebraic results . . . 301
  Arithmetical symbols must be kept in mind . . . 302–314
  The meaning of algebra . . . 302
  Translation . . . 303
  Mechanical work . . . 303
  The central topic of algebra, the equation . . . 304–314
  The backbone of long drill problems . . . 304–306
  Omission . . . 305
  The equations of condition and of identity . . . 306
  Existence of a solution . . . 307
  Equivalence of equations . . . 308
  The study of the variation of polynomials . . . 308
  The function concept . . . 309
  The functions . . . 310
  General equations . . . 311
  Putting into equations . . . 311
  Interpretation of problems . . . 312
  Solution of problems . . . 312
  The language of algebra . . . 312

CONTENTS

CHAPTER
  Discussion of results . . . 314
  Determinants . . . 314
  Miscellaneous points . . . 314–323
  Oral algebra . . . 314
  Extension of the number system . . . 314–318
  Nature of positive and negative numbers . . . 316
  Multiplication of negative numbers . . . 318
  Factoring . . . 318
  Exponents . . . 319–322
  Logarithms . . . 320
  Slide rule . . . 321
  Irrational numbers . . . 321
  Manipulation of formulas . . . 322
  Algebra applied in physics . . . 323
  An outline order of treatment . . . 325

XV. LIMITS . . . 327–331
  Geometric limits . . . 327
  Incommensurable segments . . . 327
  The real difficulty numerical . . . 328
  Omit treatment of incommensurable cases . . . 328–331
  The area of the circle . . . 329
  What can be done in the class-room . . . 330
  Why treatment has been retained hitherto . . . 330
  Numerical limits . . . 330–342
  Limits in the domain of rational numbers . . . 331–334
  Strict definition of limit . . . 331
  Limits in common parlance . . . 332
  Illustrations . . . 332
  Limits and values . . . 333
  Limits of indeterminate expressions . . . 333
  Irrational limits . . . 334–342
  Irrational numbers . . . 334–339
  Meaning of $\sqrt{2}$ times $\sqrt{3}$ not obvious . . . 335
  Definition of $\sqrt{3}$ . . . 336
  Definition of sum . . . 337
  Definition of positive and negative numbers . . . 337
  Definition of subtraction and multiplication . . . 338
  How to prove $\sqrt{2} \cdot \sqrt{3} = \sqrt{6}$ . . . 338
  An important theorem . . . 338
  Definition of limit extended to irrational numbers . . . 339
  The area of the circle . . . 339
  Remarks . . . 339–341
  Class-room treatment . . . 341

CONTENTS

CHAPTER
  Infinity . . . 342–345
  The series of integers infinite . . . 342
  Meaning of infinity . . . 342
  Intersection of parallel straight lines . . . 343
  Division by zero . . . 343
  Utility of the term "infinity." . . . 343
  When needed . . . 344
  Summary . . . 344
  Supplemental Bibliography . . . 345

INDEX . . . 355

CHAPTER III.

Methods and Modes.

METHODS AND MODES: THE DISTINCTION.

In the study of the pedogogy of mathematics, the point of view is sometimes that of the manner in which the subject matter is arranged and developed; at others that of the manner in which it is presented to the pupils. To introduce this distinction into the nomenclature, the former has sometimes been called *method* and the latter *mode*. In this usage, one would speak of the analytic *method*, but of the recitation *mode*. The distinction is not always easy to make; not all processes of instruction can be readily classified as relating distinctly and exclusively either to the sequence and interrelation of the subject matter, or to the devices by which it is made clear to the pupil. Nevertheless, the broad distinction exists, and even though the term "method" has been used to denote both phases indiscriminately, it may help to keep the distinction more explicitly in mind to use the terms, in the present chapter at least, loosely in the sense cited.

METHODS IN MATHEMATICS.

Methods to be considered. As leading methods in mathematics may be mentioned: the synthetic, the analytic, the deductive, the inductive, the socratic, the heuristic, the laboratory. The characteristics of these methods will be indicated briefly in the sequel. They are not mutually exclusive; they shade into each other, and the classification of the treatment of a subject, topic, or problem under one or another method is often difficult. But though classification is sometimes hard or even impossible, the classes exist, and in their most typical and pronounced forms each of the methods has its marked characteristics and its peculiar adaptation to special situations.

The Synthetic and the Analytic Method. The *synthetic* and the *analytic method* are so familiar that their characteristics need only be recalled by a word. The synthetic proceeds from the known to the unknown; the analytic traces out a path from the unknown to the known. The synthetic says, "Since A is true, it follows that B is true"; the analytic says, "To prove that B is true, it is sufficient to prove that A is true." The synthetic "puts together" known truths, and by the combination perceives a truth theretofore unknown; the analytic "pulls apart" the statement under question into simpler statements whose truth or falsity is more easily determined.

Examples. The usual form of statements of proofs in text-books of elementary geometry is a good example of the synthetic method. Beginning with known definitions and assumptions (axioms), each proof, each step, is deduced from what is known.

The solution of a quadratic equation may be taken as a specimen of analytic procedure.

The problem is to find for what value or values of x, if any,

$$x^2 + px = q.$$

The problem is solved if the same problem is solved for

$$x^2 + px + \frac{p^2}{4} = q + \frac{p^2}{4},$$

$$\text{or for } \left(x + \frac{p^2}{4} \right)^2 = q + \frac{p}{4},$$

$$\text{or for } x + \frac{p}{2} = \pm \sqrt{q + \frac{p^2}{4}}.$$

The last is solved if *both*

$$x + \frac{p}{2} = + \sqrt{q + \frac{p^2}{4}} \text{ and } x + \frac{p}{2} = - \sqrt{q + \frac{p^2}{4}}$$

are solved.

Examples of geometric analysis will be given in the chapter on the teaching of geometry. In a previous chapter, an example of analytic reasoning outside of the domain of mathematics has already been given (pp. 28–30).

The Function of these Methods. The analytic method is the method of the mathematical worker, the synthetic method is that in which he usually presents his results. That the analytic method should in general be that of the class-room admits therefore of little doubt. Each step in an analytic march has its reason, its purpose. In the synthetic method the steps follow more or less blindly; the truth of each is evident, but why this step should be taken rather than some other is a mystery, and the final result is often reached with a disagreeable shock. "How did the author find this proof?" is frequently asked by pupils. The reply is that in all probability he found it in an entirely different way from that in which he presented it to the world. Not one proof out of a hundred is found by synthetic steps, and many synthetic forms of statement bear little trace of the analytic path of their discovery, so that the pupil justly has the feeling of one led about blindfold. The synthetic method *proves*, but often does not *explain*.

The great advantage of the analytic method is that if it connects with the known at any point, no matter where, its task is achieved; the synthetic method, on the other hand, has only a single point to reach. The synthetic method seeks "a needle in a haystack"; in the analytic method the needle seeks to get out of the haystack.

The synthetic method is that of logical exposition; it will usually succeed most rapidly in producing the conviction that particular statements are true, but it does this at the price of the minimum of intellectual benefit to the learner. Since the attitude of the pupil should in general be active, not passive, that of the discoverer, not that of the learner, the mathematical subject matter should usually come to him in analytic form.

For permanent record, in printed books, for example, the synthetic form has the advantage of being more finished, more certain, more formal, while the analytic method is informal, tentative, and, when reduced to cold black and white, may even seem colloquial. In how far text-books should be written analytically is an open question, but there is no question that the atmosphere of the mathematical class-room should be analytic from the primary school to the University.

The Synthetic Method in the Class-room. Has, then, the synthetic method no place in the class-room? It has, and a most important place. It is the method in which, in the class-room as well as in publications, the discoveries made analytically may usually be best arranged and surveyed. The synthetic presentation shows the unfaltering, sure-footed march of mathematical demonstration from the known to the unknown, and a demonstration reached after much analytic groping, with many "if only's" and "how's," should at once be cast into permanent shape in the synthetic mold.

For formal statements of proofs obtained, for their permanent record, for summaries, for reviews, the synthetic method is invaluable in the class-room.

Geometric Analysis. What has been said applies equally to the geometric and the algebraic side of mathematics. The terms *Geometry* and *Analysis* are sometimes used in contrast, and the usage is no doubt due to the fact that analytic forms of presentation were used in the algebraic field earlier than in geometry. But there is *geometric analysis* as well as algebraic analysis, and the demonstrations of algebra and of analytic geometry may also be cast in synthetic form.

The Deductive and the Inductive Method. A word will serve to recall the character of the *deductive* and the *inductive method.* The deductive method proceeds from the general to the particular; the inductive, from the particular to the general. A typical deductive syllogism is:

All men are mortal.

Socrates is a man.

Therefore, Socrates is mortal.

A typical inductive inference is:

The sun has risen each past day of which we have any knowledge: therefore the sun rises every day.

The deductive type of inference is precisely what has been defined in the previous chapter as the *mathematical* type. It is the final form of all mathematical reasoning, but it does not follow that the reasoning which leads to the result is entirely or even in part of this type. On the contrary, it is usually largely inductive. "This problem seems like such and such that I have met before; I solved them in a certain way. Therefore I can solve the present problem in the same way."

Mathematical Discovery Inductive. Mathematics in the synthetic finished form is deductive; mathematics in the making is inductive. Not only is the plan for the work inductive, but the theorems or processes themselves are very often discovered inductively, by the consideration of special examples. For the learner, the inductive method of approach is as a rule decidedly the best. By the consideration of quite a number of special instances he begins to see some general theorem or property underlying them all, and is thus led to try to find a deductive proof of the truth of the theorem or the existence of the property.

The belief that the theorem holds was reached by real induction and a purely inductive science would be obliged to leave it thus, but it is one of the chief glories of mathematics that it can take its theorems from the realm of inductive probability into that of deductive certainty. The question of whether or not an inductive inference is correct is one that need not be left unsettled in mathematics.

Induction in the Class-room. These considerations have important bearing upon the work of the class-room. Even in mathematics, which far more than all other sciences is regarded as a deductive science, induction must have a prominent part. The teacher cannot study too carefully the rôles that inductive and deductive reasoning play in mathematics, but it need hardly be said that the pupil would profit little by any formal discussion of these methods. His attention should be confined to the actual reasoning, and not diverted to any more or less introspective discussion of the character of the reasoning. As to the work the pupil is asked to do, the opinion is widely held that inductive work should be given a more prominent part in the class-room work. It is now extensively believed that it is not best to announce a theorem, then give a strict deductive proof of it, and finally, perhaps, apply it in some problems. The more modern method would be: First, to give the pupil some specific problems, as practical as possible, foreshadowing or leading up to the theorem in question, this to be continued until the pupil himself (with some prompting, if necessary) announces the theorem and sees the need for its rigorous proof. He is now ready for this proof, and after it is given, more applications of it should follow.

An Example. The theorem of Pythagoras, for example, would be begun by telling the pupil to draw a tessellated pavement (see figure [identified here as fig. 1]), and by counting small triangles to compare the areas of the squares marked more heavily. Then various right triangles with integral sides might be constructed and the areas of the squares compared by measurement, and (in a few cases) by weighing. The pupil will thus be led to announce the Pythagorean theorem himself and will welcome a proof of it, or hints enabling him to devise a proof. The proof might well be in the first instance a "dissection proof," which the pupil would actually cut out himself; for example, that indicated in the figure. [See fig. 2.]

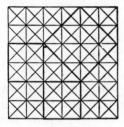

Figure 1   Figure 2

The Socratic Method. The *Socratic method* [1] consists in securing the pupil's assent to the conclusion desired by a series of easy leading questions. The character of the method can best be shown by an example.[2] (The boy is an illiterate slave.)

Soc. Tell me, boy, do you know that a figure like this is a square?

Boy. I do.

Soc. And do you know that a square figure has these four lines equal?

Boy. Certainly.

Soc. And these lines which I have drawn through the middle of the square are also equal?

Boy. Yes.

Soc. A square may be of any size?

Boy. Certainly.

Soc. And if one side of the square be of two feet and the other side be of two feet, how much will the whole be? Let me explain: If in one direction the space was of two feet and in the other direction of one foot, the whole would be of two feet taken once?

Boy. Yes.

---

1. Some idea of the pedagogic writings of antiquity, and of the method of Socrates in particular, may be obtained (without reference to the originals or to scattered translations) by means of Saffroy et Noel, *Les Écrivains pédagogiques de l'Antiquité, Extraits des Oeuvres de Xenophon, Platon, Aristotle, Quintilien, Plutarque.* Paris, 1897.

The book is very readable, and will not increase the reader's readiness to concede to the "new" views and theories of the day all the novelty which they claim.

2. Plato's Dialogues; Meno. Jowett's translation.

Soc. But since this side is also of two feet, there are twice two feet?

Boy. There are.

Soc. Then the square is of twice two feet?

Boy. Yes.

Soc. And how many are twice two feet? Count and tell me.

Boy. Four, Socrates.

Soc. And might there not be another square twice as large as this, and having, like this, the lines equal?

Boy. Yes.

Soc. And of how many feet will that be?

Boy. Of eight feet.

Soc. And now try and tell me the length of the line which forms the side of that double square: this is two feet—what will that be?

Boy. Clearly, Socrates, that will be double.

Soc. Do you observe, Meno, that I am not teaching the boy anything, but only asking him questions; and now he fancies that he knows how long a line is necessary in order to produce a figure of eight square feet; does he not?

Men. Yes.

Soc. And does he really know?

Men. Certainly not.

Soc. He only guesses that because the square is double, the line is double.

Men. True.

Soc. Observe him while he recalls the steps in regular order. (*To the boy.*) Tell me, boy, do you assert that a double space comes from a double line? Remember that I am not speaking of an oblong but of a square, and of a square twice the size of this one,—that is to say, of eight feet, and I want to know whether you still say that a double square comes from a double line?

Boy. Yes.

Soc. But does not the line become doubled if we add another such line here?

Boy. Certainly.

Soc. And four such lines will make a space containing eight feet?

Boy. Yes.

Soc. Let us describe such a figure; is not that what you would say is the figure of eight feet?

Boy. Yes.

Soc. And are there not these four divisions in the figure, each of which is equal to the figure of four feet?

Boy. True.

Soc. And is not that four times four?

Boy. Certainly.

Soc. And four times is not double?

Boy. No, indeed.

Soc. But how much?

Boy. Four times as much.

.   .   .   .

Soc. Then the line which forms the side of the square of eight feet ought to be more than this line of two feet and less than the other of four feet?

Boy. It ought.

Soc. Try and see if you can tell me how much it will be.

Boy. Three feet.

Soc. How much are three times three feet?

Boy. Nine.

Soc. And how much is the double of four?

Boy. Eight.

Soc. Then the figure of eight is not made out of a line of three?

Boy. No.

Soc. But from what line? Tell me exactly, and if you would rather not reckon, point out the line.

Boy. Indeed, Socrates, I do not know.

Soc. Do you see, Meno, what advances he has made in his power of recollection. He did not know at first, and he does not know now, what is the side of a figure of eight feet; but then he thought that he knew and answered confidently, as if he knew and had no difficulty; but now he has a difficulty, and neither knows nor fancies that he knows.

The Value of the Socratic Method. As used by Socrates it was generally *destructive,* used to overthrow some false opinion held by the pupil. To-day it is also used by teachers *constructively,* to lead the pupil to formulate a right opinion. Occasionally it may be of good service for this purpose, but its chief value, now as then, is the demolition of the false. A series of skilful leading questions may serve better than any other means to convince the pupil of the falsity of some opinion which he holds; still the Socratic method should be employed with caution. The very leading character of its questions and the consequent passive attitude of the pupil, makes its frequent employment inadvisable.

The Heuristic Method. Like the Socratic method, the *heuristic method* (named from the Greek word εὑρίσκω, *I find*) tells the pupil little directly, but leads him on by questions and problems. It avoids the leading character

267

of the questions of the Socratic method but aims to put the pupil into the attitude of a discoverer, by proposing questions and problems whose replies are not obvious though within the power of the pupil. This method, which is a mode as well, is essentially active and constructive, and deserves a dominating place in mathematical instruction. Owing to its great importance it will receive more detailed treatment in a subsequent chapter.

The Laboratory Method. The system of procedure which has recently been discussed extensively under the name *laboratory method* is very markedly a mode as well as a method. As a method, its characteristics are much emphasis on the inductive genesis of the mathematical deductions; much work with the concrete before passing to the abstract, with the particular before passing to the general. The method will be taken up at length in a subsequent chapter.

MODES IN MATHEMATICS.

Modes to be considered. A number of modes of instruction may be mentioned: The examination, the recitation, the lecture, the genetic, the heuristic, the individual, the laboratory. The descriptions to be given must necessarily be of the fully pronounced, typical forms: in practice the extreme form of any mode is the exception; they shade into each other, and few teachers use any one mode exclusively.

The Examination Mode. In the *examination mode* the teacher assigns certain tasks to be done, usually a portion of a text-book to be learned (memorized) or problems to be solved. The class period is taken up by what is tantamount to an examination of the pupils by the teacher, who thus finds out, by means of various tests, whether or not the pupils have performed the task. In its unmitigated form this mode reduces the teacher to little more than a machine. He gives no more help, stimulus, or inspiration to his pupils than the time clock which the workman must punch to record his arrival at his post, or the scales which weigh the result of his toil. In fact, it is easy to imagine a sort of phonograph which would do the work just as well, remaining quiescent as long as the words of a certain text were being said into it, but shouting "Wrong! The next!" as soon as aught else was said into it. It is difficult to think of anything to be said in favor of this method, and it has happily well-nigh gone out of use.

An actual instance of this mode has been described as follows:[3]

"A theorem was assigned. Next time the pupils had each to recite its demonstration *verbatim* according to the book. Those who could do this were assigned the next, to be learned from the book. Those who could not had to repeat the first theorem. By and by the pupils had each a different

3. Reidt, *Math. Unterricht,* pp. 29, 30.

theorem. The class exercise was conducted as follows: On entering the class, the teacher made a signal to the first pupil to say his theorem, then to the second, and so on to the others. By a special signal, the pupils who had said their theorem well were directed to prepare the next for the next time, and by another signal others received the order to repeat their theorem. The teacher prided himself on the fact that he could thus conduct an entire class exercise without saying a single word."

Probably this extreme is no longer to be found anywhere, but it is not certain that all are sufficiently far away from it to warrant taking down the danger signals. Rote teaching has not yet been so thoroughly eliminated as to prevent an educator, an onlooker as far as mathematics is concerned, from saying very recently:

"They both (Latin and algebra) belong to the group of *memoriter* subjects and are reasonably free from any taxing demands upon the higher rational processes." [4]

The Recitation Mode. The *recitation mode* is a modification of the preceding. As its name implies, it is chiefly characterized by the fact that the pupil "recites" what he has previously learned, and under this mode the class exercise is appropriately called a "recitation."

It agrees with the previous mode in having as chief characteristic that the pupil repeats in the class matter which he has learned by himself elsewhere. It differs from the preceding in that this repetition (recitation) is not regarded by the teacher exclusively as a test, but also as affording opportunity to aid the pupil to a better understanding of the matter in hand.

With the "recitation" there also is often combined some anticipatory work or explanation of the assignment made for the next recitation. The recitation mode may vary from a slight modification of the examination mode, through many possible combinations with other modes. It may at times be used (and with profit) in instruction in which other modes predominate.

The mode of instruction used by any teacher would be classed as the recitation mode whenever it has as its central feature the rehearsal in class of work previously assigned for outside preparation. With this elastic definition, instruction which is valuable, strong, and of high grade can undoubtedly be given by this mode, but it is exposed to serious dangers which must be combated actively and constantly by the teacher. There is a decided tendency to incline too far towards the examination mode, if not actually gravitating into it; the work of both teachers and pupils may be-

4. A. H. Sage, Wisconsin State Normal School, *School Science*, May, 1903, p. 68. An analogous statement was made by Herbert Spencer (*Liberal Education and Where to Find it*). "I doubt if one boy in five hundred ever heard the explanation of a rule of arithmetic, or knows his Euclid otherwise than by rote."

come mechanical, and the opportunities for rote and parrot-like work ("recitations") on the part of the pupils are great.

The Lecture Mode. In the *lecture mode,* the subject matter is presented by the teacher in the form of a connected discourse. The pupils (hearers) take notes which they may afterwards complete and study if they like. The mode is used in the mathematical work of the German and the French universities, and, with modifications, to a large extent in that of the American universities. It is by no means certain that the unmodified lecture mode is the best even for this advanced grade of work, and with rare exceptions it is entirely out of place in secondary work. In Germany, where all the secondary teachers have had at least three years of university training, the danger that they may at times drop into the lecture mode is considerable. In America the danger is growing with the increasing number of men and women of more or less university training who take up secondary work.

In the later years of the course, and in more advanced mathematics, there is larger need for the acquisition of mathematical facts as such, and these facts may sometimes be best learned from books or through direct impartation by the teacher. This would be a passing use of the lecture method, and in such cases an immediate test of some sort should be applied, such as asking the pupil to give back what he has just learned, in order that the teacher may be certain that the matter in hand has been mastered, and to give him an opportunity to correct misconceptions and to strengthen weak points.

The Genetic Mode. In the *genetic mode,* the subject matter is developed by the class guided by the teacher. All work and think together, the pupils expressing their views as permitted or requested by the teacher, who acts as chairman or leader, assists by questions, hints, and suggestions, sees to it that the discussion reaches the desired result in a reasonable length of time, but allows it all the latitude consistent herewith.[5] All new matter is first developed in the class in this manner.

The teacher is the heart of such work. The text serves for reference, and to obviate the need of taking full notes of the class work. The outside study has as end the fixing in mind of what was brought out in the class, the completion of minor points, the necessary practice and drill in computations.

To test the comprehension of the pupils and to assure their diligence in outside work, the recitation mode may well be combined with the present as one of its minor features. This mode is undoubtedly one of the best, and it is a cause for congratulation that its use is widespread and growing.

The Heuristic Mode. The genetic mode implies the heuristic *method,* but there exists a heuristic *mode* as well, which may be combined with the

5. Stenographic reports of some class exercises which may be classified under the genetic mode are given by C. S. Osborne in Thought Values in beginning Algebra, *School Review,* 1902, pp. 169–184.

heuristic method. It differs from the genetic mode in the greater stress which it lays upon work by each pupil independently of the others, as distinguished from the class working together as a unit under the genetic mode. It permits a much more important share of the work to be accomplished by the pupil outside the class, and offers greater possibilities of combination with the recitation mode. The latter mode, even the examination mode, may conceivably be applied to matter presented in a text written on the heuristic method. The heuristic mode will be discussed further in a subsequent chapter.

The Individual Mode. The *individual mode* aims to shape the work so that there may be individual progress according to individual strength. In mathematics, progress is conditioned on understanding *everything*. One point left obscure retards progress; several not grasped usually prevent progress. The different rates at which various pupils can work present a very real and serious difficulty to the teacher of mathematics which the individual mode aims to meet. The mode will be discussed in detail in a subsequent chapter.

The Laboratory Mode. As mode, the essence of the *laboratory mode* consists in the performing of the bulk, if not all, of the work in the mathematical class-room (laboratory) which should be equipped with appliances for the graphic, the experimental, and the concrete phases of the work. The teacher acts as director of the laboratory, pupils work individually or in small groups, and analogies with the work in the physical laboratory are emphasized. The mode will be discussed in detail later.

To characterize some of these modes in a word, it may be said that in the recitation mode the pupil works *before* the class session, in the lecture mode he works *after* it, in the laboratory mode he works *during* the session.

No one Mode to be used always. After this enumeration of modes, the question naturally arises, What mode should be used? The good teacher will not confine himself to any one mode. Different modes will be employed at different times, often even in the same class exercise, and procedures will be used which so combine features of various ones of the modes named that they can be classified under none of them. The nature of the topic discussed, the character of the class, the needs of individuals, the material surroundings and class-room equipment, all exercise influence on the determination of the best mode. Not the least potent is the teacher's personality and the stage of mathematical and pedagogic advancement at which he stands. No teacher can select even for himself a permanent mode of handling any subject or topic. The teacher must grow, and next year's viewpoint may require modification in what is really the most successful mode for him to-day.

The Test of the Best Mode. Modes are but means; that mode is in any instance the best which in that instance advances the pupil most towards the real ends of his study of mathematics. The teacher must be an active agent in this progress. *If the mode used is such that the pupil makes no more progress than he would have made without the teacher, this on the face of matters condemns that mode under those circumstances.*

This criterion necessitates unhesitating condemnation of the examination mode. Some of the other modes may easily be so handled as to expose them to the same condemnation. The test of any, of every mode, is whether or not it is, at the time when it is employed, the mode which enables the teacher to give to the class, to every pupil, the most of himself, of his knowledge, of his experience, of his guidance, of his enthusiasm, of his inspiration. If at the close of the class hour any pupil can say that the presence of the teacher has been of no help to him in any way, that the teacher has given him nothing, has simply examined him, heard him recite, or allowed him to work by himself, the mode employed with that pupil by that teacher at that time has been a complete failure. The very ease and simplicity of mathematics enables many a pupil to gain a real mastery of the subject even though the teacher gives him no aid, even in spite of teaching which actually hinders, and yet there is no subject in which good teaching so effectively stimulates and aids as in mathematics. It might not be out of place for the teacher to make an "examination of conscience" at the close of the class hour.

The Teacher's Self-examination. "Has each pupil profited by my presence in the class-room to-day? Has the mode of instruction employed enabled me to give the class, taken as a whole, more help, more insight, more inspiration than any other mode would have permitted? Is it possible for any pupil to say that he came to my class ready and willing to learn but that his teacher gave him no help? Could the class have obtained all that they got in the class hour to-day equally well from a lifeless book, from one another, or from private study?"

What has been said must not be construed or understood to advocate that the pupil be trained to undue dependence upon the teacher. The preceding chapter will have been written in vain if it has not given unmistakable expression to the thought that the instruction in mathematics should be dominated and determined by the aim to lead the pupil to think for himself. The present chapter simply changes the emphasis: to *lead*, not to *drive*. As soon as the teaching aims at active and independent thinking on the part of the pupil, its constant tendency will also be to diminish dependence on the teacher.

Training to use Books. The opinion is sometimes expressed that the pupils should learn "how to use books." This is quite true, but so far as mathematics is concerned it would be difficult to think of a practicable mode of teaching the subject which would not train the pupil sufficiently to make all needful use of mathematical books. The subject matter of mathematics is such that the use of a text, or at least of a collection of exercises, is usually advisable; and even in the extreme case that the work is carried on without use of a text so much as for reference, a mathematical proof once understood is recognized in print with sufficient ease to meet all emergencies likely to arise. It is quite desirable that the school library contain various texts, and that the pupils be given specific references to them, and this is quite compatible with any of the good modes of instruction.

THE TEACHING OF
ARITHMETIC

BY

DAVID EUGENE SMITH
PROFESSOR OF MATHEMATICS IN TEACHERS COLLEGE
COLUMBIA UNIVERSITY

GINN AND COMPANY
BOSTON · NEW YORK · CHICAGO · LONDON

CONTENTS

CHAPTER   PAGE

    I. THE HISTORY OF ARITHMETIC   I

   II. THE REASONS FOR TEACHING ARITHMETIC   11

  III. WHAT ARITHMETIC SHOULD INCLUDE   19

  IV. THE NATURE OF THE PROBLEMS   24

   V. THE TEXTBOOK   32

  VI. METHOD   38

 VII. MENTAL OR ORAL ARITHMETIC   54

VIII. WRITTEN ARITHMETIC   60

  IX. CHILDREN'S ANALYSES   67

   X. IMPROVEMENTS IN THE TECHNIQUE OF ARITHMETIC   72

  XI. CERTAIN GREAT PRINCIPLES OF TEACHING ARITH-

      METIC   84

 XII. SUBJECTS FOR EXPERIMENT   88

XIII. INTEREST AND EFFORT   102

XIV. NUMBER GAMES FOR CHILDREN   107

 XV. WORK OF THE FIRST SCHOOL YEAR   127

XVI. WORK OF THE SECOND SCHOOL YEAR   140

XVII. WORK OF THE THIRD SCHOOL YEAR   151

XVIII. WORK OF THE FOURTH SCHOOL YEAR   159

XIX. WORK OF THE FIFTH SCHOOL YEAR   165

 XX. WORK OF THE SIXTH SCHOOL YEAR   173

XXI. WORK OF THE SEVENTH SCHOOL YEAR   183

XXII. WORK OF THE EIGHTH SCHOOL YEAR   189

INDEX   195

CHAPTER VI.

Method.

Of all the terms used in educational circles "method" is perhaps the most loosely defined. Efforts have been made to limit its meaning, to divide its responsibilities with such terms as "mode" and "manner," but it still stands, and is likely to stand, as a convenient name for all sorts of ideas and theories and devices. Nevertheless, it has been most often used in arithmetic in speaking of the general plan of some individual for introducing the subject, as when we speak of the Pestalozzi or Tillich or Grube method, although it is also applied to such arrangements of material as are indicated by the expressions "topical method" and "spiral method," and to such an emphasis of some particular feature as has given name to the ratio method. It is not the intention to attempt any definition of the term that shall include all of these ramifications, but to take it as it stands, to characterize in simple language some of these "methods," and then to speak briefly of the subject as a whole.

Pestalozzi's method was really a creation of his followers. What this great master did for arithmetic was to introduce it much earlier into the school course, to use objects more systematically to make the number relations clear, to abandon arbitrary rules, to drill incessantly on abstract oral work, and to emphasize the unit by considering a number like 6 as "6 times 1." For the time in which he lived (about 1800) all this was a healthy protest against the stagnant education that he found. To-day it is only an incidental lesson to the teacher, although Pestalozzi's spirit and several of his ideas may well command the admiration and respect of all who study the results of his great work.

The method of Tillich, who followed Pestalozzi by a few years, consisted largely of making a systematic use of sticks cut in various lengths, say, from 1 inch to 10 inches. It is evident that such a collection allowed for emphasizing the notion of tens, for treating fractions as ratios, and for visualizing in a very good way the simpler number relations. On the other hand, it is also evident that the use of only a single kind of material is based upon a much narrower idea than that of Pestalozzi, who purposely made use of as wide a range of material as he could.

The Grube method, which created such a stir in America a generation ago, was not very original with Grube (1842). Essentially it was an adaptation of the concentric-circle plan that had already been used, a kind of spiral arrangement of matter to meet the growing powers of the child. It contained some absurdities, such as the exhausting of the work on one number before proceeding to the next, as of studying 25 in all its relations before learning 26, but on the whole it made somewhat for progress by assisting to develop a sane form of the spiral idea as adapted to the first three grades.

It is not worth while to speak of other individual methods, since they have little of value to the practical teacher, and the student of the history of education can easily have access to them. Enough has been said to show that one of the easiest things in the teaching of arithmetic is the creation of "method"—and one of the most useless. We may start off upon the idea that all number is measure, and hence that arithmetic must consist of measuring everything in sight—and we have a "measuring method." It will be a narrow idea—we shall neglect much that is important; but if we put energy back of it, we shall attract attention and will very likely turn out better computers than a poor teacher who is wise enough to have no method, in this narrow sense of the term. Again, we may say that every number is a fraction, the numerator being an integral multiple of the denominator in the case of whole numbers. From this assumption we may proceed to teach arithmetic only as the science of fractions. It will be hard work, but, given enough energy and patience and skill, the children will survive it and will learn more of arithmetic than may be the case with listless teaching on a better plan. We might also start with the idea that every lesson should be a unit, and that in it should come every process of arithmetic, so far as this is possible, and we could stir up a good deal of interest in our "unit method." Or, again, we could begin with the idea that all action demands reaction, and that every lesson containing addition should also contain subtraction; that $6 + 4 = 10$ should be followed by $10 - 6 = 4$ and $10 - 4 = 6$; and that $2 \times 5 = 10$ should be followed by $10 \div 2 = 5$ and $10 \div 5 = 2$. By sufficient ingenuity a very taking scheme could be evolved, and the "inverse method" would begin to make a brief stir in the world. This in fact has been the genesis, rise, and decline of methods: given a strong but narrow-minded personality, with some little idea such as those above mentioned; this idea is exploited as a panacea; it creates some little stir in circles more or less local; it is tried in a greater or less number of schools; the author and his pupils die, and in due time the method is remembered, if at all, only by some inscription in those pedagogical graveyards known as histories of education.

The object in writing thus is manifest. For the teacher with but little experience there is a valuable lesson, namely, that there is no method that will lead to easy victory in the teaching of arithmetic. There are a few great principles that may well be taken to heart, but any single narrow plan and any single line of material must be looked upon with suspicion. Certain of the general principles of Pestalozzi are eternal, but the reckoning-chest of Tillich is practically forgotten.

And here it is proper to say a word as to what schools of observation and practice should stand for in these matters of method and purpose. It would be a very easy thing to concentrate on some single point, some device of teaching, some particular line of problems, and to carry the work to an extreme that would attract attention and produce results that would be remarked upon. This is the temptation of those who direct such schools. But is it a wise policy? These schools are established to train teachers to well-balanced leadership, not to be extremists to the neglect of essential features of education. The graduates of such schools should know the best that there is in every theory of education, but they should also avoid the worst. The prime desideratum in arithmetic is the ability to work accurately, with reasonable rapidity and with interest, and to know how to apply numbers to the ordinary affairs of life. To secure accuracy alone, to secure speed alone, to have arithmetic mere play without accuracy and speed, or to know how to apply numbers to life in a slovenly way—these are extremes that should be avoided at any cost, including the tempting cost of sensationalism. It is the mission of the training school or college to make the earnest, well-balanced teacher, first of all. With this duty goes the laudable one of reasonable experiment, of trying out suggestions from whatever source; but normal schools and teachers colleges must at all hazards guard against the mistake of having it appear that an experiment is an accomplished result, or of sacrificing our children in unnecessary quasi-clinical work that is doomed to failure. In this connection one of the resolutions adopted by the National Educational Association in 1908 may be read with profit as voicing the sentiment of that saner element in education that is, after all, the strength of our profession.

"We recommend the subordination of highly diversified and overburdened courses of study in the grades to a thorough drill in essential subjects; and the sacrifice of quantity to an improvement in the quality of instruction. *The complaints of business men that pupils from the schools are inaccurate in results and careless of details is a criticism that should be removed.* The principles of sound and accurate training are as fixed as natural laws and should be insistently followed. *Ill-considered experiments and indiscriminate methodizing should be abandoned, and attention devoted to the persevering and continuous drill necessary for accurate and efficient training;* and we hold that no course of study in any public school should be so advanced or so rigid as to prevent instruction to any student, who may need it, in the essential and practical parts of the common English branches."

Such advice will be scoffed at by many reformers of twenty-five or thirty, but these very ones will be its stanch advocates at forty. It is the advice of experience, the protest of those who have seen the futility of spasms in education.

One thing that must be said in favor of the multitude of methods, most

278

of them bad, that are announced from time to time, is that they are confined to the first year or so of the primary grades. The harm is therefore limited in extent. This is the case with the much-exploited Montessori method at present, quite the most skillfully advertised one that has appeared in this generation, but one the permanent effect of which on education seems properly to be doubted by scientific observers.

In general it may be said that there has for a century been a tendency away from what is called the direct method of imparting number facts, and toward the rational method. This means that instead of stating to a class that $4 + 5 = 9$, and drilling upon this and similar relations, the schools have generally tended to have the pupils discover the fact and then memorize it. The experience of a century shows that this tendency is a healthy one. A child likes to be a discoverer, to find out for himself how to add and multiply, always under the skillful guidance of the teacher, and to see how to solve a problem before he knows of any dominating rule. It is only when the teacher decides that the child is never to be told anything, never to be helped over difficulties, and never to be shown a short path before habit has determined upon a long one, that the danger of the rational method appears.

.
.
.

UNITED STATES BUREAU OF EDUCATION

BULLETIN, 1911, NO. 13 - - - - - - - WHOLE NUMBER 460

MATHEMATICS
IN THE ELEMENTARY SCHOOLS
OF THE UNITED STATES

INTERNATIONAL COMMISSION ON THE TEACHING
OF MATHEMATICS

THE AMERICAN REPORT

COMMITTEES I AND II

WASHINGTON

GOVERNMENT PRINTING OFFICE

1911

INTERNATIONAL COMMISSION ON THE TEACHING OF MATHEMATICS.

General Officers.

President, F. Klein, Reg.-Rat., the University of Göttingen.
Vice President, Sir George Greenhill, F. R. S., London.
General Secretary, H. Fehr, the University of Geneva.

American Commissioners.

David Eugene Smith, chairman, Teachers College, Columbia University. New York, N.Y.
W. F. Osgood, Harvard University, Cambridge, Mass.
J. W. A. Young, the University of Chicago, Chicago, Ill.

THE AMERICAN REPORT

Committee No. I. General Elementary Schools.

Superintendent, C. N. Kendall, Indianapolis, Ind., chairman.
Professor W. W. Hart, University of Wisconsin, Madison, Wis., vice chairman.
Hon. David Snedden, commissioner of education of the State of Massachusetts, Boston, Mass.
Professor Patty Hill, Teachers College, Columbia University, New York, N. Y.
Miss Theda Gildemeister, State Normal School, Winona, Minn.
Professor F. G. Bonser, Teachers College, Columbia University, New York, N. Y.
Professor Ira S. Condit, Iowa State Teachers College, Cedar Falls, Iowa.

.
.
.

SUBCOMMITTEE 2. MATHEMATICS IN THE KINDERGARTEN.

Professor Patty Hill, Teachers College, Columbia University, New York, N. Y., chairman.
Miss Alice Temple, Kindergarten Department, School of Education, the University of Chicago, Chicago, Ill.
Miss Elizabeth Harrison, Kindergarten College, Chicago, Ill.

SUBCOMMITTEE 3. MATHEMATICS IN GRADES 1-6.

Miss Theda Gildemeister, State Normal School, Winona, Minn., chairman.
Miss Harriet Peat, State Normal School, Salem, Mass.
Miss Julia Martin, Howard University, Washington, D. C.

Professor Henry Suzzallo, Teachers College, Columbia University, New York, N. Y.
Dr. C. W. Stone, State Normal School, Farmville, Va.

.
.
.

SUBCOMMITTEE 5. MATHEMATICS IN GRADES 7 AND 8.

Professor W. W. Hart, University of Wisconsin, Madison, Wis., chairman.
Professor William L. Benitz, Notre Dame, Ind.
Dr. Henry V. Gummere, Drexel Institute, Philadelphia, Pa.

.
.
.

CONTENTS.

Subcommittee 1. Schematic survey of American educational institutions—
  their sequence and interrelations 7
General divisions 7
Types of public education 9
Agencies of public schools 12
Types of public schools 13
Nonpublic agencies schools 15
Types of nonpublic schools 15
Committee No. I. General elementary schools 16
  I. The aim and organization of the elementary schools 33
  II. The curriculum in mathematics in the elementary schools . 36
  III. Examinations in arithmetic 42
  IV. Method of instruction in arithmetic 44
  V. Training and qualifications of teachers 44
  VI. Typical courses of study 45
    Introduction 55
    A State course of study 65
    A city course of study in the kindergarten 68
Subcommittee 2. Mathematics in grades 1 to 6 68
Subcommittee 3. Mathematics in grades 1 to 6 78
  I. Introduction 85
  II. The organization of schools and the general relation of each kind
    of school to the others 89
  III. The mathematical curriculum in each type of school 93
  IV. The question of examinations from the point of view of the
    school 120
  V. The methods employed in teaching elementary mathematics .. 122
Subcommittee 4. Preparation of teachers for grades 1 to 6 122
  Introduction 124
  Subject-matter courses 125
  Professional courses 127
  Constructive suggestions 127
Subcommittee 5. Mathematics in grades 7 and 8 of the public and paro-
  chial schools 127
    Introduction 128
    Summary of data 128
    Scope of this report 129
    Sources of information 129
    Definitions of terms 130
    Special interest in these grades 131
    Influence of psychological studies 131
    Influence of completion of elementary course 131
    Influence of preparation for high school 131
    Influence of European curricula 131
    Rural and private schools 131

CONTENTS.

Committee No. I. General elementary schools—Continued.
  Subcommittee 5. Mathematics in grades 7 and 8 of the public and paro-
    chial schools—Continued.
      Organization—Continued.
        The mathematics of the grades 131
        Courses containing the curriculum 131
        Purpose of algebra 134
        Geometry of algebra in the grades 134
        Examinations in the grades 136
        Methods of instruction 136
        Class instruction 138
        Recitation and study time 138
        Division and study time 139
        Rapidity of the class time 139
        Concrete methods and accuracy 140
        Departmental teaching 140
        Induction and deduction 141
        The parochial schools 141
  Subcommittee 6. Preparation of teachers for grades 7 and 8 ... 142
    I. Present state of organization 144
    II. The training of teachers of seventh and eighth grade
      teachers of mathematics 144
        1. City training schools 148
        2. University schools 148
        3. State normal and college departments of education ... 148
        4. Private normal schools 149
        5. The forward movement in New York 149
        6. General opinions concerning the national preparation of
          teachers for grades 7 and 8 149
  Conclusion 149
Committee No. II. Special kinds of elementary schools 150
  General report 152
    Intermediate industrial, preparatory, trade, or vocational schools. 153
    Trade schools 153
    Technical schools 154
    Apprenticeship schools: Day courses 155
    Evening schools 156
    Part-time schools 156
    Trade schools 157
    Correspondence schools 159
    Schools for the colored races 159
  Subcommittee 1. Industrial classes in the public schools 160
  Subcommittee 2. Corporation industrial schools 170
  Subcommittee 3. Preparation of teachers of mathematics for trade and
    industrial schools 178
Index 183

Subcommittee 2. Mathematics in the Kindergarten.

In the early history of the kindergarten as an educational movement, there was a somewhat unanimous opinion current regarding the direct mathematical training and the instructions to be given to the children through concrete experiences with Frœbel's educational materials.

The gifts and occupations (the technical names given to Frœbel's play materials) form a related series planned to meet the creative and constructive impulses of the child, through activities involving the analysis and synthesis of geometric forms. The gifts begin with the ball (sphere), the cube, and the cylinder, progressing through the analysis of these to the study of surfaces, lines, and points. The occupations are based upon such activities as perforating, sewing, drawing, weaving, the folding and cutting of paper, and modeling. They reverse the geometric evolution, embodying the synthesis of form from the point, through lines and surfaces, back to the solid.

The traditional method of using these materials in the early history of the kindergarten tended toward a much more direct process of instruction, bringing to the children a consciousness of the geometric relations embodied in the gifts and occupations.

As the modern primary school reduced the amount of conscious arithmetical knowledge and instruction in the course of study for the younger children, a parallel movement took place in the kindergarten. As a consequence, the more direct method of mathematical instruction, which the geometric basis of the Frœbelian materials made possible, gradually gave place to a more indirect approach to number, measurements, and geometric relations, through a more incidental, organic, and fundamental emphasis upon these aspects of the materials in the moral activities of work and play.

The present tendency seems to point toward a valuation of the mathematical possibilities of the Frœbelian materials as means to a higher end; that is, as structural, functional, or organic means necessary to realize the playful, the creative, or constructive impulses of the child through which these mathematical values may begin to come to consciousness.

The fact that the Frœbelian gifts and occupations are based upon a geometric analysis and synthesis of form, need not reduce or interfere with their creative and playful opportunities, except in the hands of a kindergartner who clings to the formal use of them as a means of direct mathematical instruction. On the other hand, the very fact that their structure and use involve such unconscious activities as counting, addition, subtrac-

284

tion, multiplication, and division, some consciousness of these mental processes and their results will gradually come to the child whether the teacher emphasizes or ignores them.

The very nature of the material familiarizes the child, through playful concrete experiences, with the mental processes involved in the solution of problems in fractions and all the elementary activities of mathematics which may be brought to consciousness later through the more direct methods of instruction in the elementary school. To what degree the mathematical values involved in these playful activities should be brought to consciousness at the kindergarten period, is still under discussion, with much less decided differences of opinion than would have been apparent five or ten years ago.

While the structural and functional use of the activities of counting, measuring, adding, subtracting, and dividing seems to be on the increase, there is an equally evident growth in the appreciating of the fact that they must not be left to chance experience without due attention to ways and means for providing opportunities for further progress. In other words, there is a decided feeling that in mathematical experiences, as with all others in the kindergarten, the teacher must provide conditions which insure steady progress from the simple to the more complex, from the unconscious activities involving mathematical values to the more conscious abstraction of these, and to a continuous growth in the appreciation and control of the mathematical possibilities which are normal to the child at this period.

As a knowledge of mathematics in some form underlies all industrial activities of mankind and in the foundation of all true proportion in the art world, the kindergarten brings the child to a gradual consciousness of numerical and geometric relations, the former by such features as simple counting, measuring, and adding, as his work and play may demand, and the latter by the use of the geometric gifts and not by abstract exercises. In this way the younger children get arithmetical and geometric impressions incidentally, and the older children come into a more definite knowledge of mathematical relations, and thus begin an intelligent mastery of the material world.

The kindergarten which represents the progressive school makes no attempt to teach mathematics in a formal or direct way, since the child of kindergarten age is not interested in and can not grasp anything so abstract as number or geometric form apart from the use he may need to make of each in carrying on his play activities successfully. But in his experimenting and play with different materials he discovers certain facts in regard to number and special relations; for example, that if he uses four of his eight building blocks to make a square table, he has four left to use as chairs. Later he will make use of the knowledge thus gained, and will acquire further knowledge of the same sort in his efforts to carry out his ideas and purposes.

Often the hand work requires the division of material into halves, quarters, etc., or some material needs to be measured and cut to fit. Through such experiences the child acquires a working knowledge of certain satisfactory methods of dividing and measuring material. Furthermore, he becomes familiar with a number of geometric solids through using them in building, and he learns to select the kind that will best express his idea. The same is true of his work with paper cut in the form of squares, circles, and triangles. The games sometimes call for the grouping of children in threes or fours, and there are many occasions when counting is advantageous. The child in the kindergarten thus gains considerable knowledge which may be termed mathematical. Such knowledge comes at first incidentally and unconsciously through play, and later as the result of conscious efforts to reach ends which appeal to him as valuable.

After due investigation an effort was made by this committee to arrive at some conclusion regarding the amount of mathematical knowledge which kindergarten children could acquire, without direct instruction, through the normal activities of work and play. As a result the committee has agreed upon the following:

(1) Ability to count up to 35 or 40 can be secured through the children's helping to keep the daily record of attendance.

(2) Ability to know and name correctly the sphere, cube, and cylinder, and the most characteristic surface forms such as circles, squares, rectangles, and the right triangles.

(3) Ability to know groups of objects up to five or six.

(4) Ability to know, construct, and use intelligently halves, thirds, and quarters, by the help of blocks and the kindergarten occupations.

(5) Ability to add, subtract, divide, and multiply small numbers through constructive play. For example: (a) $2 + 2, 2 + 3, 2 + 4, 3 + 3, 3 + 4, 4 + 4, 5 + 5$; (b) $2 \times 2, 2 \times 3, 2 \times 4$; (c) $4 - 2, 6 - 3, 8 - 4$.

As to method, the committee calls attention to the following points:

(a) The concreteness of the work.

(b) The work is functional and structural, as means to an end, through the activities of work and play.

(c) Knowledge is acquired through self-active experience.

(d) In an incidental but not accidental fashion, as a result of definitely planning the experiences which involve steady progress in the use and control of mathematical facts, the child comes to realize ends that are of worth and interest.

That a better knowledge of the child is leading to a greater unanimity of opinion is quite evident from this report, since it is prepared by members who were selected because they were supposed to represent widely different points of view that obtained a few years since.

Subcommittee 3. Mathematics in Grades 1 to 6.

.
.
.

III. THE MATHEMATICAL CURRICULUM IN EACH TYPE OF SCHOOL.

Information concerning the course of study for the first six years of the elementary schools was obtained from the replies to a questionnaire sent to all States and leading cities and from an examination of a large number of printed courses of study.

Of the 48 States and Territories to which questionnaires were sent, 40 were heard from either directly through the State superintendent or from a representative city within the State. The eight from whom no replies came were in all cases States of small population. Of the 25 largest cities, 24 replied; of the 50 largest, 37 replied. The total number of cities heard from was 52. The total number of questionnaires sent out was 200; the number of usable replies, 90.

The replies from the leading private schools were limited and, as far as they could be interpreted, differed but little from those of the public schools. The replies from the State superintendents were inadequate owing to the impossibility of making generalizations upon the work of a State where there is of necessity, with few exceptions, great variability in the courses of study. The most valuable replies were those from the leading cities of the country. A statistical report was therefore made from these. The 52 city school systems which formed the basis for the work represented in the aggregate 2,480,000 pupils. Every section of the country was represented, but the most densely populated States, such as New York, Pennsylvania, Ohio, and Massachusetts, were proportionately largely represented.

The questionnaire was in three sections. The first section asked for the means employed to broaden the scope of arithmetic, the second for means used to narrow the field, and the third asked for specific information as to the time the study of number was commenced and the year in which different arithmetical topics were studied.

The questions as to the means employed to broaden the scope were: (1) Are geometric forms studied? (2) Are the equation and a literal notation used in the solution of problems? (3) Is the application of number to manual training emphasized? To geography and nature study? To prac-

287

tical affairs? (4) What other means are used to broaden the scope of arithmetic?

In reply to the question as to the means used to broaden the scope of arithmetic through the study of geometric forms 72 per cent of the school systems replied in the affirmative, 23 per cent were in a qualified affirmative, such as "somewhat," "a little," making a total affirmative of 95 per cent and a total negative of 5 per cent. The questions on the equation and literal notation were, it was evident, understood to include seventh and eighth grades instead of the grades within the limits of the investigation. The replies, although of little value for this report, were as follows: Affirmative for the use of the equation, 51 per cent; qualified affirmative, 36 per cent; negative, 13 per cent; affirmative for the use of a literal notation, 9 per cent; qualified affirmative, 50 per cent. (all labeled for seventh and eighth grades); negative, 41 per cent. In reply to the question on the application of number (1) to manual training, 50 per cent of the school systems replied in the affirmative; 35 per cent with a qualified affirmative "somewhat," making a total affirmative of 85 per cent and a negative of 15 per cent; (2) to geography and nature study, affirmative, 50 per cent; qualified affirmative, 18 per cent; total affirmative, 68 per cent; negative, 32 per cent; (3) to practical affairs, affirmative, 95 per cent; negative, 5 per cent. Typical replies to the fourth question as to other means used to broaden the scope of arithmetic were: "Our tendency is to concrete work in all grades in terms of a child's experience;" "Data for exercises taken from actual measurements and actual affairs;" "Practical affairs cover the ground;" "Arithmetic throughout is considered a social study;" "Use of actual tax bills, gas bills, water bills, etc. (forms borrowed from public service companies);" "Arithmetic not valued as formerly for its worth in discipline, but it is being made very practical;" "Connected with home life and local industries."

The questions on the means used to narrow the field were: (1) Do you have the children do more work with small numbers and less with numbers in the millions than formerly? (2) Do you teach only those arithmetic topics for which children have immediate use, excluding such topics as interest and wall papering? (3) Other tendencies?

Of the replies as to the use of smaller numbers 91 per cent were affirmative, 3 per cent qualified affirmative, making a total affirmative of 94 per cent and a negative of 6 per cent. In reply to the question on the choice of those subjects for which the children had immediate use, 44 per cent replied in the affirmative, 32 per cent gave a qualified affirmative, making a total of 76 per cent affirmative and 24 per cent negative. The replies to the third question "Other tendencies" ran as follows: "Toward simplification," "Our tendency is toward the elimination of topics not clearly serviceable," "We emphasize mental and oral work with small numbers to secure facility in common processes," "Insistence upon simple problems and proficiency within narrow limits," "Toward simplification, accuracy; certainty," "Much work with small numbers; simplified problems," "The elimination of topics; emphasis on mental work."

In the third section of the questionnaire the following questions were asked: In what year is the study of arithmetic commenced? The four fundamental processes completed? The study of fractions commenced? The study of fractions emphasized? Ratio studied? Percentage commenced?

The replies answering these specific questions as to the order of work were as follows: Number was recorded as commenced in first grade in 71½ per cent of the school systems replying; in second grade in 22 per cent of the schools and in third grade in 6½ per cent. The four fundamental processes were reported as completed in the third grade in 5 per cent of the schools replying; in fourth grade in 78 per cent of the schools; and in fifth grade in 17 per cent. Fractions were commenced in the first grade in 14 per cent of the schools replying, in second grade in 21 per cent, in third grade in 17 per cent, in fourth grade in 21 per cent, and in fifth grade in 27 per cent. Fractions were emphasized in the third grade in 2 per cent of the schools replying, in fourth grade in 10 per cent of the schools, in fifth grade in 63 per cent, in sixth grade in 23 per cent, in seventh grade in 2 per cent. Ratio was studied somewhere in the lower grades as a basis for later work in 40 per cent of the schools, in the middle grades (fourth, fifth, and sixth) in 30 per cent of schools and left entirely for upper grades (seventh, eighth, and ninth) in 30 per cent of the schools. Percentage was commenced in the fourth grade in 5 per cent of the schools, in fifth grade in 30 per cent of the schools, in sixth grade in 45 per cent, and in seventh grade in 20 per cent.

It is difficult to get at the real truth in any situation through a system of questions and answers for the reason that almost any question which can be formulated admits of misinterpretation. By comparison of the replies to the questionnaire with the printed courses of study it was found that the greatest liability to misinterpretation lay in the first section of the questionnaire, which refers to the means used to broaden the scope of arithmetic. The replies throughout the section included in many cases the seventh and eighth years of the elementary school. This makes it necessary to interpret not only the answers in the equation and literal notation in a different way from which the replies indicated (attention has already been called to this), but the answers also on the application of arithmetic to manual training, geography, and nature study. In the second section of the questionnaire there was no difficulty. In the third section there was some difference in the interpretation of the question on the year in which number was commenced. In several schools where number was introduced incidentally in the first grade it was sometimes recorded as commenced there and sometimes not. The report, therefore, gives an idea of an earlier commencement of the formal study of arithmetic than actually exists. There was a similar confusion between incidental and formal work in fractions and ratio. Much incidental work in fractions is done in the first three years, but the study of a fraction as a fraction is left in the majority of cases to the fourth and fifth years. Ratio forms the basis of several special methods of teaching number used in many localities throughout the country. In such cases it is recorded as studied in the primary grades. Ratio and proportion as such are usually put down in the printed courses of study as work for the seventh and eighth years.

The summary is indicative of an advance in the work in general. One step forward is the tendency to broaden the scope of arithmetic so that it is less a series of exercises for the manipulation of figures and more of an introduction to mathematics in general. If we may take the summary as typical of the state of affairs, the study of geometric forms is becoming current, and in the seventh and eighth grades the use of the equation and of literal notation is making some headway. It is possibly wise that the latter are not used below these years, owing to the fact that the substitution of a formal means of solving a problem for a child's own natural logic is likely to cause confusion in his mind. The tendency to correlate arithmetic with other subjects and make it a thoroughly practical subject is strong. An equally striking demand throughout the country is the cry for the simplification of arithmetic through the use of smaller numbers, the elimination of topics, the simplification of problems, and an emphasis on mental rather than written work. The tendency is to limit the work to what comes within the child's experience and expect greater efficiency within the narrower field. As to the program of work there is a tendency to begin number somewhat later in the primary school than formerly; to devote the years before the fifth grade to the four fundamental processes with integers, the fifth year to fractions, and the sixth year to fractions and percentage.

Since the cities as a usual thing are in advance of the smaller communities and the rural districts and serve, more or less as their leaders, the summary is more indicative of the trend of the courses of study than of the state of things as they actually exist. It shows a more advanced state of affairs than would be found extant if an average could be made of the work of the country as an entirety.

.
.
.

V. The Methods Employed in Teaching Elementary Mathematics.

·
·
·

III. THE EFFECT OF THE CHANGING STATUS OF TEACHING METHOD.

Teaching method in the school is primarily a readjustment of forms of knowledge and experience so as more effectively to stimulate and improve the immature responses of children. Two important movements have been responsible for the development of special methods of teaching during the past few decades—one is humanitarian and the other scientific. On the one hand, there has been a growth in reverence and sympathy for childhood. As yet it has scarcely expressed itself with fullness. The wide acceptance of the "doctrine of interest" in teaching; the enrichment of the curriculum; specialized schools for truants and defectives; individual instruction—these are the schoolmaster's recognition of the modern attitude toward childhood. Under such conditions teaching becomes less and less a ruthless external imposition of adult views, and more a means of sympathetic ministry to those inner needs of child life which make for desirable qualities of character. While it is true that teaching method is a condescension to childhood, it is a socially profitable condescension in that it is a guarantee of more effective and enduring mastery of the life that is revealed at school. Since the child's acquisition tends the more to be part and parcel of his own life under such sympathetic teaching, the products of such instruction are enduring.

Such a humanitarian movement naturally called for knowledge of the child. The wisdom of common sense soon exhausts itself and more scientific data is demanded. Thus the "child study movement" came into existence. Since then, a saner psychological foundation has been laid for educational procedure, one which is criticising and reconstructing teaching method at every turn. Hitherto teaching methods had been improved fitfully through a crude empiricism. Now a body of general psychological knowledge, rich in its criticism of old methods and in its suggestion of new means of procedure, gives a scientific basis to teaching method.

The public elementary school teacher is conservative indeed who will deny that there is anything worthy in the notion of "method!" As a class,

291

teachers have faith in the special professional technique which is included under the term. They are critical of the many abuses which have been committed in the name of method. Method can not be a substitute for scholarship. It can not be a "cut-and-dried" procedure indiscriminately or uniformly applied to classroom instruction. Like every other technical means, teaching method is subject to its own limitations and strengthens a fad which the average teacher recognizes.

In spite of the fact that the majority of elementary teachers keep reasonably sane on the problem of method in teaching, it must be admitted that a considerable proportion of teachers are inclined to be attracted by systems of method that greatly overemphasize a single element of procedure. The hold which the "Grube method" with its unnatural logical thoroughness and progression gained in this country two or three decades ago is scarcely explicable to-day. Scarcely less baffling is the very large appeal made by a series of textbooks which laid the stress upon the acquisition of arithmetic through the idea of ratio and by means of measuring. Manual work as the source of arithmetical experiences is another special emphasis, which, like the others, has had its enthusiastic adherents. Again, it is "arithmetic without a pencil" or some other overextension of a legitimate local method into a "panacea" or "cure-all" which confronts us. The promulgation and acceptance of such unversatile and one-sided systems of teaching method are indicative of two defects in the professional equipment of teachers: (1) The lack of a clear, scientific notion as to the nature and function of teaching method, and (2) a lack of psychological insight into the varied nature of classroom situations. Untrained teachers we still have among us, and others, too, to whom a little knowledge is a dangerous thing. These are frequently carried away by the enthusiastic appeals of the reformer with a system far too simple to meet the complex needs of human nature. Our experiences seem to have sobered us somewhat, the increase of supervision has made responsible officers cautious, and increased professional intelligence has put a wholesome damper upon naïve and futile proposals to make teaching easy.

A more serious evil than that just mentioned is the tendency of the supervising staff to overprescribe specific methods for classroom teachers. Recently there has developed, more particularly in large city systems, a tendency to demand a uniform mode of teaching the same school subject throughout the city. This has been brought about by the prevalent tendencies of large school systems to centralize their authority and demand uniformity of procedure. The prime causes of this tendency are to be found (1) in the specialization of grade teaching, and the interdependence of one teacher on another; (2) in the mobility of the school population which involves considerable lost energy if teachers do not operate along similar lines.

The result of such imposed uniformity is a reduction of spontaneity in teaching. The process of instruction proceeds in a more or less mechanical fashion, the teacher working for bulk results by a persistent and general application of the methods laid down. That teaching, which at every moment tends to adjust itself skillfully to the changes of human doubt and interest, difficulty and success, discouragement and insight, now taking care of a whole group at once, now aiding an individual straggler, now resolutely following a prescribed lead, now pursuing a line of least resistance previously unsuspected, can not thrive under such conditions. It stifles teaching as a fine art and makes of it a mechanical business. Under these conditions only those activities which fit the machine routine can go on. Thus it happens that we memorize, cram, drill, and review, and soon the subtler processes of thinking and evaluating, which are the best fruit of education, cease to exist.

Fortunately the one-method system of teaching will soon belong to the past, and the imposition of uniform methods is beginning to lose ground even in our cities. For the most part, the common sense of teachers and the positive statements of our better theorists keep teaching methods in a position of useful status. Teaching methods should be infinitely variable as the conditions calling for their use are endlessly changeable. Not one method but many are necessary, for their function is supplementary rather than compulsive. No one method should be used with a preestablished rigidity; each must be flexible in its uses, so as to accomplish the varied work to be done. The teacher directly facing the intellectual and emotional crises of childhood is the best interpreter of conditions and the best chooser of the tools of workmanship. The supervisor may advise and may point out certain fundamental laws of growth and procedure; but the concrete method which is the application of these must be of the teacher's making.

Arithmetical teaching, like the instruction in other subjects, has suffered from these widespread ventures of teaching method. In this respect it has shared the common professional lot. But in addition it has had special difficulties and adventures of its own. We have now to note those special phases of teaching method which are peculiar and local to mathematical instruction.

IV. METHOD AS AFFECTED BY THE DISTRIBUTION AND ARRANGEMENT OF ARITHMETICAL WORK.

THE TENDENCY TOWARD SHORTENING THE TIME DISTRIBUTION.

Several decades ago arithmetic, as a formal subject, was begun in the first school year and continued throughout the grades to the last school year. This is no longer a characteristic condition, much less a uniform one. There have been forces operating to complete the subject of arithmetic prior to the eighth year, and to delay its first systematic presentation in the primary grades for a period varying from six months to two years.

The attempt to shorten the period of formal instruction in arithmetic has had its effects upon the methods of teaching as well as upon the arrangement of the course of study. The presence of a large number of children who leave school by the seventh year, the example of a varied European practice, the overcrowded curriculum—all these have combined to suggest a shortened treatment of arithmetic. Hence economy, through the elimination of obsolete and unimportant topics in the course of study and through better methods of instruction, has become a pressing matter. Its influence on method is obvious.

It has focused attention upon "teaching method" and given it an increasing importance in the eyes of mathematical teachers. Specifically, it has tended to reduce the amount of objective work, to eliminate the explanation or rationalization of processes which in life are done automatically; it has made teachers satisfied with teaching one manner of solution where before two or three were given; it has laid the emphasis upon utilizing old knowledge in new places, rather than on acquiring new means.

The by-product of this belief is that any arithmetic taught during these first few years should be taught "incidentally," as a chance accompaniment of their other studies. Only after one or two years of incidental work should the formal arithmetic instruction be given. This "incidental" method of teaching beginners is difficult to estimate. It has been so variously treated that a comparative measure of its worth is difficult to obtain. The contention that children who are taught incidentally for two years and systematically for two years more have at the end of four years of school life as good a command of arithmetic as those who have had a systematic course through four school years is difficult to substantiate or deny on scientific grounds. Sometimes "incidental" teaching required by the course of study becomes "systematic" in the hands of the teacher. Sometimes the two years of "systematic" teaching that follows the incidental teaching means more than two years, since the teachers, in order to catch up, give more time and emphasis to the subjects than the relative time allotment of any general schedule would seem to warrant. Such have been the facts frequently revealed by a classroom inspection that penetrates beyond the course of study, the time schedule, and the regulations of the school board.

In the lack of specific comparative measures of the worth of such methods of instruction, there is a growing conviction (1) that beginning school children are mature enough for the systematic study of all the arithmetic that the modern course of study would assign to these grades; (2) that considering the quantity and quality of their experiences they can think or reason quite as well as memorize; and (3) that what the school requires of the child can be better done in a responsible, systematic manner than by any haphazard system of incidental instruction.

These reactionary attitudes by no means imply a return to systematic teaching of arithmetic in the first two school years, nor to such formal methods as had previously been employed. Other grounds forbid. The crude, uninteresting memoriter methods of the past have gone for good. Objective work, plays, games, manual activities make arithmetical study easier and more efficient. Indeed, these newer methods have been a large factor in convincing teachers that children have the ability to master the first steps in arithmetic during the first two years.

There are other problems of method that are not so much concerned with the beginning of the study of arithmetic, or with the span of school life that the subject is supposed to cover. These deal with the arrangement of subtopics, within the course of study, or with the manner of progression from one aspect of arithmetical experience to another.

The methods that have been employed in the United States for the arrangement or ordering of topics within the course of study have varied considerably from time to time, but all these variations may be grouped around two types: (1) The "logical" types of arrangement and (2) the "psychological" types of arrangement. If the course of study proceeds primarily by units that are characteristic of the mathematics of a mature adult mind, the type may be said to be "logical." If the course of study proceeds primarily by units that are characteristic of the manner in which an immature child's mind approaches the subject, then the type may be said to be "psychological."

The older "logical" plans are thorough and definite in their demands; the teacher always knows just what he is about. But such a system of procedure is unnatural and remote from the child; it lacks appeal and motive. The child pursues the subject as a task laid down for him, not as an answer to his own curiosities or necessities. The newer psychological plans meet the different levels of child maturity effectively; they are nearer the natural order of acquiring knowledge. But it is not easy for the teachers to keep account of the work of their own, previous, or subsequent grades. Nor does the supervising official find it easy to locate responsibility for definite arithmetical subtopics. As an order of teaching it is psychologically natural but administratively ineffective.

The result is that to-day the two types of arrangement are modifying each other and giving a mixed method, partly logical and partly psychological. That line of least resistance in which the children study arithmetical facts and processes with greatest success is modified by definite demands that topics, e. g., addition, be mastered thoroughly "then and there." The method is partly "topical" and partly "spiral." The child in the second grade may have a little of all the fundamental processes, a few simple fractions, and United States money, but just there he will be held definitely responsible for a very considerable number of the addition combinations. The pupil may have had fractions in every grade, but the fifth grade will be responsible for a thorough and systematic mastery of the same. Such is the mixed method of arrangement which is to-day prevalent in American schools.

V. OBJECTIVE TEACHING.

The use of objects in teaching arithmetic is current in the elementary school. Particularly is this true in the lowest grades of the school, in primary work. It may be said that there is a very large quantity of objective teaching in the first year of school and that it decreases more or less gradually as the higher grades are approached. By the time the highest grammar grades are reached the use of objects has reached its minimum, the underlying assumption being that the use of objects has a teaching value that decreases as the maturity of the pupils increases. Current practice does not proceed far beyond the application of the simple and somewhat crude psychological statement that the youngest children must have much objective teaching, the older less, the oldest least of all.

Reform in the direction of a more refined and exact use of object teaching has already suggested itself in the treatment of fractions and mensuration, where, regardless of the increased maturity of the children studying these topics, a large amount of objective method is utilized. This is a considerable departure from the slight objective treatment of other arithmetical topics taught in the same grades. Such exceptional practices suggest that the novelty of an arithmetical topic is the condition calling for objective work in instruction. It is immaturity in a special subject or situation which determines the amount of basal objective work. The correlation is not with the age of the pupil but with his experience with the special problem or subject in hand. It is, of course, true that the less experienced the student is the greater the likelihood that any subject presented will be novel and strange. Only in this indirect manner does the novelty of subject matter coincide with mere youth as an essential principle in determining the need of objective presentation. The naïve assumption of the older enthusiastic reformers that objective work is a good thing psychologically, one of which the pupil can not have too much, is by no means the accepted view of the new reformer. With the latter, objective presentation is an excellent method at a given stage of immaturity in the special topic involved, but it may be uneconomical, even an obstacle to efficiency, if pushed beyond.

There is then a certain coincidence of the scientific criticism of the psychologist and of the common-sense criticism of the conservative teachers who look suspiciously upon a highly extended object teaching. The teachers, on grounds of experience, say that too much objective teaching is confusing and delays teaching. The psychological critics say it is unnecessary and wasteful. The result is that, in these later days, the distribution of objective work has changed somewhat. More subjects are developed in the higher grades through objective instruction than before. Perhaps no fewer subjects in the lower grades are presented objectively, but the extent of objective treatment of each of these has undergone considerable curtailment.

The existing defects in objective teaching are not restricted to a false placing or distribution. The quality of teaching with the aid of objects is likewise open to serious criticism. Object teaching is a device, so successful as against prior nonobjective teaching that it has come to be a standard of instruction as well as a means. As long as objects—any convenient objects—are used, the teaching is regarded as good. Given such a sanction, the inevitable result is an indiscriminating use of objects. The process of objectifying tends not to be regulated by the needs of the child's thinking life; it is determined by the enthusiasm of the teacher and materials convenient for school use.

The first fact which asserts itself in observing objective teaching is the artificiality of the materials employed. Primary children count, add, etc., with things they will never be concerned with in life. Lentils, sticks, tablets and the like are the stock objective stuff of the schools, and to a considerable degree this will always be the case. Cheap and convenient material suitable for individual manipulation on the top of a school desk is not plentiful. But instances where better and more normal material has been used are frequent enough in the better schools to warrant the belief that more could be done in this direction in the average classroom. The "playing at store", the use of actual applications of the tables of weight and measures are cases that might be cited.

The materials used are not only more artificial than they need be, but they are too restricted in range. More forms of even the artificial material should be used, thus minimizing the danger of monotony.

Even the narrow range of materials in general use might be better employed than it is. There is, of course, a distinct tendency to vary the objects, merely because a child gets tired of it as a material. It is too frequently the case that the teacher will treat the fundamental addition combinations with one set of objects, e. g., lentils. In all the child's objective experience within that field there are two persistent associations—"lentils" and "the relation of addition." The accidental element has been emphasized as frequently as the essential one, and being concrete has had even a better chance to impress itself.

The nature of the materials proper to objective teaching has likewise been too narrowly interpreted. Objective teaching has meant almost exclusively instructing or developing through three-dimensional representation, whereas another form has been neglected, which for all the psychological purposes of education has as much worth as so-called objects, namely, use of such material as pictures. Such quasi-objective material has been little used by teachers save as it appears in textbooks. There are, of course, obvious disadvantages to pictures and diagrams. The things represented in and by them are not capable of personal manipulation by the child in the ordinary sense. But they have a superiority all their own. They offer a wider, more natural, and more interesting range of concrete experiences.

There are other curious phases of narrowness in the current pedagogical interpretation as to what constitutes a concrete or objective experience. It will be noted that visual objects are the ones generally employed and that they are generally inanimate objects. Of late there has been some tendency to use hearing and touch in giving a concrete basis to teaching. Advantage is taken of the social plays of children and their games with things. Here the children themselves and their relations and acts are the experiences from which the numerical units are obtained. With some of the best teachers in the lowest grades it is no longer unusual to see children moving about in all sorts of play designed to add reality to and increase interest in number facts.

Inductive teaching has been one of several movements affecting objective teaching. The effort of teachers to escape the slavishness of mere memoriter methods and to approximate real thinking led to the introduction of inductive teaching. Necessarily objective teaching became more or less identified with the new movement and was influenced by it. So, it has been said of objective work in arithmetic, as it has been said of laboratory work in the sciences, that such instruction is a method of "discovery" or "rediscovery." Such an alliance has had its beneficial effects upon objective teaching; it has redeemed it from the aimless "observational work" of an earlier "objective study." But in the teaching of arithmetic, at any rate, it confused an objective mode of presentation with a scientific method of learning truth, two activities having a common logical basis, but not at all the same. Under the assumption that the developmental method is one of rediscovery, the tendency is to give the child as complete a range of concrete evidences as would be necessary on the part of the scientist in substantiating a new fact. The result is, that long after the child is convinced of the truth, say that 4 and 2 are 6, the teacher persists in giving further objective illustrations of the fact. The child loses interest in the somewhat monotonous continuance of objective manipulations, and the teacher has naturally wasted time and energy.

Another modern movement in teaching method which has had a conspicuous effect on objective teaching is the movement toward "self-activity" on the part of the child. The recent favor enjoyed by manual training, nature study, self-government, and other active phases of school life is an index of the general movement in mind. Its influence has not only forced the introduction of new subjects; it has changed the manner of presenting the older subjects of the elementary curriculum. Arithmetic has responded along with the other subjects and an active use of objects by the children themselves is found in increased degree.

VI. THE USE OF METHODS OF RATIONALIZATION.

It is perfectly natural that, in shifting the teacher's attention from her own activities to those of the children, the interest of the child should be considered in increasing degree. If the child is to learn directly, with a maximum use of his initiative, it is absolutely essential that the teacher should provide some motive. This implies that the child is to be interested in some fundamental way in the activities in which he is to engage. Instead of thumbing the fundamental facts with his memory, in an artificial and effortful manner, "singsonging" the tables rhythmically, so as to make dull business less dull, the teacher begins at once to use the child's own life as the basis for instruction. The number story, the arithmetical game, playing at adult activities, constructive work, measuring, and other vital interests of the child and community life become increasingly the basis of instruction in number. Such is the pronounced tendency wherever the movement is away from the traditional rote-learning or drill.

Of course there is the slight tendency in American elementary schools where a soft and false interpretation of the doctrine of interest is gospel to teach only those things which can be taught in an interesting fashion. But this tendency is less operative in arithmetic than in other subjects. Here the logical interdependence of one arithmetical skill on another has quickly pointed the failure of such a haphazard mode of instruction.

There is, however, in "advanced", as well as in reactionary quarters, a revolt against the tendency to objectify, explain, or rationalize everything taught in arithmetic. On the whole it is a discriminating movement, for this opposition to "rationalization" in arithmetical teaching, and in favor of "memorization" or "habituation," bases its plea on rational grounds, mainly derived from the facts of modern psychology.

It is specifically opposed to explaining why "carrying" in addition, and "borrowing" in subtraction are right modes of procedure. These acts are to be taught as memory or habit, inasmuch as they are to be performed by that method forever after. To develop such processes rationally or to demand a reason for the procedure once it is acquired, is merely to stir up unnecessary trouble, trouble unprompted by any demands of actual efficiency.

A study of the actual arithmetical facts upon which this opposition expresses itself suggests the four following general principles as to the use of "rationalization" and "habituation" as methods of mastery: (1) Any fact or process which always recurs in the same identical manner, and occurs with sufficient frequency to be remembered, ought not to be "rationalized" for the pupil, but "habituated." The correct placing of partial products in the multiplication of two numbers of two or more figures is a specific case. (2) If a process does recur in the same manner, but is so little used in after life that any formal method of solution would be forgotten, then the teacher should "rationalize" it. The process of finding the square root of a number illustrates this series of facts. (3) If the process always does occur in the same manner, but with the frequency of its recurrence in doubt, the teacher should both "habituate" and "rationalize." The division of a fraction by a fraction is frequently taught both "mechanically" and "by thinking it out." (4) When a process or relation is likely to be expressed in a variable form, then the child must be taught to think through the relations involved, and should not be permitted to treat it mechanically through a mere act of habit or memory. All applied examples are to be dealt with in this manner, for such problems are of many types, and no two of the same type are ever quite alike. These laws will, of course, not be interpreted to mean that no reason is to be given a child in a process like "carrying" in addition. The reason is not essential to efficient mastery, but it may be given to add interest or to satisfy the specially curious.

VII. SPECIAL METHODS FOR OBTAINING ACCURACY, INDEPENDENCE, AND SPEED

It is not alone the first stages in the acquisition of an arithmetical process which have received attention in the reorganization of teaching methods, though, to be sure, the problem of first presentations has in recent decades been given the most attention. More and more the American tendency is to watch every step in the learning process, to provide for all necessary transitions, and to safeguard against avoidable confusions. It might be suggested that constant intermediation of the teacher in the child's work at every step might destroy the pupil's initiative and independence. Apparently, however, those who are so deeply interested that the child should not be permitted to fall into the errors which unsupervised drill would convert into habit, are fully as cautious to provide steps for forcing the child to assume an increasing responsibility for his own work. The distinction made is that an over-early independence is as fatal to accurate and rapid mathematical work as an over-delayed dependence.

One of the specific controversies much argued in the primary school concerns the medium through which arithmetical examples and problems shall be transmitted to young children. There are three typical ways in which a situation demanding arithmetical solution may be brought to the child's mind: (1) The situation when visible may be presented through itself; that is, objectively; (2) the situation may be described through the medium of spoken language, the teacher usually giving the dictation; (3) the situation may be conveyed through written language, as when the child reads from blackboard or text. Inasmuch as objects are a universal language, no difficulty arises through this basic method of presentation. It is when a language description of a situation is substituted for the situation itself that difficulty arises. The child might be able to solve the problem if he really understood the situation the language was meant to convey. Owing to the difficulty that primary children have in getting the thought out of language, it has been urged that problems in any unfamiliar field should be presented in the following order: (1) Objectively or graphically; (2) when the fundamental idea is grasped, through spoken language; and (3) after the type of situation is fairly familiar, through written or printed language. It is seriously urged by some teachers that no written presentation should be used in the first four grades. Such an extreme tendency would practically abolish the use of primary textbooks. There are many exceptional teachers who do not put a primary text in the hands of children at all. Such a tendency is increasing. Particularly is this true among primary teachers in the schools of the foreign quarters of large cities. Accurate communication through the English language is always more difficult here. Hence, the period of objective teaching is necessarily prolonged, dependence on the "number stories" told by the teacher increased, and the solution of written problems much longer delayed than elsewhere.

The situation is somewhat different, almost the opposite in fact, when "examples" rather than "problems" are presented, meaning by "example" a "problem" expressed through the use of mathematical signs. It is easier to present "examples" in written form on blackboard or in text than it is to dictate them orally. This obviates the necessity of holding the examples in mind during solution. The permanence of the visual presentation saves the restatement frequently necessary in oral presentation. Hence it is a common practice to supply the youngest children with mimeographed or written sheets of "examples." It is with older children or with younger children at a latter stage in the mastery of a typical difficulty, that oral presentation of examples is stressed. Then we have that type of work which is called "mental" or "silent" arithmetic.

There is some tendency toward the provision of better transitions from the objective presentation of applied problems to the symbolic presentation of abstract examples. The nature of such a transition is scarcely reasoned out as so much psychological science, but is the accompaniment of a widening professional movement for the enlarged use of pictures, diagrams, number stories, and the like. A critical examination of the various means of presenting arithmetical situations would order them as follows in making the transition from objective concreteness to symbolic abstractions: (1) Objects, (2) pictures, (3) graphs, (4) the concrete imagery of words, (5) more abstract verbal presentations, (6) presentations through mathematical symbols. No such minuteness of adjustment is apparent in existing methods, though it might seem desirable in teaching young children. There are four typical ways in which the child does his work, the names of which are derived from the differentiating element: (1) The "silent" method, otherwise spoken of as "mental arithmetic," "arithmetic without a pencil," etc. (2) The "oral" method, where the child works aloud—that is, expresses his procedure step by step in speech. (3) The "written" method, where the child writes out in full his analysis and calculations. (4) The "mixed" method, where the child uses all three of the previously mentioned methods, in alternation, as necessary for ease and efficiency.

The worth of these four methods of work is necessarily variable. The rapidity of the "silent method" with simple figures is obvious. The "silent method" and the "mixed method" (which is more slow but more manageable with complex processes and calculations) are the two methods normally employed in social and business life. The purely "oral" and "written" methods, with their tendency toward analysis and calculation fully expressed in oral or written language, are highly artificial. They are valuable as school devices for revealing the action of the child's mind to the teacher so that the same may be corrected, guided, and generally controlled. The present tendency is toward an over-use of these methods and toward an under-use of the other two, more particularly the "mixed" method. It would seem that there is little conscious attempt to make certain that the child moves from full oral or written statements to the judicious application of the more natural "silent" and "mixed" methods. It may be that full oral and written statements of work have seriously hampered the right use of the more natural methods of statement.

It is well to recall that in all these efforts to control the child's activity there is a tendency to leave the child overdependent upon the teacher. It is vitally important that a child should be kept free of any error which unsupervised drill would fix into the stubbornness of habit, but it is likewise important that the child should acquire some self-reliance. While not always clearly defined, there is a distinct tendency in the direction of releasing the teacher's control of the child. A characteristic practice would be one in which the teacher's work with the child would pass through various stages, each one of which would mark a decrease in the control of the process by the teacher and an increase in the freedom of the child to do his example, or problem, by himself.

One characteristic series of stages quite frequently used in the presentation of a single topic in arithmetic, say "carrying" in addition, is the following: (1) The teacher performs the process on the blackboard in the presence of the class, the children not being allowed to attempt the process by themselves until after the process is clearly understood from the teacher's development. (2) The children are then allowed to perform the process upon the blackboard, where it is exceedingly easy for the teacher to keep the work of every child under her eye. An error is caught by a quick glance at the board and immediately corrected before the child can reiterate a false impression. (3) More of the same type of example, or problem, are assigned to the children at their seats, where they work upon paper, still under the supervision of the teacher; a supervision which is less adequate, however. (4) The same difficulty, after the careful safeguarding of the previous stages, is then assigned for "home work," where the child relies almost completely upon himself. Once more it is necessary to suggest that these stages are merely roughly implied in the variations of existing practice.

Most of the methods discussed in this chapter have had as their sanction the attainment of accuracy in thinking and calculating. Some efforts to insure independent power on the part of the child have already been noted. But nothing has been said of the effort to add speed to accuracy in getting efficient results. Such special efforts have been made. These efforts may be classified into two groups: (1) Those aiming to quicken the rate of mental response. (2) Those aiming at short-cut processes of calculation.

Typical of the first are (*a*) the use of an established rhythm as the child attacks a column of additions; (*b*) the device of having children race for quick answers, having them raise their hands or stand when they have gotten the answer; (*c*) the assignment of a series of problems for written work under the pressure of a restricted time allotment for the performance of each. These and similar devices are much used in the schools. They are open to the objection that they quicken the rate of the better students, but foster confusion, error, and discouragement among the less able children, not infrequently, actually retarding speed.

The various shorter methods which represent the effort to reduce the number of mental processes required are usually not of general applicability, and consequently have not attained any general currency in the elementary schools, where the object is to teach one generally available and effective method, even though it requires more time, special expertness being left to later development in the special school of business which requires it.

It has come to be quite a common recognition of teachers that the fundamental element in rapid arithmetical work is certain and accurate work. If pupils know their tables of combinations and are sure of each detail of calculation, there is no confusion or hesitancy; speed then follows as a matter of course. This belief, as much as anything else, explains why the lower schools have developed few special means for attaining speed apart from those already mentioned.

VIII. THE USE OF SPECIAL ALGORISMS, ORAL FORMS, AND WRITTEN ARRANGEMENTS

The methods of teaching arithmetic are influenced not only by the aims of such instruction, but by the peculiar nature of the matter taught. The use of special algorisms, temporary algoristic aids or teaching "crutches," oral and written forms of analysis are of considerable moment in determining the difficulties and therefore the methods of teaching. Their condition and influence will need to be given some slight notice.

The use of special and temporary algoristic aids or learning "crutches" in mathematical calculation is one of the problems of method under constant controversy. Teachers seem fairly evenly divided upon the question. Typical situations in which such "crutches" are used may be noted as follows: Changing the figures of the upper number in "borrowing" in subtraction; rewriting figures in adding and subtracting fractions, in the broad sense any algorism which is used during the teaching or learning process temporarily, to be abandoned completely later, is an "accessory algorism" or "crutch." The objections to their use lie in the fact (1) that skill in manipulation is learned in connection with stages and forms not characteristic of final practical use; (2) that this implies, psychologically at any rate, the waste of learning two forms or usages instead of one; and (3) that it decreases the speed with which mathematical calculation is done. If there is a drift in any direction, it is probably toward the abandonment of "crutches."

The division of opinion, which exists in connection with the temporary use of special algorisms or "crutches," likewise exists with reference to the use of "full forms" and "short forms" of manipulation and statement. The temporary use of a "full form," in a case where a "short form" will finally be used, is similar to the employment of a "crutch." There is one important difference, however, which explains the relatively larger presence of temporary "full forms" than of "crutches." The "full form" is an accurate form which is used somewhere, in a more complex stage of the same process or in some other process; the "crutch" is not. Thus, a "full form," in column addition (with partial totals and a final total of partial totals) will be utilized in column multiplication; the "long-division form" of doing "short division" (that is the fully expressed form of dividing by a number of one figure) will be utilized in division by numbers of more than one figure.

The problem of form applies not alone to the algorism or special method of computation, but it likewise applies to the special methods of reasoning used in determining the specific series of steps to be taken in achieving the answer. In every problem the child solves he must not only decide what is to be done (reason), but he must do it (calculate). There are forms of reasoning as there are forms of calculation. As any calculation may have several algorisms the solution of a problem may be expressed in several forms. It is the latter difficulty which appears in the teacher's demands for "formal analysis" of problems. The analysis is usually required in full statement.

A conservative protest against the old formal expression of reasoned steps is found in omitting for the most part the linguistic statements dealing with the logic of the problem and merely "labeling" the numbers that occur in the calculation. This is a more restricted form of statement, much more used at the present time than hitherto. But it is still open to psychological objections that make the more scientific critics protest. There are many stages in a calculation where there is no association whatever with the concrete problem in hand. The concrete problem is studied, the decision is made that all the factors named are to be added. They are added, purely abstractly, and a number is given as the total. The result is then thought of in terms of the concrete problem in hand. A disposition to label each item in the addition may be necessary in the rendering of a bill, but it is a false and obstructing activity in the actual solving of the problem. The same situation exists where there are two or three processes to be utilized in series. Once the child has grasped his concrete situation and reasoned what to do he may proceed to mechanical manipulation, never thinking of the concrete applications till he is done.

The same tendency which is making for a reduction of verbal forms is increasing the use of mathematical symbols. As logical relations are less frequently written out, a simple sign such as $+$ or $\div$ is used. The algebraic x is supplied in place of a whole roundabout series of awkward preliminary statements or assumptions. With it, of course, come changed methods of manipulation, as in the use of the algebraic equation.

It is doubtless true that the rigidity of full logical forms is giving way to a more flexible and natural mode of expressing the child's thoughts. Fixed oral and written forms of exposition may assist the child, much as the acquisition of a definite symbol fixes an abstract meaning, which remains unwieldly until it attaches itself to a word by which it is to be recalled. But increasing care is manifested that children shall use only those forms that will conform to practical need upon the one hand, and to natural, efficient, and economy mastery on the other.

IX. EXAMPLES AND PROBLEMS.

The teaching of arithmetic is usually classified under two aspects, formal work and applied work. The formal work deals mainly with the memorization of fundamental facts, processes, and other details of manipulation. The applied work, as the name implies, is the formal work utilized in the setting of a concrete situation demanding a solution. These two aspects of arithmetical instruction are very frequently sharply separated, the child working alternately with one or the other. The characteristic practice is to deal with them without relating them as closely as the highest efficiency would demand.

Formal exercises in arithmetic are usually presented through the "example;" the exercises in application through the "problem;" the distinction being that one is an abstract and symbolical statement of numerical facts and the other a concrete and descriptive statement.[1] In the first case the mathematical sign tells the child what to do, whether to add, subtract, multiply, or divide; the example being a kind of prereasoned problem, the child has only to manipulate according to the sign, his whole attention throughout being focused on the formal calculation. In the second case the child has two distinct functions: He must, from the description of the situation presented, decide, through the process of reasoning, what he is to do (add, subtract, divide or multiply), and, having rendered his judgment, he must proceed through the formal calculation.

As the problem involves two types of mental processes in a single exercise, and the example but one, the usual procedure in arithmetic is to take up the formal side through examples first, and, later on, the applied side through the use of problems. This means that the first emphasis is on formal and abstract work rather than on a treatment of natural, concrete situations, an emphasis not wholly sanctioned by modern psychology and the better teaching procedure of other subjects.

The reform tendency is found mainly in the primary grades where the beginnings of new processes are made through objective presentations of the problem. But the transition from objectified problems to formal work is not immediate. The children pass from objectified situations to "number stories," which are only descriptions or narratives of a situation. This is the interesting primary-school equivalent of that more businesslike language description found in the higher grades—the arithmetical problem. But it precedes formal work and succeeds it, the formal drill being a mere intermediate drill. Here concrete presentations and formal work are more closely related and more naturally ordered.

This reform tendency, which began in the primary school, is extending to the higher grades, where it is no longer rare to find the attack upon a process preceded by careful studies of the concrete circumstances in which the process is utilized. In the case of interest, several days might be utilized in studying the institution of banking in all its more important facts and relations. Such an approach not only provides motive for the formal and mechanical work, but it gives a necessary logical basis in facts. Hence, the understanding of practical business life makes accurate reasoning possible for the child when he is called upon to solve actual problems in application of the formal work.

It is perfectly natural under the general traditional practice of putting the first emphasis on mastery of the formal work that the largest amount of attention should be given to the mechanical and technical side of arithmetic,

1. While this distinction is not general, it has sufficient currency to warrant its use here for the convenience of discussion. The expression "clothed problem" (from the German) is occasionally used to mean what is here designated as "problem," and "abstract problem" is used to mean what is here designated, as "example."

and that the concrete uses and applications should be slighted, and this is generally true of the practice of American teachers. Much more ingenuity has been used in the careful training of the child on the formal side than in teaching him to think out his problems. There is no such careful arranging and ordering of types in teaching a child to reason, as there is in teaching him to calculate.

Here and there a few thoroughly systematic attempts are made to carry the pupil through the simple types of one-step reasoning, to two-step and three-step problems with their possible variations. Just as the example isolates the difficulties of calculation, by letting the sign of + or — stand for the logic of the situation, there is a tendency to give problems without requiring the calculations. This affords a means of isolating and treating the special difficulties of reasoning. The child is merely required to tell what he would do, without doing it; the answer being checked by the gross facts. A little later, as a transition, he is permitted to give a rapid, rough approximation of what the answer is likely to be. With further command he tells what he would do and does it accurately. But such a program of teaching is still rare among teachers.

The care of the child's reasoning is largely restricted to testing his comprehension of the problem (1) by having him restate the problem to be sure he understands it, or (2) by having him give a formal oral or written analysis of the way in which he solves the problem. The first requirement may not be thoroughgoing, as the child may give a verbal repetition of the problem without really knowing its meaning. The second is a formal analysis of the finished result and does not represent the genetic method of the child's thinking. Consequently its formulas do not in any considerable degree assist him in his actual struggle with the complex of facts.

This lack of a systematic teaching of the technique of reasoning is manifest in the unreliability of children's thinking. When a child fails in a problem assigned from the textbook, the source of the error may be in one or more of three phases: (1) In failing to get the meaning of the language used to describe the details of the situation; (2) in failing to reason out what needs to be done to solve the situation; (3) in failing to make an accurate calculation. The first is a matter of language; the second, one of reasoning; the third, of memorization. The elimination of errors, due to the first and third sources, leaves a considerable proportion to be accounted for by the second. Such informal investigations as have been made seem to show that the children who fail in reasoning do not make any real effort to penetrate into the essential relations of the situation. They depend on their association of processes with specific words of relation used in the description of the problem, an association determined, of course, by their past experiences. As long as these familiar "cue" words are used, they succeed. Let unfamiliar words or phrases be utilized in their stead or let the relation be implied, and, like as not, the children will fail to do the right thing. Practical school people are familiar with the fact that children solve the problems given in the language of their own teachers and fail when the problems are set by principals or superintendents, whose language is strange to them.

A greater use of varied objects in the objective presentation of problems, and a more constantly varied use of language in the descriptive presentation of problems would prevent the child making such superficial and unthoughtful associations, and force him to think out connections between what is essential in a typical problem and the appropriate process of manipulating it. But such a deliberate application of modern psychology is far from being a conspicuous minority movement. The subject matter of the problems given to children has, however, improved greatly. Obsolete, puzzling, and unreal situations which only hinder the child's attempt to reason are less and less used in problem work.

Daily it becomes recognized with greater clearness that right reasoning depends upon a comprehension of the facts of the case, and the facts of the case in point must be within the experience of the child. This is the only way in which a problem can be real and concrete to him.

The recent effort on the part of textbook writers and teachers to make arithmetical problems "real" and "concrete" has not always recognized the above-mentioned psychological principle. The terms "real" and "concrete" have been interpreted in many ways, besides in terms of the child's consciousness. With some, "real" has meant "material," and the problems, more particularly with primary children, have, in increasing degree, been presented by objects or words connoting very vivid images. Others have defined these qualities in terms of actual existence or use in the larger social world. If these problems actually occur at the grocer's, the banker's, or the wholesaler's, it is said that they "are indeed concrete." And much effort has been expended in carrying these current problems into the classroom, in spite of the fact that they may be neither comprehensible nor interesting to the pupil. There is another social world, nearer home to the child, from which a more vital borrowing can be made. There is an opportunity to use the child's life in its quantitative aspects, to take his plays, games, and occupations, and introduce their situations into his mathematical teaching. As his world expands from year to year he will be carried by degrees from personal and local situations to those of general interest. The teacher can provide this progression without devitalizing the facts presented.

There is another error into which both the socially minded radical and the specialist in child study fall. In their eagerness to improve the arithmetic problem, they assume that problems taken from the larger social world or from the child's experience are necessarily superior to hypothetical, imaginative, or "made-up" problems. The psychological fact that needs to be forced upon the attention of the reformers is that, with proper artfulness, an imagined problem may be even more vital and real to the child than one taken from life—as a situation in a drama may be more appealing and real to a child than one on the street. This has some recognition, but not enough. Those who stand upon the side of the "made-up" problems are more likely to be reactionaries who tolerate the traditional type of problem even though its stupid artificiality is obvious to both the teacher and the child. They might better be dealing with dull problems borrowed from real life than with specially invented dullness.

Of course there is another argument for the use of actual social materials. The child must ultimately come into command of precisely these facts, since their mastery will be demanded by the business world. But must a primary school child study his arithmetic through problems taken from the dreary statistics of imports and exports merely because tariff reform is a political issue which every citizen ought finally to comprehend? There is a time for this, and, as is the case with most of such borrowed business problems, the time is later. In so far as these are current situations within the contacts of child life, let them enter. A quantitative revelation of life is important, and it is good teaching economy to gain knowledge by the way, provided it does not distract attention from whatever main business is at hand.

The socializing of arithmetical problems has one other additional good effect. It has tended to bring some topical unity into the problems constituting the assignment for a given lesson or group of lessons. Hitherto a series of problems was almost always composed of a heterogeneous lot of situations. There was no unity save that some one process was involved in each. The movement is now in the direction of attaining a more approximate unity within the subject matter of the problems themselves. The difficulties of attainment have restricted this movement to more progressive circles.

The eclectic source of arithmetic problems is apparent from the foregoing discussion. It would seem that some better texts would naturally be evolved through the implied criticism of each movement upon the other. Such is the case. Problems from child life emphasize the beginning condition to which adjustment must be made in all good teaching. Those from the greater world suggest the final goals of instruction. Those "made up" by the teacher call attention to what is too often forgotten, that the educative process in school may be artful without becoming artificial. Teaching is art, and when well done is not less effective for the fact.

X. CHARACTERISTIC MODES OF PROGRESS IN TEACHING METHODS.

The existing methods of teaching arithmetic in the American elementary schools are exceedingly varied. This is due to many causes. The democratic system of local control, as opposed to a centralized supervision of schools, has increased both the possibility and the probability of variation. Even within the units of supervision (State, county, and municipal) the opportunity for reducing variation in the direction of a more efficient uniformity is lost. This is partly due to the lack of a thoroughly trained staff of supervisors of the teaching process. Uniformity beyond the legal units of supervision has been restricted by the lack of organized professional means for investigation of and experimentation in controversial matters. Even such crude experiments as are being tried in more than one classroom, school, or system are unknown, unreported, unestimated, because no competent professional body gathers, evaluates, and diffuses such knowledge. In this respect the teaching profession is far below the efficient organization of the legal and medical professions.

It is exceedingly difficult, therefore, to analyze the characteristic aspects of teaching method except as these are interpreted in movements of general significance. These may be actual or potential, traditional or reformatory, general or local, in present acceptance. The situation is one wherein tradition is mixed with radicalism, and radicalism modified by reaction. In this medley of movements there are dominant tendencies both traditional and progressive.

It is quite impossible to indicate the progressive tendencies with clearness save in connection with the discussions of concrete difficulties in mathematical teaching. The forces that are behind these tendencies may, however, be summarized here. For convenience they may be classified into eight types of influence, extending from more or less vague and general movements to very particular scientific contributions. No attempt is made to indicate the achievement of each; the form of each influence is only roughly defined and illustrative movements or studies suggested.

1. It is obvious that any general pedagogical movement which influences the professional attitude of teachers will influence the special methods of mathematical teaching. The appearance of the doctrine of interest made mathematical instruction less formal. The growing enthusiasm for objective work enlarged the use of objects in the arithmetic period. The child-study movement laid emphasis upon the child's own plays and games as a source of problems and examples.

2. Certain special movements in methods of teaching, local to the subject of mathematics, have also been effective. Here one has only to recall the "Grube" method, with its influence on the order and thoroughness with which the elements of arithmetic are taught.

3. The tendency of every teacher who is at all sensitive to the defects of his methods is to vary his daily practice. Constant trial, with error eliminating and success justifying a departure, is thus a source of progress. The new devices of one teacher are taken up by the eager professional witness

and innovation is thus diffused. We have no ability to measure how much professional progress is due to individual variation in teaching and its conscious and unconscious imitation. The disposition of school systems to send their teachers on tours of visitation without loss of salary is a recognition of the value of this method of advance.

4. A far more efficient and radical source of change than that just mentioned is the deliberate, conscious, experimental teaching of progressive individuals. Some new idea or device occurs to the reader of original mind, and it is tried out with a fair proportion of resulting successes. An illustration of such a contribution is found in one conspicuous effort to get more rapid column addition. The first columns to be added were allowed to determine the selection and order of addition combinations learned. Thus, if $6 + 7 + 9 + 6 + 7 = 35$, is the first column to be used, then the first combinations mastered will be $6 + 7 = 13, 3 + 9 = 12, 2 + 6 = 8, 8 + 7 = 15$. Arising as a fruitful idea and seeming to give a measure of success, it has been carried, in the particular locality in mind, from school to school, and from system to system.

5. A prolific source of radical change is found in the critical application of modern psychology to teaching methods. Algorisms, types of difficulty, the order and gradation of these, as well as many other factors in method have been radically reorganized on psychological grounds. Examples of such psychological modifications of method are found in the "Courses of study for the day elementary schools of the city of San Francisco." Still more extensive critical applications are found in the "Exercises in arithmetic" devised by Dr. E. L. Thorndike, professor of educational psychology in the Teachers College, Columbia University.

6. Attempts have been made to inquire into the special psychology of arithmetical processes through careful experimentation and control. They have not been numerous, nor have they been influential on current practice. Such a field needs development. A typical attempt to investigate and formulate the special psychology of number is found in a Clark University study of "Number and its application psychologically considered." [1]

7. Educational investigations as to the efficiency of existing arithmetical teaching among school systems, sufficiently varied to be representative of American practice, have also been conducted. These have usually gone beyond the field of the special methods of presentation employed in the classroom, and have inquired into the conditions of administration and supervision, the arrangement of the courses of study, and other similar factors. Dr. J. M. Rice's studies into "The causes of success and failure in

1. Phillips, D. E. Number and its application psychologically considered. Pedagogical Seminary, vol. 5 : 211–281, 1897–98.

arithmetic" [2] investigated such specific factors as: The environment from which children come, their age, time allotment of the subject, period of school day given to arithmetic, arrangement of home work, standards, examinations, etc. A subsequent study of similar type, but employing more refined methods is that of Dr. C. W. Stone on "Arithmetical abilities and some factors determining them." [3] The main problem of this study was to find the correlation between types of arithmetical ability and different time expenditures and courses of study. These two studies have probably attracted more general notice than any other studies of arithmetical instruction. While they have largely dealt with administrative conditions that limit teaching method, rather than with the details of teaching method itself, they have stimulated the impulse to investigate conditions and practices of every type.

8. The latest source of progress in teaching method is found in the movement for comparative experimental teaching under normal but carefully controlled conditions. Several such experiments are being conducted in the Horace Mann Elementary School of Teachers College, Columbia University, under the direction of Principal Henry C. Pearson, with the cooperation of the staff of Teachers College. The experimental work conducted by the instructors and students of the Teachers College is primarily designed to determine the relative value of competing methods in actual use throughout the country, the assumption being that every substantial difference in practice implies a difference of theory and consequently a controversy that can be resolved only on the basis of careful comparative tests. Two parallel series of classes of about the same age, ability, teacher equipment, etc., are selected for this work. One series is taught by one method; the other series by the other method. The abilities of these children is measured both before and after the teaching, and the growth compared. The standards and methods of this type of comparative experimentation, together with a list of current competitive methods requiring investigation, is given in Dr. David Eugene Smith's monograph on "The teaching of arithmetic."

.
.
.

2. Rice, J. M. Educational research; Causes of success and failure in schools. Forum, **34** : 281–297, 437–452, 1902–3.

3. Stone, C. W. Arithmetical abilities and some factors determining them. Columbia University contributions to education, Teachers College, New York City, 1908, pp. 101.

Subcommittee 5. Mathematics in Grades Seven and Eight of the Public and Parochial Schools.

SCOPE OF THIS REPORT.

It was desired that this subcommittee make a special study of the following topics for grades seven and eight in public schools and in parochial schools: (*a*) The organization of the schools. (*b*) The mathematical curriculum in each type of school. (*c*) The question of examinations from the point of view of the schools. (*d*) The methods employed in the teaching of mathematics. (*e*) The parochial schools.

It was desired that the report present both present conditions and tendencies.

SOURCES OF INFORMATION.

In addition to general knowledge of the ground covered by this report, use has been made of the following sources of information: (*a*) The teaching of elementary mathematics. Prof. David Eugene Smith, Macmillan Co. (*b*) The teaching of arithmetic. Prof. David Eugene Smith, Teachers College Press. (*c*) The teaching of mathematics. Prof. J. W. A. Young, Longmans, Green & Co. (*d*) Courses of study of leading cities. (*e*) Responses to a questionnaire sent to leading cities.

DEFINITIONS OF TERMS.

The term elementary education is probably not as well defined as it might be. In general it is that education which by common practice is deemed desirable and necessary for preparation for the duties and rights of citizenship. It is made compulsory as a rule by the laws of the various States for children between the ages of 6 and 14 years. The term public as applied to schools is used to denote those schools which are conducted at the expense of and under the control of the various State and local political units; tuition in these schools is without expense. For a more complete discussion of the units see the report of the general committee number one. The term "grade" is used to denote each of certain divisions into which the work of the elementary schools is divided. As a rule there are eight such divisions.

313

One school year of from 35 to 40 weeks is required for a pupil to complete the work of one grade, excepting that bright pupils are permitted to do the work in less time. In larger cities a year or two of preliminary (kindergarten) work for children between the ages 4 and 6 is sometimes given. The eight main divisions are called respectively the first grade, second grade, etc. In some parts of this country, notably New England, there is a slightly different division of the course. The function of this committee is to study the mathematical work in the last two grades of the elementary course.

SPECIAL INTEREST IN THESE GRADES.

There are several reasons for special interest in the work of these grades. The mathematical function of the first six grades is to give the pupils control over the mechanics of arithmetic, over the fundamental number, facts and processes. The function of the upper grades has not been as well defined. There are several influences at work affecting the whole curriculum of these two grades, and especially the mathematical course. The results of certain psychological studies are especially applicable here; these two grades comprise the last part of the compulsory education of the children; they precede the high school; they correspond with certain sections of the school course of European schools, which are included in the secondary curriculum.

INFLUENCE OF PSYCHOLOGICAL STUDIES.

No effort will be made to go into great detail on this point; attention will be directed briefly to certain conclusions reached by psychologists, which are especially effective in modifying the mathematical work.

The doctrine of formal discipline is accepted now in only a modified form so that it is no longer deemed sufficient to claim for any subject that it has great disciplinary value. The educational value of all subjects, including mathematics, has been and is being subjected to close scrutiny with the result that subjects and subject matter long retained in the curriculum, through regard for tradition, are being displaced by new material, equally valuable as means of training, but more representative of current life. When this is not the result, old material is frequently dropped without any such substitution, on the ground that it neither has valuable content nor is necessary as means of training. As in all reforms, there is a tendency to go to extremes in this, especially with regard to mathematics. The willingness of the mathematicians to subject their science to the test of the new doctrine has invited the less sympathetic scrutiny of others who are not interested in the subject. The result is a tendency to demand more of mathematics in this respect than of other subjects.

The doctrine of interest as essential in training the will is generally accepted as valid. Systematic efforts to study child life and needs have served to call attention to the special interests of children between the ages of 12 and 15 years, who are just entering the adolescent period of life. The importance of safeguarding nervous energy at this time is generally recognized; the need of training the hand and the eye along with the mind, the necessity of vital contact with new material rather than theoretical study as a basis of real interest and comprehension are among the results of this movement.

INFLUENCE OF COMPLETION OF ELEMENTARY COURSE.

A large majority of the pupils of the schools do not go on to high school after completing the eighth grade. There are many reasons for this. The laws of most States do not permit the employment of children under 14 who have failed to complete the eighth grade. Many who are kept in school thereby avail themselves of the opportunity to seek employment as soon as they have completed the grade. In many cases the need of getting employment is urgent; in others, the opportunity to do so, the fact that the organization of the schools makes completion of the eighth grade a definite scholastic achievement, and the interests of pupils at this age lead many children to leave, even when their parents are in financial position to send them to high school. Many parents and pupils feel that the next stage of education is dominated too much by cultural ideals of education of so general a nature that the pupils are not trained for any form of remunerative employment. As evidence of this belief one may point to the large number of pupils who have graduated from the eighth grade who attend private schools where tuition is charged, called commercial schools, and to the fact that new forms of secondary education which have been provided in some localities seem to meet a real demand without in any way decreasing the demand for the customary forms of secondary education. For these various reasons there is a large shrinkage in the school population in the passage from the eighth grade to the high school.

Those in control of the educational work of the country are more and more allowing this fact to influence the course of study in the seventh and eighth grades. There is increasing emphasis on such training as will definitely equip the graduates for their future lives as individuals and as citizens of the community. Forms of manual training are provided and commonly, when it is impossible to furnish the equipment for all of the grades, provision is made for the pupils of the two upper grades. Owing to the realization that this vocational training is inadequate, there is at present a growing interest in industrial training. This movement which is destined to spread is certain to have its effect upon the mathematical work of the seventh and eighth grades.

INFLUENCE OF PREPARATION FOR HIGH SCHOOL.

It has been mentioned that many pupils who are ready for the high school fail to enter. It has been felt that some pupils might be led to go on to the high school if they could have in the eighth grade the beginnings of some of the high school subjects. For this reason, Latin, algebra, and a modified English course are urged as desirable eighth grade work in the hope that pupils will be unwilling to discontinue these subjects after they have once started them. In more recent years there is a reaction against this plan on the ground that these subjects are not properly within the scope of elementary education as defined. At the present time there are the beginnings of a new administrative policy to accomplish the same end. Schools are being provided in some of the systems which are designed for pupils who do plan to go on to high school or whose parents wish them to have this relatively more academic training. In these schools algebra will easily find a place. It is likely that the future will see a growth of this idea.

Again, for various reasons, the pupils who enter the high school find the work of the first year unusually difficult, so that many of them leave school during this period. It has become customary on this account to speak of the "gap" between the eighth grade and the high school, and it is generally admitted that better articulation is necessary there. The efforts to "bridge the gap" have included attempts to modify the work both in first year high school and in the eighth grade. In the eighth grade there has been an effort to concentrate upon essentials of arithmetic on the one hand, and on the other to prepare the pupils for high-school work by introducing the beginnings of algebra into the eighth grade work. There are two tendencies to-day which are likely to lessen the influence of preparation for high school as a modifying force in the eighth grade; first, there is the spirit of independence which characterizes the efforts of each of the larger units of the educational system, as an evidence of which in the elementary school is the belief that their main function is not that of serving as a feeder for the high school; and second, the spirit of responsibility on the part of each unit to take up its work where the previous unit has left off. This latter tendency is much more noticeable among secondary mathematics teachers than formerly.

INFLUENCE OF EUROPEAN CURRICULA.

The object lesson of European schools which provide under one administrative unit educational facilities for children from the age of 9 or 10 to 19 or 20, inclusive, has furnished considerable support for the idea that the essentials of elementary school work should be completed in a shorter time so that pupils may be started upon their secondary education at an earlier age.

This has been urged, especially in mathematics, where it means a change particularly in the upper grades. This idea received the support of the committee of fifteen and the committee of ten of the National Education Association.

While four influences have been enumerated, it is clear that each affects the others, so that they are not independent. In particular this last is intimately associated with the preceding one. These two in a sense are antagonistic to the other two since these place the emphasis upon secondary education, while the others throw emphasis upon the elementary phase of education. The last two are still in favor among the schoolmen especially, as in the past, whereas the former are supported equally by public opinion.

RURAL AND PRIVATE SCHOOLS

The schools of the rural districts do not feel all of these influences as strongly as do the urban schools. There is a growing effort to adapt the rural schools to the needs of the community, a movement identical with that noted in connection with urban schools. There is strong feeling of the importance of directing attention to the advantages of agricultural life. This influence will increasingly affect the work of the upper grades.

In private nonparochial schools the influences mentioned in paragraphs 7 and 8 are especially potent. The pupils of these schools usually go to the high school and college. In parochial schools there is usually reflected some of the educational policy of the public schools, in addition to the special educational policy of the parochial school. In the eighth grade of parochial schools the special function of these schools reaches its consummation in the specific training of the pupils in such sectarian studies as enable them to enter the church with which the school is connected.

ORGANIZATION OF THE GRADES

In organization there is nothing particularly distinctive about the seventh and eighth grades. In their relation to the grades below they come under the general school administration which controls the first eight grades. For a discussion of this organization see the report of the committee on general elementary schools. In their relation to the schools above there is some difference. At the close of the eighth grade the pupils are usually given a diploma as a sign of having completed a definite stage of their education. This diploma as a rule entitles the holder to admission to the high school of the same system and usually of any other school system. The diploma is obtained after compliance with the ordinary requirements for promotion. Promotion is determined by the teacher of the class with certain requirements in the way of examination, which will be discussed in a later paragraph. In some cases a special examination is required before a pupil is promoted to the high school.

THE MATHEMATICS CURRICULUM.

There is a lack of uniformity in the curricula in these two grades greater than in the lower grades. Two classes of curricula must be considered: (a) Those which do not provide any work in algebra and geometry; (b) those which do provide such work.

For those schools which do not provide any algebra in the eighth grade (and in the country at large these schools are in the majority), the mathematics course may be arranged on the topical plan, the spiral plan, or a combination of the two. By a topical plan is meant one in which the subject matter is divided according to mathematical topics; numeration, notation, and the four fundamental operations are discussed in order for integers, then the same topics for fractions in the common form; then for fractions in the decimal form; then percentage; then the applications of percentage to business life. By a spiral plan is meant one in which within a given range of numbers, say one to one hundred, notation, numeration, and certain processes are considered; later the range of numbers, the kind of numbers, the processes, and the difficulty of the applications are extended repeatedly. By a combination of the two plans is meant a course in which, while the spiral plan is adopted in spirit, at various stages of the course certain mathematical ideas are stressed so that thereafter they may be counted on as part of the working knowledge of the class, subject to recall after only slight review.

In the past the topical plan has been especially in vogue; at the present time more progressive courses of study are modeled after the third plan; the second plan has had some support, but has never had very general favor. It is probably true that the topical plan in its extreme form or in a modified form is the common plan in the majority of the schools of the country. By a modified form is meant that typified by a series of texts consisting of two or three books designed to furnish together the necessary material for an eight years' course. Each text usually covers the fundamental operations for integers, fractions, and decimals, with additional topics in each book. One book is to be used for from two to four years.

Usually the mathematics course is guided by such a text. In this event the pupils learn in the first six grades the fundamental processes for integers, fractions, and decimals, and denominate numbers. The work of the seventh and eighth grades consists of the following: A review of this foundation work; special attention to percentage and its most common application, simple interest; other business application of percentage; mensuration of plane and solid figures. The list of applications of percentage includes such topics as bank accounts, partial payments, commercial and bank discount, partnership, insurance, taxes, stocks and bonds, exchange, and interest. In mensuration is included the discussion of the area and the volume of the common plane and solid figures, square, and cube root. Besides these topics, the metric system, longitude and time, ratio, and proportion are commonly included in the texts. On account of the influences noted in former paragraphs, the tendency in the better schools of the country is to work for thoroughness and utility by omitting such topics as partial payments, partnership, exchange, bank discount on interest-bearing notes, the more difficult work in stocks and bonds, longitude and time, some portions of the mensuration of solids, cube root, and the metric system. In short, there is great freedom in omitting such topics as are not in harmony with modern life or as have been found unnecessarily confusing for the pupils. The time thus gained is devoted to the remaining topics and to additional drill on the essentials.

The problem material is contained as a rule in the book which each pupil possesses. These texts are written for the country at large, not to suit local conditions. The problems are designed to illustrate the particular mathematical idea or application under discussion; they are usually miscellaneous in character. The influences noted in former paragraphs are responsible for a new attitude toward the problem material. An effort is now made to have one set of ideas running through a particular set of problems. For example, the arithmetical idea being discussed may be percentage; instead of giving as problems a miscellaneous lot of applications of the percentage idea, the problems may all be based upon information about the population of the country for a period of years. In other words, the problem material possesses a certain unity, as a result of which information is conveyed to the pupils on the subject from which the material is drawn. A second characteristic of the problems now coming into use is that they are selected so as to give the children some insight into industrial, business, and social conditions of the city, the State, and the country. Thus there are groups of problems about the railroad, the mining, the agricultural, the manufacturing interests; about the population, area, and the wealth of the city, the State, the Nation; problems drawn from the local newspaper; problems involving the local tax rate, local real estate values, local interest, discount and commission rates, the stocks and bonds of local corporations. This material the teachers must place before the pupils either orally or on the blackboard, although some school boards are issuing pamphlets containing these supplementary problems for use in their own schools. This is a serious attempt to socialize arithmetic. It makes the course consist less of figuring and more of discussion. Under banking for example, the nature, function, and conduct of a bank is discussed; under stocks and bonds, effort is made to show again the kinds, purpose, value, and manner of sale of bonds and stocks; under taxes, the various purposes for which taxes are collected and the sources from which they are obtained. The content of the problems is considered quite as important as the solution of the problems.

COURSES CONTAINING ALGEBRA.

The other type of course in mathematics includes some work in algebra, and sometimes in geometry. These courses vary even more than those discussed previously, because the work is relatively new. In some places the arithmetic work of these two grades is curtailed and condensed so as to be completed entirely by the end of the seventh grade or by the end of the first half of the eighth grade, the latter being the more common plan; the remaining time is then devoted to algebra. In other places, work in algebra is introduced into the seventh and eighth or the eighth grade without dropping the arithmetic; there is in this case little effort to bring about any vital connection between the two subjects; the time is merely distributed so as to cover the two subjects. Again, in a few places, an effort is made to introduce the algebra into the arithmetic course in a natural way.

When algebra is taught in either of the first two ways, the work is guided by a text. This text is in some cases a brief elementary algebra written for the eighth grade classes, or consists of a few chapters added on to the arithmetic text. As a rule, the sequence of topics covered is that of the usual high-school text. When the algebra is introduced in the third form, it is presented through the regular arithmetic text, where it is introduced as opportunity permits. For example, preceding the work in percentage, the first notions of literal numbers are introduced; then the percentage law is expressed as a formula, $p = br$. Thereafter this formula is used in the solution of problems, for example, such as require the determination of the rate when the base and the percentage are given. Later this literal arithmetic may be extended, although it is quite clear that no very extended amount of algebra can be introduced in this natural manner.

So far an attempt has been made to present briefly the various forms in which algebra is taught in the grades. No definite statistics are available to form the basis of a definite statement as to the prevalence of the teaching of algebra. One investigation showed that about 30 to 35 per cent of the schools of a certain class taught algebra and these were schools of the larger cities; taking the country at large, it is unlikely that more than this percentage of them teach the subject.

PURPOSE OF ALGEBRA IN THE GRADES.

Algebra was introduced into and is retained in the grades for a number of reasons. Some hoped thereby to interest some pupils in the subject to such an extent that they would be led to enter high school to complete it; others hoped that thereby the pupils who did enter high school would have a more successful time in their mathematics work—in other words, it was a device for "bridging the gap." With others, there was the desire to "abridge and enrich" the arithmetic course; after abridging it, they felt that the natural means for maintaining the mathematical element in the curriculum was to introduce the next higher mathematical subject, which happened to be algebra. It was hoped by some that the use of the literal number and of the equation would eliminate some of the difficulties the pupils experienced in analyzing and solving some of the arithmetic problems in the eighth grade course. Those interested in the mathematical element in education desired to carry to another stage of their logical generalization certain arithmetical ideas.

Two tendencies in regard to the position of algebra are to be noted. With the public at large, the subject has never appeared as one of any "practical" value. With the current tendency to exalt in the schools those subjects which appear to have "practical" value is coming a feeling that algebra does not have a place in the eighth grade, especially in the form in which it has been taught. One of the largest cities of the country has recently entirely dropped it from the course, replacing it by the study of certain phases of local history and local business and industrial conditions. Another city, somewhat smaller in size but recognized as progressive in educational efforts has introduced about the same idea into its course, although there the next tendency to be mentioned has been recognized. These efforts, entirely independent, are typical of the feeling in some of our school systems.

The other tendency is toward an extension of the third plan of teaching algebra. There is in this country a growing belief that in the past too sharp lines of demarcation have existed between arithmetic, algebra, and geometry and there are efforts being made to bring the three into closer relation. In the elementary school, as early as the sixth grade, certainly no later than the seventh, certain elements of generalized arithmetic should be introduced and should be carried along with the arithmetic until the pupils become familiar with literal notation and the equation. This work is not properly called algebra as the number field would not necessarily be extended to include negative as well as positive numbers. This form of literal arithmetic presents all that is practical of algebra for ordinary purposes. So much of it is decidedly of utilitarian value since the mechanics of to-day who wish to read trade journals need to be familiar with it. This form of literal arithmetic has in its favor most if not all that can be said for algebra as an eighth-grade subject.

It seems probable at the present time that these two tendencies will become more pronounced, i. e., there is almost certain to be more dissatisfaction with the extreme form of algebra brought down from the high school, and as teachers are trained for the work, there is to be, it is hoped, greater interest in the form of generalized arithmetic outlined.

GEOMETRY IN THE GRADES.

The mensuration of certain geometric figures has always been included in American arithmetics. In recent years, as has been said, there has been a decrease in the extent of this work. It was formerly the practice to have this work consist mainly of definitions, formulas, and problems. This has been changed by giving experimental and intuitive verifications of the formulas. It has been uncommon to have any other form of geometry, except in isolated places where some form of constructional, inventional, or concrete geometry has been introduced. The motive has been to teach certain elementary ideas of geometric forms, to train the hand in the use of customary drawing tools, to train the eye in its judgment of geometric forms and relations, and to train the mind in such general functions as observation and generalization as pertaining to geometric data. This work has been attempted usually under the guidance of a pamphlet prepared for some specific school by those interested in such work.

The movement has not spread much. Possibly one reason for the slowness of the introduction of this work has been the custom of including in the art course usually given in American schools some "mechanical" drawing—constructions with the straightedge and compasses. This custom has been unfortunate, at least from the mathematical standpoint, as, in the drawing course, the emphasis has been upon the results; the possible cultivation of desirable habits of geometric study, and the possible training of the powers of observation and generalization have been largely neglected. A further reason for the lack of such is the scarcity of teachers acquainted with and prepared to teach geometry inductively. The majority have studied geometry only in the Euclidean form.

EXAMINATIONS.

Examinations given in the schools are of three kinds: (*a*) Those given by the teachers themselves; (*b*) those given by the supervisory officers of the schools; (*c*) those given by a school to determine the qualifications of pupils who wish to enter the school.

The examinations given by the teachers are of two kinds: The ordinary written recitation and the stated examinations which may be required by the school regulations. The first should not be called examinations in one sense of the word, since they cover usually only a short interval of previous instruction and are given as a means of affording the same sort of drill for all of the class or as a means of detecting weaknesses as a basis for further teaching. Such written lessons are left entirely to the teacher, although it is advised that they be given frequently. Such "examinations" are in every respect desirable.

The other form of examination given by teachers is more formidable. Most school systems provide that the standing of a pupil in a class shall be determined in part by examinations given at stated times. The examinations may occur monthly, quarterly, semiannually, or annually. They count from one-half down in determining a pupil's standing. When the questions are prepared by the teacher, the questions and the papers are at the disposal of the principal or other supervisors. The teacher has an opportunity to adapt the examination to the capabilities of the class, and can allow for the individuality of the pupils. Under this plan a sympathetic influence is likely to pervade the examination. As a means of administration this form of examination depends for its success upon the teachers and the opportunity of inspection. As an educational practice it is to be commended as compared with those examinations which are not prepared with the same sympathetic recognition of the pupils' interests, which the teachers are likely to display.

As a rule uniform tests are given in most school systems for administrative purposes. The questions are prepared either by the superintendent or by a committee of principals or teachers—usually principals—working under the direction of the superintendent. In few cases do the teachers have any choice concerning the questions which they submit to their classes. The teachers grade the papers and then submit them to the principals. These examinations are given to set standards of work, to interpret the course of study, to promote uniformity throughout the system, to bring out the weak points in the teaching, and to point out conditions in the school. In some cases it is urged that these examinations train the pupils to prepare their thoughts on a subject in good order in a limited time. In general the interests of the pupils are served only indirectly by these examinations as the emphasis is upon the administrative advantages. The results are sometimes used in determining a pupil's fitness for promotion, although it is seldom that failure in these examinations is allowed to retard a pupil's progress.

These examinations are an effective administrative device. Their success depends upon the experience, the wisdom, and the ideals of the supervisory staff. As a rule, these examinations do not meet with favor among the teachers. There is a feeling that the test is one of themselves rather than of their pupils. From what has been said this appears to be true, although it depends upon the purposes of the supervisors. The better teachers recognize the advantages to be gained, and, having the proper professional spirit, they are willing to have their work compared with that of their colleagues in other schools. The examinations are opposed also because of their effect upon the pupils. It is contended that the pupils are subjected to a severe nervous strain so that they do not do themselves or their teachers justice. This is possibly true. The evil results, however, may be minimized under wise supervision. If the teachers adequately prepare the pupils for the tests by reviews, and if the tests are adapted to the possible ability of the pupils, the evil results mentioned are not necessary. In the larger cities the difficulty of conducting these examinations is great, owing to the wide diversity in the population in various parts of the city. Another objection raised to such examinations is that thereby the teachers are hampered in their work, with the result that there is little progress from year to year. This again may or may not be true, dependent upon the supervision. As a rule, the supervisors of the schools will see that the tests promote rather than retard progress.

Another form of examination proposed at the present time is that designated as the "standardized" test. For a complete discussion of the nature of these tests, see the report by Dr. C. W. Stone, in the report of subcommittee No. 2 of this general committee. As to current practice, it is safe to say that little work of this nature is done in the schools. As to tendencies, there is little evidence upon which to base a statement one way or another. It would seem well for those in charge of the general tests just discussed to introduce into them such of the elements of these standardized tests as seem applicable to their needs and purposes.

In the eighth grade tests are sometimes given to determine the fitness of pupils for promotion to high school. This is not a common practice, however.

METHODS OF INSTRUCTION.

It is possible to speak only in a general way of methods of instruction as these vary with schools and with teachers. Much that can be said on this topic for the two upper grades would apply equally well for the other grades.

CLASS INSTRUCTION.

In all of the schools instruction is given to groups of pupils varying in number from 5 to 30 or more—groups called classes. The average size of classes is probably in the neighborhood of 20 and a strong effort is being made in all cities to cut down larger classes to this number. This form of instruction is called class instruction. There have been numerous attempts to modify this form of instruction by various forms of individual instruction in order to meet in a better way the needs of weak pupils. In some schools special teachers are employed to take charge of any pupils from any class who are backward in their work. As a rule, however, the regular class teacher does this herself either before or after regular school hours. An effort is made of course to organize the classes so that all pupils in the class will have as uniform ability as possible.

RECITATION AND STUDY TIME.

In most schools the arithmetic class meets daily for from 20 to 30 minutes. This time is known as recitation time. Besides this the pupils of the class usually have in school another period of equal length for the study of arithmetic. This makes the total time for arithmetic vary from 200 to 300 minutes per week. In most schools the children do no studying on arithmetic at home; in the upper grades they probably do, although the tendency to-day is to relieve pupils of any home preparation in mathematics in the elementary schools. Each pupil possesses a book. This book is not merely a collection of problems; it is usually a text providing the necessary theory and such explanation as seemed wise to the author. From the terminology used to denote the two periods, it is obvious that at some time the pupils were expected to prepare themselves in the "study" period on certain assignments in the text upon which they later recited in the "recitation" period. This was especially true in the upper grades, and unfortunately is probably true in many classrooms to-day. In the majority of schools this condition has undoubtedly changed; the recitation period should properly be called the "teaching" period and the study period might better be called the "work" period. The class time was formerly given over often to indiscriminate recitation on the solutions which the pupils had performed outside of class; it is now given over either to carefully planned drill or to instruction by the teacher on some new topic. The study time is used to supplement the class time.

DIVISION OF THE CLASS TIME.

One of the characteristic features of the teaching period is the mental work. It is common practice to direct the teachers to devote from one-third to one-half of the class time to oral-mental work. It is oral in the sense that the teacher gives the directions orally; it is mental in the sense that the pupils perform the necessary computations without use of pencil and paper. The responses of the pupils are given either orally or in writing. This work is designed either to maintain efficiency through wise drilling on topics previously taught or to lead up to and teach some new topic. This must be considered a feature of current teaching method, since formerly much of the class time was given over to "recitation" by the pupils on work which they placed upon the blackboard.

There are occasions when it is worth while to have the whole class solve problems in writing; this is especially true in the upper grades where the conditions of the problems become more confusing. As a rule, however, written work is done outside of class. In the past pupils have been required to present more or less elaborate analyses of the solutions for their problems. The desire was to have the pupil set forth in detail the process of thinking by which the solution was accomplished. The advantage of such solutions to the teacher is obvious; it is an equally obvious fact that such formality is entirely foreign to the natural, rational mode of presentation which an adult would use in ordinary life. Such a requirement is subject to criticism also because it confuses the pupils. The tendency now is to ask the pupils to give a clear presentation in good form; in the upper grades, they are encouraged to use any "short cuts" of which they know, and to do mentally as much of the computation as they can. Another reform which has been accomplished is the discontinuance of elaborate forms of ruling on the papers, a practice which has been altogether too prevalent in the past.

RAPIDITY AND ACCURACY.

The teachers of the upper two grades seek to develop in their pupils skill in computing which will enable them to perform ordinary calculations with rapidity and accuracy. In the lower grades the pupils are taught the processes and the number facts; in the upper grades the emphasis is properly turned in this other direction.

The mental work has this as its aim. The pupils are frequently given problems to solve in a limited amount of time; they are encouraged to compete with one another by being invited to rise when they have solved the problems; they are given honorable notice in various ways for achievement in these respects.

CONCRETE METHODS.

On account of the influences mentioned in former paragraphs, the teachers endeavor to make the instruction as concrete as they can without going to the extreme of objectifying relations which are obvious. Thus in the discussion of commercial forms, actual samples are exhibited; checks of some real or imaginary bank are drawn in class; account books are kept by the pupils and are balanced monthly, each child filling in records of real transactions when possible; interest-bearing and noninterest-bearing notes are shown; banks are visited or conducted in the schoolroom; the class resolves itself into a stockbroker's office, one member acting as the broker and the remaining members of the class acting as buyers or sellers of stocks or bonds. In mensuration, actual measurements are used when possible; problems are sought in the manual training department; formulas are obtained by experimental methods instead of being taken on faith and then used. The teachers endeavor to give to their classes clear impressions of a few things rather than superficial word knowledge of many things.

326

DEPARTMENTAL TEACHING.

One especially characteristic feature of the seventh and eighth grade work is the practice of having the mathematics, and some of the other subjects, taught by teachers who as a rule teach no other subjects. In the lower grades this is not common. This is known as departmental instruction. It is quite common in the larger school systems and is being extended as rapidly as circumstances permit. The teachers in charge of the departmental work are usually the more experienced teachers of the system and as a rule have had special training for their work. In many cases college graduates are obtained for these positions, whereas usually the teachers in the elementary schools do not have collegiate training.

Departmental instruction is favored because of the obvious advantage of having for this upper grade work teachers who are specially interested in and qualified to teach their subject. Departmental instruction has the disadvantage of placing the training of young children in the hands of each of several teachers, working independently, with the result that often the emphasis is placed upon teaching the subject rather than upon the education of the child. This difficulty is obviated by wise supervision, under which there will be cooperation between the various departmental teachers in any one school.

INDUCTION AND DEDUCTION

It is very likely that no conscious thought is given to these two types of teaching methods by the majority of teachers. At the same time it may be said that the instruction is either by inductive methods or by rule followed by practice. The habit of proceeding from "the known to the unknown," from "the simple to the complex," is so characteristic of the teachers that they approach new topics whenever it is possible by inductive means. For example, the nature and the meaning of "paying interest" for the use of money may be approached through the acquaintance the pupils have with the practice of paying "rent" for the use of a house; the nature and meaning of shares of stock may be approached through the pupils' experience in contributing their share toward the expense of a picnic. On the other hand, when it comes to a process such as finding the square root of a number, the books as a rule develop the process in the usual way with the aid of the formula for the square of a binomial; but the teachers are commonly advised to simply illustrate the process and then fix it in the minds of the pupils by adequate drill.

.
.
.

UNITED STATES BUREAU OF EDUCATION

BULLETIN, 1911, NO. 16 . . . . WHOLE NUMBER 463

MATHEMATICS IN THE PUBLIC AND PRIVATE SECONDARY SCHOOLS OF THE UNITED STATES

INTERNATIONAL COMMISSION ON THE TEACHING
OF MATHEMATICS

THE AMERICAN REPORT

COMMITTEES III AND IV

I. General Report pH = 36

II. Subcommittee Reports 36 — end.

WASHINGTON
GOVERNMENT PRINTING OFFICE
1911

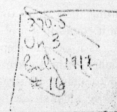

INTERNATIONAL COMMISSION ON THE TEACHING OF MATHEMATICS.

GENERAL OFFICERS.

President, F. KLEIN, Geh. Reg.-Rat., the University of Göttingen.
Vice President, SIR GEORGE GREENHILL, F. R. S., London.
General Secretary, H. FEHR, the University of Geneva.

AMERICAN COMMISSIONERS.

DAVID EUGENE SMITH, Chairman, Teachers College, Columbia University, New York, N. Y.
W. F. OSGOOD, Harvard University, Cambridge, Mass.
J. W. A. YOUNG, the University of Chicago, Chicago, Ill.

THE AMERICAN REPORT.

Committee No. III. Public General Secondary Schools.

George W. Evans, Charlestown High School, Boston, Mass.. Chairman.
Henry M. Wright, English High School, Boston, Mass.
Ernest G. Hapgood, Girls' Latin School, Boston, Mass.
Charles D. Meserve, Newton High School, Newtonville, Mass.
Charles Ammerman, McKinley High School, St. Louis, Mo.
H. D. Gaylord, Cambridge, Mass.
Professor Lewis Darwin Ames, the University of Missouri, Columbia, Mo.
Professor Arthur Sullivan Gale, the University of Rochester, Rochester, N. Y.
William Betz, East High School, Rochester, N. Y.

.
.
.

Subcommittee 9. Failures in the Technique of Secondary Teaching of Mathematics: Their Causes and Remedies.

William Betz, East High School, Rochester, N. Y., Chairman.
Miss M. E. Shea, High School for Girls, Philadelphia, Pa.
Miss Mary M. Wardwell, Central High School, Buffalo, N. Y.
H. E. Webb, High School, Newark, N. J.
Franklin T. Jones, Cleveland, Ohio.

.
.
.

329

CONTENTS.

Committee No. III. Public general secondary schools:
  I. General report.
    Organization... 11
    The curriculum... 11
    The subject-matter... 15
    The orthodox syllabus.. 17
      i. Algebra to quadratics....................................... 17
      ii. Quadratics and beyond...................................... 19
      iii. Plane geometry.. 20
      iv. Solid geometry... 21
      v. Trigonometry.. 21
      vi. Advanced algebra... 22
      vii. Arithmetic.. 22
    Growth of the college requirement: Harvard College as example.... 24
    Recent progress.. 30
    Examinations... 31
    Methods.. 34
    Aims... 36
  Subcommittee 1. Boys' high schools................................. 37
    The mathematical curriculum...................................... 37
    Examinations... 38
    Methods of teaching.. 38
    Aims of mathematical teaching.................................... 39
  Subcommittee 2. Girls' high schools................................ 39
    Organization curriculum.. 40
    Mathematical curriculum.. 42
    Examinations... 45
    Methods of teaching.. 45
    Aims of teaching... 46
  Subcommittee 3. Coeducational high schools in the East............. 47
    Report of Miss Mary Gould, of Roxbury (Mass.) High School........ 48
  Subcommittee 4. Coeducational high schools in the Middle West...... 51
    Introduction... 51
    Organization... 54
    The mathematical curriculum...................................... 55
      (a) Algebra.. 57
      (b) Geometry... 58
      (c) Mathematics.. 58
    Examinations... 59
    Methods.. 59
    Aims of mathematics teaching..................................... 61

CONTENTS.

Committee No. III. Public general secondary schools—Continued.
  II. Reports of subcommittees—Continued.
    Subcommittee 5. Mathematics in the coeducational high schools in the South.. 62
      Organization... 62
      The curriculum... 63
      The mathematics curriculum..................................... 63
      Examinations... 64
      Methods of teaching.. 64
      Aims... 66
    Subcommittee 6. Coeducational high schools on the Pacific coast.
      Organization... 66
      The curriculum... 67
      Examinations... 70
      Methods of teaching.. 71
      Aims of mathematics teaching................................... 72
    Subcommittee 7. The preparation of teachers of mathematics for the public high schools... 74
      Methods of the investigation................................... 76
      Present standard preparation of teachers in service............ 76
      Tendencies toward higher standards for teachers................ 76
      Facilities offered by universities for the special training of teachers of mathematics...................................... 77
      Desirable standards in training teachers of secondary mathematics.. 79
      Other factors in the efficiency of teachers.................... 81
    Subcommittee 8. The six-year high school......................... 82
      1. Advantages.. 83
      2. Approximations to six-year high schools..................... 84
      3. Method of the investigation................................. 84
      4. Analysis of the information received........................ 85
      5. The traditional curriculum.................................. 85
      6. Six-year high schools....................................... 85
      7. Close approximations to the six-year high school............ 86
      8. Approximations consisting of a preparatory high school and a regular high school.. 87
      9. Approximations consisting merely of departmental methods in the seventh and eighth grades.............................. 88
      10. A second form of six-year high school...................... 90
      11. The Horace Mann school..................................... 91
      12. A proposed curriculum...................................... 92
      13. General conclusion... 92
      Bibliography... 92
    Subcommittee 9. Failures in the technique of the teaching of secondary mathematics: Their causes and remedies................ 93
      Introduction... 93
      Purpose of this report... 94
      Method of investigation.. 94
      Statistics of failures... 95
      Causes of failure—preliminary analysis......................... 96
      Transforming influences in education........................... 96
      General causes of failure...................................... 98
        1. The teacher... 100
        2. The pupil... 102
        3. High-school organization.................................. 103

CONTENTS.

Committee No. III. Public general secondary schools—Continued.
  II. Reports of subcommittees—Continued.
    Subcommittee 9. Failures in the technique of the teaching of secondary mathematics: Their causes and remedies—Continued.
      Specific causes of failure..................................... 104
      Remedies... 106
      Conclusion... 108
      Appendix... 109
Committee No. IV. Mathematics in the private secondary schools of the United States... 109
  Plan of the investigation.. 113
  Extent and character of the data................................... 113
  Organization of private secondary schools.......................... 114
  The department of mathematics...................................... 117
  The course of study.. 117
  Methods.. 124
  Examinations and tests... 132
  Mathematics and coeducation.. 136
  Aim of instruction in mathematics.................................. 138
  Distinctive features in a few individual schools................... 140
  Principles underlying the course in mathematics.................... 142
  Unification of elementary mathematics as studied in the Detroit Home and Day School, Detroit, Mich. (prepared by S. A. Courtis)... 146
  Course of study—"mixed mathematics" (prepared by John S. French)... 147
  The plane geometry course in the Polytechnic Preparatory School of Brooklyn, N. Y. (prepared by George W. Meyers)................ 150
  Real problems (prepared by Eugene R. Smith)........................ 153
  A scrapbook of problems (prepared by James F. Millis).............. 156
  Reference books.. 161
  Mathematics club (prepared by C. W. Newhall)....................... 164
  Conclusion... 167
Appendix:
  A. Mathematical instructions for evening technical schools......... 170
  B. The teaching of mathematics in private correspondence schools... 177
  C. The teaching of mathematics in schools and colleges for negroes. 182

Committee No. III. Public General Secondary Schools:

I. General Report.
.
.
.

THE CURRICULUM.

Directive influences.—The curriculum in mathematics is determined in general by the admission requirements of colleges. This is, of course, confessedly so in the States in which there is a complete and State-wide organization of education, with the university recognized as the final stage. It is also true in other States, and even in the smaller communities where few, if any, of the pupils may be planning to go to college, and where the local school committee disclaim the intention of following university guidance; and it is true of the mathematical curriculum even where it is not true of other subjects of study. The reason for this nearly universal dependence on college definitions is that mathematics is not otherwise defined by any authority that the schools feel willing to accept.

The definite and legal enactment of all public high-school courses of study is in all cases made by the school committee (often called the school board, or the trustees). Only occasionally does this body contain members able or willing to decide upon details of a subject that seems to the ordinary layman so abstract as mathematics. Where the definitions of the university are not accepted bodily, the advice of the principal is generally sought, occasionally that of the head of the department, or of the special teacher of mathematics.

Importance of the textbook.—There are States in which the textbooks are prescribed; in one all the textbooks of mathematics are prescribed as those of a certain author, reliance being placed on the publishers to keep his productions up to date. Some of the teachers replying to the questions of the committee state that no deviations from the textbooks are allowed; but this is doubtless the decree of the local authorities rather than of the State, and is undoubtedly due to the unpleasant experience of trying to connect the work of a radical experimenter with that of a successor incapable of appreciating and pursuing a wide and uncharted departure from the orthodox course.

Correlation of mathematical subjects with each other.—The different branches of high-school mathematics are not in general correlated with each

331

other, but are pursued one after the other with such differences of method and of point of view that algebra is often forgotten by the time geometry is completed. Of recent years the teachers in a small number of schools have, of their own accord and with considerable difficulty, arranged the geometry work so that algebra can be applied to some of the numerical problems given in illustration of the metrical theorems. More than anything else the subject of proportion is treated algebraically. In a still smaller number of high schools there is a well-organized blending of the different subjects, algebra, geometry, and trigonometry, into a general and progressive course in mathematics.

The customary independence of these mathematical subjects is restricted almost everywhere by the requirement that a pupil must have "passed algebra" before he is permitted to begin geometry.

Correlation with science.—The mathematics work is little correlated with physics, though many schools insist on algebra at least, and sometimes geometry or even trigonometry, before beginning physics. The requirement of algebra for chemistry students also is not unknown.[1]

THE SUBJECT MATTER.

Elementary algebra and plane geometry.—Every regular high school in the United States offers algebra and plane geometry for at least one year each. Half of them give algebra for an extra half year; less than 20 per cent give algebra for two full years. A very few schools give algebra for two years and a half, and a very few give plane geometry for a year and a half.

Solid geometry, trigonometry, and college algebra.—Solid geometry for a half year, plane trigonometry (often with spherical right triangles, occasionally with the general spherical triangle[2]) for a half year, and advanced algebra, so called, including certain special topics listed below, for a half year, are given in some of the larger high schools or in some of the smaller ones that definitely prepare for college.

The textbook as evidence.—The fact that few of the high-school teachers of mathematics are thoroughly trained in their subject and that the subject matter is settled for the most part without their initiative indicates that the content of the curriculum will be closely defined by the textbooks used. This is also the comment of publishing houses in discussing new textbook proj-

---

1. An ideal state of things is described by Miss Thirmuthis Brookman, as the result of 12 years' development in the high school of Lincoln, Nebr. Here an "inspirational" half-year course in general science serves as an introduction to a course in mathematics, where each week's work is "a definite and clear-cut section of a well-proportioned system," including algebra, geometry, and trigonometry. Pupils showing marked inability in the general science introduction are not urged to enter the work in mathematics.—School Review, January, 1910.

2. More than a half year is taken in this case.

ects: "We must have a book that the ordinary teacher can follow without change; it is only the exceptional teacher that can strike out independently of its guidance."

The kind of textbook in general use up to 12 or 15 years ago, and the kind most widely used to-day, will enable us to define the subject matter and the methods of algebra, geometry, and trigonometry as presented to more than 75 per cent of the high-school pupils of the United States. Hereon is based the following outline.[3]

THE ORTHODOX SYLLABUS.

I. ALGEBRA TO QUADRATICS.

Introductory.—Definitions and "axioms," discussion of negative quantities, brief practice in algebraic expression and interpretation, one or two lessons in the use of algebra for problems so simple that algebra adds to their difficulty.

The four operations.—Addition, subtraction, multiplication, and division, completed successively in that order, with formal rules of manipulation (not necessarily stated in advance); literal and fractional coefficients and exponents used; ingeniously involved parentheses, brackets, and braces; and expressions sometimes more complicated than most of the pupils will ever see again.

Factors.—Factoring expressions, such as the difference of two squares, $ax^2 + bx + c$, $x^n \pm y^n$ (often with "demonstrations," as of the case where the sign is $+$ and n is odd); factoring "by parts;" forms like $x^4 + x^2 y^2 + y^4$; expressions such as can be obtained from the simpler forms by substituting binomials for one or more of the letters. Usually no application is made of these feats except in the reduction of fractions, and in highest common factor and least common multiple, which follow as introductory to fractions.

Highest common factor and lowest common multiple.—Highest common factor, first by factoring, then by the Euclidean method. A demonstration is usually given for this, but is hardly ever assimilated by the pupils. Not seldom the proof given is applicable only to numbers—that is, it will not hold for literal expressions in which, as is usual, some of the dividends have to be multiplied and some monomial factors have to be saved out. Lowest common multiple, generally by factoring only, with a perfunctory comment on the method which utilizes the highest common factor.

Fractions.—Fractions, with the rules of transformation formally demonstrated, and the four operations each completed in its turn. Expressions of ingenious complexity are handled under each head.

---

3. For the purpose of this outline only, "numbers" will be understood as expressed *without letters,* and "problems" will be understood as "clothed" in words.

Simple equations and problems.—"Simple" equations, that is, equations of the first degree with one unknown letter, and abounding in parentheses and fractions; and, at last, problems to be solved by means of such equations, except that the equations needed for the purpose are really simple.

Linear elimination and problems.—Two-letter linear equations, including fractional and literal equations; three-letter equations of the first degree, and occasionally simple four or five letter sets. Equations solved for the reciprocals of the letters involved. Problems leading to equations of the first degree in two or more letters. Literal equations are scattered at random under this topic and the preceding one.

Inference of equations.—The model examples worked out in the textbook generally indicate the inference of an equation from the preceding work by means of phrases printed at the side, such as "transposing," "clearing of fractions," "adding to eliminate the x terms," etc. No expectation is indicated that the pupil will use any substitute for these annotations.

Neglect of practice in devising equations.—The number of problems given under this topic and the preceding one is generally insufficient to give real facility in algebraic expression, and their introduction seems isolated, an interruption in the progress of manipulation. Haste or neglect at this point is explained by the fact that no topic is more difficult to test adequately in a written examination than the devising of equations, and where time is scant it will be devoted to topics that show.

Involution and evolution.—Under the title "Involution" next are treated powers of numbers and of monomials, and squares and cubes of binomials; under the title "Evolution" are treated square roots and cube roots of polynomials. Some details of the theory of exponents are necessarily included under these heads.

Radicals and radical equations.—Radicals, including the rationalization of binomial denominators, and the square root of a binomial surd (generally given without adequate demonstration); radical equations, carefully selected or constructed so as to give, upon rationalization, equations of the first degree. Extraneous solutions, sometimes declared admissible because of the "ambiguous" sign of the square root. Problems again, few in number, leading with suitable choice of letters to radical equations.

Exponents.—Theory of exponents, without any mention of logarithms; good correlation with the preceding topic.

II. QUADRATICS AND BEYOND.

Quadratics in one and two unknowns.—Quadratics in one unknown, first without the second term ("pure" quadratics) and then complete quadratics ("affected" quadratics); problems leading to such quadratics. Linear-quadratic pairs, elimination by substitution; special cases of quadratic pairs solved by devices suited to each case; special emphasis on symmetrical equations, solved by reducing to values for $x + y$ and $x - y$. Very few problems. Literal equations at random under this topic.

Ratio and proportion.—Ratio and proportion, including the traditional transformations of a proportion; examples of literal equations and problems to which proportion can be applied if one insists; no mention of its application in geometry, and no comment on the relation of this subject to fractional equations. This topic is not referred to under any other part of the work in algebra.

The progressions.—Arithmetical progression; formulas for the nth term and for the sum of the terms, any three of the five constants being given, to find the other two.

Geometrical progression; formulas for the nth term and for the sum of the terms, certain groups of three of the five constants being given to find the other two constants. Formula for the "sum of the series" when the ratio is less than one and the number of terms indefinitely great; recurring decimals.

Inserting means.—Arithmetic and geometric mean; insertion of two or more arithmetic or geometric means between two given numbers.

Binomial theorem.—The binomial theorem for positive integral exponents; proof of the same;[4] application to powers of a binomial of which the terms may be complicated with fractions, with radical signs or with exponents that may or may not be positive or integral. Formula by which any term of any power may be written down.

III. PLANE GEOMETRY.

The five books.—The sequence in all the ordinary textbooks is that of Legendre; five books, the first on lines, angles, triangles, and other polygons; the second on circles and the measurement of angles; the third on proportion (treated as an algebraic subject) and similar figures; the fourth on areas; the fifth on regular polygons and the measurement of the circle.

Incommensurables.—Incommensurable ratios occur in Books II, III, IV, and V; in most schools an attempt is made at every one of these points to master the explanations given in the book.

Construction.—Geometrical constructions, to be made as with Euclid by the use of the compass and unmarked straightedge, are given in a logical place among the other propositions. Locus theorems are given, beginning with the bisectors of angles and the perpendicular bisectors of lines in Book I.

Original exercises ("riders").—Exercises are given for practice in the invention of demonstrations similar to those in the text, and in the application of available theorems to numerical data. These exercises reach the number

4. In most classes this proof is omitted in teaching.

of 500 or 600, and are often accompanied by suggestive notes or diagrams. They are for the most part rigidly confined to subject matter like that in the text, so that successful practice with them does not add materially to the geometrical information of the student.

IV. SOLID GEOMETRY.

Order of topics.—This includes successively the following topics: Perpendicular and parallel lines and planes; diedral, triedral and polyedral angles (including the ratio of incommensurable diedrals) ; equivalence and congruence among, and the measurement of, parallelopipeds, prisms, pyramids, cylinders, and cones; the geometry of great-circle diagrams on a spherical surface, with scant reference to the corresponding polyedral angles at the center of the sphere; the surface and volume of the sphere.

Mensuration theorems.—Development is almost never used for the lateral areas of cones and cylinders, and the assumption that there is a quantity spoken of as "the area" of a cylinder, cone, or a sphere is tacitly made (a similar assumption having been made for the "length" of the circumference in plane geometry), the areas of successively approximating figures approaching this assumed quantity as a limit. The important distinction between area and volume in this respect is not commented upon.

Method of limits.—There are about a dozen places in plane and solid geometry in which the method of limits is used to deal with the incommensurable numbers which have arisen in the work. In nearly all cases the proofs are so cast that a variable number is determined in two different ways independent of each other, and use is made of the following "Theorem of Limits":

"If two variables are equal and each approaches a limit, the limits are equal."

Pupils seem to be able to learn to repeat the words of this theorem while failing in many cases to appreciate the cogency of the proof in which it is used. The treatment of limits in geometry is the source of much discontent not only among the teachers themselves, but also among the university examiners and professors.

V. TRIGONOMETRY.

Introductory.—Definition of the functions of an acute angle; generalization to angles in any quadrant. Representation of the functions by lines drawn on a unit circle; change in the values of functions from one quadrant to another.

Formulas.—Proof of the formulas for the sine and cosine of the sum and of the difference of two angles; of the tangent of the sum and of the difference; of the sine, cosine, and tangent of the double and the half of an angle; formulas for the transformation of the sum or the difference of two sines or two cosines into products; practice in the use of all these formulas in reductions.

Logarithms.—Generally logarithms are studied at this point.

Triangles.—Application of logarithms to computation of a right triangle; proofs of formulas for an oblique triangle, using trigonometric algebra as much as possible. Simple applications to surveying and navigation.

VI. ADVANCED ALGEBRA.

Topics treated.—Under this head are given various disconnected topics including: Theory of quadratic equations, with graphs of $y = ax^2 + bx + c$; solution of numerical equations of higher degree in one unknown, with graphical illustration; occasionally successive derivatives of algebraic polynomials, geometrically interpreted, are incidentally taken up as far as advisable in utilizing graphs for explanation; occasionally trigonometric solutions are given for certain equations. Choice and chance. Determinants, with practice in reduction and evaluation (the multiplication theorem omitted). Indeterminate coefficients.

Purpose.—The sole purpose in this course seems to be to furnish information that may be useful in later mathematical study.

Confusion of title.—In many schools the latter part of the course in elementary algebra described previously is styled "Advanced algebra." This usage is confusing and should be avoided.

VII. ARITHMETIC.

In addition to the subjects which are generally recognized as secondary school studies, many high schools give a half year in arithmetic. In smaller schools and in districts where the elementary schools are not so effective, either on account of short terms or on account of more recent establishment of public school education, this is given at the beginning of high school work; in other schools it is given after the years devoted to algebra and geometry, and is called "Advanced arithmetic." The topics are not in any respect different from those treated in elementary schools, though the problems are somewhat more difficult and aim at a closer correlation with commercial practice. There is a decided purpose to attain facility and accuracy in routine operations. Little or no effort is made to treat arithmetic as a science, or as having any real connection with the other mathematical subjects in high school work.

.
.
.

RECENT PROGRESS.

The last 10 years.—In the last 10 years changes in the details of high-school mathematics have been radical and rapid.[5] They are largely the result of the active interest taken in the work of high-school teachers by university professors, and of the conference between high-school men of different localities. Both of these influences have made themselves felt through teachers' associations. So far as the changes and tendencies referred to have actually begun to affect teaching, they appear in recently published textbooks in good use. For this reason the committee has examined some thirty of the recent high-school books on algebra, geometry, and trigonometry, and presents the results of that examination here.

The order of topics.—In almost all these books geometry is supposed to follow a year's work in algebra, though there are one or two books, whose success is still not completely assured, which essay a combination of the two subjects. A combination (or "blending") of plane and solid geometry does not seem to have been seriously attempted.

In algebra the order of topics is only slightly varied from the following:

1. Introduction, negative numbers, etc.
2. "The four operations."
3. Factors, H. C. F. and L. C. M. by factoring.
4. Fractions.
5. Simple equations and problems.
6. Elimination, linear systems.
7. Powers and roots, exponents, radicals.
8. Quadratic equations.
9. Elimination of quadratics.
10. Literal equations, generalization.
11. Proportion, "the progressions," logarithms.
12. The binomial theorem.

In geometry the order of development is still mostly that of Legendre, the five books of plane geometry being successively polygons, circles, similar figures, areas, and regular polygons; and the solid-geometry order being planes and lines, polyhedral angles, prisms and pyramids, and the "three round bodies." Two books transpose the third and fourth books of plane geometry; here and there also is shown a disposition to group propositions in smaller lists than the "books," without, however, changing the order much.

The textbooks in trigonometry agree fairly well on the topics which

---

5. See "Present Tendencies in the Teaching of Geometry" (in the United States) in A. W. Stamper's History of the Teaching of Geometry, New York, Columbia University (1906).

should be taken, but differ widely in their estimate of the relative importance of these topics.

A common arrangement of topics is the following: Functions of an acute angle; solution of right triangles by natural functions and by logarithms; functions of any angle; general value of an angle; the addition and subtraction formulas; formulas for double an angle and half an angle; the conversion formulas; and the solution of oblique triangle by logarithms. In addition to these topics, we find the radian measure, inverse functions, and the line representation of functions, and, in some books, graphical discussion of functions and a careful treatment of the measurement of angles near $0°$ and $90°$.

Graphical methods of discussion.—For some 15 years there has been increasing pressure for the introduction of Cartesian coordinates as an instrument of study in elementary algebra. It began to appear in the schoolbooks about 1898. All but one of the books here examined make use of this device; sometimes it is given in a separate chapter, in one case in an appendix. In a few others it is made an effective part of the structure of the subject. The word "function" is sometimes used, but even without it the work generally begins by plotting curves in which y is a non-algebraic function of x, so that the student gets some insight into the functional relation.

The graph of a two-letter linear equation is pointed out as a straight line. No proof is given, though one book remarks that the "proof follows easily from the geometry of similar triangles." Elimination of linear pairs is illustrated, generally also linear-quadratic and quadratic pairs. No comment is made, as a general thing, on the limitation of this illustration to two-letter equations.

In about one-half of the books the solution of a numerical quadratic equation by the use of a standard parabola ($y = x^2$) and a straight edge is mentioned, and its use recommended as a check on the solution obtained by the algebraic process.

Computation.—In spite of the fact that John Perry's propositions for reform in mathematical teaching have been widely and on the whole favorably considered in this country, not one of the textbooks of algebra, and only one of those in geometry, makes any reference to the number of significant figures in a number as a criterion of the degree of approximation. None gives any directions for economical methods of computation having regard to the degree of accuracy warranted by the data, or gives problems with data appropriate for such practice.

In a geometry textbook of excellent character and long use, problems appear in which the data are such as would occur under the actual circumstances described in the problem; but no directions were given for dealing economically with the difficulties of arithmetic thus introduced, and the problems were considered unsuitable by the schools. In the more modern books here examined the data are all of the predigested sort (one or two-figure integers).

In trigonometry the subject of approximate computation in general, and the fact that only approximate results can be obtained by the use of trigonometric functions, are rarely referred to.

Checks.—The practice of checking the solution of an equation in algebra by substituting the roots, and checking an algebraic transformation by substituting arbitrary values, appears in almost all the algebra textbooks. In trigonometry the subject of checks for the solution of triangles is not carefully treated—several books give no checks except the obvious one for the angles when the sides of the triangle are given. The topic does not appear at all in geometry. No reference is made anywhere to methods of checking the details of computation; it being assumed, no doubt, that the matter has been adequately treated in the study of arithmetic. The textbooks in that subject, and the irresponsible habits of the pupils in computing, do not furnish good ground for such an assumption.

Notation.—In algebra there is a tendency to break the monopoly that the letter x has had in representing numbers whose value is sought. The symbol $\neq$ for "is not equal to" and the symbol $\equiv$ for algebraic identity have come into use. In geometry the symbol $\equiv$ is apparently favored for congruence, instead of $\cong$, which already had good authority. For the exceedingly mysterious thing which some authors call the "intrinsic" sign of a number, a diminutive plus or minus sign is sometimes used.

The notation of lower-case letters for lines and for lengths of lines has at last been introduced into elementary geometry textbooks, to the great advantage of the algebraic proofs. This appears in three of these books, one of which applies it very imperfectly. The same book also uses lower-case letters to represent the number of degrees in an angle, though analogy to the unlimited and the limited straight lines would suggest using a capital for both the point and its associated magnitude, the angle.

Logical terms.—The technical terms of logic are mostly avoided. The term "reductio ad absurdum" occurs in three; the same thing is called "indirect proof" in four others; the "method of exclusion" is pointed out in three. "Reductio ad absurdum" and the "method of exclusion" are both classified as "indirect proof" in one book, while "indirect proof" and the "method of exclusion" are both classified as "reductio ad absurdum" in another. One book manages to avoid all mention of these terms.

The logical inverse is called the converse in all current textbooks, and there is no exception in these latest books. The obverse is so called in one book, is called the opposite in two others, and is omitted in the rest. The contraposite is so called in one, is called, curiously, the contradictory in another, and is not mentioned in the rest, although one book points out the equivalence of the converse and the opposite.

The term "immediate inference" is given and much used in one book. Homothetic position is used for the similarity theorems in two of these textbooks, but under different names ("radially situated," "in perspective"), and in only one of them is it systematically used as a means of demonstration.

Innovations.—The changes in the subject matter of algebra have been referred to under preceding heads. Those in geometry are much less extensive, no doubt because of a widespread belief in the invulnerability of the logical structure represented by the successively dependent propositions. The treatment of incommensurable magnitudes in geometry seems, in particular, to be protected by sacred tradition.

The theorem of limits, namely, that "if two variables are equal and each approaches a limit, the limits are equal," is used systematically in all but two of the books examined, and one of these puts it in an appendix.

The similarity theorems are based on the area theorems in two. Axial and central symmetry are both used in three, and neither appears alone. The idea of symmetry is used for comment and illustration rather than as a method of attack or as a resource in argument.

A decided innovation is the custom of explaining methods of attack for new theorems; this is contained in almost all of the newer textbooks.

The word "congruent" is used in four books, one of the others using the old-fashioned phrase, "equal in all respects." Only one of the books using the word "congruent" uses the word "equal" in the sense of "equivalent."

In solid geometry also there are few innovations—that is, innovations so far as really popular use is concerned. Among them are shaded figures or photographs of actual models, the spherical degree (or "spherid" as one book calls it) as the unit of area on the sphere, and the prismoidal formula. None of the books speaks of a "unit of solid angle;" it is always a "unit of area on the sphere." Some, even of the most enterprising of these authors, adhere to the trirectangular triangle as a unit. The prismoidal formula is apparently not introduced as a means of simplifying the logical structure; it is rather a new addition to the old task.

Problems in algebra.—Much more space is given to equations, and to problems giving rise to equations, as a response to the frequently repeated contention of teachers, uttered in magazine articles and in teachers' associations, that the equation should be the fundamental work at least for the first year. In most cases, however, the preparatory study of transformations (multiplication and division, factoring, fractions, etc.) is carried to a degree far beyond what is necessary for the manipulation of any reasonably probable equations, certainly beyond what are given during first-year work. The study presents, therefore, a somewhat disconnected aspect—first, transformations treated in a systematic and fairly complete fashion, with a few intrusive illustrations of the application of them to equations that do not need much; then, equations treated as material for practice of a small part of this manipulation; and, finally, problems, hopefully sought from newer quarries, designed to show how equations might arise that could be managed by this manipulative skill.

It would probabaly be easy for a young person of good judgment, engaged in reviewing his high-school algebra, to learn that problems cause the invention of equations, and that transformations are necessary for the solution of equations. The prominence given, however, to this systematic development of what must be considered the mechanical side of algebra tends to weaken the interest of the pupil in that part of the subject that is of most value, not only to him whose education stops with the high school, but surely also with the future student of engineering or of pure mathematics; the study, that is, of expressing the conditions of actuality in mathematical form, and of interpreting mathematical results in terms of time, space, and things.

The problems in all these books are very plentiful; sometimes the teacher is warned that the work should not include the solution of *all* the problems, and that their profusion is his opportunity to vary his work from class to class and to specify fresh problems for review lessons. While the character of the problems in three of the books is strictly orthodox, the others take their data freely from geometry, physics, and even from engineering and dietetics (!). There is no hesitation in utilizing the properties of similar triangles, or the phenomena of falling bodies; but there is a chaste reluctance to do anything more than mention the existence of reasons at the back of the facts and formulas used. Our old friend the clock problem survives the dead and buried hare and hound, and the solution in odd elevenths of a second continues to pass without challenge.

Long division, square root, and generally cube root of algebraic expressions are still treated at length, without any comment on the futility of the pupil's attempt when the result does not "come out even."[6]

The comment that an extraneous root of a radical equation can be made to satisfy the equation "by suitably choosing between the two possible signs of a square root" is passing out of use.

Problems in geometry.—The number of "original" exercises to which the pupil is expected to apply his newly acquired knowledge varies from 600 to 1,200 in plane geometry, and from 300 to 600 in solid. Some of them use freely the results of the modern geometry of the triangle and of projective geometry, but without any introduction of the corresponding modern methods in the text. One book, however, includes the nine-point circle, the radical axis, and the notion of reciprocal theorems in the regular text, but omits all mention of symmetry.

6. See Missouri Teachers' Course in Algebra, § I (*b*), § X, (*c*). School Science, April, 1908.

Some effort is made to create a "practical" atmosphere, and one or two modern books are rich in allusions to and illustrations of such things as surveying, parquetry, and architecture. They are dealt with, however, by the sometimes cumbrous methods of Euclidean geometry, instead of by such means as practical men would use.

The fundamental definitions of trigonometry appear, and in a couple of books the tables of natural functions; in one there are two-place tables, in the other a four-place, while in both is used what seems to be a three-figure angle (degrees, and tenths by interpolation).

Loci.—The definition of a locus is introduced at the very beginning in one textbook; in Book II in another; in most of them it appears in Book I in connection with the theorems about perpendiculars and bisectors. In no textbook does the locus of an algebraic equation in two variables appear, though this would seem a not inadvisable corollary of the introduction of graphs into algebra. The nearest thing to it is the problem to find the locus of a point moving so that the figures determining it retain certain numerical properties, as in the locus of the vertex of a triangle with fixed base and constant perimeter. The "real" or "practical" locus problem is still rare; a type of such is the artisan's way of testing the cross-section of a cylindrical core box with a steel square.

While no reference whatever is made to the locus of an equation in the text books on geometry, some of the trigonometries use it in tracing the changes in the values of sine, tangent, etc., as the angle varies; all of them, however, make some reference to the representation of the trigonometric ratios by lines related to a unit circle. Only one comments on the important fact that here we have a line representing a pure number.

Problems in trigonometry.—The problems in trigonometry textbooks comprise the proofs of identities and the numerical solution of equations as opportunities for practice in the transformations of trigonometric expressions; and also the solutions of plane triangles, with applications to questions of surveying, civil engineering, and navigation. The pupil is expected to remember all the formulas referred to on page 21.

Spherical trigonometry is usually considered a college subject, but spherical right (and quadrantal) triangles are often dealt with in the secondary school. With these the so-called Napier's Rules furnish the possibility of memorizing formulas, apparently an indispensable requisite in subjects offered for admission examinations.

Only one of these books mentions the fact that oblique triangles may be solved by dividing them into right triangles. The idea of projection and of the angle functions as projection ratios does not enter into these books. One book refers to it, but makes little use of it.

The solution of oblique triangles comes late, following the addition and subtraction formulas. One book gives a geometric proof for the tangent formula. Angles are generally expressed in degrees, minutes, and seconds; two books have degrees, minutes, and decimals of a minute, and one has a set of examples in which degrees and decimals of a degree are used. Few books have a discussion of the theory of logarithms. It is evidently assumed that the student has received from algebra a knowledge of the nature and properties of logarithms sufficient for the practical application to the solution of triangles. The use of the augmented characteristic in the case of a negative logarithm is almost universal.

We find in one textbook the radian measurement introduced on the second page in the book and no further use made of it, while in another book it is found well along in the book, where an excellent discussion of it is given, and frequent use is made of it in equations, identities, and problems. We find a similar condition of affairs when we look for the inverse functions.

Only one of the books completes the solution of plane oblique triangles before entering upon the discussion of the standard formulas of trigonometric algebra.

.
.
.

METHODS.

Relative popularity.—In the questionnaire issued by this committee 12 methods were listed, the names being taken from well-known books on the teaching of mathematics. The replies indicated clearly, by practice or preference, that five of these methods were most popular:

Measurement and computation.
Laboratory method.
Use of models.
Use of cross-section paper.
Individual method.

Next in order of popularity, after a considerable interval, come the following:

Combination of algebra and geometry.
Out-of-door work.
Paper folding.
Observational geometry, to precede deductive geometry.

The least popular of the 12 suggestions offered were the combination of plane and solid geometry and of geometry and trigonometry; next to them in unpopularity, curiously enough, is the "heuristic" method; and, in view of the noticeable tendency in recent and widely adopted textbooks, the inference is unavoidable that this apparent unpopularity is due to the fact that "heuristic" is a hard word.

On the other hand, the low position of "observational" geometry in these reports is significant. A progressive teacher in Arkansas writes: "We tried a six weeks' course in observational geometry in the second high-school year and saved time by it, but the pupils did not like it; they were too old." The most successful work in observational geometry has been in schools where it could be done by pupils of 12 years of age; the six-year high school is probably a necessary condition for the best use of this expedient.

Outdoor work and paper folding depend on local conditions and individual teachers, respectively. One high-school teacher borrows a transit from the city engineer every spring. Paper folding, used occasionally for symmetry propositions at the beginning of geometry, has not been found available for much else.

The combination of algebra and geometry has a good start in the sense that algebra is applied to the discussion of geometry problems involving numerical relations, but except in isolated cases there has been no blending or interweaving of the two subjects into one.

The five topics listed as the most popular emphasize the decided tendency to cultivate the intuitional side, to utilize sight, touch, and muscular sense as avenues to the pupils' intelligence.

Separate problem book.—One or two attempts have been made by publishers to present algebra by means of a manual and an exercise book separately, but except for review work this plan is hardly ever followed. Principles and practice appear not only in the same book, but as nearly as possible on the same page.

The use of models.—Models, in most cases made by the pupils themselves with cardboard, wire, and fine cord, or thread, are very much used in solid geometry.

The model for equivalent parallelopipeds and for the dissection of a triangle prism into three equivalent pyramids can not generally be so made, and the school owns the patterns, if it is not so fortunate as to own the right sort of teacher. The spherical blackboard is generally used.

Squared paper.—Cross-section paper is very much used, generally for the illustration of elimination, sometimes also for the introduction of the idea of function. A considerable opportunity here for the correlation of algebra and geometry seems to be entirely neglected. Little or no attempt is made to find approximate solutions graphically, in cases where elementary algebra will not help out.

Computation.—Measurement and computation are undertaken in true schoolroom style. No attempt is made to work to a specified degree of accuracy, or to acquire convenient and systematic habits of computation. Logarithms are only used in the trigonometry class, and the slide rule has not appeared in high schools.

Improvement of problems.—Search is being made everywhere for problems that make a more direct appeal to the interest of the pupil than the collections handed down by previous generations. Even in the not infrequent case where these problems are themselves highly improbable as instances of perplexity in human beings, some gain is made by clothing the inventions of the schoolmaster in the words of people that walk the streets to-day, and a great many of them are "real" problems of "practical" import.

.
.
.

AIMS.

General culture and college.—The aim of high-school education, so far as mathematics is concerned, is general culture, and at the same time is preparation for college. There is a slight preponderance of popularity in favor of the former reply, but the latter is close enough to it to make it clear that in the minds of school committees and other official bodies, general culture seems to need the sort of mathematics that is prescribed for admission to college. A considerable fraction—from 25 per cent in the Middle West to 75 per cent in the Atlantic States—include preparation for technical institutes as a part of the purpose that mathematical education is to fulfill.

Not for occupation.—Of the careers that teachers are consciously looking forward to for their pupils, those of the merchant or accountant, the civil or mechanical engineer, the teacher, the farmer, and the "woman of the house" are frequently mentioned. It may well be doubted whether the mathematical training received in high schools gives added efficiency to any degree, in any of these callings; that is to say, the effect of the kind formerly acclaimed and now discredited under the name of general discipline; certainly not to any greater degree than the same amount of time and interest applied to geology, or chemistry, or even to music. The pupil learns to solve algebraic equations, but does not apply them to devising balanced rations for the farm stock out of the crop he raises; he learns about similar triangles, but knows not so much as his grandfather about the thrust on a girder, or about the way of mapping a river, or of estimating the amount of excavation in grading the house lot. He is brighter and keener, because he has been educated, and he has self-reliance because he has done things by his own thinking power; but he has had nothing directly contributory to the special knowledge or aptitude required for these occupations that he may follow—except teaching; surely he can teach what he has been taught, and he does. Thus schools inherit.

The college determines the aim of high-school work.—Since the high school does not prepare by means of mathematical teaching for occupations in which the pupils may subsequently engage, and since mathematics as deemed desirable for general culture is defined by the entrance examinations

346

of the university, the whole question of the aim of this subject in high schools must be decided by the views of university people, and made known, aside from the scanty information of catalogues, by the character of examination questions. On this account the report on examinations will be of great interest.

The presumption is, then, that the subjects of high-school mathematics contain information and cultivate aptitudes that are necessary and useful in college mathematical work; or that so far as they do not do so, they are more useful in other ways than subjects that would do so. This is not true.

No systematic study of the desiderata.—The subject of geometry, for example, passed down from the university to the high school, continued to be taught with little change of content or method as a consequence of the transfer. There is no indication that the present syllabus of high-school mathematics has been adjusted by university professors to the needs of their departments. Nobody knows what parts of it are absolutely necessary for subsequent work in exact science, or whether any of the necessary parts could with advantage be postponed to the university and replaced by topics of interest and of greater value to high-school pupils.

The question is not discussed in such a systematic way as that. Changes that have been brought about, mostly additions, have been fortunate guesses, proposed by tentative examination questions and afterwards reenforced by argument and formal demand. Such are the locus problem and the "original" or "rider" in geometry, the use of graphs in algebra. Within a few years some inconsiderable omissions have been made, such as the division process for H. C. F. in algebra, the square root of a binomial surd, and so on; and a decidedly critical attitude has been maintained against the traditional type of problems based on highly impractical data. All these things, while not aimless, can fairly be called tinkering rather than scientific reconstruction.

Influence of teachers' associations.—The formation of associations of mathematical teachers, in which university professors are actively interested, is bringing about a different attitude on this subject. Several of them have prepared and published reports on aims and methods in algebra and geometry. The most thorough and scientific work may be expected from the committee appointed recently by the National Education Association to form a syllabus of elementary geometry. The plans of that committee include an inquiry into all the considerations that should weigh in determining the scope of the subject, and its membership is such as to warrant the expectation of valuable results.

II. Reports of Subcommittees.

.
.
.

SUBCOMMITTEE 9. FAILURES IN THE TECHNIQUE OF THE TEACHING OF SECONDARY MATHEMATICS: THEIR CAUSES AND REMEDIES.

INTRODUCTION.

In this commercial age, which makes efficiency the controlling factor in all walks of life, the teacher must not expect to escape a searching scrutiny of his results or criticism of his methods. The general public has at last begun to watch with interest, not entirely free from meddlesome curiosity, the work of its tax-supported schools. It is well that it should be so. For may not many of the educational crises of the past be traced to the aloofness of the average teacher from the active world? Separated from the noise and the merciless competition of real life, the school frequently fails to make those unavoidable readjustments which a business establishment effects almost automatically in its effort to remain "up to date."

Thus it happens that the educational process so often is "behind the times." With majestic inertia the school system glides on in its accustomed and "approved" course, long after the familiar landmarks have disappeared and the compass needle points to strange and untried seas. Finally there are dangerous collisions and the passengers complain of the wearisome, aimless trip. Then the educational pilots are roused from their stupor and frantic efforts are made to ascertain the "new course." A "reform wave" is suddenly espied, and carried by this "new movement" the distressed craft tries to regain its bearings.

Another reason for this lack of adjustment lies in the difficulty of the educational process. A new machine is easily installed. A mechanical improvement can readily be tested. Not so the infinitely subtle machinery of the mind. A well-known psychologist frankly admitted that in regard to many aspects of the educational problem psychology is as silent as a sphinx. Scientific pedagogy is only in its infancy. It will be found that in most cases the successful teacher, cautioned of course by scientific study against obvious blunders, rises on the basis of sympathy and tact to the experimental acquisition of a satisfactory technique. But all experimenting takes time. Unless

348

undertaken with the utmost care, it is almost sure to mean educational waste. To this should be added the fact that the average teacher holds office for a short period only and that many schools have practically new faculties every year. The new and inexperienced teacher either follows the rut left by his predecessors or indulges in experimentation of a more or less doubtful character. Only a small percentage of secondary teachers have specialized in their work sufficiently to become really creative.

Thus we have a constant oscillation from stagnation to frantic reform. And it is difficult to determine which is more amusing: The abyssal, cocksure self-complacency of the orthodox old-timer, or the innocent glee of the reformer who announces a new patent remedy for all educational ills. What we really need is a less jerky and erratic development, less dangerous stagnation and more genuine progress.

PURPOSE OF THIS REPORT.

The present inquiry was undertaken with a view to answering the following questions:

(1) Are the results obtained in the teaching of secondary mathematics satisfactory?

(2) If not, is mathematics taught more poorly than other high-school subjects?

(3) In case it is taught as well, and yet the results are poor, what general or specific causes of failure can be pointed out?

(4) What remedies can be suggested?

•
•
•

CAUSES OF FAILURE—PRELIMINARY ANALYSIS.

If we turn now to a consideration of the causes of failure, it becomes at once apparent that our problem is both general and specific. General, in that mathematics is not alone in its inferior results, a fact proved beyond dispute by statistics. Specific, in that we must determine the particular aspects which this general deficiency assumes in the mathematical classroom, as well as the particular remedies that mathematics may offer for overcoming the general weakness. The individual teacher, when confronted by a large number of failures, rarely takes a sufficiently broad view of the situation. In some cases he frankly blames his own limited preparation, his prosaic and uninteresting methods, his lack of enthusiasm. Usually it is the pupils who are condemned in toto, or it is the school system or any number of other factors.

There is little doubt that nearly every high school subject is taught with clearer perception of its aim, methods, and content than a generation ago.

It is even claimed by some that results are better than formerly. (Cf. Report on the Norwich tests, School Review, May, 1910.) If in spite of this improvement and this increased effort our expectations are so poorly realized, must we not first of all look for underlying causes and conditions beyond the control of the average teacher or even the average school?

It has been said over and over again that we are living in a transition period. Old standards are being replaced by uncertainty and scepticism. Education is powerfully affected by this general unrest. Hence, any consideration of the causes of failure would be incomplete and meaningless without a study—however brief and imperfect—of the influences that are transforming our educational system.

TRANSFORMING INFLUENCES IN EDUCATION.

For a brief summary of the present tendencies in education we may refer to a paper read by the chairman of this committee at the Cleveland meeting of the N. E. A. (published in School Science and Mathematics, November, 1908). The following quotations are taken from it:

1. In the first place, modern industrialism, with its demand for tangible success, has led to a great outcry for more practical school work. There is an increasing contempt of "mere theory." This feeling finds its expression in the establishment of trade and technical schools. Mathematics, as usually taught, furnishes a welcome target to the utilitarian educator. As a result there is a growing fear that we may drift too far from the ideal of liberal culture and that the direct bread-winning power of a subject may be made the sole criterion of its usefulness.

2. Our large cities, the natural centers of industry, are also becoming great centers of population. Naturally the struggle for existence is becoming keener. Many parents are now sending their children to the high school to fit them, in the briefest possible time, for a more comfortable life than they themselves enjoy. This has made the high school population more diversified than ever before, and the demands imposed upon the schools have become more numerous from year to year. *For the first time in history, secondary education is truly democratic.* But it can not be denied that the assimilation of so much raw material from homes giving no cultural impulses, and of so many students having no intention of entering higher institutions of learning, is one of the most serious problems of the high school.

3. More far-reaching than these changes of ideal and environment have been certain revolutions in school curricula and methods of instruction. The natural sciences have risen from comparative obscurity to great prominence. Their inductive method of investigation is considered by many as the great panacea for all our troubles. The influence of the laboratory method is undeniable. It is reacting, for example, on the teaching of history and the languages. In so far as it insists on self-reliance and definiteness of results and is productive of greater interest, it is excellent. But it lengthens school hours, calls for costly equipment, and demands much outside work on the part of pupil and teacher.

4. It would be difficult, moreover, to overestimate the effect of the "new education." Its fundamental precept that all work must be arranged psychologically and adapted strictly to the child's power of comprehension is eminently sound. But it has also given us the enriched curriculum, and the doctrine of interest which replaces all objective standards by the subjective attitude of the child. Unquestionably this means at once a distinct advance and a very real source of danger. The complaint is not

infrequent that in many cases the young are learning to depend too much upon the inspirational powers of the teacher, that all real difficulties are carefully avoided, and that the very aim of all true education, to develop a strong character and to create self-activity and initiative, is thereby defeated.

During the past five years we have heard much of the social function of the school. Playgrounds, evening schools, social centers, school clubs, a multitude of new school activities, claim the attention of teachers and pupils. A prominent professor kindly informed us that until exercises in spelling, mental arithmetic, and formal grammar should have become merely incidental and subsidiary, the high-water mark in teaching would not have been reached. It is exaggerations of this sort that rob many otherwise excellent ideas of their legitimate influence and place upon them the stigma of the faddist.

A corollary of this new gospel of social efficiency is the new doctrine of mental discipline. Although not yet clearly formulated, its main contentions are: (1) That mental discipline as ordinarily conceived is a myth, in the sense that no "general training" is to be derived from the intensive study of one or more subjects, such as Latin, algebra, etc.; (2) that the disciplinary value of a subject is a function of the interest which it inspires and of the motive guiding the student; (3) that the cultural value of a subject depends on the extent to which that subject can be, and actually is, linked with the activities and the thought content of real life. In this way the old static, historic, idealistic conception of mental discipline is being replaced by a dynamic, realistic, practical view. (Cf. Formal Discipline, by C. J. C. Bennett, in Teachers College Series, Columbia University.)

It is not so much this new theory itself, as the hasty inferences drawn from it by superficial minds that we must regard as dangerous. In the first place, it requires no proof that the mere completion, however mechanical and stereotyped, of so much "prescribed" Latin or mathematics does not make an educated person. It is equally true that not all boys and girls find the old school subjects profitable, and for a certain number of them industrial or commercial studies are preferable. This proves nothing concerning the presence or absence of inherent disciplinary value in the present curriculum. The early and onesided introduction of professionalism, no matter how successfully managed, is always deplorable. Wherever it becomes imperative, it should be looked upon as a necessary evil. For "it is difference in culture, far more than difference in wealth or position, which separates man from man, and class from class." The blending of liberal education and technical training is the supreme educational problem of our day. In Europe it has been solved by a differentiation of schools. America may have to follow that plan. Secondly, the new theory of discipline does not imply the cultural equivalence of all subjects. On the contrary, it demolishes that view completely. If it can be shown that mathematics can be linked with a larger range of actual thought processes and activities than typewriting or bookkeeping, for example, then the greater disciplinary value of mathematics will have been established. Hence, instead of crowding out the "old studies," the new conception of mental discipline simply gives a better criterion for testing their value and should have the effect of securing better training.

Last, not least, the mathematical curriculum has been affected powerfully by two other, mutually opposing, forces. The Perry movement, a direct outgrowth of the trend toward more practical mathematics, aims to abolish from the course all unnecessary details and to substitute experimental verification for logical deduction. On the other hand, the tremendous progress of scientific research, effected by men like Pasch, Peano, Klein, Hilbert, Veronese, Poincaré, has called attention to the many flaws in the logic of our text-books and has given new impetus to the demand for genuine mathematical rigor.

GENERAL CAUSES OF FAILURE

All these transforming influences if overlooked or ignored by the teacher may become prolific sources of failure. The constant shifting of the educational background demands on the part of the teacher sound judgment, quick insight, wide training, and the capacity for sane, conservative, readjustment. The new situation makes each educational factor both an active and a passive participant in the educational process. The latter distinction is important, as it should save many teachers from unnecessary discouragement. We shall proceed to examine briefly the principal educational factors as causes of failure, either in an active or in a passive rôle.

1. THE TEACHER.

Granted that the teacher meets all the obvious preliminary requirements, such as a strong and yet sympathetic personality, tact, enthusiasm, he nevertheless frequently becomes a serious cause of failure through any one of the following factors:

(1) *Lack of professional preparation.*—This is perhaps the most vital and distressing point of weakness in American secondary education. The only hopeful thing about it is that we are beginning to feel this weakness. Much pounding was required to rouse us. At first it was the foreign critic, or the acclimated American, who put his finger on the sore. Who has not read Prof. Münsterberg's scathing criticisms? And now every number of the educational magazines sings the same melody. "Wanted—a teacher," exclaimed James H. Canfield, of Columbia University, 10 years ago (Educational Review, December, 1900). Some reported cases of professional ignorance seem almost incredible. Time was when everybody thought he could teach everything. This miserable Jacotot fallacy gradually dominated American education, because it harmonized so splendidly with the American spirit of self-activity and independence. Mr. E. George Payne, in a report published by the Kentucky Department of Education, 1909, tells of a young

352

woman who planned to make her entire preparation to teach German in "one of the leading high schools" in Kentucky by spending six weeks on the subject at a summer school. Then he says, "I insist that 90 per cent of those attempting to teach the modern languages in the American schools, especially in the Kentucky schools, do not perform better work than this lady did in first-year German." (See School Review, June, 1910, p. 433.) Shocking, if true. New York State three years ago had only 32.2 per cent of college graduates among its 4,668 secondary teachers. This means that the remaining number had only the equivalent of a high-school education in mathematics. Their horizon was only a little above that of their pupils. How many high-school teachers of mathematics at the present day have ever studied analytics, not to speak of the calculus? How many have ever seen Crystal's Algebra, or Hilbert's Foundations of Geometry, or have read the pedagogical works of Smith or Young? All honor to the noble men and women who, in spite of serious handicaps, have done good work. But every effort should be made from now on by individuals and by schools to secure better professional equipment.

(2) *Lack of professional contact.*—Owing to the vast extent of the country it has been hard to develop esprit de corps outside of the big centers. Departmental organization in the large schools was the first step in the right direction. Associations of teachers soon followed, and any ambitious teacher can now make it possible to meet his colleagues at the educational gatherings. For those who can not go to these meetings the printed reports published in the new mathematical journals furnish a substitute. Lack of contact has been and still is a great source of stagnation. Let us hope it may speedily be removed.

(3) *Overwork.*—It need hardly be said that any teacher who has more than 25 periods a week of required work can not do that work effectively. Entirely indefensible is the practice of loading on a teacher three or four different subjects, especially if they are entirely "out of her line." Careless, half-hearted, indifferent teaching or incessant worry is the inevitable result in most cases. Many classes are altogether too large. We hear so much about individual instruction and personal attention and yet expect a teacher to inspire 40 young people at a time. So long as these conditions prevail to any considerable extent no improvement can follow.

(4) *Short and unstable tenure of office.*—Another very real source of failure: There is altogether too much shifting of positions. It takes several years to grow into a new position. A teacher who finds herself at a different school every two or three years can not expect to be of great service to that school. A very large number of teachers drop out every year, either to be married or to begin a different occupation. At the 1909 meeting of the American Association for the Advancement of Science Prof. William C. Ruediger, of George Washington University, presented the results of some

investigations of the qualities of merit in teachers. He claimed that the best teachers had taught an average of *14 years* and the poorest *8 years*. No teacher who ranked first or second had taught less than 5 years. (See Science, for Apr. 15, 1910.) The shortness of the average teacher's service is due largely to the appallingly low salaries and to the uncertainty of tenure of office. Salaries often are not up to the standard of even the street laborer. No great improvement in teaching need be expected until we shall have (1) better salaries, (2) permanent appointment after a limited trial period, (3) a pension guarantee after a fixed term of service.

2. THE PUPIL.

So long as human nature is imperfect the problem of the pupil will remain with us, especially during the critical period of adolescence. However, many of the difficulties besetting the teacher would all but disappear if it were not for the following great causes of failure:

(1) *Immaturity.*—This is an entirely indefensible factor, in view of the work done in European schools by pupils of the same age. The enrollment of the Chicago public schools in January, 1909, showed the following arrangement of ages:

High school.	Ages.										Total.
	11	12	13	14	15	16	17	18	19	20+	
First-year pupils ..	2	45	708	2,291	2,104	1,045	257	60	14	19	6,555
Second-year pupils .	0	2	47	467	1,236	1,062	532	159	27	14	3,546

(2) *Lack of preparation.*—A large majority of the teachers reporting to us emphasized this point. It seems that our elementary schools either find the problem of democratic education too big a task or use methods that do not produce lasting results. A very large percentage of children do not complete the school course (Chicago, 1909: First grade, 38,239; eighth grade, 14,795).

(3) *Aimlessness.*—The "life-career motive," discussed by President Eliot at the 1910 meeting of the National Education Association, is becoming more essential in proportion as increased competition demands greater technical or professional equipment. Altogether too many pupils have no dominant purpose that might keep them at work. A moderate vocational tendency may prove a partial remedy, although it would be a grievous mistake to make vocational studies the sole basis of our secondary education.

(4) *Social diversions.*—Pupils must, of course, have a certain amount of relaxation. But many pupils have too much fun, too much athletics of the grand-stand type, too many social functions. They often develop the habits

of grown-ups, become priggish, domineering, sluggish, and incapable of persistent effort. Lack of home training is responsible for much of this. A real educational crusade must be begun to convince parents of the necessity of careful moral and social training of their children. The increasing agitation against fraternities and athletics is a welcome indication of a sound reaction against the social evils of the high school.

3. HIGH-SCHOOL ORGANIZATION

The fact is that the high school has outgrown its present form of organization. It is sinning every moment against the law that two material bodies can not occupy the same space at the same time. It loses a tremendous number of its pupils (Chicago, 1909: First year, 6,555; fourth year, 1,467). Those who graduate have an education that must be pronounced both unsymmetric and superficial.

(1) *Lack of symmetry.*—This defect is apparent not only in the curriculum as a whole, but is felt in nearly every subject, especially in mathematics, history, and science. The average high-school graduate can at best solve an ordinary quadratic equation or analyze a simple geometric problem. The geometry of solids remains foreign to him, the most helpful trigonometric relations do not form part of his equipment, and, above all, he has not learned to apply his mathematics to the realities of life. This meager outfit, so laboriously acquired, is speedily lost because it is not broad enough to be of real use.

(2) *Lack of thoroughness.*—President Rush Rhees, of the University of Rochester, after a year abroad devoted to a careful inspection of European technical schools, stated at a recent educational meeting that lack of thoroughness is the most widespread defect of the educational work of our American schools. He said that the American educational system gives intellectual power, but fails to impart intellectual life, and that in practical work it fails with reference to methods of study. In mathematics all these defects become accentuated through the tandem system—first algebra, then geometry, then a year of complete interruption, then a review of entirely forgotten principles. A fairly good algebraic foundation may be laid in a year, but geometry most certainly requires more time. A comparison of the percentage of failures in elementary algebra and plane geometry in the tables of the appendix shows that geometry is less successfully taught than algebra, although the poorest pupils drop out at the end of the first year, thus leaving a smaller and more mature body of students.

The effort to make the elective system remedy these defects may be likened to an attempt to cure dyspepsia with liberal doses of olive oil. The digestive apparatus would probably function normally if proper mastication were not rendered impossible by too rapid and ill-arranged feeding. The group system, which is now being substituted for an excessive elective system, will secure greater thoroughness, but not necessarily greater symmetry. Hence, unless the principle of a cosmopolitan high school is to be given up and vocational schools are to take its place a different remedy must be found.

SPECIFIC CAUSES OF FAILURE.

Under this head we must limit ourselves to a brief consideration of the aim, the content, and the methods of secondary mathematics teaching.

Aim.—The one-sided doctrine of mental discipline must go. There need not be any antagonism between theory and practice. Neither Euclid alone nor Perry alone should be our guide. We ought to have a fusion of the abstract and the concrete, a fusion dictated by common sense and free from radicalism in either direction. A teacher who dwells exclusively on half-comprehended, nonproductive subtleties is as much to blame as one who emphasizes merely the How and not the Why. Real applications should be introduced systematically, but the acquisition of a satisfactory technique must not be allowed to suffer. Much of the indifference so often prevailing in mathematical classrooms would disappear if the teachers would take pains to make x and y talk realities and if they poured some life blood into the chimerical formulas of geometry.

Subject matter.—In very many classrooms the textbook or the syllabus of an examining body seems to be the only authority for the content and the relative prominence of the topics considered. Very many pupils fail to get the right point of view. In algebra the whole course must be built around two leading ideas, (1) the equation as a means of stating and solving numerical relations, (2) the development of the number system. In geometry propositions should be arranged topically, and theorems having small inherent value or not serving as building stones for the whole system should be omitted. The teaching of incommensurables and limits will soon become optional. In all cases the "thought nodes" should stand out prominently in the pupil's mind. The course in secondary mathematics should not be a monotonous array of facts stretching away on an endless wire, but a landscape showing a few towering mountains and many connecting valleys.

Method.—A discussion of method is always dangerous, for here the experienced teacher considers himself on terra firma. It would be the height of conceit, however, not to acknowledge a connection between our poor results and our methods of instruction.

1. In the first place, our school hours should be periods of instruction, of actual thinking and doing, and not merely "recitations." There is no doubt that the "little red schoolhouse," with its insufficient equipment, is responsible for the plan of assigning lessons from a book without previous classroom discussion. In that little school such a practice was a deplorable necessity, since the one teacher in charge was not equal to the task of in-

structing many classes at once, or of mastering all the prescribed subjects. When the pupils had done their "studying," they were kept busy at the board or were given much written work to do. In this way the textbook and the blackboard gradually usurped the place of the teacher, who soon became a lesson-hearing automaton registering the "marks." That which at first had been a mere makeshift, finally crystallized, under the misunderstood maxims of Rousseau, Fröbel, Jacotot, into a national policy. For this system of teaching was supposed to give full play to the development of individual initiative, of self-activity, etc. Thus it seemed to meet all the requirements of an ideal education. Apparently it turned out self-made men— and it was cheap. How many slow pupils remained submerged forever was not determined. That this outgrowth of the pioneer days of the country should retain so much of its power in the modern high school is a new proof of the overwhelming influence of Anglo-Saxon conservatism. The grotesqueness of the idea becomes apparent when we imagine Socrates assigning a lesson from Homer to Plato or Aristotle.

2. The "recitations" should be less monotonous and less mechanical. The usual procedure consists in giving a brief explanation of the advanced lesson, then sending a large number of pupils to the board, where they consume from five minutes to a whole period. In geometry there is a little more variation. It has been said, to be sure, that mathematics must be written into the mind. But mechanical writing is useless. First the thought, then the symbol. How little real thinking excessive written work often represents is proved by those pupils who get splendid marks in algebra but are put down as hopeless cases in gometry. The blackboard is a very valuable piece of furniture, but it should be reserved for reviews or snappy drill work. Some teachers have very good success with a system of cards, kept in a filing cabinet. These cards are given out to pupils for miscellaneous blackboard drill.

3. The class, and not the individual, should be the working unit. This is true because individual instruction is usually impossible. Training a class from the beginning to respond in a body makes for greater economy of effort, secures more uniform results, and leaves time for applied work and laboratory methods. This is the real secret of the excellent results obtained in many European schools. Every teacher of mathematics should read Prof. J. W. A. Young's "The Teaching of Mathematics in the Schools of Prussia." Two members of this committee in recent years made a personal comparative study of American and European schools, Mr. Betz in Germany and Miss Wardwell in England. A detailed account of the French system, from the American standpoint, was furnished to the Rochester section of the Association of Teachers in the Middle States and Maryland by Prof. Etzel, of Rochester, the latter having taught more than two decades in French secondary schools. The reports all agree in finding in European schools greater concentration of effort, as well as greater certainty and uni-

formity of good training, although these results are perhaps obtained at the expense of originality and spontaneity. The first thing that astonishes the American visitor is the small blackboard and the immense amount of oral work. A limited use of the Prussian method can be recommended unconditionally. A number of American teachers have tried it and speak highly of it.

And yet, no method can possibly take the place of a real enthusiastic teacher. The true teacher is an artist. He is ever watching for improvements. He is not dogmatic, but eclectic. The best thoughts of all ages and climes help him to wield an influence which, through his skillful leadership, produces a satisfactory harmony.

REMEDIES

Throughout this report remedies have been considered in connection with the causes of failure. The remedies suggested in our questionnaire were all received favorably by the teachers except the first, which called for "more through teaching by taking more time, e. g., six-year curriculum." Only a small number expressed an opinion in regard to it, thus indicating that the plan is not sufficiently clear.

At the risk of some repetition we propose the following additional remedies:

I. *A six-year curriculum, to begin at the end of the present sixth grade.*— Not a single valid objection can be urged against the plan. The present cramped curriculum seriously interferes with—

(1) The right sort of approach to each subject.

(2) Thoroughness of assimilation.

(3) Permanence of impressions.

(4) Applications of vital interest to pupils.

(5) The coordination and proper sequence of studies.

Many other reasons may be presented why we need more time than formerly. The following list might easily be extended:

(1) We must get away from mechanical textbook teaching.

(2) The prevalence of laboratory methods consumes more time. The spirit of discovery is inconsistent with machine routine.

(3) The old curriculum paid almost no attention to the demands of actual life. It ignored applications.

(4) The requirements of the higher institutions and of the professions are becoming more intensive and extensive.

(5) The complexity of modern life furnishes so many distractions to the young student that more thorough teaching and more reviews are necessary than formerly.

The plan has been tried in some American cities. For a detailed account we must refer to the report of subcommittee 8. The six-year curriculum seems to solve many of our difficulties. All possible objections should be removed by considerations such as the following:

1. It has been tried in Europe. In England, France, and Germany secondary education begins much earlier, usually at the age of 9. This long-continued, unified period of instruction, administered by carefully prepared teachers, is primarily responsible for the supremacy of Europe in science and—perhaps—in foreign commerce. Excellent accounts of the Prussian system may be found in the above-named book of Prof. Young, and in Prof. Klein's Vorträge über den Mathematischen Unterricht an den höheren Schulen (Leipzig, 1907). A brief résumé of present-day teaching of geometry in Europe and America is given in A. W. Stamper's "A History of the Teaching of Elementary Geometry" (Teachers College, Columbia University, 1909). The German high-school boy, in the three types of secondary schools, is given a total of 1,360, 1,680, 1,880 hours, respectively, of unified mathematical instruction. This work is compulsory, and all but the first two or three years of it corresponds to secondary mathematics in our country; so that 960, 1,280, 1,480 hours, respectively, are given to secondary mathematics. Plane geometry extends over a period of from five to six years; solid geometry over a period of four years; trigonometry, four years; algebra, six years.[7] Compare with this our less than 200 algebra periods and 200 geometry periods. A pupil who takes four years of mathematics in our high schools gets a maximum of less than 800 periods of instruction, while the German minimum is 960.

2. A six-year curriculum will secure closer contact with the elementary schools.

3. There is no reason why our educational system should not consist of three periods of equal length—primary (6–12), secondary (13–18), higher (19–24).

4. In a more extended secondary course it will be easier to discover a pupil's special aptitudes.

5. The proper psychological moment for teaching certain subjects, e. g., modern languages, can be utilized.

6. An increasing number of pupils find it impossible to complete the present course in four years. Instead of compelling them to fail and drop out, we could adapt the work better to their capacity.

7. The six-year curriculum offers the only hope of overcoming the tandem system. All efforts to secure unified mathematical instruction have been useless under existing conditions.

II. The mathematics teachers of the future must lay a much broader foundation in their own preparation. No candidate lacking a knowledge of

---

7. It is of course necessary to remember that ordinarily four weekly periods are devoted to unified mathematics, not to algebra or geometry alone.

the rudiments of trigonometry, analytics, the calculus, and elementary mechanics, ought to be appointed to a high-school position in mathematics. A familiarity with surveying and shop work is also very desirable. Salaries must be made sufficiently high to justify this increased requirement.

III. There must be more expert supervision. This should not be of the nature of petty fault-finding, but should be administered with a spirit of cooperation and inspiration. The experience of other countries justifies the belief that this is a much more effective method of stimulating teachers to better efforts than our periodic examinations, which frequently seem to be narrow and pedantic, and to select incidentals rather than essentials.

.
.
.

PART THREE: 1920–1937

The "1923 Report" and Connectionism in Arithmetic

The major historical document of this period is clearly *The Reorganization of Mathematics in Secondary Education,* the report of the National Committee on Mathematical Requirements which is commonly called the "1923 Report." Because of this report's significance and lack of general availability, all of part 1 of the report has been selected. The report was written by many notables of the time, including David Eugene Smith, J. W. A. Young, and E. H. Moore.

Of particular importance in this report was the solidification of the junior high school–senior high school curriculum. The foundations for the junior high school program were laid in the prior period. The result, as seen in this period, was the integrated or fused course we now frequently call "general mathematics." General mathematics, as originally conceived, is best represented by the mathematics course commonly taught today in grades 7 and 8. This course was conceived as a course for all students rather than as a separation point for college-bound and non-college-bound students. Only later did the grade 9 course act as a separation point.

The influence of the "1923 Report" continued until the report in 1959 of the Commission on Mathematics of the College Entrance Examination Board (chapters of which are included in Part Four). That this influence did not create a corresponding change in practice was due mainly to the traditional inertia in educational practice and the depression of the 1930s.

A major report which has received less stress is the mathematics report of the Commission on the Reorganization of Secondary Education appointed by the National Education Association. (The same commission prepared *Cardinal Principles of Secondary Education* in 1918.) The report, *The Problem of Mathematics in Secondary Education,* was published in 1920. It had fewer mathematics educators of distinction as authors; and only one man, Raleigh Schorling, served on this commission and also worked on the "1923 Report." *The Problem of Mathematics in Secondary Education* discusses needs for mathematics and the needs of students, and it spends little time on course outlines. The committee concentrated on the curriculum for junior high school.

The geometry selection written by George D. Birkhoff and Ralph Beatley (1930) is an example of material that appeared before its time. Their approach to geometry anticipated the recent surge in secondary geometry curriculum and methodology.

In arithmetic, the first decade of the 1920–37 interval was marked by the arrival of connectionism as the dominant psychology. Two major interpreters of this theory, Edward L. Thorndike and Frederick B. Knight, selections from whose writings are included here, were themselves psychologists. Each wrote influential series of arithmetic texts. But like the "faculty" doctrine popular fifty years earlier and the "methods" of the turn of the century, connectionism was seen to be overapplied. An alternative theory that gained some acceptance was Gestalt psychology. Gestalt theory made insight and discovery key elements in learning and denied the connectionistic tenet that learning consists of stimulus-response bonds induced by drill.

William Brownell's meaning theory, expounded in an article included in this section, was compatible with the Gestalt point of view. Meaning theory was, however, less bound to any school of psychology or philosophy than its predecessor. For while the theory is generally consistent Gestalt psychology, it is worthy of note that Brownell does not cite psychological sources in justification of his theory in the major statement included here. Although Brownell denied being eclectic, he can be seen to fulfill the interpretive function of the mathematics educator in the tradition of David Eugene Smith.

DEPARTMENT OF THE INTERIOR
BUREAU OF EDUCATION

BULLETIN, 1920, No. 1

THE PROBLEM OF MATHEMATICS IN SECONDARY EDUCATION

A REPORT OF THE COMMISSION ON
THE REORGANIZATION OF SECOND-
ARY EDUCATION, APPOINTED BY THE
NATIONAL EDUCATION ASSOCIATION

WASHINGTON
GOVERNMENT PRINTING OFFICE
1920

CONTENTS.

	Page.
Membership of the committee on the problem of mathematics.	3
Membership of the reviewing committee of the commission	3
Letter of transmittal	7
Preface	8
I. Introduction	9
II. The demand for an inquiry	9
III. Analysis of the situation	11
1. The problem of presentation	11
2. The several needs for mathematics	11
3. Comparative values	14
4. Formal discipline	15
5. The needs of the several groups	16
6. Selecting mathematical ability	17
IV. Suggestions as to courses	20
1. The work of the junior high school	21
2. Trade mathematics	22
3. Preliminary engineering	23
4. For the specializers	23

5

COMMITTEE ON THE PROBLEM OF MATHEMATICS IN SECONDARY EDUCATION.

William H. Kilpatrick, *chairman*, professor of education, Teachers College, Columbia University, New York, N. Y.

Fred R. Hunter, superintendent of schools, Oakland, Calif.

Franklin W. Johnson, principal University High School, University of Chicago, Ill.

J. H. Minnick, assistant professor of educational methods, University of Pennsylvania, Philadelphia, Pa.

Raleigh Shorling, Lincoln School, 646 Park Avenue, New York, N. Y.

J. C. Stone, head of department of mathematics, State Normal School, Montclair, N. J.

Milo H. Stuart, principal Technical High School, Indianapolis, Ind.

J. H. Withers, superintendent of schools, St. Louis, Mo.

The Problem of Mathematics in Secondary Education.

I. Introduction.

Few subjects taught in the secondary school elicit more contradictory statements of view than does mathematics. What should be taught, how much of it, to whom, how, and why, are matters of disagreement. There is every variety of position. A conservative group would keep substantially unchanged the customary content and division into courses, and find the hope of improvement in a more adequate preparation of teachers. To this limited reform an increasing number object, with little agreement, however, among themselves. Amid the conflict of opinions the committee on the problem of mathematics in secondary education believes that a reconsideration of the whole question is desirable.

To present the finished details of a working plan would have been most gratifying to the committee, but this has been judged impossible. The situation seems to force the limitation. To carry weight, such a detailed plan would have to be based upon a wider range of experiment than in fact exists. Only recently has there been serious effort to consider the problem of the proper content and arrangement of the courses in secondary mathematics. The pertinent experiments available for study do not as yet present a variety of type and testing sufficient to establish the necessary conclusions. Within the time allotment available to the committee there seemed then only the choice between no report and an admittedly preliminary report. The committee has chosen the latter alternative, and proposes to lay before the American educational public (1) some of the considerations that demand a fresh study of the problems involved, (2) some of the factors that bear upon the solution of the problem, and (3) certain tentative suggestions for experimentation to develop new and better courses.[1] It is but fair to say that few of the specific suggestions made are in fact new, many being already somewhere actually in practice.

1. It is gratifying to note that the Mathematical Association of America is pushing a program of study and experimentation along lines quite similar to those here discussed.

II. The Demand for an Inquiry.

An inquiry into the advisability of reorganizing and reconstituting secondary mathematics is demanded from a variety of considerations.

1. It is being insisted as never before that each subject and each item in the subject justify itself; or, negatively, that no subject or item be retained in any curriculum unless its value, viewed in relation to other topics and to time involved, can be made reasonably probable. No longer should the force of tradition shield any subject from this scrutiny. A better insight into the conditions of social welfare, and the many changes among these conditions, alike make inherently probable a different emphasis upon materials in the curriculum, if not a different selection of actual subject matter. This calls for a review and revaluation, in particular, of all our older studies, mathematics not least.

2. Moreover, a growing science of education has come to place appreciably different values upon certain psychological factors involved, chief among which is that relating to "mental discipline." No one inclusive formulation of the older position can be asserted, yet on the whole there was acceptance of the "faculty" psychology with an uncritical belief in the possibility of a good-for-all training of the several "faculties." To the extremist of this school the "faculty of reasoning," for example, could be trained on any material where reasoning was involved (the more evident the reasoning, the better the training), and any facility of reasoning gained in that particular activity, could, it was thought, be accordingly directed at will with little loss of effectiveness to any other situation where good reasoning was desired. In probably no study did this older doctrine of "mental discipline" find larger scope than in mathematics, in arithmetic to an appreciable extent, more in algebra, most of all in geometry.

With the scientific scrutiny of the conditions under which "transfer" of training takes place, the inquiry grows continually more insistent as to whether our mathematical courses should continue unchanged, now that so much of their older justification has been modified. Possibly both purpose and content need to be changed.

3. Yet another demand for reconstruction is found in the now generally accepted belief that not all high-school pupils should take the same studies. The fact of marked individual differences has been scientifically established. The principles of adaptation to such individual differences, that is, to individual needs and capacities, is now widely accepted in the high schools

of America. The exception calls for scrutiny. Traditionally, algebra and geometry have been required for graduation. Is this necessary or advisable? In this growing practice of differentiation and adaptation we have then a third reason for at least reconsidering the customary mathematics courses.

4. A demand for reconsideration well worthy of our attention is found in the insistent question whether a content chosen to furnish preparation for further but remote study does necessarily or even probably include the wisest selection of knowledge useful for those who do not reach that advanced stage of study. Whether all should learn first the more assuredly useful topics, or whether alternative courses should be offered, are proper subjects of inquiry. In either event we find in this consideration a fourth reason for studying anew the offerings of our high-school mathematics.

5. A fifth reason for reconsideration is found in the problem of method. Educators are studying now with new zeal the proper presentation of subject matter in all school work. Should not this study extend to secondary mathematics? Have we arranged the subject matter of that field in the best form for appropriation? Might it even be possible that mathematics should be reorganized in a way to run across customary lines of division? Or might this be true of some parts of mathematics for some groups of pupils and not be true of all? The proper answers to such questions are not at once evident, but certainly there is enough point in the inquiry to add a fifth reason for our proposed investigation.

III. Analysis of the Situation.

1. *The problem of presentation.*—Far-reaching differences of method carry with them widely different organizations of subject matter, especially in introductory courses. From this consideration, at least, there are certain advantages in discussing as the first factor in the situation the problem of presentation.

The traditional school method has been that based upon the "logical" arrangement of subject matter. Thus our fathers studied English grammar before they took up composition, the "science" being "logically" anterior to the "art." The science, in this case grammar, began with a definition of itself and the analysis of the subject into its four principal divisions. Then came the definitions of the "parts of speech." It was a long—and generally dreary —road before the pupil could see any bearing of what he learned upon anything else. At length, after toilsome memorizing, there appeared within the subject itself a new variety of mental gymnastics which called forth from some a certain show of activity. In the end the survivors caught some glimpse of what it had all been about. But when they took up the "art" of composition, the "science" proved of small assistance. Somehow the "art" had to be learned as if it alone faced the actual demand.

From an implicit reliance upon this "logical" arrangement there has come a revolt, not yet universal, but still unmistakably at hand. The demand has now become insistent that in arranging subject matter for learning, consideration be given, not to "logic" as formerly conceived, but to economy in learning and effective control of subject matter. This reversal of method, coupled with a distrust of the theory of discipline, has thus not only reduced grammar to a small fraction of its former self, but has, besides, greatly rearranged and rewritten the study.

Keeping before us the demand for economy in learning and effective control of subject matter, what can we say about method? How does learning in fact take place? (1) Repetition is a factor in learning known to all. (2) An inclusive "set" which shall predispose the attention, focus available inner resources, and secure repetition is a necessary condition less commonly considered. (3) The effect of accompanying satisfaction to foster habit formation is a third factor to be noted.[2] These three factors are neces-

---

2. The behaviorist psychologist by definition rejects the subjective connotation of "satisfaction." If we had access to the actual psychology involved, possibly the difference of statement would in effect disappear.

sary, then, to adequate consideration of the problem of method. It accords with these considerations and with undisputed observation that, other things being equal, any item is more readily learned if its bearing and need are definitely recognized. The felt need predisposes attention, calls into play accessory mental resources, and in proportion to its strength secures the necessary repetition. As the need is met, satisfaction ensues. All factors thus cooperate to fix in place the new item of knowledge. The element of felt need thus secures not only the learning of the new item, but it has at the same time called into play the allied intellectual resources so that new and old are welded together in effective organization with reference to the need which originally motivated the process.

Lest some should fear that by need is here meant a mere "bread and butter demand," the committee hastens to say that it is psychologic and not economic need which acts as the factor in learning. Economic need may indeed be felt; and, if so, may then serve to influence learning; but there is nothing in the foregoing argument to deny that a purely "theoretic" interest might not be as potent as any other to bring about the learning and organization of subject matter.

To speak of the bearing and need of any new material is to imply the presence and functioning of already existent purposes and interests. From this consideration thus related to the foregoing the committee believes that, speaking generally, introductory mathematics—ordinarily conceived as separate courses in algebra, geometry, and trigonometry—should be given in connection with the solving of problems and the executing of projects in fields where the pupils already have both knowledge and interest. This would make the study of mathematics more nearly approximate a laboratory course, in which individual differences could be considered and the effective devices of supervised study be utilized. The minimum of the course might well in this way be cared for in the recitation period, reserving the outside work rather for allied projects and problems in which individual interests and capacities were prominent factors.

The significant element in this conception is the utilization of ideas and interests already present with the pupils as a milieu within which the mathematical conception or process to be taught finds a natural setting, and from which a need to use the conception or process can as a consequence be easily developed. Where this state of affairs exists, the bearing and felt need utilize the laws of learning as was discussed above, and the mathematical knowledge or skill is fixed in a manner distinctly economical as regards both present effort and future applicability.

As was stated at the outset, this suggested procedure reaches beyond the questions of economy of learning and application—controlling though these here are—to the question of content. The procedure here contemplated makes definite demand for an appropriate introductory content. To work along this line there must be made a selection of conceptions and processes which can serve the pupils as instruments to the attainment of the ends set before them in the projects or problems upon which they are at work. This instrumental character becomes then the essential factor in any introductory course. It is these instrumental needs and not "logical" interconnectedness which must give unity to such a course. A content thus instrumentally selected will, on the one hand, be free of the old formal puzzles, the complex instances, the verbal problems which in the past have wasted so much time and destroyed so much potential interest; and will, on the other, run across the divisions heretofore separating algebra, geometry, and trigonometry.

A distinct advantage in the procedure here suggested is the better promise it holds out of meeting in one introductory course the needs of both those who will go on to advanced study in mathematical lines and those who will not. Where the basis of selection and procedure is instrumental, all can begin together. The future specializers in mathematics will as the course proceeds take increasing interest in the mathematical relationships involved and will stress this aspect in their individual problems and projects. Those whose tastes and aptitudes lead them elsewhere will in the meanwhile have had the opportunity to learn in practical situations some of the mathematical concepts and processes which they will later use in their own chosen fields. Their individual projects in the course can serve well as connecting links between the mathematics taught and their later field of vocational application.

After the introductory course has been completed, and differentiation has begun, the same principles still hold, though in the different fields. Those who have chosen to continue the study of mathematics as such will find their problems or projects within the field of mathematics itself, quite likely examining anew in the light of wider acquaintance assumptions freely made in the earlier period. Euclid's system of axioms and postulates might here receive its first careful consideration. Those who had elected to prepare for engineering and the like might continue to find their mathematics in connection with problems or projects devoted now particularly to a preliminary engineering content. Conceptions usually reserved for college analytics and calculus—if not indeed already used in the introductory course—can well have a place here. Their rich instrumental character will justify their presence, even if they lack somewhat in relationship to a fully developed logical system.

2. *The several needs for mathematics*—Among the multiplicity of specific occasions for using mathematics and among the various types of subject matter, there are certain possible groupings which promise aid in the determination of the mathematical courses.

Without implying the possibility always of sharp differentiation, we may distinguish in the realm of mathematical knowledge (i) those items the immediate use of which involve a minimum of thinking, as, for example, adding a column of figures, and (ii) those items which are primarily used as notions or concepts in the furtherance of thinking. It is clear that the distinction here is of the way in which the knowledge is used and not of the knowledge itself; for any item of knowledge might at one time serve one function and at another time the other. It would still remain true, however, that certain groups of people might have characteristically different needs along the two lines. Under the first head we should include the mechanic's use of a formula, the surveyor's use of his tables, the statistician's finding of the quartile. The man in the street would call this the "practical" use of mathematics. Under the other head we should include the intelligent reader's use of mathematical language by which he would understand an account of Kepler's three famous laws. Some may wish to call this the "cultural" use of mathematics. The term "interpretative" might, however, more exactly express the differentiating idea.

We may next ask whether there are differentiable groups among high-school pupils whose probable destinations or activities determine within reasonable limits the extent and type of their future mathematical needs. In a democracy like ours, questions of probable destination are of course very difficult. There must be no caste-like perpetuation of economic and cultural differences; and definite effort must be made to keep wide open the door of further study for those who may later change their minds. But differentiating choices are in fact made; and in view of the wealth of offerings on the one hand and of individual differences on the other, such choices must be made. Properly safeguarded by an intelligent effort to adopt social demands to individual taste and aptitude, these choices should work to the advantage both of the individual and of the group. The committee considers that four groups of users of mathematics may be distinguished:

(*a*) The "general readers," who will find their use of mathematics beyond arithmetic confined largely to the interpretative function described above.

(*b*) Those whose work in certain trades will make limited, but still specific, demand for the "practical" use of mathematics.

(*c*) Those whose practical work as engineers or as students of certain sciences requires considerable knowledge of mathematics.

(*d*) Those who specialize in the study of mathematics with a view either to research or to teaching or to the mere satisfaction of extended study in the subject.

It is at once evident that these groups are not sharply marked off from each other; and that the needs of the first group are shared by the others. It is, moreover, true that the "general readers" represent a wide range of interest. The committee has taken all these things into account, and still believes that the division here made will prove of substantial utility in arranging the offerings of high-school mathematics.

3. *Comparative values.*—Out of the conflict of topics for a place in the program there emerges one general principle, already suggested in these pages, which is being increasingly accepted for guidance by students of education. In briefest negative terms: *No item shall be retained for any specific group of pupils unless, in relation to other items and to time involved, its (probable) value can be shown.* So stated the principle seems a truism, but properly applied it proves a grim pruning hook to the dead limbs of tradition. A final method of ascertaining such comparative values remains to be worked out; but the feasibility of a reasonable application of the principle will hardly be denied. In accordance with this, many topics once common have been dropped from the curriculum and more are marked to go. Thus our better practice has ceased to include the Euclidian method of finding the H. C. F., because the knowledge of this method is nowhere serviceable in life; and in secondary algebra itself little if anything else depends on it. Indeed, the H. C. F. itself might well go, as it is used almost exclusively in simplifying fractions made for the purpose.

In a full discussion, many terms of the statement would need consideration. What constitutes value is probably the point where most questioning would arise. The committee takes this term in its broadest sense, specifically denying restriction to a "bread and butter" basis or other mere material utility, though affirming that remunerative employment is normally a worthy part of the worthy life. What the statement then in fact demands is (i) that the value of the topic be not a mere assumption—a positive case must be made out; and (ii) that the value of the topic so shown be sufficiently great in relation to other topics and to the element of cost (as regards time, labor, money outlay, etc.) to warrant its inclusion in the curriculum.

This principle of exclusion seems especially applicable to those items which now remain merely as a heritage from the past and to those which have been introduced mainly to round out the subject or where the unity of the subject matter has been found in the content itself and not in the relation of the content to the needs of the pupil.

In offering such a principle for guidance, the committee considers that it is merely stating explicitly what has been implicitly assumed in all such controversies. The committee none the less believes that conscious insistence on the point is necessary in order to disclose whatever indefensible elements may be in our present program of studies.

4. *"Formal discipline."*—A full discussion of this topic, of course, is impossible within the limits of this paper. Such a discussion is, moreover, for our purpose unnecessary, because we shall wish to use only the most general conclusion, in which there is substantial concurrence. We can thus

avoid the niceties of elaboration, about which agreement has not yet been reached. The older doctrine assumed uncritically a very high degree of what we now call "general transfer" of training. Modern investigation, to speak generally, restricts very considerably the amount of transfer which may reasonably be expected, and inquires strictly into the conditions of transfer. Under the older doctrine it was a sufficient justification for the requiring of any subject that pupils should gain through it increased ability in the use of any important "faculty," because the increase in ability was naively assumed to mean an increase in the equally naively assumed faculty itself and would accordingly be effective wherever the faculty was used. As pupils show such an increase of ability in one or more "faculties" by the simple fact of learning any new subject, the convenience of this older doctrine for curriculum defense is evident. When this old psychological doctrine was first called in question by scientific measurement, the idea gained popular currency that all transfer was denied. No such claim has serious support. The psychologists, however, have so far found it difficult to agree upon any final situation as to the amount of transfer which in any particular situation may be a priori expected. All agree, none the less, in greatly reducing the old claim both as to the amount and as to the generality of conditions under which transfer may be expected. In accordance with these considerations the committee has not used the factor of "formal discipline" in determining the content of the mathematical courses to be recommended in this report.

5. *The needs of the several groups.*—With these several principles and factors before us, we are now ready to consider more fully the needs of the several groups of users as distinguished above. We are particularly concerned to ask whether or not their respective group needs are compatible with one introductory course to be taken in common; and if yes, when the differentiation from such a common course should begin.

(1) *The "general readers."*—This group will need to use in "practical" fashion but little of mathematics other than ordinary arithmetic. As general readers, however, they will still require a certain acquaintance with mathematical language and concepts. Just what terms, symbols, and concepts would meet the requirements of this group will have to be determined by extensive inductive studies. Assuming, however, ordinary arithmetic and mensuration, some items can be at once named as fairly certain to be included: How to interpret and evaluate a simple literal formula; the meaning and use of an algebraic equation of one unknown; the notion and use of negative numbers in such simple cases as temperature, latitude, and stock fluctuations; the simpler conception of space relations (inductively obtained); the notion of function (the dependence of one quantity upon another); the graph as a means of interpreting statistical information, with such terms as average and median.

(2) *The group preparing for certain trades.*—Under this head the committee would group those whose use of "practical" mathematics is, while generally quite definite, still relatively small—such, for example, as machinists, plumbers, sheet-metal workers, and the like. The general run of the need here contemplated can be gathered from the requirements laid down for machinists in one of the more recent vocational surveys—simple equations, use of formulas, measurement of angles, measurements of areas and volumes, square root, making and reading of graphs, solution of right triangles, geometry of the circle. Much practice would of course be necessary to make even this small amount of mathematics function adequately.

It is at once evident that if no more algebra is needed than formulas, simple equations and the graph, and no more geometry than is here suggested, then the ordinary high-school courses in these subjects are but ill-adapted to the needs of such pupils. It would seem to follow that this group of pupils has no need to follow courses in mathematics other than (i) arithmetic, (ii) the "interpretative" (introductory) mathematics discussed above, and (iii) the special applications of these to the specific subject matter of their several specializations.

This group might then well study in common with the preceding until the completion of the work there laid out. The presentation of this common course along the lines previously laid down (p. 11) would well harmonize the somewhat diverse interests of the two groups. What little additional content and whatever practice in specialized application this second group might need could then be given either in a parallel or in a succeeding course (or courses) especially devised for that purpose.

(3) *The group preparing for engineering.*—This group will consist mostly of boys intending to study in engineering schools. In contrast with the two preceding groups, appreciably more mathematics is here needed. In contrast with the following group, there are here specific aims external to mathematics itself which define and limit the mathematical knowledge and skill needed. Although recognizing that the individual teacher will require a certain leeway as regards content in getting his class effectively to work at any topic, we may still profitably ask as to the minimum content fixed for this group by its peculiar needs.

The minimum mathematical content suitable for the use of this group can probably best be secured by working simultaneously along two lines: First, to ascertain inductively what mathematics the engineer needs (including experiment to find out what part of this can best be taught in the secondary school); second, to criticize the existing courses to see what they lack and what they include that is useless for this group. It is much to be hoped that necessary inductive studies and experiments along the first line of procedure may be vigorously pushed. The second in important respects waits for the first, but it is possible from certain inherent considerations at once to exclude some matter now customarily taught.

Taking the customary high-school mathematics as a basis for comparison, we find at least three principles of criteria for exclusion from the present offerings: (*a*) Exclude all those items which are not themselves to be directly used in practical situations or which are not reasonably necessary to the intelligent mastery or use of such "practical" items; (*b*) exclude all involved and complicated instances of otherwise useful topics or applications which do not serve to clarify the main point under consideration; (*c*) exclude all such proofs and discussions as do not in fact help the pupil to an intelligent use of the topic. It is probably correct to say that these exclusions relate to material introduced from considerations of theory rather than of intelligent practical mastery; from considerations of the pleasure that theorizers (teachers mostly) get from the study of mathematics rather than from a conscious purpose to give that familiarity and grasp which the future practical man will need.

Under the head of (*a*) topics excluded as not needed in this group the committee would mention such as the H. C. F. and the L. C. M.; operations with literal coefficients (except for a few formulas); radical equations; the theory of exponents, except the simplest operations with fractional and negative exponents (these to be retained to give meaning to logarithms and the slide rule); operations with imaginaries; cube root; proportion as a separate topic (the simple equation suffices); the progressions.

Among (*b*) excluded complex applications might be mentioned the following: All lengthy exercises in multiplication and division; factoring beyond the simplest instances of the four forms (i) $ax + ay$, (ii) $a^2 - b^2$, (iii) $a^2 + 2ab + b^2$, (iv) $x^2 + (a + b) x + ab$; all but the simplest fractonal forms (the more complicated are in fact given to illustrate factoring); all radicals beyond $\sqrt{ab}$ and $\sqrt{a \div b}$; simultaneous equations of more than two unknowns; simultaneous quadratics (except possibly a quadratic and a linear); the clock, hare and hounds, and courier problems and the like; the extended formal demonstrative geometry of our ordinary schools; most trigonometry beyond the use of sine, cosine, and tangent in triangle work.

(*c*) Proofs excluded or deferred are mostly cared for in (*a*) and (*b*). The chief instances in the past (too often yet remaining for the "specializers") have been the distinction between negative quantities and negative numbers, the (supposedly) rigorous generalizing of $a^m \times a^n = {}^{m+n}$, the proof of too evident propositions in geometry, the incommensurable cases in geometry, the general proof of $\sin (x + y)$.

It may be mentioned in this connection that teachers of mathematics from arithmetic onward only too frequently deceive themselves as to the place that the presentation of a rigorously logical proof plays in bringing conviction. The worth of a sense of logical cogency can hardly be overestimated;

but we who teach not infrequently overreach ourselves in our zeal for it. The teacher of introductory mathematics can well take lessons from the laboratory, where careful measurement repeated under many different conditions will bring a conviction often otherwise unknown to the pupil who is not gifted in abstract thinking. Probably in most instances an inductively reached conviction is the best provocative of an appetite for a yet more thoroughgoing proof.

Everything so far points to one common introductory course. With this group as with the preceding, the point of differentiation would seem to come at the end of the interpretative course first discussed for the "general readers." Whether this third (engineering) group should proceed further in common with the fourth group (of specializers), we later consider further in common with the fourth group.

(4) *The group of specializers.*—This group will include those pupils, both boys and girls, who "like" mathematics. While these best of all could continue to work with the present offerings, the considerations urged under the discussion on presentation suffice, in the committee's opinion, to demand even for this group a far-reaching reorganization of practically all of secondary mathematics.

Since we are here planning for those who specialize in mathematics, we are not called upon—after meeting the interpretative need—to consider any external demands upon mathematics, but only such a selection and arrangement within the subject itself as best furthers the mathematical activity. Hitherto, the arrangement within the course has been made, as we saw in the discussion on presentation, in answer to considerations rather of "logical" organization than of psychological experiencing and growth. The results have not been satisfactory. Algebra, geometry, and, to a lesser degree, trigonometry have been treated as separate logical entities, with consequent loss to the pupil of both interest and power. The committee thinks that the selection and organization should be made in the light of experiment as to which conceptions do in fact prove successively most strategic in the pupils' continued approach to mathematical power. The result would probably take a form somewhat analogous to the "general science" course which is now being worked out in that field.

That this group should take its introductory work in common with the others has perhaps been sufficiently implied. The intelligent choice of a specialty could hardly precede the actual experiencing of taste and aptitude. How far beyond the common introductory course this group should go in company with the third (the preliminary engineering) is not easy to say. In all but the largest schools administrative considerations will probably keep the two together in whatever work is offered. Where numbers and funds suffice, differentiation may well begin immediately upon the completion of the common introductory course, according to considerations already laid down. In that case the preliminary engineering group would get their mathematics more in terms of engineering content and situations; those specializing in mathematics would get theirs more directly in terms of "pure" mathematics. The contents of such courses could well differ considerably.

6. *Selecting mathematical ability.*—From the point of view both of society and its needs and of the individual and his satisfactions, it is highly desirable that ability, or the lack thereof, be disclosed in order that intelligent choice may be made. Mathematical ability as expressed in mathematical achievement and application is a most powerful agency in advancing civilization. In order that society may profit by its available stock of mathematical ability, there is urgent need of some process that shall disclose this ability. Analogous considerations demand that the individual learn by a less costly process than occupational trial what degree of probable success he may expect from an occupation in which mathematical ability is an important factor. We hope much from further psychological study in this field of disclosing specific abilities, but as matters now stand the opportunity in the high school for trial of mathematical success and liking is at least one important part in the disclosing of mathematical ability. This factor must be taken into account in arranging the introductory work in mathematics.

IV. Suggestions as to Courses.

Each valid consideration in the foregoing discussion should have its effect in the resulting determination of the mathematics courses. Considerations of presentation demanded that we give up the "logical" arrangement of subject matter, especially for introductory work, and find instead an organization based upon the successful attack of projects and problems in connection with which the pupils already have both knowledge and potential interest. Four groups of pupils judged by probable destination showed four types of mathematical needs: (i) The "general readers," whose needs lie largely in the "interpretative" function of mathematics; (ii) those who, expecting to enter trades, would have a small but still definite need for "practical" mathematics; (iii) those who, as prospective engineers, would need a considerable body of content determined by the demands of engineering study and practice; (iv) those specializing in mathematics who would wish a content determined by the satisfactions inherent in the activity and by the demands of further study. From considerations of comparative values nothing should enter into the curriculum except as it can show probable value in relation to other topics and to time involved. "Formal discipline" was not considered by the committee in determining the content of courses to be recommended. Care should be given that at an early stage mathematical taste and ability may be disclosed so as to allow appropriate choice of school work and occupational preparation. It seemed clear that a new introductory course should be offered which all the students should, normally, take in common. College entrance considerations, except as inherently cared for above, are deliberately disregarded.

With these demands before us, can an appropriate school procedure be devised and feasibly operated?

The task certainly is great. Nothing short of extended study and experimentation can meet the situation. The committee makes the following tentative suggestions as possible lines along which research and trial might prove profitable.

1. *The work of the junior high school.*—It seems to the committee that the work of grades 7, 8, and 9 should, in addition to whatever review of previous arithmetic may be necessary, include—

A. A body of processes and conceptions commonly called arithmetic, where the study, however, is of social activities—trade or otherwise—which need mathematics, rather than of mathematical topics artificially "motivated" by social relationships. As a constituent part of these processes the committee would include any use of algebra or intuitive geometry within easy reach of the pupils which can prove its worth by actual service in common life outside of the school.

B. A body of mathematical symbols, concepts, information, and processes—commonly thought of as belonging to algebra and geometry or beyond—which the intelligent general reader of high school or college standing will need in order to meet the demands of his social and intellectual life. As a part of this content, it seems safe to suggest the ordinary algebraic symbols, the use of the formula, the simple equation, and the (statistical) graph.

C. The opportunity for at least a preliminary testing of mathematical taste and aptitude.[3]

D. Such additional content—relatively small in amount—as may be needed to make effective the teaching of the foregoing.

The appropriate contents of parts A and B can be fixed only by a carefully made inductive study of the demands as they actually exist; the contents of parts C and D, only after extended experimentation. The contents of B, C, and D, respectively, the committee judges to be in the descending order of size and importance. Pending the scientific determination of these several contents, the committee feels that a wide diversity of offerings is to be welcomed as a sign of healthy variation likely to promote progress.

Just what course groupings of the foregoing should be made must likewise be for some time a matter of experimentation. Some will wish to consider the whole three years' work as one unity, the various items being presented in such connections among themselves and with the situations of application as good teaching may suggest. Others will wish to give A in grade 7, and devote grades 8 and 9 to an extended treatment of B, C, D. Still others will give two years to A, probably reducing the weekly time allowance, and in the ninth grade concentrate on B, C, D.

Especial attention is called to the course to be made up of B, C, and D (whether extending through one year or two). This is the common introductory course referred to many times in these pages. It is assumed that as a rule all pupils would take it (or at least begin on it), and that no further mathematics would be customarily required for college entrance.[4]

2. *Trade mathematics.*—For the groups of small but definite "practical" use the committee judges that the foregoing will commonly suffice so far as

3. We have grounds for hoping that psychological tests may prove of material assistance in this connection.

4. Any pupil would of course be permitted to offer for entrance credit any other mathematics he had elected in his secondary school. It is, moreover, probable that certain college courses open to freshmen would specify as a necessary prerequisite an amount of mathematics greater than that here included in this "general readers' " course.

concerns specific mathematical content. In some of the trade curriculums, however, it will be necessary to provide a specific course (or courses) in which sufficient practice in the trade application can be found. The more directly such courses can be connected with the work of application the better.

3. *Preliminary engineering.*—For the preliminary engineering group there are, after the common introductory course, several possibilities. One would be to have this group work as heretofore with the "specializers" (see 4 below). This is perhaps less desirable, but will probably continue for some time to come as the more usual procedure, especially in the secondary school of not more than moderate size and income. Another possibility would be to construct a course specifically for this group from a careful study of the specific demands of their future work (see pages 18 and 19 above). Such a content could then be given according to the principles of presentation discussed earlier (see p. 11). Here again experimentation will be necessary to develop an effective organization and procedure. Such experimentation may be expected to show a wide range of variation—at the one extreme an approximation to the old formal "logical"; at the other, an effort to make all mathematics teaching purely incidental to other work. And again, a wide diversity is at the first a healthy indication.

4. *For the specializers.*—Where numbers and income warrant, there should be elective work during the grades 10, 11, and 12 for those specializing in mathematics. There is need, as previously stated, to reorganize the customary offerings for these years in such a way as to displace a presentation based on classification for a presentation based on experimentally determined conditions in growth, in interest, and power.

Such a reorganization will naturally run across the lines of division heretofore maintained, and will probably anticipate certain conceptions and procedures confined now to analytics and calculus. Where the preliminary engineering group is included with this group it may prove advisable to utilize to a considerable extent problems and projects from the natural sciences to give a certain desirable concreteness of thinking. This may well result in benefit to all concerned. With progress in the work should come, however, for the group of specializers an increased interest in and desire for mathematics on its own account. Such a reorganization as is suggested above would probably reduce in appreciable degree the quantity of formal demonstrative geometry, a result that the committee anticipates with equanimity. It seems probable that by suitable experimentation a new course can be worked out which will prove more alluring to the pupil and at the same time furnish a better introduction to the further study of the subject. Various efforts tending to corroborate this belief have already been made both in this country and abroad.

It may be asked whether all secondary schools should try to make full offerings of the courses here suggested. The committee thinks not. It will expect that work substantially equivalent to that here suggested for the grades 7, 8, and 9 will everywhere be offered; that the trade courses will naturally be restricted to trade curriculums; but that the elective work for the senior high school may be restricted in small schools where the income is not large. It seems probable that the relative reduction attending elective mathematics in the college will extend itself similarly to the secondary school. The committee in conclusion deprecates the continued disposition on the part of some colleges unwisely to dictate the contents of courses in secondary schools. It feels that such a usurpation of power operates to prevent the secondary school from making the most intelligent adaptation of its work to the needs of its pupils.

THE

REORGANIZATION OF MATHEMATICS

IN

SECONDARY EDUCATION

A Report by

THE NATIONAL COMMITTEE
ON
MATHEMATICAL REQUIREMENTS

under the auspices of

THE MATHEMATICAL ASSOCIATION
OF AMERICA, INC.

THE MATHEMATICAL ASSOCIATION OF AMERICA, INC.

1923

The National Committee on Mathematical Requirements

(Under the auspices of The Mathematical Association of America, Inc.)

J. W. Young, chairman, Dartmouth College, Hanover, N. H.

J. A. Foberg, vice chairman, State Department of Public Instruction, Harrisburg, Pa.

MEMBERS.

A. R. Crathorne, University of Illinois.

C. N. Moore, University of Cincinnati.[1]

E. H. Moore, University of Chicago.

David Eugene Smith, Columbia University.

H. W. Tyler, Massachusetts Institute of Technology.

J. W. Young, Dartmouth College.

W. F. Downey, English High School, Boston, Mass.,
  representing the Association of Teachers of Mathematics in New England.[2]

Vevia Blair, Horace Mann School, New York City,
  representing the Association of Teachers of Mathematics in the Middle States and Maryland.

J. A. Foberg, director of mathematical instruction, State Department, Harrisburg, Pa.,[3]
  representing the Central Association of Science and Mathematics Teachers.

A. C. Olney, Commissioner of Secondary Education, Sacramento, Calif.

Raleigh Schorling, The Lincoln School, New York City.

P. H. Underwood, Ball High School, Galveston, Tex.

Eula A. Weeks, Cleveland High School, St. Louis, Mo.

---

[1] Prof. Moore took the place vacated in 1918 by the resignation of Oswald Veblen, Princeton University.

[2] Mr. Downey took the place vacated in 1919 by the resignation of G. W. Evans, Charlestown High School, Boston, Mass.

[3] Until July, 1921, of the Crane Technical High School, Chicago, Ill.

PREFACE

The National Committee on Mathematical Requirements was organized in the late summer of 1916 under the auspices of The Mathematical Association of America for the purpose of giving national expression to the movement for reform in the teaching of mathematics, which had gained considerable headway in various parts of the country, but which lacked the power that coördination and united effort alone could give.

The original nucleus of the committee, appointed by E. R. Hedrick, then president of the association, consisted of the following: A. R. Crathorne, University of Illinois; E. H. Moore, University of Chicago; D. E. Smith, Columbia University; H. W. Tyler, Massachusetts Institute of Technology; Oswald Veblen, Princeton University; and J. W. Young, Dartmouth College, chairman. This committee was instructed to add to its membership so as to secure adequate representation of secondary school interests, and then to undertake a comprehensive study of the whole problem concerned with the improvement of mathematical education and to cover the field of secondary and collegiate mathematics.

This group held its first meeting in September, 1916, at Cambridge, Mass. At that meeting it was decided to ask each of the three large associations of secondary school teachers of mathematics (The Association of Teachers of Mathematics in New England, The Association of Teachers of Mathematics in the Middle States and Maryland, and The Central Association of Science and Mathematics Teachers) to appoint an official representative on the committee. At this time also a general plan for the work of the committee was outlined and agreed upon.

In response to the request above referred to the following were appointed by the respective associations: Miss Vevia Blair, Horace Mann School, New York City, representing the Middle States and Maryland Association; G. W. Evans, Charlestown High School, Boston,. Mass., representing the New England Association;[1] and J. A. Foberg, Crane Technical High School, Chicago, Ill., representing the Central Association.

At later dates the following members were appointed: A. C. Olney, Commissioner of Secondary Education, Sacramento, Calif.; Raleigh Schorling, The Lincoln School, New York City; P. H. Underwood, Ball High School,

---

1. Mr. Evans resigned in the summer of 1919, owing to an extended trip abroad; his place was taken by W. F. Downey, English High School, Boston, Mass.

Galveston, Tex.; and Miss Eula A. Weeks, Cleveland High School, St. Louis, Mo.

From the very beginning of its deliberations the committee felt that the work assigned to it could not be done effectively without adequate financial support. The wide geographical distribution of its membership made a full attendance at meetings of the committee difficult if not impossible without financial resources sufficient to defray the traveling expenses of members, the expenses of clerical assistance, etc. Above all, it was felt that, in order to give to the ultimate recommendations of the committee the authority and effectiveness which they should have, it was necessary to arouse the interest and secure the active coöperation of teachers, administrators, and organizations throughout the country—that the work of the committee should represent a coöperative effort on a truly national scale.

For over two years, owing in large part to the World War, attempts to secure adequate financial support proved unsuccessful. Inevitably also the war interfered with the committee's work. Several members were engaged in war work[2] and the others were carrying extra burdens on account of such work undertaken by their colleagues.

In the spring of 1919, however, and again in 1920, the committee was fortunate in securing generous appropriations from the General Education Board of New York City for the prosecution of its work.[3]

This made it possible greatly to extend the committee's activities. The work was planned on a large scale for the purpose of organizing a truly nation-wide discussion of the problems facing the committee, and J. W. Young and J. A. Foberg were selected to devote their whole time to the work of the committee. Suitable office space was secured and adequate stenographic and clerical help was employed.

The results of the committee's work and deliberations are presented in the following report. A word as to the methods employed may, however, be of interest at this point. The committee attempted to establish working contact with all organizations of teachers and others interested in its problems and to secure their active assistance. Nearly 100 such organizations have taken part in this work. A list of these organizations will be found in the appendix to this report (p. 632). Provisional reports on various phases of the problem were submitted to these coöperating organizations in advance of publication, and criticisms, comments, and suggestions for improvement were invited from individuals and special coöperating committees. The reports previously published for the committee by the United States Bureau of

2. Professor Veblen resigned in 1917 on account of the pressure of his war duties. His place was taken on the committee by Professor C. N. Moore, University of Cincinnati.

3. Again in November, 1921, the General Education Board made appropriations to cover the expense of publishing and distributing the present report and to enable the committee to carry on certain phases of its work during the years 1922-1923.

Education[4] and in The Mathematics Teacher[5] and designated as "preliminary" are the result of this kind of coöperation. The value of such assistance can hardly be overestimated and the committee desires to express to all individuals, organizations, and educational journals that have taken part its hearty appreciation and thanks. The committee believes it is safe to say, in view of the methods used in formulating them, that the recommendations of this final report have the approval of the great majority of progressive teachers throughout the country.

No attempt has been made in this report to trace the origin and history of the various proposals and movements for reform nor to give credit either to individuals or organizations for initiating them. A convenient starting point for the history of the modern movement in this country may be found in E. H. Moore's presidential address before the American Mathematical Society in 1902.[6] But the movement here is only one manifestation of a movement that is world-wide and in which very many individuals and organizations have played a prominent part. The student interested in this phase of the subject is referred to the extensive publications of the International Commission on the Teaching of Mathematics, to the Bibliography of the Teaching of Mathematics, 1900-1912, by D. E. Smith and C. Goldziher (U. S. Bureau of Education, Bulletin, 1912, No. 29) and to the bibliography (since 1912) to be found in this report (Chap. XVI, p. 539*f*).

The National Committee expects to maintain its office, with a certain amount of clerical help, during the year 1922-23 and perhaps for a longer period. It is hoped that in this way it may continue to serve as a clearing house for all activities looking to the improvement of the teaching of mathematics in this country, and to assist in bringing about the effective adoption in practice of the recommendations made in the following report, with such modifications of them as continued study and experimentation may show to be desirable.

4. The Reorganization of the First Courses in Secondary School Mathematics, U. S. Bureau of Education, Secondary School Circular, No. 5, February, 1920. 11 pp. Junior High School Mathematics, U. S. Bureau of Education, Secondary School Circular, No. 6, July, 1920. 10 pp. The Function Concept in Secondary School Mathematics, Secondary School Circular, No. 8, June, 1921. 10 pp.

5. Terms and Symbols in Elementary Mathematics, The Mathematics Teacher, Vol. 14 (March, 1921), pp. 107-118. Elective Courses in Mathematics for Secondary Schools, The Mathematics Teacher, vol. 14 (April, 1921), pp. 161-170. College Entrance Requirements in Mathematics. The Mathematics Teacher, vol. 14 (May, 1921), pp. 224-245.

6. E. H. Moore: On the Foundations of Mathematics, Bulletin of the American Mathematical Society, vol. 9 (1902-3), p. 402; Science, vol. 17, p. 401.

TABLE OF CONTENTS

PART I. GENERAL PRINCIPLES AND RECOMMENDATIONS

PAGE

CHAPTER I. A brief outline of the report 3

CHAPTER II. Aims of mathematical instruction—general principles ... 5

CHAPTER III. Mathematics for years seven, eight and nine 19

CHAPTER IV. Mathematics for years ten, eleven and twelve 32

CHAPTER V. College entrance requirements 43

CHAPTER VI. List of propositions in plane and solid geometry 55

CHAPTER VII. The function concept in secondary school mathematics .. 64

CHAPTER VIII. Terms and symbols in elementary mathematics 74

PART II. INVESTIGATIONS CONDUCTED FOR THE COMMITTEE

CHAPTER IX. The present status of disciplinary values in education
by Vevia Blair.. 89

CHAPTER X. The theory of correlation applied to school grades
by A. R. Crathorne 105

CHAPTER XI. Mathematical curricula in foreign countries
by J. C. Brown.. 129

CHAPTER XII. Experimental courses in mathematics
by Raleigh Schorling 177

CHAPTER XIII. Standardized tests in mathematics for secondary schools
by C. B. Upton 279

CHAPTER XIV. The training of teachers of mathematics
by R. C. Archibald.. 429

CHAPTER XV. Certain questionnaire investigations 509

CHAPTER XVI. Bibliography on the teaching of mathematics
by D. E. Smith and J. A. Foberg...................... 539

Appendix: List of Co-operating Organizations.............. 632

Index.. 639

Part I. General Principles and Recommendations

CHAPTER I

A Brief Outline of the Report

The present chapter gives a brief general outline of the contents of this report for the purpose of orienting the reader and making it possible for him to gain quickly an understanding of its scope and the problems which it considers.

The valid aims and purposes of instruction in mathematics are considered in Chapter II. A formulation of such aims and a statement of general principles governing the committee's work is necessary as a basis for the later specific recommendations. Here will be found the reasons for including mathematics in the course of study for all secondary school pupils.

To the end that all pupils in the period of secondary education shall gain early a broad view of the whole field of elementary mathematics, and, in particular, in order to insure contact with this important element in secondary education on the part of the very large number of pupils who, for one reason or another, drop out of school by the end of the ninth year, the National Committee recommends emphatically that the course of study in mathematics during the seventh, eighth, and ninth years contain the fundametal notions of arithmetic, of algebra, of intuitive geometry, of numerical trigonometry, and at least an introduction to demonstrative geometry, and that this body of material be required of all secondary school pupils.

A detailed account of this material is given in Chapter III. Careful study of the later years of our elementary schools, and comparison with European schools, have shown the vital need of reorganization of mathematical instruction, especially in the seventh and eighth years. The very strong tendency now evident to consider elementary education as ceasing at the end of the sixth school year, and to consider the years from the seventh to the twelfth inclusive as comprising years of secondary education, gives impetus to the movement for reform of the teaching of mathematics at this stage.

While Chapter III is devoted to a consideration of the body of materials of instruction in mathematics that is regarded as of sufficient importance to form part of the course of study for all secondary school pupils, Chapter IV is devoted to consideration of the types of material that properly enter into courses of study for pupils who continue their study of mathematics beyond the minimum regarded as essential for all pupils. Here will be found recommendations concerning the traditional subject matter of the tenth, eleventh, and twelfth school years, and also certain material that heretofore has been looked upon in this country as belonging rather to college courses of study; as, for instance, the elementary ideas and processes of the calculus.

Chapter V is devoted to a study of the types of secondary school instruction in mathematics that may be looked upon as furnishing the best preparation for successful work in college. This study leads to the conclusion that there is no conflict between the needs of those pupils who ultimately go to college and those who do not. Certain very definite recommendations are made as to changes that appear desirable in the statement of college entrance requirements and in the type of college entrance examination.

Chapter VI contains lists of propositions and constructions in plane and in solid geometry. The propositions are classified in such a way as to separate from others of less importance those which are regarded as so fundamental that they should form the common minimum of any standard course in the subject.

The statement previously made in preliminary reports of the National Committee and repeated in Chapter II, that the function concept should serve as a unifying element running throughout the instruction in the mathematics of the secondary school, has brought many requests for a more precise definition of the rôle of the function concept in secondary school mathematics. Chapter VII is intended to meet this demand.

Recommendations as to the adoption and use of terms and symbols in elementary mathematics are contained in Chapter VIII. It is intended to present a norm embodying agreement as to best current practice.

The remaining chapters (Part II) give for the most part the results of special investigations conducted for the National Committee. The contents of these chapters are indicated sufficiently in the general table of contents and in the tables of contents preceding many of the chapters in question.

CHAPTER II

Aims of Mathematical Instruction—General Principles

I. INTRODUCTION.

A discussion of mathematical education, and of ways and means of enhancing its value, must be approached first of all on the basis of a precise and comprehensive formulation of the valid aims and purposes of such education.[1] Only on such a basis can we approach intelligently the problems relating to the selection and organization of material, the methods of teaching and the point of view which should govern the instruction, and the qualifications and training of the teachers who impart it. Such aims and purposes of the teaching of mathematics, moreover, must be sought in the nature of the subject, the rôle it plays in the practical, intellectual, and spiritual life of the world, and in the interests and capacities of the students.

Before proceeding with the formulation of these aims, however, we may properly limit to some extent the field of our enquiry. We are concerned primarily with the period of secondary education—comprising, in the modern junior and senior high schools, the period beginning with the seventh and ending with the twelfth school year, and concerning itself with pupils ranging in age normally from 12 to 18 years. References to the mathematics of the grades below the seventh (mainly arithmetic) and beyond the senior high school will be only incidental.

Furthermore, we are primarily concerned at this point with what may be described as "general" aims, that is to say aims which are valid for large sections of the school population and which may properly be thought of as contributing to a general education as distinguished from the specific needs of vocational, technical, or professional education.

---

1. Reference may here be made to the formulation of the principal aims in education to be found in the Cardinal Principles of Secondary Education, published by the U. S. Bureau of Education as Bulletin No. 55, 1918. The main objectives of education are there stated to be: 1. Health; 2. Command of fundamental processes; 3. Worthy home membership; 4. Vocation; 5. Citizenship; 6. Worthy use of leisure; 7. Ethical character. These objectives are held to apply to all education—elementary, secondary, and higher —and all subjects of instruction are to contribute to their achievement.

II. THE AIMS OF MATHEMATICAL INSTRUCTION

With these limitations in mind we may now approach the problem of formulating the more important aims that the teaching of mathematics should serve. It has been customary to distinguish three classes of aims: (1) Practical or utilitarian, (2) disciplinary, (3) cultural; and such a classification is indeed a convenient one. It should be kept clearly in mind, however, that the three classes mentioned are not mutually exclusive and that convenience of discussion rather than logical necessity often assigns a given aim to one or the other of these classes. Indeed, any truly disciplinary aim is practical and, in a broad sense, the same is true of cultural aims.

Practical aims.—By a practical or utilitarian aim, in the narrower sense, we mean then the immediate or direct usefulness in life of a fact, method, or process in mathematics.

1. The immediate and undisputed utility of the *fundamental processes of arithmetic* in the life of every individual demands our first attention. The first instruction in these processes, it is true, falls outside the period of instruction which we are considering. By the end of the sixth grade the child should be able to carry out the four fundamental operations with integers and with common and decimal fractions accurately and with a fair degree of speed. This goal can be reached in all schools—as it is being reached in many—if the work is done under properly qualified teachers and if drill is confined to the simpler cases which alone are of importance in the practical life of the great majority. (See more specifically, Chapter III, p. 21.) Accuracy and facility in numerical computation are of such vital importance, however, to every individual that effective drill in this subject should be continued throughout the secondary school period, not in general as a separate topic, but in connection with the numerical problems arising in other work. In this numerical work, besides accuracy and speed, the following aims are of the greatest importance:

(*a*) A progressive increase in the pupil's understanding of the nature of the fundamental operations and power to apply them in new situations. The fundamental laws of algebra are a potent influence in this direction. (See 3, below.)

(*b*) Exercise of common sense and judgment in computing from approximate data, familiarity with the effect of small errors in measurements, the determination of the number of figures to be used in computing and to be retained in the result, and the like.

(*c*) The development of self-reliance in the handling of numerical problems through the consistent use of checks on all numerical work.

2. Of almost equal importance to every educated person is *an understanding of the language of algebra* and the ability to use this language intelligently and readily in the expression of such simple quantitative rela-

tions as occur in every-day life and in the normal reading of the educated person.

Appreciation of the significance of formulas and ability to work out simple problems by setting up and solving the necessary equations must nowadays be included among the minimum requirements of any program of universal education.

3. The development of the ability to understand and to use such elementary algebraic methods involves a study of the *fundamental laws of algebra* and at least a certain minimum of drill in algebraic technique, which, when properly taught, will furnish the foundation for an understanding of the significance of the processes of arithmetic already referred to. The essence of algebra as distinguished from arithmetic lies in the fact that algebra concerns itself with the operations upon numbers *in general*, while arithmetic confines itself to operations on *particular* numbers.

4. The ability to understand and interpret correctly *graphic representations* of various kinds, such as nowadays abound in popular discussions of current scientific, social, industrial, and political problems, will also be recognized as one of the necessary aims in the education of every individual. This applies to the representation of statistical data which are becoming increasingly important in the consideration of our daily problems, as well as to the representation and understanding of various sorts of dependence of one variable quantity upon another.

5. Finally, among the practical aims to be served by the study of mathematics should be listed familiarity with the *geometric forms* common in nature, industry, and life; the elementary properties and relations of these forms, including their *mensuration;* the development of *space-perception;* and the exercise of *spatial imagination*. This involves acquaintance with such fundamental ideas as congruence and similarity and with such fundamental facts as those concerning the sum of the angles of a triangle, the pythagorean proposition, and the areas and volumes of the common geometric forms.

Among directly practical aims should also be included the acquisition of the ideas and concepts in terms of which the quantitative thinking of the world is done, and of ability to think clearly in terms of those concepts. It seems more convenient, however, to discuss this and, in a broad sense, the same is true of cultural aims.

Disciplinary aims.—We would include here those aims which relate to mental training, as distinguished from the acquisition of certain specific skills discussed in the preceding section. Such training involves the development of certain more or less general characteristics and the formation of certain mental habits which, besides being directly applicable in the setting in which they are developed or formed, are expected to operate also in more or less closely related fields—that is, to "transfer" to other situations.

The subject of the transfer of training has for a number of years been a very controversial one. Only recently has there been any evidence of agreement among the body of educational psychologists. We need not at this point go into detail as to the present status of disciplinary values since this forms the subject of a separate chapter (Chap. IX; see also Chap. X). It is sufficient for our present purpose to call attention to the fact that most psychologists have abandoned two extreme positions as to transfer of training. The first asserted that a pupil trained to reason well in geometry would thereby be trained to reason equally well in any other subject; the second denied the possibility of any transfer and hence the possibility of any general mental training. That the effects of training do transfer from one field of learning to another is now, however, recognized. The amount of transfer in any given case depends upon a number of conditions. If these conditions are favorable, there may be considerable transfer, but in any case the amount of transfer is difficult to measure. Training in connection with certain attitudes, ideals, and ideas is now almost universally admitted by psychologists to have general value. It may, therefore, be said that, with proper restrictions, general mental discipline is a valid aim in education.

The aims which we are discussing are so important in the restricted domain of quantitative and spatial (i. e., mathematical or partly mathematical) thinking which every educated individual is called upon to perform that we do not need for the sake of our argument to raise the question as to the extent of transfer to less mathematical situations.

In formulating the disciplinary aims of the study of mathematics the following should be mentioned:

(1) The acquisition, in precise form, of those *ideas or concepts in terms of which the quantitative thinking of the world is done*. Among these ideas and concepts may be mentioned ratio and measurement (lengths, areas, volumes, weights, velocities, and rates in general, etc.), proportionality and similarity, positive and negative numbers, and the dependence of one quantity upon another.

(2) The development of *ability to think clearly in terms of such ideas and concepts*. This ability involves training in—

(a) Analysis of a complex situation into simpler parts. This includes the recognition of essential factors and the rejection of the irrelevant.

(b) The recognition of logical relations between interdependent factors and the understanding and, if possible, the expression of such relations in precise form.

(c) Generalization; that is, the discovery and formulation of a general law and an understanding of its properties and applications.

(3) The acquisition of *mental habits and attitudes* which will make the above training effective in the life of the individual. Among such habitual reactions are the following: a seeking for relations and their precise

expression; an attitude of enquiry; a desire to understand, to get to the bottom of a situation; concentration and persistence; a love for precision, accuracy, thoroughness, and clearness, and a distaste for vagueness and incompleteness; a desire for orderly and logical organization as an aid to understanding and memory.

(4) Many of these disciplinary aims are included in the broad sense of *the idea of relationship or dependence*—in what the mathematician in his technical vocabulary refers to as a "function" of one or more variables. Training in "functional thinking," that is thinking in terms of and about relationships, is one of the most fundamental disciplinary aims of the teaching of mathematics.

Cultural aims.—By cultural aims we mean those somewhat less tangible but none the less real and important intellectual, ethical, esthetic or spiritual aims that are involved in the development of appreciation and insight and the formation of ideals of perfection. As will be at once apparent the realization of some of these aims must await the later stages of instruction, but some of them may and should operate at the very beginning.

More specifically we may mention the development or acquisition of—

(1) *Appreciation of beauty* in the geometrical forms of nature, art, and industry.

(2) *Ideals of perfection* as to logical structure, precision of statement and of thought, logical reasoning (as exemplified in the geometric demonstration), discrimination between the true and the false, etc.

(3) *Appreciation of the power of mathematics*—of what Byron expressively called "the power of thought, the magic of the mind"[2]—and the rôle that mathematics and abstract thinking, in general, have played in the development of civilization; in particular in science, in industry, and in philosophy. In this connection mention should be made of the religious effect, in the broad sense, which the study of the infinite and of the permanence of laws in mathematics tends to establish.[3]

III. THE POINT OF VIEW GOVERNING INSTRUCTION

The practical aims enumerated above, in spite of their vital importance, may without danger be given a secondary position in seeking to formulate the general point of view which should govern the teacher, provided only

2. D. E. Smith: Mathematics in the Training for Citizenship, Teachers College Record, vol. 18 (May, 1917), p. 6.

3. For an elaboration of the ideas here presented in the barest outline, the reader is referred to the article by D. E. Smith already mentioned and to his presidential address before the Mathematical Association of America. "Religio Matematici", American Mathematical Monthly, vol. 28 (Oct., 1921), pp. 339-349, also published in The Mathematics Teacher, vol. 14 (Dec., 1921), pp. 413-426.

that they receive due recognition in the selection of material and that the necessary minimum of technical drill is insisted upon.

The primary purposes of the teaching of mathematics should be to develop those powers of understanding and of analyzing relations of quantity and of space which are necessary to an insight into and control over our environment and to an appreciation of the progress of civilization in its various aspects, and to develop those habits of thought and of action which will make these powers effective in the life of the individual.

All topics, processes, and drill in technique which do not directly contribute to the development of the powers mentioned should be eliminated from the curriculum. It is recognized that in the earlier periods of instruction the strictly logical organization of subject-matter[4] is of less importance than the acquisition, on the part of the pupil, of experience as to facts and methods of attack on significant problems, of the power to see relations, and of training in accurate thinking in terms of such relations. Care must be taken, however, through the dominance of the course by certain general ideas that it does not become a collection of isolated and unrelated details.

Continued emphasis throughout the course must be placed on the development of ability to grasp and to utilize ideas, processes, and principles in the solution of concrete problems rather than on the acquisition of mere facility or skill in manipulation. The excessive emphasis now commonly placed on manipulation is one of the main obstacles to intelligent progress. On the side of algebra, the ability to understand its language and to use it intelligently, the ability to analyze a problem, to formulate it mathematically, and to interpret the result must be dominant aims. *Drill in algebraic manipulation should be limited to those processes and to the degree of complexity required for a thorough understanding of principles and for probable applications either in common life or in subsequent courses which a substantial proportion of the pupils will take.* It must be conceived throughout as a means to an end, not as an end in itself. Within these limits, skill in algebraic manipulation is important, and drill in this subject should be extended far enough to enable students to carry out the essential processes accurately and expeditiously.

On the side of geometry the formal demonstrative work should be preceded by a reasonable amount of informal work of an intuitive, experimental, and constructive character. Such work is of great value in itself; it is needed also to provide the necessary familiarity with geometric ideas, forms, and relations, on the basis of which alone intelligent appreciation of formal demonstrative work is possible.

The one great idea which is best adapted to unify the course is that of

---

4. "The logical from the standpoint of subject matter represents the goal, the last term of training, not the point of departure." Dewey, "How We Think," p. 62.

the *functional relation*. The concept of a variable and of the dependence of one variable upon another is of fundamental importance to everyone. It is true that the general and abstract form of these concepts can become significant to the pupil only as a result of very considerable mathematical experience and training. There is nothing in either concept, however, which prevents the presentation of specific concrete examples and illustrations of dependence even in the early parts of the course. Means to this end will be found in connection with the tabulation of data and the study of the formula and of the graph and of their uses.

The primary and underlying principle of the course should be the idea of relationship between variables, including the methods of determining and expressing such relationship. The teacher should have this idea constantly in mind, and the pupil's advancement should be consciously directed along the lines which will present first one and then another of the ideas upon which finally the formation of the general concept of functionality depends. (For a more detailed discussion of these ideas see Chapter VII).

The general ideas which appear more explicitly in the course and under the dominance of one or another of which all topics should be brought are: (1) The formula, (2) graphic representation, (3) the equation, (4) measurement and computation, (5) congruence and similarity, (6) demonstration. These are considered in more detail in a later section of the report (Chaps. III and IV).

IV. THE ORGANIZATION OF SUBJECT MATTER

"General" courses.—We have already called attention to the fact that, in the earlier periods of instruction especially, logical principles of organization are of less importance than psychological and pedagogical principles. In recent years there has developed among many progressive teachers a very significant movement away from the older rigid division into "subjects" such as arithmetic, algebra, and geometry, each of which shall be "completed" before another is begun, and toward a rational breaking down of the barriers separating these subjects, in the interest of an organization of subject-matter that will offer a psychologically and pedagogically more effective approach to the study of mathematics.

There has thus developed the movement toward what are variously called "composite," "correlated," "unified," or "general" courses. The advocates of this new method of organization base their claims on the obvious and important interrelations between arithmetic, algebra, and geometry (mainly intuitive), which the student must grasp before he can gain any real insight into mathematical methods and which are inevitably obscured by a strict adherence to the conception of separate "subjects." The movement has gained considerable new impetus by the growth of the junior high school, and there can be little question that the results already achieved by those who are experimenting with the new methods of organization war-rant the abandonment of the extreme "water-tight compartment" method of presentation.

The newer method of organization enables the pupil to gain a broad view of the whole field of elementary mathematics early in his high-school course. In view of the very large number of pupils who drop out of school at the end of the eighth or the ninth school year or who for other reasons then cease their study of mathematics, this fact offers a weighty advantage over the older type of organization under which the pupils studied algebra alone during the ninth school year, to the complete exclusion of all contact with geometry.

It should be noted, however, that the specific recommendations as to content given in the next two chapters do not necessarily imply the adoption of a different type of organization of the materials of instruction. A large number of high schools will for some time continue to find it desirable to organize their courses of study in mathematics by subjects—algebra, plane geometry, etc. Such schools are urged to adopt the recommendations made with reference to the content of the separate subjects. These, in the main, constitute an essential simplification as compared with present practice. The economy of time that will result in courses in ninth-year algebra, for instance, will permit of the introduction of the newer type of material, including intuitive geometry and numerical trigonometry, and thus the way will be prepared for the gradual adoption in larger measure of the recommendations of this report.

At the present time it is not possible to designate any particular order of topics or any organization of the materials of instruction as being the best or as calculated most effectively to realize the aims and purposes here set forth. More extensive and careful experimental work must be done by teachers and administrators before any such designation can be made that shall avoid undesirable extremes and that shall bear the stamp of general approval. This experimental work will prove successful in proportion to the skill and insight exercised in adapting the aims and purposes of instruction to the interests and capacities of the pupils. One of the greatest weaknesses of the traditional courses is the fact that both the interests and the capacities of pupils have received insufficient consideration and study. For a detailed account of courses in mathematics at a number of the most successful experimental schools the reader is referred to Chapter XII of this report.

Required courses.—The National Committee believes that the material described in the next chapter should be required of all pupils and that under favorable conditions this minimum of work can be completed by the end of the ninth school year. In the junior high school, comprising grades seven, eight, and nine, the course for these three years should be planned as a unit *with the purpose of giving each pupil the most valuable mathematical train-ing he is capable of receiving in those years, with little reference to courses which he may or may not take in succeeding years.* In particular, college en-trance requirements should, during these years, receive no specific considera-tion. Fortunately there appears to be no conflict of interest during this period between those pupils who ultimately go to college and those who do not; a course planned in accordance with the principle just enunciated will form a desirable foundation for college preparation. (See Châpter V; also, the experience of the schools described in Chapter XII.)

Similarly, in case of the at present more prevalent 8-4 school organiza-tion, the mathematical material of the seventh and eighth grades should be selected and organized as a unit with the same purpose; the same applies to the work of the first year (ninth grade) of the standard four-year high school, and to later years in which mathematics may be a required subject.

In the case of some elective courses the principle needs to be modified so as to meet whatever specific vocational or technical purposes the courses may have. (See Chap. IV.)

The movement toward correlation of the work in mathematics with other courses in the curriculum, notably those in science, is as yet in its infancy. The results of such efforts will be watched with the keenest interest.

The junior high-school movement.—Reference has several times been made to the junior high school. The National Committee adopted the fol-lowing resolution on April 24, 1920:

> The National Committee approves the junior high school form of organi-zation, and urges its general adoption in the conviction that it will secure greater efficiency in the teaching of mathematics.

The committee on the reorganization of secondary education, appointed by the National Education Association, in its pamphlet on the "Cardinal Principles of Secondary School Education," issued in 1918 by the Bureau of Education, advocates an organization of the school system whereby the first six years shall be devoted to elementary education and the following six years to secondary education to be divided into two periods which may be designated as junior and senior periods.

To those interested in the study of the questions relating to the history and present status of the junior high school movement, the following books are recommended: Principles of Secondary Education, by Inglis (Houghton Mifflin & Co., 1918) ; The Junior High School, The Fifteenth Yearbook (Pt. III) of the National Society for the Study of Education (Public School Pub-lishing Co., 1919) ; The Junior High School, by Bennett (Warwick & York, 1919) ; The Junior High School, by Briggs (Houghton Mifflin & Co., 1920) ; and The Junior High School, by Koos (Harcourt, Brace & Howe, 1920).

398

V. THE TRAINING OF TEACHERS

While the greater part of this report concerns itself with the content of courses in mathematics, their organization and the point of view which should govern the instruction, and investigations relating thereto, the National Committee must emphasize strongly its conviction that even more fundamental is the problem of the teacher—his qualifications and training, his personality, skill, and enthusiasm.

The greater part of the failure of mathematics is due to poor teaching. Good teachers have in the past succeeded, and will continue to succeed, in achieving highly satisfactory results with the traditional material; poor teachers will not succeed even with the newer and better material.

The United States is far behind Europe in the scientific and professional training required of its secondary school teachers (see Chap. XIV). The equivalent of two or three years of graduate and professional training in addition to a general college course is the normal requirement for secondary school teachers in most European countries. Moreover, the recognized position of the teacher in the community must be such as to attract men and women of the highest ability into the profession. This means not only higher salaries but smaller classes and more leisure for continued study and professional advancement. It will doubtless require a considerable time before the public can be educated to realize the wisdom of taxing itself sufficiently to bring about the desired result. But if this ideal is continually advanced and supported by sound argument there is every reason to hope that in time the goal may be reached.

In the meantime everything possible should be done to improve the present situation. One of the most vicious and widespread practices consists in assigning a class in mathematics to a teacher who has had no special training in the subject and whose interests lie elsewhere because in the construction of the time schedule he or she happens to have a vacant period at the time. This is done on the principle, apparently, that "anybody can teach mathematics" by simply following a textbook and devoting 90 per cent of the time to drill in algebraic manipulation or to the recitation of the memorized demonstration of theorems in geometry.

It will be apparent from the study of this report that a successful teacher of mathematics must not only be highly trained in his subject and have a genuine enthusiasm for it but must have also peculiar attributes of personality and above all insight of a high order into the psychology of the learning process as related to the higher mental activities. Administrators should never lose sight of the fact that while mathematics if properly taught is one of the most important, interesting, and valuable subjects of the curriculum, it is also one of the most difficult to teach successfully.

Standards for teachers.—It is necessary at the outset to make a fundamental distinction between standards in the sense of requirements for appointment to teaching positions, and standards of scientific attainment which shall determine the curricula of colleges and normal schools aiming to give candidates the best practicable preparation. The former requirements should be high enough to insure competent teaching, but they must not be so high as to form a serious obstacle to admission to the profession even for candidates who have chosen it relatively late. The main factors determining the level of these requirements are the available facilities for preparation, the needs of the pupils, and the economic or salary conditions.

Relatively few young people deliberately choose before entering college the teaching of secondary mathematics as a life work. In the more frequent or more typical case, the college student who will ultimately become a teacher of secondary mathematics makes the choice gradually, perhaps unconsciously, late in the college course or even after its completion, perhaps after some trial of teaching in other fields. The possible supply of young people who have the real desire to become teachers of mathematics is so meager in comparison with the almost unlimited needs of the country that every effort should be made to develop and maintain that desire and all possible encouragement given those who manifest it. If, as will usually be the case, the desire is associated with the necessary mathematical capacity, it will not be wise to hamper the candidate by requiring too high attainments, though as a matter of course he will need guidance in continuing his preparation for a profession of exceptional difficulty and exceptional opportunity.

Another factor which must tend to restrict requirements of high mathematical attainment is the importance to the candidate of breadth of preparation. In college he may be in doubt as to becoming a teacher of mathematics or physics or some other subject. It is unwise to hasten the choice. In many cases the secondary teacher must be prepared in more than one field, and to the future teacher of mathematics preparation in physics and drawing, not to mention chemistry, engineering, etc., may be at least as valuable as purely mathematical college electives beyond the calculus.

In the second sense—of standards of scientific attainment to be held by the colleges and normal schools—these institutions should make every effort—

1. To awaken interest in the subject and the teaching of it in as many young people of the right sort as possible.
2. To give them the best possible opportunity for professional preparation and improvement, both before and after the beginning of teaching.

How the matter of requirements for appointment will actually work out in a given community will inevitably depend upon conditions of time and place, varying widely in character and degree. In many communities it is already practicable and customary to require not less than two years of college work in mathematics, including elementary calculus, with provision for additional electives. Such a requirement the committee would strongly recommend, recognizing, however, that in some localities it would be for the present too restrictive of the supply. In some cases preparation in the pedagogy, philosophy, and history of mathematics could be reasonably demanded or at least given weight; in other cases, any considerable time spent upon them would be of doubtful value. In all cases requirements should be carefully adjusted to local conditions with a view to recognizing the value both of broad and thorough training on the part of those entering the profession and of continued preparation and improvement by summer work and the like. Particular pains should be taken that such preparation is made accessible and attractive in the colleges and normal schools from which teachers are drawn.

It is naturally important that entrance to the profession should not be much delayed by needlessly high or extended requirements, and the danger of creating a teacher who may be too much a specialist for school work and too little for college teaching must be guarded against. There may naturally also be a wide difference between requirements in a strong school offering many electives and a weaker one or a junior high school. Practically, it may be fair to expect that the stronger schools will maintain their standards not by arbitrary or general requirements for entrance to the profession but often by recruiting from other schools teachers who have both high attainments and successful teaching experience.

Programs of courses for colleges and normal schools preparing teachers in secondary mathematics will be found in Chapter XIV, together with an account of existing conditions.

CHAPTER III

Mathematics for Years Seven, Eight, and Nine

I. INTRODUCTION

There is a well-marked tendency among school administrators to consider grades one to six, inclusive, as constituting the elementary school and to consider the secondary school period as commencing with the seventh grade and extending through the twelfth.[1] Conforming to this view, the content of the courses of study in mathematics for grades seven, eight, and nine are considered together. In the succeeding chapter the content for grades ten, eleven, and twelve is considered.

The committee is fully aware of the widespread desire on the part of teachers throughout the country for a detailed syllabus by years or half-years which shall give the best order of topics with specific time allotments for each. This desire can not be met at the present time for the simple reason that no one knows what is the best order of topics, nor how much time should be devoted to each in an ideal course. The committee feels that its recommendations should be so formulated as to give every encouragement to further experimentation rather than to restrict the teacher's freedom by a standardized syllabus.

However, certain suggestions as to desirable arrangements of the material are offered in a later section (Sec. III) of this chapter, and in Chapter XII there will be found detailed outlines giving the order of presentation and time allotments in actual operation in schools of various types. This material should be helpful to teachers and administrators in planning courses to fit their individual needs and conditions.

It is the opinion of the committee that the material included in this chapter should be required of all pupils. It includes mathematical knowl-

1. "We therefore recommend a reorganization of the school system whereby the first six years shall be devoted to elementary education designed to meet the needs of pupils of approximately 6 to 12 years of age; and the second six years to secondary education designed to meet the needs of approximately 12 to 18 years of age. * * * The six years to be devoted to secondary education may well be divided into two periods, which may be designated as the junior and senior periods." Cardinal Principles of Secondary Education, p. 18.

edge and training which is likely to be needed by every citizen. Differentiation due to special needs should be made after and not before the completion of such a general minimum foundation. Such portions of the recommended content as have not been completed by the end of the ninth year should be required in the following year.

The general principles which have governed the selection of the material presented in the next section and which should govern the point of view of the teaching have already been stated (Chap. II). At this point it seems desirable to recall specifically what was then said concerning principles governing the organization of material, the importance to be attached to the development of insight and understanding and of ability to think clearly in terms of relationships (dependence), and the limitations imposed on drill in algebraic manipulation. In addition we would call attention to the following considerations:

It is assumed that at the end of the sixth school year the pupil will be able to perform with accuracy and with a fair degree of speed the fundamental operations with integers and with common and decimal fractions. The fractions here referred to are such simple ones in common use as are set forth in detail under A(c) in the following section. It may be pointed out that the standard of attainment here implied is met in a large number of schools, as is shown by various tests now in use (see Chap. XIII), and can easily be met generally if time is not wasted on the relatively unimportant parts of the subject.

In adapting instruction in mathematics to the mental traits of pupils care should be taken to maintain the mental growth too often stunted by secondary school materials and methods, and an effort should be made to associate with inquisitiveness, the desire to experiment, the wish to know "how and why" and the like, the satisfaction of these needs.

In the years under consideration it is also especially important to give the pupils as broad an outlook over the various fields of mathematics as is consistent with sound scholarship. These years especially are the ones in which the pupil should have the opportunity to find himself, to test his abilities and aptitudes, and to secure information and experience which will help him choose wisely his later courses and ultimately his life work.

II. MATERIAL FOR GRADES SEVEN, EIGHT, AND NINE

In the material outlined in the following pages no attempt is made to indicate the most desirable order of presentation. Stated by topics rather than years the mathematics of grades seven, eight, and nine may properly be expected to include the following:

A. Arithmetic.—*(a)* The fundamental operations of arithmetic.

(*b*) Tables of weights and measures in general practical use, including the most common metric units (meter, centimeter, millimeter, kilometer, gram, kilogram, liter). The meaning of such foreign monetary units as pound, franc, and Mark.

(*c*) Such simple fractions as ½, ⅓, ⅔, ¼, ¾, ⅕, ⅛; others than these to have less attention.

(*d*) Facility and accuracy in the four fundamental operations; time tests, taking care to avoid subordinating the teaching to the tests or to use the tests as measures of the teacher's efficiency. (See Chap. XIII.)

(*e*) Such simple short cuts in multiplication and division as that of replacing multiplication by 25 by multiplying by 100 and dividing by 4.

(*f*) Percentage. Interchanging common fractions and per cents; finding any per cent of a number; finding what per cent one number is of another; finding a number when a certain per cent of it is known; and such applications of percentage as come within the student's experience.

(*g*) Line, bar, and circle graphs, wherever they can be used to advantage.

(*h*) Arithmetic of the home: household accounts, thrift, simple bookkeeping, methods of sending money, parcel post.

Arithmetic of the community: property and personal insurance, taxes.

Arithmetic of banking: savings accounts, checking accounts.

Arithmetic of investment: real estate, elementary notions of stocks and bonds, postal savings.

(*i*) Statistics: fundamental concepts, statistical tables and graphs; pictograms; graphs showing simple frequency distributions.

It will be seen that the material listed above includes some material of earlier instruction. This does not mean that this material is to be made the direct object of study but that drill in it shall be given in connection with the new work. It is felt that this shift in emphasis will make the arithmetic processes here involved much more effective and will also result in a great saving of time.

The amount of time devoted to arithmetic as a distinct subject should be greatly reduced from what is at present customary. This does not mean a lessening of emphasis on drill in arithmetic processes for the purpose of securing accuracy and speed. The need for continued arithmetic work and numerical computation throughout the secondary school period is recognized elsewhere in this report. (Chap. II.)

The applications of arithmetic to business should be continued late enough in the course to bring to their study the pupil's greatest maturity, experience, and mathematical knowledge, and to insure real significance of this study in the business and industrial life which many of the pupils will enter at the close of the eighth or ninth school year. (See I, below.) In this connection care should be taken that the business practices taught in the schools are in accord with the best actual usage. Arithmetic should not be completed before the pupil has acquired the power of using algebra as an aid.

B. Intuitive geometry.—*(a)* The direct measurement of distances and angles by means of a linear scale and protractor. The approximate character of measurement. An understanding of what is meant by the degree of precision as expressed by the number of "significant" figures.

(*b*) Areas of the square, rectangle, parallelogram, triangle, and trapezoid; circumference and area of a circle; surfaces and volumes of solids of corresponding importance; the construction of the corresponding formulas.

(*c*) Practice in numerical computation with due regard to the number of figures used or retained.

(*d*) Indirect measurement by means of drawings to scale; use of square ruled paper.

(*e*) Geometry of appreciation; geometric forms in nature, architecture, manufacture, and industry.

(*f*) Simple geometric constructions with ruler and compasses, T-square, and triangle, such as that of the perpendicular bisector, the bisector of an angle, and parallel lines.

(*g*) Familiarity with such forms as the equilateral triangle, the 30°–60° right triangle, and the isosceles right triangle; symmetry; a knowledge of such facts as those concerning the sum of the angles of a triangle and the pythagorean relation; simple cases of geometric loci in the plane and in space.

(*h*) Informal introduction to the idea of similarity.

The work in intuitive geometry should make the pupil familiar with the elementary ideas concerning geometric forms in the plane and in space with respect to shape, size, and position. Much opportunity should be provided for exercising space perception and imagination. The simpler geometric ideas and relations in the plane may properly be extended to three dimensions. The work should, moreover, be carefully planned so as to bring out geometric relations and logical connections. Before the end of this intuitive work the pupil should have definitely begun to make inferences and to draw valid conclusions from the relations discovered. In other words, this informal work in geometry should be so organized as to make it a gradual approach to, and provide a foundation for, the subsequent work in demonstrative geometry.

C. Algebra.—1. The formula—its construction, meaning, and use (*a*) as a concise language; (*b*) as a shorthand rule for computation; (*c*) as a general solution; (*d*) as an expression of the dependence of one variable upon another.

The pupil will already have met the formula in connection with intuitive geometry. The work should now include translation from English into algebraic language, and vice versa, and special care should be taken to make sure that the new language is understood and used intelligently. The nature of the dependence of one variable in a formula upon another should be examined and analyzed, with a view to seeing "how the formula works." (See Chap. VII.)

2. Graphs and graphic representations in general—their construction and interpretation in (*a*) representing facts (statistical, etc.); (*b*) representing dependence; (*c*) solving problems.

After the necessary technique has been adequately presented graphic representation should not be considered as a separate topic but should be used throughout, whenever helpful, as an illustrative and interpretative instrument.

3. Positive and negative numbers—their meaning and use: (*a*) as expressing both magnitude and one of two opposite directions or senses; (*b*) their graphic representation; (*c*) the fundamental operations applied to them.

4. The equation—its use in solving problems:

(*a*) Linear equations in one unknown—their solution and applications.

(*b*) Simple cases of quadratic equations when arising in connection with formulas and problems.

(*c*) Equations in two unknowns, with numerous concrete illustrations.

(*d*) Various simple applications of ratio and proportion in cases in which they are generally used in problems of similarity and in other problems of ordinary life. In view of the usefulness of the ideas and training involved, this subject may also properly include simple cases of variation.

5. Algebraic technique: (*a*) The fundamental operations.

Their connection with the rules of arithmetic should be clearly brought out and made to illuminate numerical processes. Drill in these operations should be limited strictly in accordance with the principle mentioned in Chapter II, page 11. In particular, "nests" of parentheses should be avoided, and multiplication and division should not involve much beyond monomial and binomial multipliers, divisors, and quotients.

(*b*) Factoring. The only cases that need be considered are (i) common factors of the terms of a polynomial; (ii) the difference of two squares; (iii) trinomials of the second degree that can be easily factored by trial.

(*c*) Fractions. Here again the intimate connection with the corresponding processes of arithmetic should be made clear and should serve to illuminate such processes. The four fundamental operations with fractions should be considered only in connection with simple cases and should be applied constantly throughout the course so as to gain the necessary accuracy and facility.

(*d*) Exponents and radicals. The work done on exponents and radicals should be confined to the simplest material required for the treatment of formulas. The laws for positive integral exponents should be included. The consideration of radicals should be confined to transformations of the following types: $\sqrt{a^2 b} = a\sqrt{b}, \sqrt{a/b} = \frac{1}{b}\sqrt{ab}$ and $\sqrt{a/b} = \sqrt{a}/\sqrt{b}$, and to the numerical evaluation of simple expressions involving the radical sign. A process for finding the square root of a number should be included, but not for finding the square root of a polynomial.

(*e*) Stress should be laid upon the need for checking solutions.

D. Numerical trigonometry.—(*a*) Definition of sine, cosine, and tangent.

(*b*) Their elementary properties as functions.

(*c*) Their use in solving problems involving right triangles.

(*d*) The use of tables of these functions (to three or four places).

The introduction of the elementary notions of trigonometry into the earlier courses in mathematics has not been as general in the United States as in foreign countries. (See Chap. XI.) Among the reasons for an early introduction of this topic are these: Its practical usefulness for many citizens; the insight it gives into the nature of mathematical methods, particularly those concerned with indirect measurement, and into the rôle that mathematics plays in the life of the world; the fact that it is not difficult and that it offers wide opportunity for concrete and significant application; and the interest it arouses in the pupils. It should be based upon the work in intuitive geometry, with which it has intimate contacts (see B, *d*, *h*, above), and should be confined to the simplest material needed for the numerical treatment of the problems indicated. Relations between the trigonometric functions need not be considered.

E. Demonstrative geometry.—The demonstration of a limited number of propositions, with no attempt to limit the number of fundamental assumptions, the principal purpose being to show to the pupil what "demonstration" means.

Many of the geometric facts previously inferred intuitively may be used as the basis upon which the demonstrative work is built. This is not intended to preclude the possibility of giving at a later time rigorous proofs of some of the facts inferred intuitionally. It should be noted that from the strictly logical point of view the attempt to reduce to a minimum the list of axioms, postulates, or assumptions is not at all necessary, and from a pedagogical point of view such an attempt in an elementary course is very undesirable. It is necessary, however, that those propositions which are to be used as the basis of subsequent formal proofs be explicitly listed and their logical significance recognized.

In regard to demonstrative geometry some teachers have objected to the introduction of such work below the tenth grade on the ground that with such immature pupils as are found in the ninth grade nothing worth while could be accomplished in the limited time available. These teachers may be right with regard to conditions prevailing or likely to prevail in the majority of schools in the immediate future. The committee has therefore in a later section of this chapter (Sec. III) made alternative provision for the

407

omission of work in demonstrative geometry.

On the other hand, it is proper to call attention to the fact that certain teachers have successfully introduced a limited amount of work in demonstrative geometry into the ninth grade (see Chap. XII) and that it would seem desirable that others should make the experiment when conditions are favorable. Much of the opposition is probably due to a failure to realize the extent to which the work in intuitive geometry, if properly organized, will prepare the way for the more formal treatment, and to a misconception of the purposes and extent of the work in demonstrative geometry that is proposed. In reaching a decision on this question teachers should keep in mind that it is one of their important duties and obligations, in the grades under consideration, to show their pupils the nature, content, and possibilities of later courses in their subject and to give to each pupil an opportunity to determine his aptitudes and preferences therefor. The omission in the earlier courses of all work of a demonstrative nature in geometry would disregard one educationally important aspect of mathematics.

F. History and biography.—Teachers are advised to make themselves reasonably acquainted with the leading events in the history of mathematics, and thus to know that mathematics has developed in answer to human needs, intellectual as well as technical. They should use this material incidentally throughout their courses for the purpose of adding to the interest of the pupils by means of informal talks on the growth of mathematics and on the lives of the great makers of the science.

G. Optional topics.—Certain schools have been able to cover satisfactorily the work suggested in sections A to F before the end of the ninth grade (see Chap. XII). The committee looks with favor on the efforts, in such schools, to introduce earlier than is now customary certain topics and processes which are closely related to modern needs, such as the meaning and use of fractional and negative exponents, the use of the slide-rule, the use of logarithms and of other simple tables, and simple work in arithmetic and geometric progressions, with modern applications to such financial topics as interest and annuities and to such scientific topics as falling bodies and laws of growth.

H. Topics to be omitted or postponed.—In addition to the large amount of drill in algebraic technique already referred to, the following topics should, in accordance with our basic principles, be excluded from the work of grades seven, eight, and nine; some of them will properly be included in later courses (see Chap. IV):

Highest common factor and lowest common multiple, except the simplest cases involved in the addition of simple fractions.

The theorems on proportion relating to alternation, inversion, composition, and division.

Literal equations, except such as appear in common formulas, including the derivation of formulas and of geometric relations, or to show how needless computation may be avoided.

Radicals, except as indicated in a previous section.

Square root of polynomials.

Cube root.

Theory of exponents.

Simultaneous equations in more than two unknowns.

The binomial theorem.

Imaginary and complex numbers.

Radical equations except such as arise in dealing with elementary formulas.

I. Problems.—As already indicated, much of the emphasis now generally placed on the formal exercise should be shifted to the "concrete" or "verbal" problem. The selection of problem material is, therefore, of the highest importance.

The demand for "practical" problems should be fully met in so far as the maturity and previous experience of the pupil will permit. But above all, the problems must be "real" *to the pupil*, must connect with his ordinary thought, and must be within the world of his experience and interest. "The educational utility of problems is not to be measured by their commercial or scientific value, but by their degree of reality for the pupils. . . . They must exemplify those leading ideas which it is desired to impart, and they must do so through media which are real to those under instruction. The reality is found in the students, the utility in their acquisition of principles."[2]

There should be, moreover, a conscious effort through the selection of problems to correlate the work in mathematics with the other courses of the curriculum, especially in connection with courses in science. The introduction of courses in "general science" increases the opportunities in this direction.

J. Numerical computation, use of tables, etc.—The solution of problems should offer opportunity throughout the grades under consideration for considerable arithmetical and computational work. In this connection attention should be called to the importance of exercising common sense and judgment in the use of approximate data, keeping in mind the fact that all data secured from measurement are approximate. A pupil should be led to see the absurdity of giving the area of a circle to a thousandth of a square inch when the radius has been measured only to the nearest inch. He should understand the conception of "the number of significant figures" and should not retain more figures in his result than are warranted by the accuracy of his data. The ideals of accuracy and of self-reliance and the necessity of checking all numerical results should be emphasized. An insight into the nature of tables, including some elementary notions as to

2. Carson: Mathematical Education, pp. 42-45.

interpolation, is highly desirable. The use of tables of various kinds (such as squares and square roots, interest, and trigonometric functions) to facilitate computation and to develop the idea of dependence should be encouraged.

III. SUGGESTED ARRANGEMENTS OF MATERIAL

In approaching the problem of arranging or organizing this material it is necessary to consider the different situations that may have to be met.

1. The junior high school.—In view of the fact that under this form of school organization pupils may be expected to remain in school until the end of the junior high school period instead of leaving in large numbers at the end of the eighth school year, the mathematiĉs of the three years of the junior high school should be planned as a unit, and should include the material recommended in the preceding section. There remains the question as to the order in which the various topics should be presented and the amount of time to be devoted to each. The committee has already stated its reasons for not attempting to answer this question (see Sec. I of this chapter). The following plans for the distribution of time are, however, suggested in the hope that they may be helpful; but no one of them is recommended as superior to the others, and only the large divisions of material are mentioned.

PLAN A.

First year: Applications of arithmetic, particularly in such lines as relate to the home, to thrift, and to the various school subjects; intuitive geometry.

Second year: Algebra; applied arithmetic, particularly in such lines as relate to commercial, industrial and social needs.

Third year: Algebra, trigonometry, demonstrative geometry.

By this plan the demonstrative geometry is introduced in the third year, and arithmetic is practically completed in the second year.

PLAN B.

First year: Applied arithmetic (as in plan A); intuitive geometry.

Second year: Algebra, intuitive geometry, trigonometry.

Third year: Applied arithmetic, algebra, trigonometry, demonstrative geometry.

By this plan trigonometry is taken up in two years, and the arithmetic is transferred from the second year to the third year.

PLAN C.

First year: Applied arithmetic (as in plan A), intuitive geometry, algebra.

Second year: Algebra, intuitive geometry.

Third year: Trigonometry, demonstrative geometry, applied arithmetic.

By this plan Algebra is confined chiefly to the first two years.

PLAN D.

First year: Applied arithmetic (as in plan A), intuitive geometry.

Second year: Intuitive geometry, algebra.

Third year: Algebra, trigonometry, applied arithmetic.

By this plan Algebra is confined chiefly to the first two years.

PLAN E.

First year: Intuitive geometry, simple formulas, elementary principles of statistics, arithmetic (as in plan A).

Second year: Intuitive geometry, algebra, arithmetic.

Third year: Geometry, numerical trigonometry, arithmetic.

2. Schools organized on the 8-4 plan.—It cannot be too strongly emphasized that, in the case of the older and at present more prevalent plan of the 8-4 school organization, the work in mathematics of the seventh, eighth, and ninth grades should also be organized to include the material here suggested.

The prevailing practice of devoting the seventh and eighth grades almost exclusively to the study of arithmetic is generally recognized as a wasteful marking of time. It is mainly in these years that American children fall behind their European brothers and sisters. No essentially new arithmetic principles are taught in these years, and the attempt to apply the previously learned principles to new situations in the more advanced business and economic aspects of arithmetic is doomed to failure on account of the fact that the situations in question are not and cannot be made real and significant to pupils of this age. We need only refer to what has already been said in this chapter on the subject of problems (I, Sec. II).

The same principles should govern the selection and arrangement of material in mathematics for the seventh and eighth grades of a grade school as govern the selection for the corresponding grades of a junior high school, with this exception: Under the 8-4 form of organization many pupils will leave school at the end of the eighth year. This fact must receive due consideration. The work of the seventh and eighth years should be so planned as to give the pupils in these grades the most valuable mathematical information and training that they are capable of receiving in those years, with little reference to courses that they may take in later years. As to possibilities for arrangement, reference may be made to the plans given above for the first two years of the junior high school. When the work in mathematics of the seventh and eighth grades has been thus reorganized, the work of the first year of a standard four-year high school should complete the program suggested.

Finally, there must be considered the situation in those four-year high schools in which the pupils have not had the benefit of the reorganized instruction recommended for grades seven and eight. It may be hoped that this situation will be only temporary, although it must be recognized that, owing to a variety of possible reasons (lack of adequately prepared teachers in grades seven and eight, lack of suitable textbooks, administrative inertia,

411

and the like), the new plans will not be immediately adopted and that, therefore, for some years many high schools will have to face the situation implied.

In planning the work of the ninth grade under these conditions teachers and administrative officers should again be guided by the principle of giving the pupils the most valuable mathematical information and training which they are capable of receiving in this year with little reference to future courses which the pupil may or may not take. It is to be assumed that the work of this year is to be required of all pupils. Since for many this will constitute the last of their mathematical instruction, it should be so planned as to give them the widest outlook consistent with sound scholarship.

Under these conditions it would seem desirable that the work of the ninth grade should contain both algebra and geometry. It is, therefore, recommended that about two-thirds of the time be devoted to the most useful parts of algebra, including the work on numerical trigonometry, and that about one-third of the time be devoted to geometry, including the necessary informal introduction and, if feasible, the first part of demonstrative geometry.

It should be clear that owing to the greater maturity of the pupils much less time need be devoted in the ninth grade to certain topics of intuitive geometry (such as direct measurement, for example) than is desirable when dealing with children in earlier grades. Even under the conditions presupposed, pupils will be acquainted with most of the fundamental geometric forms and with the mensuration of the most important plane and solid figures. The work in geometry in the ninth grade can then properly be made to center about indirect measurement and the idea of similarity (leading to the processes of numerical trigonometry), and such geometric relations as the sum of the angles of a triangle, the pythagorean proposition, congruence of triangles, parallel and perpendicular lines, quadrilaterals, and the more important simple constructions.

CHAPTER IV

Mathematics for Years Ten, Eleven, and Twelve

I. INTRODUCTION

The committee has in the preceding chapter expressed its judgment that the material there recommended for the seventh, eighth, and ninth years should be required of all pupils. In the tenth, eleventh, and twelfth years, however, the extent to which election of subjects is permitted will depend on so many factors of a general character that it seems unnecessary and inexpedient for the present committee to urge a positive requirement beyond the minimum one already referred to. The subject must, like others, stand or fall on its intrinsic merit or on the estimate of such merit by the authorities responsible at a given time and place. The committee believes nevertheless that every standard high school should not merely offer courses in mathematics for the tenth, eleventh, and twelfth years, but should encourage a large proportion of its pupils to take them. Apart from the intrinsic interest and great educational value of the study of mathematics, it will in general be necessary for those preparing to enter college or to engage in the numerous occupations involving the use of mathematics to extend their work beyond the minimum requirement.

The present chapter is intended to suggest for students in general courses the most valuable mathematical training that will appropriately follow the courses outlined in the previous chapter. Under present conditions most of this work will normally fall in the last three years of the high school; that is, in general, in the tenth, eleventh, and twelfth years.

The selection of material is based on the general principles formulated in Chapter II. At this point attention need be directed only to the following:

1. In the years under consideration it is proper that some attention be paid to the students' vocational or other later educational needs.

2. The material for these years should include as far as possible those mathematical ideas and processes that have the most important applications in the modern world. As a result, certain material will naturally be included that at present is not ordinarily given in secondary school courses; as, for instance, the material concerning the calculus. On the other hand, certain other material that is now included in college entrance requirements

413

will be excluded. The results of an investigation made by the National Committee in connection with a study of these requirements indicates that modifications to meet these changes will be desirable from the standpoint of both college and secondary school (see Chap. V).

3. During the years now under consideration an increasing amount of attention should be paid to the logical organization of the material, with the purpose of developing habits of logical memory, appreciation of logical structure, and ability to organize material effectively.

It cannot be too strongly emphasized that the broadening of content of high school courses in mathematics suggested in the present and in previous chapters will materially increase the usefulness of these courses to those who pursue them. It is of prime importance that educational administrators and others charged with the advising of students should take careful account of this fact in estimating the relative importance of mathematical courses and their alternatives. The number of important applications of mathematics in the activities of the world is today very large and is increasing at a very rapid rate. This aspect of the progress of civilization has been noted by all observers who have combined a knowledge of mathematics with an alert interest in the newer developments in other fields. It was revealed in very illuminating fashion during the recent war by the insistent demand for persons with varying degrees of mathematical training for many war activities of the first moment. If the same effort were made in time of peace to secure the highest level of efficiency available for the specific tasks of modern life, the demand for those trained in mathematics would be no less insistent; for it is in no wise true that the applications of mathematics in modern warfare are relatively more important or more numerous than its applications in those fields of human endeavor which are of a constructive nature.

There is another important point to be kept in mind in considering the relative value to the average student of mathematical and various alternative courses. If the student who omits the mathematical courses has need of them later, it is almost invariably more difficult, and it is frequently impossible, for him to obtain the training in which he is deficient. In the case of a considerable number of alternative subjects a proper amount of reading in spare hours at a more mature age will ordinarily furnish him the approximate equivalent to that which he would have obtained in the way of information in a high school course in the same subject. It is not, however, possible to make up deficiencies in mathematical training in so simple a fashion. It requires systematic work under a competent teacher to master properly the technique of the subject, and any break in the continuity of the work is a handicap for which increased maturity rarely compensates. Moreover, when the individual discovers his need for further mathematical training it is usually difficult for him to take the time from his other activities for systematic work in elementary mathematics.

414

II. RECOMMENDATIONS FOR ELECTIVE COURSES

The following topics are recommended for inclusion in the mathematical electives open to pupils who have satisfactorily completed the work outlined in the preceding chapter, comprising arithmetic, the elementary notions of algebra, intuitive geometry, numerical trigonometry, and a brief introduction to demonstrative geometry.

1. Plane demonstrative geometry.—The principal purposes of the instruction in this subject are: To exercise further the spatial imagination of the student, to make him familiar with the great basal propositions and their applications, to develop understanding and appreciation of a deductive proof and the ability to use this method of reasoning where it is applicable, and to form habits of precise and succinct statement, of the logical organization of ideas, and of logical memory. Enough time should be spent on this subject to accomplish these purposes.

The following is a suggested list of topics under which the work in demonstrative geometry may be organized:[1] (*a*) Congruent triangles, perpendicular bisectors, bisectors of angles; (*b*) arcs, angles, and chords in circles; (*c*) parallel lines and related angles, parallelograms; (*d*) the sum of the angles for triangle and polygon; (*e*) secants and tangents to circles with related angles, regular polygons; (*f*) similar triangles, similar figures; (*g*) areas; numerical computation of lengths and areas, based upon geometric theorems already established.

Under these topics constructions, loci, originals and other exercises are to be included.

It is recommended that the formal theory of limits and of incommensurable cases be omitted, but that the ideas of limit and of incommensurable magnitudes receive informal treatment.

It is believed that a more frequent use of the idea of motion in the demonstration of theorems is desirable, both from the point of view of gaining greater insight and of saving time.[2]

If the great basal theorems are selected and effectively organized into a logical system, a considerable reduction (from 30 to 40 per cent) can be made in the number of theorems given either in the Harvard list or in the report of the Committee of Fifteen. Such a reduction is exhibited in the lists prepared by the committee and printed later in this report (Chap. VI). In this connection it may be suggested that more attention than is now customary may profitably be given to those methods of treatment which make

1. It is not intended that the order here given should imply anything as to the order of presentation. (See also Chap. VI.)
2. Reference may here be made to the treatment given in recent French texts such as those by Bourlet and Méray.

consistent use of the idea of motion (already referred to), continuity (the tangent as the limit of a secant, etc.), symmetry, and the dependence of one geometric magnitude upon another.

If the student has had a satisfactory course in intuitive geometry and some work in demonstration before the tenth grade, he may find it possible to cover a minimum course in demonstrative geometry, giving the great basal theorems and constructions, together with exercises, in the 90 periods constituting a half year's work.

2. Algebra.—*(a) Simple functions of one variable:* Numerous illustrations and problems involving linear, quadratic, and other simple functions including formulas from science and common life. More difficult problems in variation than those included in the earlier course.

(*b*) *Equations in one unknown:* Various methods for solving a quadratic equation (such as factoring, completing the square, use of formula) should be given. In connection with the treatment of the quadratic a very brief discussion of complex numbers should be included. Simple cases of the graphic solution of equations of degree higher than the second should be discussed and applied.

(*c*) *Equations in two or three unknowns:* The algebraic solution of linear equations in two or three unknowns and the graphic solution of linear equations in two unknowns should be given. The graphic and algebraic solution of a linear and a quadratic equation and of two quadratics that contain no first degree term and no xy term should be included.

(*d*) *Exponents, radicals, and logarithms:* The definitions of negative, zero, and fractional exponents should be given, and it should be made clear that these definitions must be adopted if we wish such exponents to conform to the laws for positive integral exponents. Reduction of radical expressions to those involving fractional exponents should be given as well as the inverse transformation. The rules for performing the fundamental operations on expressions involving radicals, and such transformations as

$$\sqrt[n]{a/b} = \frac{1}{b} \sqrt[n]{ab^{n-1}}, \ \sqrt[n]{a^n b} = a \sqrt[n]{b}, \ \frac{a}{\sqrt{b} + \sqrt{c}} = \frac{a(\sqrt{b} - \sqrt{c})}{b - c}$$

should be included. In close connection with the work on exponents and radicals there should be given as much of the theory of logarithms as is involved in their application to computation and sufficient practice in their use in computation to impart a fair degree of facility.

(*e*) *Arithmetic and geometric progressions:* The formulas for the nth term and the sum of n terms should be derived and applied to significant problems.

(*f*) *Binomial theorem:* A proof for positive integral exponents should be given; it may also be stated that the formula applies to the case of negative and fractional exponents under suitable restrictions, and the problems may include the use of the formula in these cases as well as in the case of positive integral exponents.

3. Solid geometry.—The aim of the work in solid geometry should be to exercise further the spatial imagination of the student and to give him both a knowledge of the fundamental spatial relationships and the power to work with them. It is felt that the work in plane geometry gives enough training in logical demonstration to warrant a shifting of emphasis in the work on solid geometry away from this aspect of the subject and in the direction of developing greater facility in visualizing spatial relations and figures, in representing such figures on paper, and in solving problems in mensuration.

For many of the practical applications of mathematics it is of fundamental importance to have accurate space perceptions. Hence it would seem wise to have at least some of the work in solid geometry come as early as possible in the mathematical courses, preferably not later than the beginning of the eleventh school year. Some schools will find it possible and desirable to introduce the more elementary notions of solid geometry in connection with related ideas of plane geometry.

The work in solid geometry should include numerous exercises in computation based on the formulas established. This will serve to correlate the work with arithmetic and algebra and to furnish practice in computation.

The following provisional outline of subject matter is submitted:

(a) Propositions relating to lines and planes, and to dihedral and trihedral angles.

(b) Mensuration of the prism, pyramid, and frustum; the (right circular) cylinder, cone and frustum, based on an informal treatment of limits; the sphere, and the spherical triangle.

(c) Spherical geometry.

(d) Similar solids.

Such theorems as are necessary as a basis for the topics here outlined should be studied in immediate connection with them.

Desirable simplification and generalization may be introduced into the treatment of mensuration theorems by employing such theorems as Cavalieri's and Simpson's, and the Prismoid Formula; but rigorous proofs or derivations of these need not be included.

Beyond the range of the mensuration topics indicated above, it seems preferable to employ the methods of the elementary calculus (see Section 6, below).

It should be possible to complete a minimum course covering the topics outlined above in not more than one-third of a year.

The list of propositions in solid geometry given in Chapter VI should be considered in connection with the general principles stated at the beginning of this section. By requiring formal proofs to a more limited extent than has been customary, time will be gained to attain the aims indicated and to extend the range of geometric information of the pupil. Care must be exercised to make sure that the pupil is thoroughly familiar with the facts, with the associated terminology, with all the necessary formulas, and that he secures the necessary practice in working with and applying the information acquired to concrete problems.

4. Trigonometry.—The work in elementary trigonometry begun in the earlier years should be completed by including the logarithmic solution of right and oblique triangles, radian measure, graphs of trigonometric functions, the derivation of the fundamental relations between the functions and their use in proving identities and in solving easy trigonometric equations. The use of the transit in connection with the simpler operations of surveying and of the sextant for some of the simpler astronomical observations, such as those involved in finding local time, is of value; but when no transit or sextant is available, simple apparatus for measuring angles roughly may and should be improvised. Drawings to scale should form an essential part of the numerical work in trigonometry. The use of the slide-rule in computations requiring only three-place accuracy and in checking other computations is also recommended.

5. Elementary statistics.—Continuation of the earlier work to include the meaning and use of fundamental concepts and simple frequency distributions with graphic representations of various kinds and measures of central tendency (average, mode, and median).

6. Elementary calculus.—The work should include:

(*a*) The general notion of a derivative as a limit indispensable for the accurate expression of such fundamental quantities as velocity of a moving body or slope of a curve.

(*b*) Applications of derivatives to easy problems in rates and in maxima and minima.

(*c*) Simple cases of inverse problems; e.g., finding distance from velocity, etc.

(*d*) Approximate methods of summation leading up to integration as a powerful method of summation.

(*e*) Applications to simple cases of motion, area, volume, and pressure.

Work in the calculus should be largely graphic and may be closely related to that in physics; the necessary technique should be reduced to a minimum by basing it wholly or mainly on algebraic polynomials. No formal study of analytic geometry need be presupposed beyond the plotting of simple graphs.

It is important to bear in mind that, while the elementary calculus is sufficiently easy, interesting, and valuable to justify its introduction, special pains should be taken to guard against any lack of thoroughness in the fundamentals of algebra and geometry; no possible gain could compensate for a real sacrifice of such thoroughness.

It should also be borne in mind that the suggestion of including elementary calculus is not intended for all schools nor for all teachers or all pupils in any school. It is not intended to connect in any direct way with college entrance requirements. The future college student will have ample opportunity for calculus later. The capable boy or girl who is not to have the college work ought not on that account to be prevented from learning something of the use of this powerful tool. The applications of elementary calculus to simple concrete problems are far more abundant and more interesting than those of algebra. The necessary technique is extremely simple. The subject is commonly taught in secondary schools in England, France, and Germany, and appropriate English texts are available.[3]

7. History and biography.—Historical and biographical material should be used throughout to make the work more interesting and significant.

8. Additional electives.—Additional electives such as *mathematics of investment, shop mathematics, surveying and navigation, descriptive* or *projective geometry* will appropriately be offered by schools which have special needs or conditions, but it seems unwise for the National Committee to attempt to define them pending the results of further experience on the part of these schools.

III. PLANS FOR ARRANGEMENT OF THE MATERIAL

In the majority of high schools at the present time the topics suggested can probably be given most advantageously as separate units of a three-year program. However, the National Committee is of the opinion that methods of organization are being experimentally perfected whereby teachers will be enabled to present much of this material more effectively in combined courses unified by one or more of such central ideas as functionality and graphic representation.

As to the arrangement of the material the committee gives below four plans which may be suggestive and helpful to teachers in arranging their courses. No one of them is, however, recommended as superior to the others.

PLAN A.

Tenth year: Plane demonstrative geometry, algebra.
Eleventh year: Statistics, trigonometry, solid geometry.
Twelfth year: The calculus, other elective.

PLAN B.

Tenth year: Plane demonstrative geometry, solid geometry.

---

3. Quotations and typical problems from one of these texts will be found in a supplementary note appended to this chapter.

Eleventh year: Algebra, trigonometry, statistics.
Twelfth year: The calculus, other elective.

PLAN C.

Tenth year: Plane demonstrative geometry, trigonometry.
Eleventh year: Solid geometry, algebra, statistics.
Twelfth year: The calculus, other elective.

PLAN D.

Tenth year: Algebra, statistics, trigonometry.
Eleventh year: Plane and solid geometry.
Twelfth year: The calculus, other elective.

Additional information on ways of organizing this material will be found in Chapter XII.

SUPPLEMENTARY NOTE ON THE CALCULUS AS A HIGH SCHOOL SUBJECT.

In connection with the recommendations concerning the calculus, such questions as the following may arise: Why should a college subject like this be added to a high school program? How can it be expected that high school teachers will have the necessary training and attainments for teaching it? Will not the attempt to teach such a subject result in loss of thoroughness in earlier work? Will anything be gained beyond a mere smattering of the theory? Will the boy or girl ever use the information or training secured? The subsequent remarks are intended to answer such objections as these and to develop more fully the point of view of the committee in recommending the inclusion of elementary work in the calculus in the high school program.

By the calculus we mean for the present purpose a study of *rates of change*. In nature all things change. How much do they change in a given time? How fast do they change? Do they increase or decrease? When does a changing quantity become largest or smallest? How can rates of changing quantities be compared?

These are some of the questions which lead us to study the elementary calculus. Without its essential principles these questions cannot be answered with definiteness.

The following are a few of the specific replies that might be given in answer to the questions listed at the beginning of this note: The difficulties of the college calculus lie mainly outside the boundaries of the proposed work. The elements of the subject present less difficulty than many topics now offered in advanced algebra. It is not implied that in the near future many secondary school teachers will have any occasion to teach the elementary calculus. It is the culminating subject in a series which only relatively strong

420

schools will complete and only then for a selected group of students. In such schools there should always be teachers competent to teach the elementary calculus here intended. No superficial study of calculus should be regarded as justifying any substantial sacrifice of thoroughness. In the judgment of the committee the introduction of elementary calculus necessarily includes sufficient algebra and geometry to compensate for whatever diversion of time from these subjects would be implied.

The calculus of the algebraic polynomial is so simple that a boy or girl who is capable of grasping the idea of limit, of slope, and of velocity, may in a brief time gain an outlook upon the field of mechanics and other exact sciences, and acquire a fair degree of facility in using one of the most powerful tools of mathematics, together with the capacity for solving a number of interesting problems. Moreover, the fundamental ideas involved, quite aside from their technical applications, will provide valuable training in understanding and analyzing quantitative relations—and such training is of value to everyone.

The following typical extracts from an English text intended for use in secondary schools may be quoted:

"It has been said that the calculus is that branch of mathematics which schoolboys understand and senior wranglers fail to comprehend. * * * So long as the graphic treatment and practical applications of the calculus are kept in view, the subject is an extremely easy and attractive one. Boys can be taught the subject early in their mathematical career, and there is no part of their mathematical training that they enjoy better or which opens up to them wider fields of useful exploration. * * * The phenomena must first be known practically and then studied philosophically. To reverse the order of these processes is impossible."

The text in question, after an interesting historical sketch, deals with such problems as the following:

A train is going at the rate of 40 miles an hour. Represent this graphically.

At what rate is the length of the daylight increasing or decreasing on December 31, March 26, etc.? (From tabular data.)

A cart going at the rate of 5 miles per hour passes a milestone, and 14 minutes afterwards a bicycle, going in the same direction at 12 miles an hour, passes the same milestone. Find when and where the bicycle will overtake the cart.

A man has 4 miles of fencing wire and wishes to fence in a rectangular piece of prairie land through which a straight river flows, the bank of the stream being utilized as one side of the enclosure. How can he do this so as to inclose as much land as possible?

A circular tin canister closed at both ends has a surface area of 100 square centimeters. Find the greatest volume it can contain.

Post-office regulations prescribe that the combined length and girth of a parcel must not exceed 6 feet. Find the maximum volume of a parcel whose shape is a prism with the ends square.

A pulley is fixed 15 feet above the ground, over which passes a rope 30 feet long with one end attached to a weight which can hang freely, and the other end is held by a man at a height of 3 feet from the ground. The man walks horizontally away from beneath the pulley at the rate of 3 feet per second. Find the rate at which the weight rises when it is 10 feet above the ground.

The pressure on the surface of a lake due to the atmosphere is known to be 14 pounds per square inch. The pressure in the liquid x inches below the surface is known to be given by the law $dp/dx = 0.036$. Find the pressure in the liquid at a depth of 10 feet.

The arch of a bridge is parabolic in form. It is 5 feet wide at the base and 5 feet high. Find the volume of water that passes through per second in a flood when the water is rushing at the rate of 10 feet per second.

A force of 20 tons compresses the spring buffer of a railway stop through 1 inch, and the force is always proportional to the compression produced. Find the work done by a train which compresses a pair of such stops through 6 inches.

These may illustrate the aims and point of view of the proposed work. It will be noted that not all of them involve calculus, but those that do not lead up to it.

CHAPTER V

College Entrance Requirements

The present chapter is concerned with a study of topics and training in elementary mathematics that will have most value as preparation for college work, and with recommendations of definitions of college entrance requirements in elementary algebra and plane geometry.

General considerations.—The primary purpose of college entrance requirements is to test the candidate's ability to benefit by college instruction. This ability depends, so far as our present inquiry is concerned, upon (1) general intelligence, intellectual maturity, and mental power; (2) specific knowledge and training required as preparation for the various courses of the college curriculum.

Mathematical ability appears to be a sufficient but not a necessary condition for general intelligence.[1] For this, as well as for other reasons, it would appear that *college entrance requirements in mathematics should be formulated primarily on the basis of the special knowledge and training required for the successful study of courses which the student will take in college.*

The separation of prospective college students from the others in the early years of the secondary school is neither feasible nor desirable. It is therefore obvious that secondary school courses in mathematics cannot be planned with specific reference to college entrance requirements. Fortunately there appears to be no real conflict of interest between those students who ultimately go to college and those who do not, so far as mathematics is concerned. It will be made clear in what follows that a course in this subject, covering from two to two and one-half years in a standard four-year high school, and so planned as to give the most valuable mathematical training which the student is capable of receiving, will provide adequate preparation for college work.

---

1. A recent investigation made by the department of psychology at Dartmouth College showed that all students of high rank in mathematics had a high rating on general intelligence; the converse was not true, however.

Topics to be included in high-school courses.—In the selection of material of instruction for high school courses in mathematics, its value as preparation for college courses in mathematics need not be specifically considered. Not all college students study mathematics; it is therefore reasonable to expect college departments in this subject to adjust themselves to the previous preparation of their students. Nearly all college students do, however, study one or more of the physical sciences (astronomy, physics, chemistry) and one or more of the social sciences (history, economics, political science, sociology). Entrance requirements must therefore insure adequate mathematical preparation in these subjects. Moreover, it may be assumed that adequate preparation for these two groups of subjects will be sufficient for all other subjects for which the secondary schools may be expected to furnish the mathematical prerequisites.

The National Committee recently conducted an investigation for the purpose of securing information as to the content of high school courses of instruction most desirable from the point of view of preparation for college work. A number of college teachers, prominent in their respective fields, were asked to assign to each of the topics in the following table an estimate of its value as preparation for the elementary courses in their respective subjects. Table 1 gives a summary of the replies, arranged in two groups— "Physical sciences," including astronomy, physics, and chemistry; and "Social sciences," including history, economics, sociology, and political science.

The high value attached to the following topics is significant: Simple formulas—their meaning and use; the linear and quadratic functions and variation; numerical trigonometry; the use of logarithms and other topics relating to numerical computation; statistics. These all stand well above such standard requirements as arithmetic and geometric progression, binomial theorem, theory of exponents, simultaneous equations involving one or two quadratic equations, and literal equations.

These results would seem to indicate that a modification of present college entrance requirements in mathematics is desirable from the point of view of college teachers in departments other than mathematics. It is interesting to note how closely the modifications suggested by this inquiry correspond to the modifications in secondary school mathematics foreshadowed by the study of needs of the high school pupil irrespective of his possible future college attendance. The recommendations made in Chapter II that functional relationship be made the "underlying principle of the course," that the meaning and use of simple formulas be emphasized, that more attention be given to numerical computation (especially to the methods relating to approximate data), and that work on numerical trigonometry and statistics be included, have received widespread approval throughout the country. That

424

TABLE 1.—*Value of topics as preparation for elementary college courses.*

[In the headings of the table, E = essential, C = of considerable value, S = of some value, O = of little or no value, N = number of replies received. The figures in the first four columns of each group are percentages of the number of replies received.]

	Physical sciences.					Social sciences.				
	E.	C.	S.	O.	N.	E.	C.	S.	O.	N.
Negative numbers—their meaning and use	79	5	10	5	39	45	17	22	17	18
Imaginary numbers—their meaning and use	23	21	25	31	39	13	13	37	37	16
Simple formulas—their meaning and use	93	5	2	—	41	47	26	21	5	19
Graphic representation of statistical data	57	25	15	3	40	57	24	14	5	21
Graphs (mathematical and empirical):										
(a) As a method of representing dependence	62	16	22	—	37	15	54	15	15	13
(b) As a method of solving problems	45	20	28	6	25	18	18	46	18	11
The linear function, $y = mx + b$	78	14	8	—	37	29	29	14	29	14
The quadratic function, $y = ax^2 + bx + c$	59	21	17	3	34	8	8	33	50	12
Equations: Problems leading to—										
Linear equations in one unknown	98	2	—	—	41	40	7	20	33	15
Quadratic equations in one unknown	78	15	5	2	40	31	8	8	54	13
Simultaneous linear equations in 2 unknowns	71	24	3	3	38	33	8	—	58	12
Simultaneous linear equations in more than 2 unknowns	43	29	23	6	35	8	8	17	67	12
One quadratic and one linear equation in 2 unknowns	40	24	27	9	33	—	9	9	82	11
Two quadratic equations in 2 unknowns	31	19	28	22	32	—	9	—	91	11
Equations of higher degree than the second	10	32	32	26	31	—	—	9	91	11
Literal equations (other than formulas)	43	18	32	7	28	—	10	40	50	10
Ratio and proportion	84	8	3	5	39	37	26	32	5	19
Variation	50	13	20	17	30	17	33	25	25	12
Numerical computation:										
With approximate data—rational use of significant figures	61	36	—	3	39	40	27	20	13	12
Short-cut methods	27	38	24	10	37	29	35	23	12	17
Use of logarithms	62	29	7	2	42	12	29	29	29	17
Use of other tables to facilitate computation	24	45	26	5	38	18	29	41	12	17
Use of slide-rule	24	39	26	12	38	11	39	28	22	18
Theory of exponents	36	31	25	8	36	—	21	21	57	14
Theory of logarithms	34	26	21	18	38	7	13	20	60	15
Arithmetic progression	16	32	38	13	37	23	29	12	35	17
Geometric progression	19	27	40	14	37	23	25	18	35	17
Binomial theorem	35	32	18	13	37	13	20	27	40	15
Probability	9	32	41	19	32	20	35	35	10	20
Statistics:										
Meaning and use of elementary concepts	23	28	31	17	29	55	36	5	5	22
Frequency distributions and frequency curves	15	19	35	32	26	47	33	10	10	21
Correlation	11	18	39	32	28	33	47	14	5	21
Numerical trigonometry:										
Use of sine, cosine, and tangent in the solution of simple problems involving right triangles	68	21	3	8	38	—	—	25	75	12
Demonstrative geometry	68	15	12	6	34	—	21	43	36	14
Plane trigonometry (usual course)	57	27	11	5	37	8	23	31	38	13
Analytic geometry:										
Fundamental conceptions and methods in the plane	32	45	19	3	31	—	15	38	46	13
Systematic treatment of—										
Straight line	34	37	20	9	35	9	9	18	64	11
Circle	29	43	20	9	35	—	18	9	73	11
Conic sections	18	41	26	15	34	—	9	18	73	11
Polar coordinates	18	26	41	15	34	—	—	18	82	11
Empirical curves and fitting curves to observations	12	38	38	12	34	8	—	25	67	12

they should be in such close accord with the desires of college teachers in the fields of physical and social sciences as to entrance requirements is striking. We find here the justification for the belief expressed earlier in this report that there is no real conflict between the needs of students who ultimately go to college and those who do not.

TABLE 2.—*Topics in order of value as preparation for elementary college courses.*

[The figures in the column headed "E" are taken from Table 1, taking in each case the higher of the two "E" ratings there given. The column headed "E+C" gives in each case the sum of the two ratings for "E" and "C." An asterisk indicates that the topic in question is now included in the definitions of the College Entrance Examination Board.[2]]

	E.	E+C.
Linear equations in one unknown...	98	100
Simple formulas—their meaning and use.....................................	93	98
*Ratio and proportion..	84	92
*Negative numbers—their meaning and use....................................	79	84
*Quadratic equations in one unknown.......................................	78	93
The linear function: $y = mx + b$..	78	92
*Simultaneous linear equations in two unknowns..............................	71	95
Numerical trigonometry—the use of the sine, cosine, and tangent in the solution of simple problems involving right triangles... .'..	68	89
*Demonstrative geometry..	68	83
Use of logarithms in computation..	62	91
*Graphs as a method of representing dependence..............................	62	78
Computation with approximate data—rational use of significant figures.......	61	97
The quadratic function: $y = ax^2 + bx + c$...................................	59	80
Plane trigonometry—usual course..	57	84
Graphic representation of statistical data....................................	57	82
Statistics—meaning and use of elementary concepts...........................	55	91
Variation. .'...	50	63
Statistics—frequency distributions and curves................................	47	80
*Graphic solution of problems..	45	65
*Literal equations...	43	61
*Simultaneous linear equations in more than 2 unknowns.....................	43	72
*Simultaneous equations, one quadratic, one linear...........................	40	64
*Theory of exponents..	36	67
*Binomial theorem...	35	67
Analytic geometry of the straight line.......................................	34	71
Theory of logarithms...	34	60
Statistics—correlation...	33	80
Analytic geometry—Fundamental Conceptions................................	32	77
*Simultaneous quadratic equations..	31	50
Analytic geometry of the circle...	29	72
Short-cut methods of computation...	29	65
Use of tables in computation (other than logarithms).........................	24	69
Use of slide rule...	24	63
*Arithmetic progression..	23	52
*Geometric progression..	23	48
Imaginary numbers...	23	44
Probability..	20	55
Conic sections...	18	59
Polar coordinates..	18	44
Empirical curves and fitting curves to observations...........................	12	50
Equations of higher degree than the second..................................	10	42

The attitude of the colleges.—Mathematical instruction in this country is at present in a period of transition. While a considerable number of our most progressive schools have for several years given courses embodying most of the recommendations contained in Chapters II, III, and IV of the present report, the large majority of schools are still continuing the older types of courses or are only just beginning to introduce modifications. The movement toward reorganization is strong, however, throughout the country,

2. The list includes all the requirements of the college entrance examination board except those relating to algebraic technique. The topic of "Negative numbers" has also been given an asterisk, as it is clearly implied, though not explicitly mentioned in the C. E. E. B. definitions.

not only in the standard four-year high schools but also in the newer junior high schools.

During this period of transition it should be the policy of the colleges, while exerting a desirable steadying influence, to help the movement toward a sane reorganization. In particular, they should take care not to place obstacles in the way of changes which are clearly in the interest of more effective college preparation, as well as of better general education.

College entrance requirements will continue to exert a powerful influence on secondary school teaching. Unless they reflect the spirit of sound progressive tendencies, they will constitute a serious obstacle.

In the present chapter revised definitions of college-entrance requirements in plane geometry and elementary algebra are presented. So far as plane geometry is concerned, the problem of definition is comparatively simple. The proposed definition of the requirement in plane geometry does not differ from the one now in effect under the College Entrance Examination Board. A list of propositions and constructions has however been prepared and is given in the next chapter for the guidance of teachers and examiners.

In elementary algebra a certain amount of flexibility is obviously necessary both on account of the quantitative differences among colleges and of the special conditions attending a period of transition. The former differences are recognized by the proposal of a minor and a major requirement in elementary algebra. The second of these includes the first and is intended to correspond with the two-unit rating of the C. E. E. B.

In connection with this matter of units, the committee wishes particularly to disclaim any emphasis upon a special number of years or hours. The unit terminology is doubtless too well established to be entirely ignored in formulating college entrance requirements, but the standard definition of unit[3] has never been precise, and will now become much less so with the inclusion of the newer six-year program. A time allotment of 4 or 5 hours per week in the seventh year can certainly not have the same weight as the same number of hours in the twelfth year, and the disparity will vary with different subjects. *What is really important is the amount of subject matter and the quality of work done in it.* The "unit" can not be anything but a crude approximation to this. The distribution of time in the school program should not be determined by any arbitrary unit scale.

As a further means of securing reasonable flexibility, the committee recommends that for a limited time—say five years—the option be offered be-

---

3. The following definition, formulated by the National Committee on Standards of Colleges and Secondary Schools, has been given the approval of the C. E. E. B. "A unit represents a year's study in any subject in a secondary school, constituting approximately a quarter of a full year's work. A four-year secondary school curriculum should be regarded as representing not more than 16 units of work."

tween examinations based on the old and on the new definitions, so far as differences between them may make this desirable.

In view of the changes taking place at the present time in mathematical courses in secondary schools, and the fact that college entrance requirements should so soon as possible reflect desirable changes and assist in their adoption, the National Committee recommends that either the American Mathematical Society or the Mathematical Association of America (or both) maintain a permanent committee on college entrance requirements in mathematics, such a committee to work in close coöperation with other agencies which are now or may in the future be concerned in a responsible way with the relations between colleges and secondary schools.

PROPOSED DEFINITION OF COLLEGE ENTRANCE REQUIREMENTS

ELEMENTARY ALGEBRA.

Minor requirement.—The meaning, use, and evaluation (including the necessary transformations) of simple formulas involving ideas with which the student is familiar and the derivation of such formulas from rules expressed in words.

The dependence of one variable upon another. Numerous illustrations and problems involving the linear function $y = mx + b$. Illustrations and problems involving the quadratic function $y = kx^2$.

Graphs and graphic representations in general; their construction and interpretation, including the representation of statistical data and the use of the graph to exhibit dependence.

Positive and negative numbers; their meaning and use.

Linear equations in one unknown quantity; their use in solving problems.

Sets of linear equations involving two unknown quantities; their use in solving problems.

Ratio, as a case of simple fractions; proportion without the theorems on alternation, etc.; and simple cases of variation.

The essentials of algebraic technique. This should include—

(a) The four fundamental operations.

(b) Factoring of the following types: Common factors of the terms of a polynomial; the difference of two squares; trinomials of the second degree (including the square of a binomial) that can be easily factored by trial.

(c) Fractions, including complex fractions of a simple type.

(d) Exponents and radicals. The laws for positive integral exponents; the meaning and use of fractional exponents, but not the formal theory. The consideration of radicals may be confined to the simplification of expressions of the form $\sqrt{a^2 b}$ and $\sqrt{a/b}$ and to the evaluation of simple expressions involving the radical sign. A process for extracting the square root of a number should be included but not the process for extracting the square root of a polynomial.

Numerical trigonometry. The use of the sine, cosine, and tangent in solving right triangles. The use of three or four place tables of natural functions.

Major requirement.—In addition to the minor requirement as specified above, the following should be included:

Illustrations and problems involving the quadratic function $y = ax^2 + bx + c$.

Quadratic equations in one unknown; their use in solving problems.

Exponents and radicals. Zero and negative exponents, and more extended treatment of fractional exponents. Rationalizing denominators. Solution of simple types of radical equations.

The use of logarithmic tables in computation without the formal theory.

Elementary statistics, including a knowledge of the fundamental concepts and simple frequency distributions, with graphic representations of various kinds.

The binomial theorem for positive integral exponents less than 8; with such applications as compound interest.

The formula for the nth term, and the sum of n terms, of arithmetic and geometric progressions, with applications.

Simultaneous linear equations in three unknown quantities and simple cases of simultaneous equations involving one or two quadratic equations; their use in solving problems.

Drill in algebraic manipulation should be limited, particularly in the minor requirement, by the purpose of securing a thorough understanding of important principles and facility in carrying out those processes which are fundamental and of frequent occurrence either in common life or in the subsequent courses that a substantial proportion of the pupils will study. Skill in manipulation must be conceived of throughout as a means to an end, not as an end in itself. Within these limits, skill and accuracy in algebraic technique are of prime importance, and drill in this subject should be extended far enough to enable students to carry out the fundamentally essential processes accurately and with reasonable speed.

The consideration of literal equations, when they serve a significant purpose, such as the transformation of formulas, the derivation of a general solution (as of the quadratic equation), or the proof of a theorem, is important. As a means for drill in algebraic technique they should be used sparingly.

The solution of problems should offer opportunity throughout the course for considerable arithmetical and computational work. The conception of algebra as an extension of arithmetic should be made significant both in numerical applications and in elucidating algebraic principles. Emphasis should be placed upon the use of common sense and judgment in computing from approximate data, especially with regard to the number of figures retained, and on the necessity for checking the results. The use of tables to facilitate computation (such as tables of squares and square roots, of interest, and of trigonometric functions) should be encouraged.

PLANE GEOMETRY.

The usual theorems and constructions of good textbooks, including the general properties of plane rectilinear figures; the circle and the measurement of angles; similar polygons; areas; regular polygons and the measurement of the circle. The solution of numerous original exercises, including locus problems. Applications to the mensuration of lines and plane surfaces.

The scope of the required work in plane geometry is indicated by the List of Fundamental Propositions and Constructions, which is given in the next chapter. This list indicates in Section I the type of proposition which, in the opinion of the committee, may be assumed without proof or given informal treatment. Section II contains 52 propositions and 19 constructions which are regarded as so fundamental that they should constitute the common minimum of all standard courses in plane geometry. Section III gives a list of subsidiary theorems which suggests the type of additional propositions that should be included in such courses.

College entrance examinations.—College entrance examinations exert in many schools, and especially throughout the eastern section of the country, an influence on secondary school teaching which is very far-reaching. It is, therefore, well within the province of the National Committee to inquire whether the prevailing type of examination in mathematics serves the best interests of mathematical education and of college preparation.

The reason for the almost controlling influence of entrance examinations in the schools referred to is readily recognized. Schools sending students to such colleges for men as Harvard, Yale, and Princeton, to the larger colleges for women, or to any institution where examinations form the only or prevailing mode of admission, inevitably direct their instruction toward the entrance examination. This remains true even if only a small percentage of the class intends to take these examinations, the point being that the success of a teacher is often measured by the success of his or her students in these examinations.

In the judgment of the committee, the prevailing type of entrance examination in algebra is primarily a test of the candidate's skill in formal manipulation, and not an adequate test of his understanding or of his ability to apply the principles of the subject. Moreover, it is quite generally felt that the difficulty and complexity of the formal manipulative questions, which have appeared on recent papers set by colleges and by such agencies as the College Entrance Examination Board, has often been excessive. As a result, teachers preparing pupils for these examinations have inevitably been led to devote an excessive amount of time to drill in algebraic technique, without insuring an adequate understanding of the principles involved. Far from providing the desired facility, this practice has tended to impair it. For "practical skill, modes of effective technique, can be intelligently, non-mechanically used only when intelligence has played a part in their acquisition." (Dewey, *How We Think*, p. 52.)

Moreover, it must be noted that authors and publishers of textbooks are under strong pressure to make their content and distribution of emphasis conform to the prevailing type of entrance examination. Teachers in turn are too often unable to rise above the textbook. An improvement in the examinations in this respect will cause a corresponding improvement in textbooks and in teaching.

On the other hand, the makers of entrance examinations in algebra cannot be held solely responsible for the condition described. Theirs is a most difficult problem. Not only can they reply that as long as algebra is taught as it is, examinations must be largely on technique,[4] but they can also claim with considerable force that technical facility is the only phase of algebra that can be fairly tested by an examination; that a candidate can rarely do himself justice amid unfamiliar surroundings and subject to a time limit on questions involving real thinking in applying principles to concrete situations; and that we must face here a real limitation on the power of an examination to test attainment. Many, and perhaps most, teachers will agree with this claim. Past experience is on their side; no generally accepted and effective "power test" in mathematics has as yet been devised and, if devised, it might not be suitable for use under conditions prevailing during an entrance examination.

But if it is true that the power of an examination is thus inevitably limited, the wisdom and fairness of using it as the sole means of admission to college is surely open to grave doubt. That many unqualified candidates are admitted under this system is not open to question. Is it not probable that many qualified candidates are at the same time excluded? If the entrance examination is a fair test of manipulative skill only, should not the colleges use additional means for learning something about the candidate's other abilities and qualifications?

Some teachers believe that an effective "power test" in mathematics is possible. Efforts to devise such a test should receive every encouragement.

In the meantime, certain desirable modifications of the prevailing type of entrance examination are possible. The College Entrance Examination Board recently appointed a committee to consider this question and a con-

---

4. The vicious circle is now complete. Algebra is taught mechanically because of the character of the entrance examination; the examination, in order to be fair, must conform to the character of the teaching.

ference[5] on this subject was held by representatives of the College Entrance Examination Board, members of the National Committee, and others. The following recommendations are taken from the report of the committee just referred to:

Fully one-third of the questions should be based on topics of such fundamental importance that they will have been thoroughly taught, carefully reviewed, and deeply impressed by effective drill. . . . They should be of such a degree of difficulty that any pupil of regular attendance, faithful application, and even moderate ability may be expected to answer them satisfactorily.

There should be both simple and difficult questions testing the candidate's ability to apply the principles of the subject. The early ones of the easy questions should be really easy for the candidate of good average ability who can do a little thinking under the stress of an examination; but even these questions should have genuine scientific content.

There should be a substantial question which will put the best candidates on their mettle, but which is not beyond the reach of a fair proportion of the really good candidates. This question should test the normal workings of a well-trained mind. It should be capable of being thought out in the limited time of the examination. It should be a test of the candidate's grasp and insight—not a catch question or a question of unfamiliar character making extraordinary demands on the critical powers of the candidate or one the solution of which depends on an inspiration. Above all, this question should lie near to the heart of the subject as all well-prepared candidates understand the subject.

As a rule, a question should consist of a single part and be framed to test one thing—not pieced together out of several unrelated and perhaps unequally important parts.

Each question should be a substantial test on the topic or topics which it represents. It is, however, in the nature of the case impossible that all questions be of equal value.

Care should be used that the examination be not too long. * * * The examiner should be content to ask questions on the important topics, so chosen that their answers will be fair to the candidate and instructive to the readers; and beyond this merely to sample the candidate's knowledge of the minor topics.

The National Committee suggests the following additional principles: The examination as a whole should, as far as practicable, reflect the principle that algebraic technique is a means to an end, and not an end in itself.

Questions that require of the candidate skill in algebraic manipulation beyond the needs of actual application should be used very sparingly.

5. At this conference the following vote was unanimously passed: "Voted, that the results of examinations (of the College Entrance Examination Board), be reported by letters A, B, C, D, E and that the definition of the groups represented by these letters should be determined in each year by the distribution of ability in a standard group of papers representing widely both public and private schools."

An effort should be made to devise questions which will fairly test the candidate's understanding of principles and his ability to apply them, while involving a minimum of manipulative complexity.

The examinations in geometry should be definitely constructed to test the candidate's ability to draw valid conclusions rather than his ability to memorize an argument.

A chapter on mathematical terms and symbols is included in this report.[6] It is hoped that examining bodies will be guided by the recommendations there made relative to the use of terms and symbols in elementary mathematics.

The College Entrance Examination Board, early in 1921, appointed a commission to recommend such revisions as might seem necessary in the definitions of the requirements in the various subjects of elementary mathematics. The recommendations contained in the present chapter have been laid before this commission. It is hoped that the commission's report, when it is finally made effective by action of the College Entrance Examination Board and the various colleges concerned, will give impetus to the reorganization of the teaching of elementary mathematics along the lines recommended in the report of the National Committee.

6. See Chap. VIII.

CHAPTER VI

List of Propositions in Plane and Solid Geometry

General basis of the selection of material.—The subcommittee appointed to prepare a list of basal propositions made a careful study of a number of widely used textbooks on geometry. The bases of selection of the propositions were two: (1) The extent to which the propositions and corollaries were used in subsequent proofs of important propositions and exercises; (2) the value of the propositions in completing important pieces of theory. Although the list of theorems and problems is substantially the same in nearly all textbooks in general use in this country, the wording, the sequence, and the methods of proof vary to such an extent as to render difficult a definite statement as to the number of times a proposition is used in the several books examined. A tentative table showed, however, less variation than might have been anticipated.

Classification of propositions.—The classification of propositions is not the same in plane geometry as in solid geometry. This is partly due to the fact that it is generally felt that the student should limit his construction work to figures in a plane and in which the compasses and straight edge are sufficient. The propositions have been divided as follows:

Plane geometry: I. Assumptions and theorems for informal treatment; II. Fundamental theorems and constructions: A. Theorems, B. Constructions; III. Subsidiary theorems.

Solid geometry: I. Fundamental theorems; II. Fundamental propositions in mensuration; III. Subsidiary theorems; IV. Subsidiary propositions in mensuration.

PLANE GEOMETRY

I. Assumptions and theorems for informal treatment.—This list contains propositions which may be assumed without proof (postulates) and theorems which it is permissible to treat informally. Some of these propositions will appear as definitions in certain methods of treatment. Moreover, teachers should feel free to require formal proofs in certain cases, if they desire to do so. The precise wording given is not essential, nor is the order in which the propositions are here listed. The list should be taken as representative of the type of propositions which may be assumed, or treated informally, rather than as exhaustive.

434

1. Through two distinct points it is possible to draw one straight line, and only one.

2. A line segment may be produced to any desired length.

3. The shortest path between two points is the line segment joining them.

4. One and only one perpendicular can be drawn through a given point to a given straight line.

5. The shortest distance from a point to a line is the perpendicular distance from the point to the line.

6. From a given center and with a given radius one and only one circle can be described in a plane.

7. A straight line intersects a circle in at most two points.

8. Any figure may be moved from one place to another without changing its shape or size.

9. All right angles are equal.

10. If the sum of two adjacent angles equals a straight angle, their exterior sides form a straight line.

11. Equal angles have equal complements and equal supplements.

12. Vertical angles are equal.

13. Two lines perpendicular to the same line are parallel.

14. Through a given point not on a given straight line, one straight line, and only one, can be drawn parallel to the given line.

15. Two lines parallel to the same line are parallel to each other.

16. The area of a rectangle is equal to its base times its altitude.

II. Fundamental theorems and constructions.—It is recommended that theorems and constructions (other than originals) to be proved on college entrance examinations be chosen from the following list. Originals and other exercises should be capable of solution by direct reference to one or more of these propositions and constructions. It should be obvious that any course in geometry that is capable of giving adequate training must include considerable additional material. The order here given is not intended to signify anything as to the order of presentation. It should be clearly understood that certain of the statements contain two or more theorems, and that the precise wording is not essential. The committee favors entire freedom in statement and sequence.

A. Theorems.

1. Two triangles are congruent if [1] (a) two sides and the included angle of one are equal, respectively, to two sides and the included angle of the other; (b) two

---

1. Teachers should feel free to separate this theorem into three distinct theorems and to use other phraseology for any such proposition. For example, in 1, "Two triangles are equal if * * *", " a triangle is determined by * * *", etc. Similarly in 2, the statement might read: "Two right triangles are congruent if, besides the right angles, any two parts (not both angles) in the one are equal to corresponding parts of the other."

angles and a side of one are equal, respectively, to two angles and the corresponding side of the other; (c) the three sides of one are equal, respectively, to the three sides of the other.

2. Two right triangles are congruent if the hypotenuse and one other side of one are equal, respectively, to the hypotenuse and another side of the other.

3. If two sides of a triangle are equal, the angles opposite these sides are equal; and conversely.[2]

4. The locus of a point (in a plane) equidistant from two given points is the perpendicular bisector of the line segment joining them.

5. The locus of a point equidistant from two given intersecting lines is the pair of lines bisecting the angles formed by these lines.

6. When a transversal cuts two parallel lines, the alternate interior angles are equal; and conversely.

7. The sum of the angles of a triangle is two right angles.

8. A parallelogram is divided into congruent triangles by either diagonal.

9. Any (convex) quadrilateral is a parallelogram (a) if the opposite sides are equal; (b) if two sides are equal and parallel.

10. If a series of parallel lines cut off equal segments on one transversal they cut off equal segments on any transversal.

11. (a) The area of a parallelogram is equal to the base times the altitude.

(b) The area of a triangle is equal to one-half the base times the altitude.

(c) The area of a trapezoid is equal to half the sum of its bases times its altitude.

(d) The area of a regular polygon is equal to half the product of its apothem and perimeter.

12. (a) If a straight line is drawn through two sides of a triangle parallel to the third side it divides these sides proportionally.

(b) If a line divides two sides of a triangle proportionally it is parallel to the third side. (Proofs for commensurable cases only.)

(c) The segments cut off on two transversals by a series of parallels are proportional.

13. Two triangles are similar if (a) they have two angles of one equal, respectively, to two angles of the other; (b) they have an angle of one equal to an angle of the other and the including sides are proportional; (c) their sides are respectively proportional.

14. If two chords intersect in a circle, the product of the segments of one is equal to the product of the segments of the other.

15. The perimeters of two similar polygons have the same ratio as any two corresponding sides.

16. Polygons are similar, if they can be decomposed into triangles which are similar and similarly placed; and conversely.

17. The bisector of an (interior or exterior) angle of a triangle divides the

---

2. It should be understood that the converse of a theorem need not be treated in connection with the theorem itself, it being sometimes better to treat it later. Furthermore, a converse may occasionally be accepted as true in an elementary course, if the necessity for proof is made clear. The proof may then be given later.

opposite side (produced if necessary) into segments proportional to the adjacent sides.

18. The areas of two similar triangles (or polygons) are to each other as the squares of any two corresponding sides.

19. In any right triangle the perpendicular from the vertex of the right angle on the hypotenuse divides the triangle into two triangles each similar to the given triangle.

20. In a right triangle the square on the hypotenuse is equal to the sum of the squares on the other two sides.

21. In the same circle or in equal circles, if two arcs are equal, their central angles are equal; and conversely.

22. In any circle angles at the center are proportional to their intercepted arcs. (Proof for commensurable case only.)

23. In the same circle or in equal circles, if two chords are equal their corresponding arcs are equal; and conversely.

24. (*a*) A diameter perpendicular to a chord bisects the chord and the arcs of the chord. (*b*) A diameter which bisects a chord (that is not a diameter) is perpendicular to it.

25. The tangent to a circle at a given point is perpendicular to the radius at that point; and conversely.

26. In the same circle or in equal circles, equal chords are equally distant from the center; and conversely.

27. An angle inscribed in a circle is equal to half the central angle having the same arc.

28. Angles inscribed in the same segment are equal.

29. If a circle is divided into equal arcs, the chords of these arcs form a regular inscribed polygon and tangents at the points of division form a regular circumscribed polygon.

31.[3] The area of a circle is equal to πr^2. (Informal proof only.)

30. The circumference of a circle is equal to $2\pi r$. (Informal proof only.)

The treatment of the mensuration of the circle should be based upon related theorems concerning regular polygons, but it should be informal as to the limiting processes involved. The aim should be an understanding of the concepts involved, so far as the capacity of the pupil permits.

B. Constructions.

1. Bisect a line segment and draw the perpendicular bisector.

2. Bisect an angle.

3. Construct a perpendicular to a given line through a given point.

4. Construct an angle equal to a given angle.

5. Through a given point draw a straight line parallel to a given straight line.

6. Construct a triangle, given (*a*) the three sides; (*b*) two sides and the included angle; (*c*) two angles and the included side.

7. Divide a line segment into parts proportional to given segments.

3. The total number of theorems given in this list when separated, as will probably be found advantageous in teaching, including the converses indicated, is 52.

8. Given an arc of a circle, find its center.
9. Circumscribe a circle about a triangle.
10. Inscribe a circle in a triangle.
11. Construct a tangent to a circle through a given point.
12. Construct the fourth proportional to three given line segments.
13. Construct the mean proportional between two given line segments.
14. Construct a triangle (polygon) similar to a given triangle (polygon).
15. Construct a triangle equal to a given polygon.
16. Inscribe a square in a circle.
17. Inscribe a regular hexagon in a circle.

III. Subsidiary list of propositions.—The following list of propositions is intended to suggest some of the additional material referred to in the introductory paragraph of Section II. It is not intended, however, to be exhaustive; indeed, the committee feels that teachers should be allowed considerable freedom in the selection of such additional material, theorems, corollaries, originals, exercises, etc., in the hope that opportunity will thus be afforded for constructive work in the development of courses in geometry.

1. When two lines are cut by a transversal, if the corresponding angles are equal or if the interior angles on the same side of the transversal are supplementary, the lines are parallel.
2. When a transversal cuts two parallel lines, the corresponding angles are equal, and the interior angles on the same side of the transversal are supplementary.
3. A line perpendicular to one of two parallels is perpendicular to the other also.
4. If two angles have their sides respectively parallel or respectively perpendicular to each other, they are either equal or supplementary.
5. Any exterior angle of a triangle is equal to the sum of the two opposite interior angles.
6. The sum of the angles of a convex polygon of n sides is $2(n - 2)$ right angles.
7. In any parallelogram (a) the opposite sides are equal; (b) the opposite angles are equal; (c) the diagonals bisect each other.
8. Any (convex) quadrilateral is a parallelogram, if (a) the opposite angles are equal; (b) the diagonals bisect each other.
9. The medians of a triangle intersect in a point which is two-thirds of the distance from a vertex to the mid-point of the opposite side.
10. The altitudes of a triangle meet in a point.
11. The perpendicular bisectors of the sides of a triangle meet in a point.
12. The bisectors of the angles of a triangle meet in a point.
13. The tangents to a circle from an external point are equal.
14.[4] (a) If two sides of a triangle are unequal, the greater side has the greater

4. Such inequality theorems as these are of importance in developing the notion of dependence or functionality in geometry. The fact that they are placed in the "Subsidiary list of propositions" should not imply that they are considered of less educational value than those in List II. They are placed here because they are not "fundamental" in the same sense that the theorems of List II are fundamental.

angle opposite it, and conversely.

(*b*) If two sides of one triangle are equal respectively to two sides of another triangle, but the included angle of the first is greater than the included angle of the second, then the third side of the first is greater than the third side of the second, and conversely.

(*c*) If two chords are unequal, the greater is at the less distance from the center, and conversely.

(*d*) The greater of two minor arcs has the greater chord, and conversely.

15. An angle inscribed in a semicircle is a right angle.

16. Parallel lines cutting a circle intercept equal arcs on the circle.

17. An angle formed by a tangent of a circle and a chord drawn through the point of contact is measured by half the intercepted arc.

18. An angle formed by two intersecting chords is measured by half the sum of the intercepted arcs.

19. An angle formed by two secants or by two tangents to a circle is measured by half the difference between the intercepted arcs.

20. If from a point without a circle a secant and a tangent are drawn, the tangent is the mean proportional between the whole secant and its external segment.

21. Parallelograms or triangles of equal bases and equal altitudes are equal.

22. The perimeters of two regular polygons of the same number of sides are to each other as their radii and also as their apothems.

SOLID GEOMETRY

In the following list the precise wording and the sequence are not considered:

I. Fundamental Theorems.

1. If two planes meet, they intersect in a straight line. .

2. If a line is perpendicular to each of two intersecting lines at their point of intersection it is perpendicular to the plane of the two lines.

3. Every perpendicular to a given line at a given point lies in a plane perpendicular to the given line at the given point.

4. Through a given point (internal or external) there can pass one and only one line perpendicular to a plane.

5. Two lines perpendicular to the same plane are parallel.

6. If two lines are parallel, every plane containing one of the lines and only one is parallel to the other.

7. Two planes perpendicular to the same line are parallel.

8. If two parallel planes are cut by a third plane, the lines of intersection are parallel.

9. If two angles not in the same plane have their sides respectively parallel in the same sense, they are equal and their planes are parallel.

10. If two planes are perpendicular to each other, a line drawn in one of them perpendicular to their intersection is perpendicular to the other.

11. If a line is perpendicular to a given plane, every plane which contains this

line is perpendicular to the given plane.

12. If two intersecting planes are each perpendicular to a third plane, their intersection is also perpendicular to that plane.

13. The sections of a prism made by parallel planes cutting all the lateral edges are congruent polygons.

14. An oblique prism is equal to a right prism whose base is equal to a right section of the oblique prism and whose altitude is equal to a lateral edge of the oblique prism.

15. The opposite faces of a parallelopiped are congruent.

16. The plane passed through two diagonally opposite edges of a parallelopiped divides the parallelopiped into two equal triangular prisms.

17. If a pyramid (or a cone) is cut by a plane parallel to the base:

(*a*) The lateral edges (or elements) and the altitude are divided proportionally;

(*b*) The section is a figure similar to the base;

(*c*) The area of the section is to the area of the base as the square of the distance from the vertex is to the square of the altitude of the pyramid (or cone).

18. Two triangular pyramids having equal bases and equal altitudes are equal.

19. All points on a circle of a sphere are equidistant from either pole of the circle.

20. On any sphere a point which is at a quadrant's distance from each of two other points not the extremities of a diameter is a pole of the great circle passing through these two points.

21. If a plane is perpendicular to a radius at its extremity on a sphere, it is tangent to the sphere.

22. A sphere can be inscribed in or circumscribed about any tetrahedron.

23. If one spherical triangle is the polar of another, then reciprocally the second is the polar triangle of the first.

24. In two polar triangles each angle of either is the supplement of the opposite side of the other.

25. Two symmetric spherical triangles are equal.

II. Fundamental Propositions in Mensuration.

26. The lateral area of a prism or a circular cylinder is equal to the product of a lateral edge or element, respectively, by the perimeter (circumference) of a right section.

27. The volume of a prism (including any parallelopiped) or of a circular cylinder is equal to the product of its base by its altitude.

28. The lateral area of a regular pyramid or a right circular cone is equal to half the product of its slant height by the perimeter (circumference) of its base.

29. The volume of a pyramid or a cone is equal to one-third the product of its base by its altitude.

30. The area of a sphere.

31. The area of a spherical polygon.

32. The volume of a sphere.

III. Subsidiary Theorems.

33. If from an external point a perpendicular and obliques are drawn to a plane, (*a*) the perpendicular is shorter than any oblique; (*b*) obliques meeting the plane

at equal distances from the foot of the perpendicular are equal; (c) of two obliques meeting the plane at unequal distances from the foot of the perpendicular, the more remote is the longer.

34. If two lines are cut by three parallel planes, their corresponding segments are proportional.

35. Between two lines not in the same plane there is one common perpendicular, and only one.

36. The bases of a cylinder are congruent.

37. If a plane intersects a sphere, the line of intersection is a circle.

38. The volume of two tetrahedrons that have a trihedral angle of one equal to a trihedral angle of the other are to each other as the products of the three edges of these trihedral angles.

39. In any polyhedron the number of edges increased by two is equal to the number of vertices increased by the number of faces.

40. Two similar polyhedrons can be separated into the same number of tetrahedrons similar each to each and similarly placed.

41. The volumes of two similar tetrahedrons are to each other as the cubes of any two corresponding edges.

42. The volumes of two similar polyhedrons are to each other as the cubes of any two corresponding edges.

43. If three face angles of one trihedral angle are equal, respectively, to the three face angles of another the trihedral angles are either congruent or symmetric.

44. Two spherical triangles on the same sphere are either congruent or symmetric if (a) two sides and the included angle of one are equal to the corresponding parts of the other; (b) two angles and the included side of one are equal to the corresponding parts of the other; (c) they are mutually equilateral; (d) they are mutually equiangular.

45. The sum of any two face angles of a trihedral angle is greater than the third face angle.

46. The sum of the face angles of any convex polyhedral angle is less than four right angles.

47. Each side of a spherical triangle is less than the sum of the other two sides.

48. The sum of the sides of a spherical polygon is less than 360°.

49. The sum of the angles of a spherical triangle is greater than 180° and less than 540°.

50. There can not be more than five regular polyhedrons.

51. The locus of points equidistant (a) from two given points; (b) from two given planes which intersect.

IV. Subsidiary Propositions in Mensuration.

52. The volume of a frustum of (a) a pyramid or (b) a cone.

53. The lateral area of a frustum of (a) pyramid or (b) a cone of revolution.

54. The volume of a prismoid (without formal proof).

441

CHAPTER VII

The Function Concept in Secondary School Mathematics [1]

In Chapter II, and incidentally in later chapters, considerable emphasis has been placed on the function concept or, better, on the idea of relationship between variable quantities as one of the general ideas that should dominate instruction in elementary mathematics. Since this recommendation is peculiarly open to misunderstanding on the part of teachers, it seems desirable to devote a separate chapter to a rather detailed discussion of what the recommendation means and implies.

It will be seen in what follows that there is no disposition to advocate the teaching of any sort of function *theory*. A prime danger of misconception that should be removed at the very outset is that teachers may think it is the notation and the definitions of such a theory that are to be taught. Nothing could be further from the intention of the committee. Indeed, it seems entirely safe to say that the word "function" had best not be used at all in the early courses.

What is desired is that the idea of relationship or dependence between variable quantities be imparted to the pupil by the examination of numerous concrete instances of such relationship. He must be shown the workings of relationships in a large number of cases before the abstract idea of relationship will have any meaning for him. Furthermore, the pupil should be led to form the habit of thinking about the connections that exist between related quantities, not merely because such a habit forms the best foundation for a real appreciation of the theory that may follow later, but chiefly because this habit will enable him to think more clearly about the quantities with which he will have to deal in real life, whether or not he takes any further work in mathematics.

Indeed, the reason for insisting so strongly upon attention to the idea of relationships between quantities is that such relationships do occur in

1. The first draft of this chapter was prepared for the National Committee by E. R. Hedrick, of the University of Missouri. It was discussed at the meeting of the Committee, Sept. 2-4, 1920; revised by the author, and again discussed Dec. 29-30, 1920, and is now issued as part of the committee's report.

real life in connection with practically all of the quantities with which we are called upon to deal in practice. Whereas there can be little doubt about the small value to the student who does not go on to higher studies of some of the manipulative processes criticized by the National Committee, there can be no doubt at all of the value to all persons of any increase in their ability to see and to foresee the manner in which related quantities affect each other.

To attain what has been suggested, the teacher should have in mind constantly not any definition to be recited by the pupil, not any automatic response to a given cue, not any memory exercise at all, but rather a determination not to pass any instance in which one quantity is related to another, or in which one quantity is determined by one or more others, without calling attention to the fact, and trying to have the student "see how it works." These instances occur in literally thousands of cases in both algebra and geometry. It is the purpose of this chapter to outline in some detail a few typical instances of this character.

I. RELATIONSHIPS IN ALGEBRA

In algebra the instance of the function idea which usually occurs to one first is in connection with the study of graphs. While this is natural enough, and while it is true that the graph is fundamentally functional in character, the supposition that it furnishes the first opportunity for observing functional relations between quantities betrays a misconception that ought to be corrected.

1. Use of letters for numbers.—The very first illustrations given in algebra to show the use of letters in the place of numbers are essentially functional in character. Thus, such relations as $I = prt$ and $A = \pi r^2$, as well as others that are frequently used, are statements of general relationships. These should be used to accustom the student not only to the use of letters in the place of numbers and to the solution of simple numerical problems, but also to the idea, for example, that changes in r affect the value of A. Such questions as the following should be considered: If r is doubled, what will happen to A? If p is doubled, what will happen to I? Appreciation of the meaning of such relationships will tend to clarify the entire subject under consideration. Without such an appreciation, it may be doubted whether the student has any real grasp of the matter.

2. Equations.—Every simple problem leading to an equation in the first part of algebra would be better understood for just such a discussion as that mentioned above. Thus, if two dozen eggs are weighed in a basket which weighs 2 pounds, and if the total weight is found to be 5 pounds, what is the average weight of an egg? If x is the weight in ounces of one egg, the total weight with the 2-pound basket would be $24x + 32$ ounces. If the student will first try the effect of an average weight of 1 ounce, of 1½ ounces, 2 ounces, 2½ ounces, the meaning of the problem will stand out clearly. In every such problem, preliminary trials really amount to a discussion of the properties of a linear function.

3. Formulas of pure science and of practical affairs.—The study of formulas as such, aside from their numerical evaluation, is becoming of more and more importance. The actual uses of algebra are not to be found solely nor even principally in the solution of numerical problems for numerical answers. In such formulas as those for falling bodies, levers, etc., the manner in which changes in one quantity cause (or correspond to) changes in another, are of prime importance, and their discussion need cause no difficulty whatever. The formulas under discussion here include those formulas of pure science and of practical affairs which are being introduced more and more into our texts on algebra. Whenever such a formula is encountered, the teacher should be sure that the students have some comprehension of the effects of changes in one of the quantities upon the other quantity or quantities in the formula.

As a specific instance of such scientific formulas, consider, for example, the force F, in pounds, with which a weight W, in pounds, pulls outward on a string (centrifugal force) if the weight is revolved rapidly at a speed v, in feet per second, at the end of a string of length r feet. This force is given by the formula

$$F = \frac{Wv^2}{32r}$$

When such a formula is used the teacher should not be contented with the mere insertion of numerical values for W, v, and r to obtain a numerical value for F.

The advantage obtained from the study of such a formula lies quite as much in the recognition of the behavior of the force when one of the other quantities varies. Thus the student should be able to answer intelligently such questions as the following: If the weight is assumed to be twice as heavy, what is the effect upon the force? If the speed is taken twice as great, what is the effect upon the force? If the radius becomes twice as large, what is the effect upon the force? If the speed is doubled, what change in the weight would result in the same force? Will an increase in the speed cause an increase or decrease in the force? Will an increase in the radius r cause an increase or a decrease in the force?

As another instance (of a more advanced character) consider the formula for the amount of a sum of money P, at compound interest at r per cent, at the end of n years. This amount may be denoted by A_n. Then we shall have $A_n = P (1 + r)^n$. Will doubling P result in doubling A_n? Will doubling n result in doubling A_n? Since the compound interest that has accumulated

444

is equal to the difference between P and A_n, will the doubling of r double the interest? Compare the correct answers to these questions with the answers to the similar questions in the case of simple interest, in which the formula reads $A_n = P + Prn$ and in which the accumulated interest is simply Prn.

The difference between such a study of the effect produced upon one quantity by changes in another and the mere substitution of numerical values will be apparent from these examples.

4. Formulas of pure algebra.—Formulas of pure algebra, such as that for $(x + h)^2$, will be better understood and appreciated if accompanied by a discussion of the manner in which changes in h cause changes in the total result. This can be accomplished by discussing such concrete realities as the error made in computing the area of a square field or of a square room when an error has been made in measuring the side of the square. If x is the true length of the side, and if the student assumes various possible values for the error h made in measuring x, he will have a situation that involves some comprehension of the functional workings of the formula mentioned. The same formula relates to such problems as the change from one entry to the next entry in a table of squares.

A similar situation, and a very important one, occurs with the pure algebraic formula for $(x + a)(y + b)$. This formula may be said to govern the question of the keeping of significant figures in finding the product xy. For if a and b represent the uncertainty in x and y, respectively, the uncertainty in the product is given by this formula. The student has much to learn on this score, for the retention of meaningless figures in a product is one of the commonest mistakes of both student and teacher in computational work.

Such formulas occur throughout algebra, and each of them will be illuminated by such a discussion. The formulas for arithmetic and geometric progression, for example, should be studied from a functional standpoint.

5. Tables.—The uses of the functional idea in connection with numerical computation have already been mentioned in connection with the formula for a product. Work which appears on the surface to be wholly numerical may be of a distinctly functional character. Thus any table, e. g., a table of squares, corresponds to or is constructed from a functional relation, e. g., for a table of squares, the relation $y = x^2$. The differences in such a table are the differences caused by changes in the values of the independent variable. Thus, the differences in a table of squares are precisely the differences between x^2 and $(x + h)^2$ for various values of x.

6. Graphs.—The functional character of graphic representations was mentioned at the beginning of this section. Every graph is obviously a representation of a functional relationship between two or more quantities. What is needed is only to draw attention to this fact and to study each graph from this standpoint. In addition to this, however, it is desirable to

445

point out that functional relations may be studied directly by means of graphs without the intervention of any algebraic formula. Thus, such a graph as a population curve, or a curve representing wind pressure, obviously represents a relationship between two quantities, but there is no known formula in either case. The idea that the three concepts, tables, graphs, algebraic formulas, are all representations of the same kind of connection between quantities, and that we may start in some instances with any of the three, is a most valuable addition to the student's mental equipment, and to his control over the quantities with which he will deal in his daily life.

II. RELATIONSHIPS IN GEOMETRY

Thus far the instances mentioned have been largely algebraic, though certain mensuration formulas of geometry have been mentioned. While the mensuration formulas may occur to one first as an illustration of functional concepts in geometry, they are by no means the earliest relationships that occur in that study.

1. Congruence.—Among the earliest theorems are those on the congruence of triangles. In any such theorem, the parts necessary to establish congruence evidently determine completely the size of each other part. Thus, two sides and the included angle of a triangle evidently determine the length of the third side. If the student clearly grasps this fact, the meaning of this case of congruence will be more vivid to him, and he will be prepared for its important applications in surveying and in trigonometry. Even if he never studies those subjects, he will nevertheless be able to use his understanding of the situation in any practical cases in which the angle between two fixed rods or beams is to be fixed or is to be determined, in a practical situation such as house building. Other congruence theorems throughout geometry may well be treated in a similar manner.

2. Inequalities.—In the theorems regarding inequalities, the functional quality is even more pronounced. Thus, if two triangles have two sides of one equal respectively to two sides of the other, but if the included angle between these sides in the one triangle is greater than the corresponding angle in the other, then the third sides of the triangles are unequal in the same sense. This theorem shows that as one angle grows, the side opposite it grows, if the other sides remain unchanged. A full realization of the fact here mentioned would involve a real grasp of the functional relation between the angle and the side opposite it. Thus, if the angle is doubled, will the side opposite it be doubled? Such questions arise in connection with all theorems on inequalities.

3. Variations in figures.—A great assistance to the imagination is gained in certain figures by imagining variations of the figure through all intermediate stages from one case to another. Thus, the angle between two lines that cut a circle is measured by a proper combination of the two arcs cut out of the circle by the two lines. As the vertex of the angle passes from the center of the circle to the circumference and thence to the outside of the circle, the rule changes but these changes may be borne in mind, and the entire scheme may be grasped, by imagining a continuous change from the one position to the other, following all the time the changes in the intercepted arcs. The angle between a secant and a tangent is measured in a manner that can best be grasped by another such continuous motion, watching the changes in the measuring arcs as the motion occurs. Such observations are essentially functional in character, for they consist in careful observations of the relationships between the angle to be measured and the arcs that measure it.

4. Motion.—The preceding discussion of variable figures leads naturally to a discussion of actual motion. As figures move, either in whole or in part, the relationships between the quantities involved may change. To note these changes is to study the functional relationships between the parts of the figures. Without the functional idea, geometry would be wholly *static*. The study of fixed figures should not be the sole purpose of a course in geometry, for the uses of geometry are not wholly on static figures. Indeed, in all machinery, the geometric figures formed are in continual motion, and the shapes of the figures formed by the moving parts change. The study of motion and of moving forms, the *dynamic* aspects of geometry, should be given at least some consideration. Whenever this is done, the functional relations between the parts become of prime importance. Thus a linkage of the form of a parallelogram can be made more nearly rectangular by making the diagonals more nearly equal, and the linkage becomes a rectangle if the diagonals are made exactly equal. This principle is used in practice in making a rectangular framework precisely true.

5. Proportionality theorems.—All theorems which assert that certain quantities are in proportion to certain others, are obviously functional in character. Thus even the simplest theorems on rectangles assert that the area of a rectangle is directly proportional to its height, if the base is fixed. When more serious theorems are reached, such as the theorems on similar triangles, the functional ideas involved are worthy of considerable attention. That this is eminently true will be realized by all to whom trigonometry is familiar, for the trigonometric functions are nothing but the ratios of the sides of right triangles. But even in the field of elementary geometry a clear understanding of the relation between the areas (and volumes) of similar figures and the corresponding linear dimensions is of prime importance.

III. RELATIONSHIPS IN TRIGONOMETRY

The existence of functional relationships in trigonometry is evidenced by the common use of the words "trigonometric functions" to describe the trigonometric ratios. Thus the sine of an angle is a definite ratio whose value depends upon and is determined by the size of the angle to which it refers. The student should be made conscious of this relationship and he should be asked such questions as the following: Does the sine of an angle increase or decrease as the angle changes from zero to 90°? If the angle is doubled, does the sine of the angle double? If not, is the sine of double the angle more or less than twice the sine of the original angle? How does the value of the sine behave as the angles increase from 90° to 180°? From 180° to 270°? From 270° to 360°? Similar questions may be asked for the cosine and for the tangent of an angle.

Such questions may be reinforced by the use of figures that illustrate the points in question. Thus an angle twice a given angle should be drawn, and its sine should be estimated from the figure. A central angle and an inscribed angle on the same arc may be drawn in any circle. If they have one side in common, the relations between their sines will be more apparent. Finally, the relationships that exist may be made vivid by actual comparison of the numerical values found from the trigonometric tables.

Not only in these first functional definitions, however, but in a variety of geometric figures throughout trigonometry do functional relations appear. Thus the law of cosines states a definite relationship between the three sides of a triangle and any one of the angles. How will the angle be affected by increase or decrease of the side opposite it, if the other two sides remain fixed? How will the angle be affected by an increase or a decrease of one of the adjacent sides, if the other two sides remain fixed? Are these statements still true if the angle in question is obtuse?

As another example, the height of a tree, or the height of a building, may be determined by measuring the two angles of elevation from two points on the level plain in a straight line with its base. A formula for the height (h) in terms of these two angles (A, B) and the distance (d) between the points of observation, may be easily written down $[h = d \sin A \sin B / \sin (A-B)]$. Then the effect upon the height of changes in one of these angles may be discussed.

In a similar manner, every formula that is given or derived in a course on trigonometry may be discussed with profit from the functional standpoint.

IV. CONCLUSION

In conclusion, mention should be made of the great rôle which the idea of functions plays in the life of the world about us. Even when no calculation is to be carried out, the problems of real life frequently involve the ability to think correctly about the nature of the relationships which exist between related quantities. Specific mention has been made already of this type of problem in connection with interest on money. In everyday affairs, such as the filling out of formulas for fertilizers or for feeds or for spraying mixtures on the farm, the similar filling out of recipes for cooking (on different scales from that of the book of recipes), or the proper balancing of the ration in the preparation of food, many persons are at a loss on account of their lack of training in thinking about the relations between quantities. Another such instance of very common occurrence in real life is in insurance. Very few men or women attempt intelligently to understand the meaning and the fairness of premiums on life insurance and on other forms of insurance, chiefly because they cannot readily grasp the relations of interest and of chance that are involved. These relations are not particularly complicated, and they do not involve any great amount of calculation for the comprehension of the meaning and of the fairness of the rates. Mechanics, farmers, merchants, housewives, as well as scientists and engineers have to do constantly with quantities of things, and the quantities with which they deal are related to other quantities in ways that require clear thinking for maximum efficiency.

One element that should not be neglected is the occurrence of such problems in public questions which must be decided by the votes of the whole people. The tariff, rates of postage and express, freight rates, regulation of insurance rates, income taxes, inheritance taxes, and many other public questions involve relationships between quantities—for example, between the rate of income taxation and the amount of the income—that require habits of functional thinking for intelligent decisions. The training in such habits of thinking is therefore a vital element toward the creation of good citizenship.

It is believed that transfer of training does operate between such topics as those suggested in the body of this paper and those just mentioned, because of the existence of such identical or common elements, whereas the transfer of the training given by courses in mathematics that do not emphasize functional relationships might be questionable.

While this account of the functional character of certain topics in geometry and in algebra makes no claim to being exhaustive, the topics mentioned will suggest others of like character to the thoughtful teacher. It is hoped that sufficient variety has been mentioned to demonstrate the existence of functional ideas throughout elementary algebra and geometry. The committee feels that if this is recognized, algebra and geometry can be given new meaning to many children, and indeed to many educators, and that all students will be better able to control the actual relations which they meet in their own lives.

CHAPTER VIII

Terms and Symbols in Elementary Mathematics [1]

A. Limitations imposed by the committee upon its work.—The committee feels that in dealing with this subject it should explicitly recognize certain general limitations, as follows:

1. No attempt should be made to impose the phraseology of any definition, although the committee should state clearly its general views as to the meaning of disputed terms.

2. No effort should be made to change any well-defined current usage unless there is a strong reason for doing so, which reason is supported by the best authority, and, other things being substantially equal, the terms used should be international. This principle excludes the use of all individual efforts at coining new terms except under circumstances of great urgency. The individual opinions of the members, as indeed of any teacher or body of teachers, should have little weight in comparison with general usage if this usage is definite. If an idea has to be expressed so often in elementary mathematics that it becomes necessary to invent a single term or symbol for the purpose, this invention is necessarily the work of an individual; but it is highly desirable, even in this case, that it should receive the sanction of wide use before it is adopted in any system of examinations.

3. On account of the large number of terms and symbols now in use, the recommendations to be made will necessarily be typical rather than exhaustive.

I. GEOMETRY

B. Undefined terms.—The committee recommends that no attempt be made to define, with any approach to precision, terms whose definitions are not needed as parts of a proof.

Especially is it recommended that no attempt be made to define precisely such terms as *space, magnitude, point, straight line, surface, plane,*

---

1. The first draft of this chapter was prepared by a subcommittee consisting of David Eugene Smith (chairman), W. W. Hart, H. E. Hawkes, E. R. Hedrick, and H. E. Slaught.

direction, distance, and *solid,* although the significance of such terms should be made clear by informal explanations and discussions.

C. Definite usage recommended.—It is the opinion of the committee that the following general usage is desirable:

1. *Circle* should be considered as the curve; but where no ambiguity arises, the word "circle" may be used to refer either to the curve or to the part of the plane inclosed by it.

2. *Polygon* (including *triangle, square, parallelogram,* and the like) should be considered, by analogy to a circle, as a closed broken line; but where no ambiguity arises, the word polygon may be used to refer either to the broken line or to the part of the plane inclosed by it. Similarly, *segment of a circle* should be defined as the figure formed by a chord and either of its arcs.

3. *Area of a circle* should be defined as the area (numerical measure) of the portion of the plane inclosed by the circle. *Area of a polygon* should be treated in the same way.

4. *Solids.* The usage above recommended with respect to plane figures is also recommended with respect to solids. For example, *sphere* should be regarded as a surface, its volume should be defined in a manner similar to the area of a circle, and the double use of the word should be allowed where no ambiguity arises. A similar usage should obtain with respect to such terms as *polyhedron, cone,* and *cylinder.*

5. *Circumference* should be considered as the length (numerical measure) of the circle (line). Similarly, *perimeter* should be defined as the length of the broken line which forms a polygon; that is, as the sum of the lengths of the sides.

6. *Obtuse angle* should be defined as an angle greater than a right angle and less than a straight angle, and should therefore not be defined merely as an angle greater than a right angle.

7. The term *right triangle* should be preferred to "right-angled triangle," this usage being now so standardized in this country that it may properly be continued in spite of the fact that it is not international. Similarly for *acute triangle, obtuse triangle,* and *oblique triangle.*

8. Such English plurals as *formulas* and *polyhedrons* should be used in place of the Latin and Greek plurals. Such unnecessary Latin abbreviations as *Q. E. D.* and *Q. E. F.* should be dropped.

9. The definitions of *axiom* and *postulate* vary so much that the committee does not undertake to distinguish between them.

D. Terms made general.—It is the recommendation of the committee that the modern tendency of having terms made as general as possible should be followed. For example:

1. *Isosceles triangle* should be defined as a triangle having two equal sides. There should be no limitation to two and only two equal sides.

2. *Rectangle* should be considered as including a square as a special case.

3. *Parallelogram* should be considered as including a rectangle, and hence a square, as a special case.

4. *Segment* should be used to designate the part of a straight line included between two of its points as well as the figure formed by an arc of a circle and its chord, this being the usage generally recognized by modern writers.

E. Terms to be abandoned.—It is the opinion of the committee that the following terms are not of enough consequence in elementary mathematics at the present time to make their recognition desirable in examinations, and that they serve chiefly to increase the technical vocabulary to the point of being burdensome and unnecessary:

1. *Antecedent* and *consequent*.

2. *Third proportional* and *fourth proportional*.

3. *Equivalent*. An unnecessary substitute for the more precise expressions "equal in area" and "equal in volume," or (where no confusion is likely to arise) for the single word "equal."

4. *Trapezium*.

5. *Scholium, lemma, oblong, scalene triangle, sect, perigon, rhomboid* (the term "oblique parallelogram" being sufficient), and *reflex angle* (in elementary geometry).

6. Terms like *flat angle, whole angle,* and *conjugate angle* are not of enough value in an elementary course to make it desirable to recommend them.

7. *Subtend,* a word which has no longer any etymological meaning to most students and teachers of geometry. While its use will naturally continue for some time to come, teachers may safely incline to such forms as the following: "In the same circle equal arcs *have* equal chords."

8. *Homologous,* the less technical term "corresponding" being preferable.

9. Guided by principle A2 and its interpretation, the committee advises against the use of such terms as the following: *Angle-bisector, angle-sum, consecutive interior angles, supplementary consecutive exterior angles, quader* (for rectangular solid), *sect, explement, tranverse angles*.

10. It is unfortunate that it still seems to be necessary to use such a term as *parallelepiped,* but we seem to have no satisfactory substitute. For rectangular parallelepiped, however, the use of *rectangular solid* is recommended. If the terms were more generally used in elementary geometry it would be desirable to consider carefully whether better ones could not be found for the purposes than *isoperimetric, apothem, icosahedron,* and *dodecahedron*.

F. Symbols in elementary geometry.—It should be recognized that a symbol like ⊥ is merely a piece of shorthand designed to afford an easy grasp of a written or printed statement. Many teachers and a few writers make an extreme use of symbols, coining new ones to meet their own views as to usefulness, and this practice is naturally open to objection.[2] There are, however, certain symbols that are international and certain others of which the meaning is at once apparent and which are sufficiently useful and generally enough recognized to be recommended.

For example, the symbols for triangle, $\triangle$, and circle, $\odot$, are international, although used more extensively in the United States than in other countries. Their use, with their customary plurals, is recommended.

The symbol $\perp$, generally read as representing the single word "perpendicular" but sometimes as standing for the phrase "is perpendicular to," is fairly international and the meaning is apparent. Its use is therefore recommended. On account of such a phrase as "the $\perp AB$," the first of the above readings is likely to be the more widely used, but in either case there is no chance for confusion.

The symbol $\|$ for "parallel" or "is parallel to" is fairly international and is recommended.

The symbol $\sim$ for "similar" or "is similar to" is international and is recommended.

The symbols $\cong$ and $\equiv$ for "congruent" or "is congruent to" both have a considerable use in this country. The committee feels that the former, which is fairly international, is to be preferred because it is the more distinctive and suggestive.

The symbol $\angle$ for "angle" is, because of its simplicity, coming to be generally preferred to any other and is therefore recommended.

Since the following terms are not used frequently enough to render special symbols of any particular value the world has not developed any that have general acceptance and there seems to be no necessity for making the attempt: Square, rectangle, parallelogram, trapezoid, quadrilateral, semicircle.

The symbol $\overset{\frown}{AB}$ for "arc AB" cannot be called international. While the value of the symbol $\frown$ in place of the short word *arc* is doubtful, the committee sees no objection to its use.

The symbol $\therefore$ for "therefore" has a value that is generally recognized, but the symbol $\because$ for "since" is used so seldom that it should be abandoned.

With respect to the lettering of figures, the committee calls attention for purposes of general information to a convenient method, found in certain European and in some American textbooks, of lettering triangles: Capitals represent the vertices, corresponding small letters represent opposite sides, corresponding small Greek letters represent angles, and the primed letters represent the corresponding parts of a congruent or similar triangle.

---

2. This is not intended to discourage the use of algebraic methods in the solution of such geometric problems as lend themselves readily to algebraic treatment.

This permits of speaking of α (alpha) instead of "angle A," and of "small a" instead of BC. The plan is by no means international with respect to the Greek letters. The committee is prepared, however, to recommend it with the optional use of the Greek forms.

In general, it is recommended that a single letter be used to designate any geometric magnitude whenever there is no danger of ambiguity. The use of numbers alone to designate magnitudes should be avoided by the use of such forms $A_1, A_2, \ldots$.

With respect to the symbolism for limits, the committee calls attention to the fact that the symbol $\doteq$ is a local one, and that the symbol $\rightarrow$ (for "tends to") is both international and expressive and has constantly grown in favor in recent years. Although the subject of limits is not generally treated scientifically in the secondary school, the idea is mentioned in geometry and a symbol may occasionally be needed.

While the teacher should be allowed freedom in the matter, the committee feels that it is desirable to discourage the use of such purely local symbols as the following:

$\overset{\circ}{=}$ for "equal in degrees,"
ass for "two sides and an angle adjacent to one of them," and
sas for "two sides and the included angle."

G. Terms not standardized.—At the present time there is not sufficient agreement upon which to base recommendations as to the use of the term *ray* and as to the value of terms like *coplanar, collinear,* and *concurrent* in elementary work. Many terms, similar to these, will gradually become standardized or else will naturally drop out of use.

II. ALGEBRA AND ARITHMETIC

H. Terms in algebra.—1. With respect to equations the committee calls attention to the fact that the classification according to degree is comparatively recent and that this probably accounts for the fact that the terminology is so unsettled. The Anglo-American custom of designating an equation of the first degree as a *simple equation* has never been satisfactory, because the term has no real significance. The most nearly international terms are *equation of the first degree* (or "first degree equation") and *linear equation.* The latter is so brief and suggestive that it should be generally adopted.

2. The term *quadratic equation* (for which the longer term "second degree equation" is an unnecessary synonym, although occasionally a convenient one) is well established. The terms *pure quadratic* and *affected quadratic* signify nothing to the pupil except as he learns the meaning from a book, and the committee recommends that they be dropped. Terms more

nearly in general use are *complete quadratic* and *incomplete quadratic*. The committee feels, however, that the distinction thus denoted is not of much importance and believes that it can well be dispensed with in elementary instruction.

3. As to other special terms, the committee recommends abandoning, so far as possible, the use of the following: *Aggregation* for grouping; *vinculum* for bar; *evolution* for finding roots, as a general topic; *involution* for finding powers; *extract* for find (a root); *absolute term* for constant term; *multiply an equation, clear of fractions, cancel* and *transpose*, at least until the significance of the terms is entirely clear; *aliquot part* (except in commercial work).

4. The committee also advises the use of either *system of equations* or *set of equations* instead of "simultaneous equations," in such an expression as "solve the following set of equations," in view of the fact that at present no well established definite meaning attaches to the term "simultaneous."

5. The term *simplify* should not be used in cases where there is possibility of misunderstanding. For purposes of computation, for example, the form $\sqrt{8}$ may be simpler than the form $2\sqrt{2}$, and in some cases it may be better to express $\sqrt{3/4}$ as $\sqrt{0.75}$ instead of $\frac{1}{2}\sqrt{3}$. In such cases, it is better to give more explicit instructions than to use the misleading term "simplify."

6. The committee regrets the general uncertainty in the use of the word *surd*, but it sees no reasonable chance at present of replacing it by a more definite term. It recognizes the difficulty generally met by young pupils in distinguishing between *coefficient* and *exponent*, but it feels that it is undesirable to attempt to change terms which have come to have a standardized meaning and which are reasonably simple. These considerations will probably lead to the retention of such terms as *rationalize, extraneous root, characteristic,* and *mantissa*, although in the case of the last two terms "integral part" and "fractional part" (of a logarithm) would seem to be desirable substitutes.

7. While recognizing the motive that has prompted a few teachers to speak of "positive x" instead of "plus x," and "negative y" instead of "minus y" the committee feels that attempts to change general usage should not be made when based upon trivial grounds and when not sanctioned by mathematicians generally.

I. Symbols in algebra.—The symbols in elementary algebra are now so well standardized as to require but few comments in a report of this kind. The committee feels that it is desirable, however, to call attention to the following details:

1. Owing to the frequent use of the letter x, it is preferable to use the center dot (a raised period) for multiplication in the few cases in which any symbol is necessary. For example, in a case like $1 \cdot 2 \cdot 3 \cdot \ldots (x - 1) \cdot x$, the center dot is preferable to the symbol $\times$; but in cases like $2a(x - a)$ no sym-

bol is necessary. The committee recognizes that the period (as in $a.b$) is more nearly international than the center dot (as in $a \cdot b$); but inasmuch as the period will continue to be used in this country as a decimal point, it is likely to cause confusion, to elementary pupils at least, to attempt to use it as a symbol for multiplication.

2. With respect to division, the symbol $\div$ is purely Anglo-American, the symbol: serving in most countries for division as well as ratio. Since neither symbol plays any part in business life, it seems proper to consider only the needs of algebra, and to make more use of the fractional form and (where the meaning is clear) of the symbol /, and to drop the symbol $\div$ in writing algebraic expressions.

3. With respect to the distinction between the use of $+$ and $-$ as symbols of operation and as symbols of direction, the committee sees no reason for attempting to use smaller signs for the latter purpose, such an attempt never having received international recognition, and the need of two sets of symbols not being sufficient to warrant violating international usage and burdening the pupil with this additional symbolism.

4. With respect to the distinction between the symbols $\equiv$ and $=$ as representing respectively identity and equality, the committee calls attention to the fact that, while the distinction is generally recognized, the consistent use of the symbols is rarely seen in practice. The committee recommends that the symbol $\equiv$ be not employed in examinations for the purpose of indicating identity. The teacher, however, should use both symbols if desired.

5. With respect to the root sign, $\sqrt{}$, the committee recognizes that convenience of writing assures its continued use in many cases instead of the fractional exponent. It is recommended, however, that in algebraic work involving complicated cases the fractional exponent be preferred. Attention is also called to the fact that the convention is quite generally accepted that the symbol $\sqrt{a}$ (a representing a positive number) means only the positive square root and that the symbol $\sqrt[n]{a}$ means only the principal nth root, and similarly for $a^{1/2}$, $a^{1/n}$. The reason for this convention is apparent when we come to consider the value of $\sqrt{4} + \sqrt{9} + \sqrt{16} + \sqrt{25}$. This convention being agreed to, it is improper to write $x = \sqrt{4}$, as the complete solution of $x^2 - 4 = 0$, but the result should appear as $x = \pm \sqrt{4}$. Similarly, it is not in accord with the convention to write $\sqrt{4} = \pm 2$, the conventional form being $\pm \sqrt{4} = \pm 2$; and for the same reason it is impossible to have $\sqrt{(-1)^2} = \pm 1$ since the symbol refers only to a positive root. These distinctions are not matters to be settled by the individual opinion of a teacher or a local group of teachers; they are purely matters of convention as to notation, and the committee simply sets forth, for the benefit of teachers, this statement as to what the convention seems to be among the leading writers of the world at the present time.

When imaginaries are used, the symbol i should be employed instead of $\sqrt{-1}$ except possibly in the first presentation of the subject.

7. As to the factorial symbols 5! and $\lfloor 5$, to represent $5 \cdot 4 \cdot 3 \cdot 2 \cdot 1$, the tendency is very general to abandon the second one, probably on account of the difficulty of printing it, and the committee so recommends. This question is not, however, of much importance in the general courses in the high school.

8. With respect to symbols for an unknown quantity there has been a noteworthy change within a few years. While the Cartesian use of x and y will doubtless continue for two general unknowns, the recognition that the formula is, in the broad use of the term, a central feature of algebra has led to the extended use of the initial letter. This is simply illustrated in the direction to solve for r the equation $A = \pi r^2$. This custom is now international and should be fully recognized in the schools.

9. The committee advises abandoning the double colon (: :) in proportion, and the symbol $\propto$ in variation, both of these symbols being now practically obsolete.

J. Terms and symbols in arithmetic.—1. While it is rarely wise to attempt to abandon suddenly the use of words that are well established in our language, the committee feels called upon to express regret that we still require very young pupils, often in the primary grades, to use such terms as *subtrahend, addend, minuend* and *multiplicand*. Teachers themselves rarely understand the real significance of these words, nor do they recognize that they are comparatively modern additions to what used to be a much simpler vocabulary in arithmetic. The committee recommends that such terms be used, if at all, only after the sixth grade.

2. Owing to the uncertainty attached to such expressions as "to three decimal places," "to thousandths," "correct to three decimal places," "correct to the nearest thousandth," the following usage is recommended: When used to specify accuracy in computation, the four expressions should be regarded as identical. The expression "to three decimal places" or "to thousandths" may be used in giving directions as to the extent of a computation. It then refers to a result carried only to thousandths, without considering the figure of ten-thousandths; but it should be avoided as far as possible because it is open to misunderstanding. As to the term, "significant figure," it should be noted that 0 is always significant except when used before a decimal fraction to indicate the absence of integers or, in general, when used merely to locate the decimal point. For example, the zeros italicised in the following are "significant," while the others are not: 0.5, 9.5*0*, 1*0*2, 3*0*,200. Further, the number 2396, if expressed correct to three significant figures, would be written 2400.[3] It should be noted that the context or the way in which a

---

3. The italicising of significant zeros is here used merely to make clear the committee's meaning: The device is not recommended for general adoption.

number has been obtained is sometimes the determining factor as to the significance of a 0.

3. The pupil in arithmetic needs to see the work in the form in which he will use it in practical life outside the schoolroom. His visualization of the process should therefore not include such symbols as $+$, $-$, $\times$, $\div$, which are helpful only in writing out the analysis of a problem or in the printed statement of the operation to be performed. Because of these facts the committee recommends that only slight use be made of these symbols in the written work of the pupil, except in the analysis of problems. It recognizes, however, the value of such symbols in printed directions and in these analyses.

III. GENERAL OBSERVATIONS AND RECOMMENDATIONS

K. General observations.—The committee desires also to record its belief in two or three general observations.

1. It is very desirable to bring mathematical writing into closer touch with good usage in English writing in general. That we have failed in this particular has been the subject of frequent comment by teachers of mathematics as well as by teachers of English. This is all the more unfortunate because mathematics may be and should be a genuine help toward the acquisition of good habits in the speaking and writing of English. Under present conditions, with a style that is often stilted and in which undue compression is evident, we do not offer to the student the good models of English writing of which mathematics is capable, nor indeed do we always offer good models of thought processes. It is to be feared that many teachers encourage the use of a kind of vulgar mathematical slang when they allow such words as "tan" and "cos," for tangent and cosine, and habitually call their subject by the title "math."

2. In the same general spirit the committee wishes to observe that teachers of mathematics and writers of textbooks seem often to have gone to an extreme in searching for technical terms and for new symbols. The committee expresses the hope that mathematics may retain, as far as possible, a literary flavor. It seems perfectly feasible that a printed discussion should strike the pupil as an expression of reasonable ideas in terms of reasonable English forms. The fewer technical terms we introduce, the less is the subject likely to give the impression of being difficult and a mere juggling of words and symbols.

3. While recognizing the claims of euphony, the fact that a word like "historic" has a different meaning from "historical" and that confusion may occasionally arise if "arithmetic" is used as an adjective with a different pronunciation from the noun, the committee advises that such forms as geometric be preferred to geometrical. This is already done in such terms

as analytic geometry and elliptic functions, and it seems proper to extend the custom to include *arithmetic, geometric, graphic,* and the like.

L. General recommendations.—In view of the desirability of a simplification of terms used in elementary instruction, and of establishing international usage so far as is reasonable, the committee recommends that the subject of this report be considered by a committee to be appointed by Section IV of the next International Congress of Mathematicians, such committee to contain representatives of at least the recognized international languages admitted to the meetings.

2. The committee suggests that examining bodies, contributors to mathematical journals, and authors of textbooks endeavor to follow the general principles formulated in this report.

The following two selections by Edward L. Thorndike and Frederick B. Knight were chosen to illustrate characteristics that distinguish connectionistic psychology. Among the characteristic attitudes of connectionists, the two that differentiate their views most clearly from those of others can also be seen as excesses. These two attitudes are extreme concern with ''elementary bonds,'' which led to de-emphasis of other aspects of arithmetic, and distrust of logical and mathematical structure as a basis for the structure of learning. Many connectionistic contributions to arithmetic teaching, as suggested by the tables of contents included here, are still considered to be of value—for example, concern with the amount and spacing of practice.

THE PSYCHOLOGY OF
ARITHMETIC

BY

EDWARD L. THORNDIKE

TEACHERS COLLEGE, COLUMBIA
UNIVERSITY

New York
THE MACMILLAN COMPANY
1924

PREFACE

Within recent years there have been three lines of advance in psychology which are of notable significance for teaching. The first is the new point of view concerning the general process of learning. We now understand that learning is essentially the formation of connections or bonds between situations and responses, that the satisfyingness of the result is the chief force that forms them, and that habit rules in the realm of thought as truly and as fully as in the realm of action.

The second is the great increase in knowledge of the amount, rate, and conditions of improvement in those organized groups or hierarchies of habits which we call abilities, such as ability to add or ability to read. Practice and improvement are no longer vague generalities, but concern changes which are definable and measurable by standard tests and scales.

The third is the better understanding of the so-called "higher processes" of analysis, abstraction, the formation of general notions, and reasoning. The older view of a mental chemistry whereby sensations were compounded into percepts, percepts were duplicated by images, percepts and images were amalgamated into abstractions and concepts, and these were manipulated by reasoning, has given way to the understanding of the laws of response to elements or aspects of situations and to many situations or elements thereof in combination. James' view of reasoning as "selection of essentials" and "thinking things together" in a revised and clarified form has important applications in the teaching of all the school subjects.

This book presents the applications of this newer dynamic psychology to the teaching of arithmetic. Its contents are substantially what have been included in a course of lectures on the psychology of the elementary school subjects given by the author for some years to students of elementary education at Teachers College. Many of these former students, now in supervisory charge of elementary schools, have urged that these lectures be made available to teachers in general. So they are now published in spite of the author's desire to clarify and reinforce certain matters by further researches.

A word of explanation is necessary concerning the exercises and problems cited to illustrate various matters, especially erroneous pedagogy. These are all genuine, having their source in actual textbooks, courses of study, state examinations, and the like. To avoid any possibility of invidious comparisons they are not quotations, but equivalent problems such as represent ac-

462

curately the spirit and intent of the originals.

I take pleasure in acknowledging the courtesy of Mr. S. A. Courtis, Ginn and Company, D. C. Heath and Company, The Macmillan Company, The Oxford University Press, Rand, McNally and Company, Dr. C. W. Stone, The Teachers College Bureau of Publications, and The World Book Company, in permitting various quotations.

EDWARD L. THORNDIKE.

TEACHERS COLLEGE
COLUMBIA UNIVERSITY
April 1, 1920

CONTENTS

PAGE

INTRODUCTION: THE PSYCHOLOGY OF THE ELEMENTARY SCHOOL SUBJECTS . . . xi

CHAPTER

I. THE NATURE OF ARITHMETICAL ABILITIES . . . 1
Knowledge of the Meaning of Numbers
Arithmetical Language
Problem Solving
Arithmetical Reasoning
Summary
The Sociology of Arithmetic

II. THE MEASUREMENT OF ARITHMETICAL ABILITIES . . . 27
A Sample Measurement of an Arithmetical Ability
Ability to Add Integers
Measurements of Ability in Computation
Measurements of Ability in Applied Arithmetic: the Solution of Problems

III. THE CONSTITUTION OF ARITHMETICAL ABILITIES . . . 51
The Elementary Functions of Arithmetical Learning
The Elementary Meaning of a Fraction
Knowledge of the Processes of Computation
Learning the Processes of Computation

IV. THE CONSTITUTION OF ARITHMETICAL ABILITIES (continued) . . . 70
The Selection of the Bonds to Be Formed
The Importance of Habit Formation
Desirable Bonds Now Often Neglected
Wasteful and Harmful Bonds
Guiding Principles

V. THE PSYCHOLOGY OF DRILL IN ARITHMETIC: THE STRENGTH OF BONDS . . . 102
The Need of Stronger Elementary Bonds
Early Mastery
The Strength of Bonds for Temporary Service
The Strength of Bonds with Technical Facts and Terms
The Strength of Bonds Concerning the Reasons for Arithmetical Processes
Propedeutic Bonds

VI. THE PSYCHOLOGY OF DRILL IN ARITHMETIC: THE AMOUNT OF PRACTICE AND THE ORGANIZATION OF ABILITIES . . . 122
The Amount of Practice
Under-learning and Over-learning
The Organization of Abilities

VII. THE SEQUENCE OF TOPICS: THE ORDER OF FORMATION OF BONDS . . . 141
Conventional versus Effective Orders
Decreasing Interference and Increasing Facilitation
Interest
General Principles

VIII. THE DISTRIBUTION OF PRACTICE . . . 156
The Problem
Sample Distributions
Possible Improvements

IX. THE PSYCHOLOGY OF THINKING: ABSTRACT IDEAS AND GENERAL NOTIONS IN ARITHMETIC . . . 169
Responses to Elements and Classes
Facilitating the Analysis of Elements
Systematic and Opportunistic Stimuli to Analysis
Adaptations to Elementary-school Pupils

X. THE PSYCHOLOGY OF THINKING: REASONING IN ARITHMETIC . . . 185
The Essentials of Arithmetical Reasoning
Reasoning as the Coöperation of Organized Habits

XI. ORIGINAL TENDENCIES AND ACQUISITIONS BEFORE SCHOOL . 195
The Utilization of Instinctive Interests
The Order of Development of Original Tendencies
Inventories of Arithmetical Knowledge and Skill
The Perception of Number and Quantity
The Early Awareness of Number

XII. INTEREST IN ARITHMETIC . . . 209
Censuses of Pupils' Interests
Relieving Eye Strain
Significance for Related Activities
Intrinsic Interest in Arithmetic

XIII. THE CONDITIONS OF LEARNING . . . 227
External Conditions
The Hygiene of the Eyes in Arithmetic
The Use of Concrete Objects in Arithmetic
Oral, Mental, and Written Arithmetic

XIV. THE CONDITIONS OF LEARNING: THE PROBLEM ATTITUDE . 266
Illustrative Cases
General Principles
Difficulty and Success as Stimuli
False Inferences

XV. INDIVIDUAL DIFFERENCES . . . 285
Nature and Amount
Differences within One Class
The Causes of Individual Differences
The Interrelations of Individual Differences

BIBLIOGRAPHY OF REFERENCES . . . 301

INDEX . . . 311

CHAPTER V

The Psychology of Drill in Arithmetic: The Strength of Bonds

An inventory of the bonds to be formed in learning arithmetic should be accompanied by a statement of how strong each bond is to be made and kept year by year. Since, however, the inventory itself has been presented here only in samples, the detailed statement of desired strength for each bond cannot be made. Only certain general facts will be noted here.

THE NEED OF STRONGER ELEMENTARY BONDS

The constituent bonds involved in the fundamental operations with numbers need to be much stronger than they now are. Inaccuracy in these operations means weakness of the constituent bonds. Inaccuracy exists, and to a degree that deprives the subject of much of its possible disciplinary value, makes the pupil's achievements of slight value for use in business or industry, and prevents the pupil from verifying his work with new processes by some previously acquired process.

The inaccuracy that exists may be seen in the measurements made by the many investigators who have used arithmetical tasks as tests of fatigue, practice, individual differences and the like, and in the special studies of arithmetical achievements for their own sake made by Courtis and others.

Burgerstein, using such examples as

$$28704516938276546397$$
$$+ 35869427359163827263$$

and similar long numbers to be multiplied by 2 or by 3 or by 4 or by 5 or by 6, found 851 errors in 28,267 answer-figures, or 3 per hundred answer-figures, or ⅗ of an error per example. The children were 9½ to 15 years old. Laser, using the same sort of addition and multiplication, found somewhat over 3 errors per hundred answer-figures in the case of boys and girls averaging 11½ years, during the period of their most accurate work. Holmes, using addition of the sort just described, found 346 errors in 23,713 answer-figures or about 1½ per hundred. The children were from all grades from the third to the eighth. In Laser's work, 21, 19, 13, and 10 answer-figures were obtained per minute. Friedrich with similar examples, giving the very long time of 20 minutes for obtaining about 200 answer-figures, found from 1 to

2 per hundred wrong. King had children in grade 5 do sums, each consisting of 5 two-place numbers. In the most accurate work-period, they made 1 error per 20 columns. In multiplying a four-place by a four-place number they had less than one total answer right out of three. In New York City Courtis found with his Test 7 that in 12 minutes the average achievement of fourth-grade children is 8.8 units attempted with 4.2 right. In grade 5 the facts are 10.9 attempts with 5.8 right; in grade 6, 12.5 attempts with 7.0 right; in grade 7, 15 attempts with 8.5 right; in grade 8, 15.7 attempts with 10.1 right. These results are near enough to those obtained from the country at large to serve as a text here.

The following were set as official standards, in an excellent school system, Courtis Series B being used:—

	GRADE.	SPEED ATTEMPTS.	PERCENT OF CORRECT ANSWERS.
Addition	8	12	80
	7	11	80
	6	10	70
	5	9	70
	4	8	70
Subtraction	8	12	90
	7	11	90
	6	10	90
	5	9	80
	4	7	80
Multiplication	8	11	80
	7	10	80
	6	9	80
	5	7	70
	4	6	60
Division	8	11	90
	7	10	90
	6	8	80
	5	6	70
	4	4	60

Kirby found that, in adding columns like those printed below, children in grade 4 got on the average less than 80 percent of correct answers. Their average speed was about 2 columns per minute. In doing division of the sort printed below childern of grades 3 *B* and 4 *A* got less than 95 percent of correct answers, the average speed being 4 divisions per minute. In both cases the slower computers were no more accurate than the faster ones. Practice improved the speed very rapidly, but the accuracy remained substantially unchanged. Brown found a similar low status of ability and notable improvement from a moderate amount of special practice.

3	5	6	2	3	8	9	7	4	9
7	9	6	5	5	6	4	5	8	2
3	4	7	8	7	3	7	9	3	7
8	8	4	8	2	6	8	2	9	8
2	2	4	7	6	9	8	5	6	2
6	9	5	7	8	5	2	3	2	4
9	6	4	2	7	2	9	4	4	5
3	3	7	9	9	9	2	8	9	7
6	8	9	6	4	7	7	9	2	4
8	4	6	9	9	2	6	9	8	9

$$20 = \ldots 5s$$
$$56 = \ldots 9s \text{ and } \ldots r.$$
$$30 = \ldots 7s \text{ and } \ldots r.$$
$$89 = \ldots 9s \text{ and } \ldots r.$$
$$20 = \ldots 8s \text{ and } \ldots r.$$
$$56 = \ldots 6s \text{ and } \ldots r.$$
$$31 = \ldots 4s \text{ and } \ldots r.$$
$$86 = \ldots 9s \text{ and } \ldots r.$$

It is clear that numerical work as inaccurate as this has little or no commercial or industrial value. If clerks got only six answers out of ten right as in the Courtis tests, one would need to have at least four clerks make each computation and would even then have to check many of their discrepancies by the work of still other clerks, if he wanted his accounts to show less than one error per hundred accounting units of the Courtis size.

It is also clear that the "habits of . . . absolute accuracy, and satisfaction in truth as a result" which arithmetic is supposed to further must be largely mythical in pupils who get right answers only from three to nine times out of ten!

EARLY MASTERY

The bonds in question clearly must be made far stronger than they now are. They should in fact be strong enough to abolish errors in computation, except for those due to temporary lapses. It is much better for a child to know half of the multiplication tables, and to know that he does not know the rest, than to half-know them all; and this holds good of all the elementary bonds required for computation. Any bond should be made to work perfectly, though slowly, very soon after its formation is begun. Speed can easily be added by proper practice.

The chief reasons why this is not done now seem to be the following: (1) Certain important bonds (like the additions with higher decades) are not given enough attention when they are first used. (2) The special training necessary when a bond is used in a different connection (as when the multiplications to 9 × 9 are used in examples like $\underline{\hphantom{8}8}$ where the pupil has also to choose the right number to multiply, keep in mind what is carried, use it properly, and write the right figure in the right place, and carry a figure, or remember that he carries none) is neglected. (3) The pupil is not taught to check his work. (4) He is not made responsible for substantially accurate results. Furthermore, the requirement of (4) without the training of (1), (2), and (3) will involve either a fruitless failure on the part of many pupils, or an utterly unjust requirement of time. The common error of supposing that the task of computation with integers consists merely in learning the additions to 9 + 9, the subtractions to 18 — 9, the multiplications to 8 × 9, and the divisions to 81 ÷ 9, and in applying this knowledge in connection with the principles of decimal notation, has had a large share in permitting the gross inaccuracy of arithmetical work. The bonds involved in 'knowing the tables' do not make up one fourth of the bonds involved in real adding, subtracting, multiplying, and dividing (with integers alone).

It should be noted that if the training mentioned in (1) and (2) is well cared for, the checking of results as recommended in (3) becomes enormously more valuable than it is under present conditions, though even now it is one of our soundest practices. If a child knows the additions to higher decades so that he can add a seen one-place number to a thought-of two-place number in three seconds or less with a correct answer 199 times out of 200, there is only an infinitesimal chance that a ten-figure column twice added (once up, once down) a few minutes apart with identical answers will be wrong. Suppose that, in long multiplication, a pupil can multiply to 9 × 9 while keeping his place and keeping track of what he is 'carrying' and of where to write the figure he writes, and can add what he carries without losing track of what he is to add it to, where he is to write the unit figure, what he is to multiply next and by what, and what he will then have to carry, in each case to a surety of 99 percent of correct responses. Then two identical answers got by multiplying one three-place number by another a few minutes apart, and with reversal of the numbers, will not be wrong more than twice in his entire school career. Checks approach proofs when the constituent bonds are strong.

If, on the contrary, the fundamental bonds are so weak that they do not work accurately, checking becomes much less trustworthy and also very much more laborious. In fact, it is possible to show that below a certain point of strength of the fundamental bonds, the time required for checking is so great that part of it might better be spent in improving the fundamental bonds.

For example, suppose that a pupil has to find the sum of five numbers like $2.49, $5.25, $6.50, $7.89, and $3.75. Counting each act of holding in mind the number to be carried and each writing of a column's result as equivalent in difficulty to one addition, such a sum equals nineteen single additions. On this basis and with certain additional estimates[1] we can compute the practical consequences for a pupil's use of addition in life according to the mastery of it that he has gained in school.

I have so computed the amount of checking a pupil will have to do to reach two agreeing numbers (out of two, or three, or four, or five, or whatever the number before he gets two that are alike), according to his mastery of the elementary processes. The facts appear in Table 1.

It is obvious that a pupil whose mastery of the elements is that denoted by getting them right 96 times out of 100 will require so much time for checking that, even if he were never to use this ability for anything save a few thousand sums in addition, he would do well to improve this ability before he tried to do the sums. An ability of 199 out of 200, or 995 out of 1000, seems likely to save much more time than would be taken to acquire it, and a reasonable defense could be made for requiring 996 or 997 out of 1000.

A precision of from 995 to 997 out of 1000 being required, and ordinary sagacity being used in the teaching, speed will substantially take care of it-

TABLE 1

The Effect of Mastery of the Elementary Facts of Addition upon the Labor Required to Secure Two Agreeing Answers When Adding Five Three-figure Numbers

Mastery of the Elementary Additions Times Right in 1000	Approximate Number of Wrong Answers in Sums of 5 Three-place Numbers per 1000	Approximate Number of Agreeing Answers, after One Checking, per 1000	Approximate Number of Agreeing Answers, after a Checking of the First Discrepancies	Approximate Number of Checkings Required (over and above the First General Checking of the 1000 Sums) to Secure Two Agreeing Results
960	700	90	216	4500
980	380	384	676	1200
990	190	656	906	470
995	95	819	975	210
996	76	854	984	165
997	54	895	992	115
998	38	925	996	80
999	19	962	999	40

1. These concern allowances for two errors occurring in the same example and for the same wrong answer being obtained in both original work and check work.

self. Counting on the fingers or in words will not give that precision. Slow recourse to memory of serial addition tables will not give that precision. Nothing save sure memory of the facts operating under the conditions of actual examples will give it. And such memories will operate with sufficient speed.

There is one intelligent objection to the special practice necessary to establish arithmetical connections so fully as to give the accuracy which both utilitarian and disciplinary aims require. It may be said that the pupils in grades 3, 4, and 5 cannot appreciate the need and that consequently the work will be dull, barren, and alien, without close personal appropriation by the pupil's nature. It is true that no vehement life-purpose is directly involved by the problem of perfecting one's power to add 7 to 28 in grade 2, or by the problem of multiplying 253 by 8 accurately in grade 3 or by precise subtraction in long division in grade 4. It is also true, however, that the most humanly interesting of problems—one that the pupil attacks most whole-heartedly—will not be solved correctly unless the pupil has the necessary associative mechanisms in order; and the surer he is of them, the freer he is to think out the problem as such. Further, computation is not dull if the pupil can compute. He does not himself object to its barrenness of vital meaning, so long as the barrenness of failure is prevented. We must not forget that pupils like to learn. In teaching excessively dull individuals, who has not often observed the great interest which they display in anything that they are enabled to master? There is pathos in their joy in learning to recognize parts of speech, perform algebraic simplifications, or translate Latin sentences, and in other accomplishments equally meaningless to all their interests save the universal human interest in success and recognition. Still further, it is not very hard to show to pupils the imperative need of accuracy in scoring games, in the shop, in the store, and in the office. Finally, the argument that accurate work of this sort is alien to the pupil in these grades is still stronger against *inaccurate* work of the same sort. If we are to teach computation with two- and three- and four-place numbers at all, it should be taught as a reliable instrument, not as a combination of vague memories and faith. The author is ready to cut computation with numbers above 10 out of the curriculum of grades 1–6 as soon as more valuable educational instruments are offered in its place, but he is convinced that nothing in child-nature makes a large variety of inaccurate computing more interesting or educative or germane to felt needs than a smaller variety of accurate computing!

THE STRENGTH OF BONDS FOR TEMPORARY SERVICE

The second general fact is that certain bonds are of service for only a limited time and so need to be formed only to a limited and slight degree of strength. The data of problems set to illustrate a principle or improve some habit of computation are, of course, the clearest cases. The pupil needs to remember that John bought 3 loaves of bread and that they were 5-cent loaves and that he gave 25 cents to the baker only long enough to use the data to decide what change John should receive. The connections between the total described situation and the answer obtained, supposing some considerable computation to intervene, is a bond that we let expire almost as soon as it is born.

It is sometimes assumed that the bond between a certain group of features which make a problem a 'Buy *a* things at *b* per thing, find total cost' problem or a 'Buy *a* things at *b* per thing, what change from *c*' problem or a 'What gain on buying for *a* and selling for *b*' problem or a 'How many things at *a* each can I buy for *b* cents' problem—it is assumed that the bond between these essential defining features and the operation or operations required for solution is as temporary as the bonds with the name of the buyer or the price of the thing. It is assumed that all problems are and should be solved by some pure act of reasoning without help or hindrance from bonds with the particular verbal structure and vocabulary of the problems. Whether or not they *should* be, they *are not*. Every time that a pupil solves a 'bought-sold' problem by subtraction he strengthens the tendency to respond to any problem whatsoever that contains the words 'bought for' and 'sold for' by subtraction; and he will by no means surely stop and survey every such problem in all its elements to make sure that no other feature makes inapplicable the tendency to subtract which the 'bought sold' evokes.

To prevent pupils from responding to the form of statement rather than the essential facts, we should then not teach them to forget the form of statement, but rather give them all the common forms of statement to which the response in question is an appropriate response, and only such. If a certain form of statement does in life always signify a certain arithmetical procedure, the bond between it and that procedure may properly be made very strong.

Another case of the formation of bonds to only a slight degree of strength concerns the use of so-called 'crutches' such as writing $+$, $-$, and $\times$ in copying problems like those below:—

Add	Subtract	Multiply
23	79	32
61	24	3

or altering the figures when 'borrowing' in subtraction, and the like. Since it is undesirable that the pupil should regard the 'crutch' response as essential to the total procedure, or become so used to having it that he will be disturbed by its absence later, it is supposed that the bond between the situation and the crutch should not be fully formed. There is a better way out of the difficulty, in case crutches are used at all. This is to associate the crutch with a special 'set,' and its non-use with the general set which is to be the permanent one. For example, children may be taught from the start never to write the crutch sign or crutch figure unless the work is accompanied by "Write . . . to help you to . . . ."

Write — to help you to Find the differences:—
remember that you must   39   67   78   56   45
subtract in this row.   23   44   36   26   24

Remember that you must Find the differences:—
subtract in this row.   85   27   96   38   78
                          63   14   51   45   32

The bond evoking the use of the crutch may then be formed thoroughly enough so that there is no hesitation, insecurity, or error, without interfering to any harmful extent with the more general bond from the situation to work without the crutch.

THE STRENGTH OF BONDS WITH TECHNICAL FACTS AND TERMS

Another instructive case concerns the bonds between certain words and their meanings, and between certain situations of commerce, industry, or agriculture and useful facts about these situations. Illustrations of the former are the bonds between *cube root, hectare, brokerage, commission, indorsement, vertex, adjacent, nonagon, sector, draft, bill of exchange,* and their meanings. Illustrations of the latter are the bonds from "Money being lent 'with interest' at no specified rate, what rate is charged?" to "The legal rate of the state," from "$X per M as a rate for lumber" to "Means $X per thousand board feet, a board foot being 1 ft. by 1 ft. by 1 in."

It is argued by many that such bonds are valuable for a short time; namely, while arithmetical procedures in connection with which they serve are learned, but that their value is only to serve as a means for learning these procedures and that thereafter they may be forgotten. "They are formed only as accessory means to certain more purely arithmetical knowledge or discipline; after this is acquired they may be forgotten. Everybody does in fact forget them, relearning them later if life requires." So runs the argument.

In some cases learning such words and facts only to use them in solving a certain sort of problems and then forget them may be profitable. The practice is, however, exceedingly risky. It is true that everybody does in fact forget many such meanings and facts, but this commonly means either that they should not have been learned at all at the time that they were learned, or that they should have been learned more permanently, or that details should have been learned with the expectation that they themselves would be forgotten but that a general fact or attitude would remain. For example, duodecagon should not be learned at all in the elementary school; indorsement should either not be learned at all there, or be learned for permanence of a year or more; the details of the metric system should be so taught as to leave for several years at least knowledge of the facts that there is a system so named that is important, whose tables go by tens, hundreds, or thousands, and a tendency (not necessarily strong) to connect meter, kilogram, and liter with measurement by the metric system and with approximate estimates of their several magnitudes.

If an arithmetical procedure seems to require accessory bonds which are to be forgotten, once the procedure is mastered, we should be suspicious of the value of the procedure itself. If pupils forget what compound interest is, we may be sure that they will usually also have forgotten how to compute it. Surely there is waste if they have learned what it is only to learn how to compute it only to forget how to compute it!

THE STRENGTH OF BONDS CONCERNING THE REASONS FOR ARITHMETICAL PROCESSES

The next case of the formation of bonds to slight strength is the problematic one of forming the bonds involved in understanding the reasons for certain processes only to forget them after the process has become a habit. Should a pupil, that is, learn why he inverts and multiplies, only to forget it as soon as he can be trusted to divide by a fraction? Should he learn why he puts the units figure of each partial product in multiplication under the figure that he multiplies by, only to forget the reason as soon as he has command of the process? Should he learn why he gets the number of square inches in a rectangle by multiplying the length by the width, both being expressed in linear inches, and forget why as soon as he is competent to make computations of the areas of rectangles?

On general psychological grounds we should be suspicious of forming bonds only to let them die of starvation later, and tend to expect that elaborate explanations learned only to be forgotten either should not be learned at all, or should be learned at such a time and in such a way that they would not be forgotten. Especially we should expect that the general principles of arithmetic, the whys and wherefores of its fundamental ways of manipulating numbers, ought to be the last bonds of all to be forgotten. Details of *how* you arranged numbers to multiply might vanish, but the general reasons for the placing would be expected to persist and enable one to invent the detailed manipulations that had been forgotten.

This suspicion is, I think, justified by facts. The doctrine that the customary deductive explanations of why we invert and multiply, or place the partial products as we do before adding, may be allowed to be forgotten once the actual habits are in working order, has a suspicious source. It arose to meet the criticism that so much time and effort were required to keep these deductive explanations in memory. The fact was that the pupil learned to compute correctly *irrespective of* the deductive explanations. They were only an added burden. His inductive learning that the procedure gave the right answer really taught him. So he wisely shuffled off the extra burden of facts about the consequences of the nature of a fraction or the place values of our decimal notation. The bonds weakened because they were not used. They were not used because they were not useful in the shape and at the time that they were formed, or because the pupil was unable to understand the explanations so as to form them at all.

The criticism was valid and should have been met in part by replacing the deductive explanations by inductive verifications, and in part by using the deductive reasoning as a check after the process itself is mastered. The very same discussions of place-value which are futile as proof that you must do a certain thing before you have done it, often become instructive as an explanation of why the thing that you have learned to do and are familiar with and have verified by other tests works as well as it does. The general deductive theory of arithmetic should not be learned only to be forgotten. Much of it should, by most pupils, not be learned at all. What is learned should be learned much later than now, as a synthesis and ration-ale of habits, not as their creator. What is learned of such deductive theory should rank among the most rather than least permanent of a pupil's stock of arithmetical knowledge and power. There are bonds which are formed only to be lost, and bonds formed only to be lost *in their first form,* being used in a new organization as material for bonds of a higher order; but the bonds involved in deductive explanations of why certain processes are right are not such: they are not to be formed just to be forgotten, nor as mere propædeutics to routine manipulations.

[*The final section of Chapter V, "Propaedeutic Bonds," not given here, deals with weak bonds formed for temporary purposes.*]

CHAPTER X

The Psychology of Thinking: Reasoning in Arithmetic

.
.
.

REASONING AS THE COÖPERATION OF ORGANIZED HABITS

The pedagogy of the past made two notable errors in practice based on two errors about the psychology of reasoning. It considered reasoning as a somewhat magical power or essence which acted to counteract and overrule the ordinary laws of habit in man; and it separated too sharply the 'understanding of principles' by reasoning from the 'mechanical' work of computation, reading problems, remembering facts and the like, done by 'mere' habit and memory.

Reasoning or selective, inferential thinking is not at all opposed to, or independent of, the laws of habit, but really is their necessary result under the conditions imposed by man's nature and training. A closer examination of selective thinking will show that no principles beyond the laws of readiness, exercise, and effect are needed to explain it; that it is only an extreme case of what goes on in associative learning as described under the 'piecemeal' activity of situations; and that attributing certain features of learning to mysterious faculties of abstraction or reasoning gives no real help toward understanding or controlling them.

It is true that man's behavior in meeting novel problems goes beyond, or even against, the habits represented by bonds leading from gross total situations and customarily abstracted elements thereof. One of the two reasons therefor, however, is simply that the finer, subtle, preferential bonds with subtler and less often abstracted elements go beyond, and at times against, the grosser and more usual bonds. One set is as much due to exercise and effect as the other. The other reason is that in meeting novel problems the mental set or attitude is likely to be one which rejects one after another response as their unfitness to satisfy a certain desideratum appears. What remains as the apparent course of thought includes only a few of the many bonds which did operate, but which, for the most part, were unsatisfying to the ruling attitude or adjustment.

Successful responses to novel data, associations by similarity and purposive behavior are in only apparent opposition to the fundamental laws of associative learning. Really they are beautiful examples of it. Man's

475

successful responses to novel data—as when he argues that the diagonal on a right triangle of 796.278 mm. base and 137.294 mm. altitude will be 808.022 mm., or that Mary Jones, born this morning, will sometime die—are due to habits, notably the habits of response to certain elements or features, under the laws of piecemeal activity and assimilation.

Nothing is less like the mysterious operations of a faculty of reasoning transcending the laws of connection-forming, than the behavior of men in response to novel situations. Let children who have hitherto confronted only such arithmetical tasks, in addition and subtraction with one- and two-place numbers and multiplication with one-place numbers, as those exemplified in the first line below, be told to do the examples shown in the second line.

Add	Add	Add	Subt.	Subt.	Multiply	Multiply	Multiply
8	37	35	8	37	8	9	6
5	24	68	5	24	5	7	3
		23					
		19					

Multiply	Multiply	Multiply
32	43	34
23	22	26

They will add the numbers, or subtract the lower from the upper number, or multiply 3×2 and 2×3, etc., getting 66, 86, and 624, or respond to the element of 'Multiply' attached to the two-place numbers by "I can't" or "I don't know what to do," or the like; or, if one is a child of great ability, he may consider the 'Multiply' element and the bigness of the numbers,

'9
be reminded by these two aspects of the situation of the fact that 9 multiply'
'10
gave only 81, and that 10 multiply' gave only 100, or the like; and so may report an intelligent and justified "I can't," or reject the plan of 3×2 and 2×3, with 66, 86, and 624 for answers, as unsatisfactory. What the children will do will, in every case, be a product of the elements in the situation that are potent with them, the responses which these evoke, and the further associates which these responses in turn evoke. If the child were one of sufficient genius, he might infer the procedure to be followed as a result of his knowledge of the principles of decimal notation and the meaning of 'Multiply,' responding correctly to the 'place-value' element of each digit and adding his 6 tens and 9 tens, 20 twos and 3 thirties; but if he did thus invent the shorthand addition of a collection of twenty-three collections, each of 32 units, he would still do it by the operation of bonds, subtle but real.

Association by similarity is, as James showed long ago, simply the tendency of an element to provoke the responses which have been bound to it.

abcde leads to *vwxyz* because *a* has been bound to *vwxyz* by original nature, exercise, or effect.

Purposive behavior is the most important case of the influence of the attitude or set or adjustment of an organism in determining (1) which bonds shall act, and (2) which results shall satisfy. James early described the former fact, showing that the mechanism of habit can give the directedness or purposefulness in thought's products, provided that mechanism includes something paralleling the problem, the aim, or need, in question.

The second fact, that the set or attitude of the man helps to determine which bonds shall satisfy, and which shall annoy, has commonly been somewhat obscured by vague assertions that the selection and retention is of what is "in point," or is "the right one," or is "appropriate," or the like. It is thus asserted, or at least hinted, that "the will," "the voluntary attention," "the consciousness of the problem," and other such entities are endowed with magic power to decide what is the "right" or "useful" bond and to kill off the others. The facts are that in purposive thinking and action, as everywhere else, bonds are selected and retained by the satisfyingness, and are killed off by the discomfort, which they produce; and that the potency of the man's set or attitude to make this satisfy and that annoy— to put certain conduction-units in readiness to act and others in unreadiness —is in every way as important as its potency to set certain conduction-units in actual operation.

Reasoning is not a radically different sort of force operating against habit but the organization and coöperation of many habits, thinking facts together. Reasoning is not the negation of ordinary bonds, but the action of many of them, especially of bonds with subtle elements of the situation. Some outside power does not enter to select and criticize; the pupil's own total repertory of bonds relevant to the problem is what selects and rejects. An unsuitable idea is not killed off by some *actus purus* of intellect, but by the ideas which it itself calls up, in connection with the total set of mind of the pupil, and which show it to be inadequate.

Almost nothing in arithmetic need be taught as a matter of mere unreasoning habit or memory, nor need anything, first taught as a principle, ever become a matter of mere habit or memory. $5 \times 4 = 20$ should not be learned as an isolated fact, nor remembered as we remember that Jones' telephone number is 648 J 2. Almost everything in arithmetic should be taught as a habit that has connections with habits already acquired and will work in an organization with other habits to come. The use of this organized hierarchy of habits to solve novel problems is reasoning.

THE
TWENTY-NINTH YEARBOOK

OF THE

NATIONAL SOCIETY FOR THE STUDY
OF EDUCATION

REPORT OF THE SOCIETY'S COMMITTEE
ON ARITHMETIC

PART I. SOME ASPECTS OF MODERN THOUGHT ON ARITHMETIC
PART II. RESEARCH IN ARITHMETIC

Prepared by the Society's Committee
W. A. Brownell, B. R. Buckingham, G. T. Buswell, C. E. Greene,
R. L. West, and F. B. Knight (*Chairman*)

Assisted by the Following Active Members of the Society
E. A. Beito, J. C. Brown, L. J. Brueckner, J. R. Clark, W. F. Dearborn, Arthur
Edwards, H. L. Harap, Ernest Horn, C. H. Judd, Fred Kelly, L. A. King,
R. H. Lane, Josephine MacLatchy, C. R. Mead, R. L. Morton, Elma A.
Neal, G. M. Norem, W. J. Osburn, J. R. Overman, Isidoro Pan-
lasigui, Harriet E. Peet, F. G. Pickell, A. C. Repp, G. M. Ruch,
C. W. Stone, Florence Stratemeyer, and C. W. Washburne

———

Edited by
GUY MONTROSE WHIPPLE

———

THIS YEARBOOK WILL BE DISCUSSED AT THE ATLANTIC CITY MEETING OF THE
NATIONAL SOCIETY, FEBRUARY 22 AND 25, 1930, 8:00 P.M.

———

PUBLIC SCHOOL PUBLISHING COMPANY
BLOOMINGTON, ILLINOIS
1930

TABLE OF CONTENTS

PAGE

EDITOR'S PREFACE 1

PART I. SOME ASPECTS OF MODERN THOUGHT ON ARITHMETIC

CHAP.

I. INTRODUCTION 9
   F. B. KNIGHT

II. THE SOCIAL VALUE OF ARITHMETIC 65
   B. R. BUCKINGHAM

III. THE ARITHMETIC CURRICULUM 145
   W. A. BROWNELL

IV. SOME CONSIDERATIONS OF METHOD
   B. L. WEST, CHARLES E. GREENE, AND W. A. BROWNELL

V. TESTING, DIAGNOSIS, AND REMEDIAL WORK IN ARITHMETIC 269
   F. B. KNIGHT

VI. THE TRAINING OF TEACHERS OF ARITHMETIC 319
   CHARLES E. GREENE AND G. T. BUSWELL

PART II. RESEARCH IN ARITHMETIC 411

I. THE PURPOSE AND PLAN OF PART TWO 415
   G. T. BUSWELL

II. THE TECHNIQUES OF RESEARCH EMPLOYED IN ARITHMETIC 445
   G. T. BUSWELL

III. A CRITICAL SURVEY OF PREVIOUS RESEARCH IN ARITHMETIC 473
   W. A. BROWNELL

IV. THE NUMBER ABILITIES OF CHILDREN WHEN THEY ENTER
   GRADE ONE 525
   B. R. BUCKINGHAM, Harvard University, Cambridge, Massachusetts, and JOSEPHINE MACLATCHY, Ohio State University, Columbus, Ohio

V. A CRITICAL EVALUATION OF METHODS OF ANALYZING PRACTICE IN FRACTIONS 535
   LEO J. BRUECKNER, University of Minnesota, Minneapolis, Minnesota, and FRED KELLY, Gettysburg College, Gettysburg, Pennsylvania

VI. MIXED VERSUS ISOLATED DRILL ORGANIZATION 551
   ADDISON C. RARR, State Teachers College, Flagstaff, Arizona

VII. THE LEARNING OF THE ONE HUNDRED MULTIPLICATION COMBINATIONS 551
   G. M. NOREM, State Normal School, Minot, North Dakota, and F. B. KNIGHT, State University of Iowa, Iowa City, Iowa

VIII. A MEASUREMENT OF TRANSFER IN THE LEARNING OF NUMBER COMBINATIONS 569
   E. A. BETZ, Mechanic Arts High School, St. Paul, Minnesota, and LEO J. BRUECKNER, University of Minnesota, Minneapolis, Minnesota

IX. AN EXPERIMENTAL STUDY IN IMPROVING ABILITY TO REASON IN ARITHMETIC 589
   C. W. STONE, State College of Washington, Pullman, Washington

X. A TEST IN ARITHMETIC FOR MEASURING GENERAL ABILITY OF PUPILS IN THE FIRST SIX GRADES 601
   HARLEY E. TREAT and WALTER F. DEARBORN, Harvard University, Cambridge, Massachusetts

XI. THE EFFECT OF AWARENESS OF SUCCESS OR FAILURE 611
   ISIDORO PANLASIGUI, University of the Philippines, Manila, Philippine Islands, and F. B. KNIGHT, State University of Iowa, Iowa City, Iowa

XII. A STUDY OF ERRORS IN PERCENTAGE 621
   ARTHUR EDWARDS, Superintendent of Schools, Geneva, Iowa

XIII. THE GRADE PLACEMENT OF ARITHMETIC TOPICS 641
   CARLETON W. WASHBURNE, Superintendent of Schools, Winnetka, Illinois

XIV. A REVIEW OF EXPERIMENTS ON SUBTRACTION 671
   G. M. RUCH and CYRUS D. MEAD, University of California, Berkeley, California

APPENDIX: A CRITIQUE OF THE YEARBOOK 681
   LEO J. BRUECKNER

Constitution of the National Society for the Study of Education. 711
Minutes of the Cleveland Meeting of the Society 714
Synopsis of the Proceedings of the Board of Directors During 1929 717
Audit of the Treasurer of the Society for 1928 720
List of Honorary and Active Members of the Society 723
Information Concerning the Society 744
List of the Publications of the Society 747

CHAPTER I

Introduction

I. PURPOSES OF THE YEARBOOK

In this *Twenty-Ninth Yearbook* of the Society the attempt has been made to discuss certain crucial problems of arithmetic in such a way as to bring out the theoretical aspects in so far as our present knowledge permits, and also to bring out numerous practical applications which, we trust, will make the discussions useful to supervisors and teachers. Our attempt has been facilitated by certain circumstances among which the following seem outstanding: first, the Arithmetic Committee, in ten full days of conference, secured the manifest advantage of frank exchange of opinion; second, the widespread interest in arithmetic made available for our use a large body of written discussion; third, a reviewing committee received most of the material in galley form in time to prepare a concluding critical chapter, so that this Yearbook contains not only discussions by the committee, but also a deliberate appraisal of these discussions by an independent and competent group of students of arithmetic.

II. SOME LIMITATIONS

There are certain omissions in this volume which will be recognized immediately by the reader. He will note, for instance, the absence or the scantiness of discussions directed to several important aspects of arithmetic. Thus, problems and problem-solving receive but a partial discussion, because lack of rigorous data permits no thorough and penetrating discussion at present, and in general, the main reason for our neglect of certain issues which stand in obvious need of treatment is the simple fact that there is at present an insufficient amount of consistent scientific findings to furnish a satisfactory basis for such treatments. It seemed better to remain silent when discussion could go little beyond the limits of personal opinion.

A second reason for certain omissions arises, in some instances, from a decision not to proceed beyond general principles to definite and specific suggestions and detailed directions for classroom procedure. Several considerations led to this decision. In some cases sufficiently close agreement on details could not be reached to present them without, at the same time, presenting a minority opinion. Too frequent expression of minority opinion becomes confusing to the reader. On the whole, the Yearbook is the expression of unanimous agreement of the Committee. While, of course, each member of the Committee has mental reservations about occasional paragraphs in the several chapters (on the score of pertinency as well as probable truth), the Yearbook as a whole represents the judgment of the entire Committee in the interpretation of available data. An exception to this is, of course, the concluding chapter, which is the appraisal of an independent reviewing committee.

Another factor influencing our decision to omit specifics was the desire of members of the Committee to avoid the promotion of their own particular interests in arithmetic, which can be found in print elsewhere. The Committee believes that the Yearbook does not propagandize any particular course of study, textbook, or type of instruction. In leaning backward in its effort to accomplish this purpose, the Committee may have omitted specific suggestions which would prove useful to the supervisor or to the teacher. The student may, however, by using the general points of view presented herein, be enabled to evaluate specific methods found in materials published elsewhere.

III. THE EDUCATIONAL PHILOSOPHY UNDERLYING THE YEARBOOK

Some readers may feel that this Yearbook is too conservative, that it lacks a bold and daring spirit of progressiveness. There has been a conscious attempt to avoid the urging of any point of view not supported by considerable scientific fact. It has seemed preferable to proceed slowly and on sure ground, to be content with sane and moderate progress, rather than to expound a theory of instruction which, though supported by fine hopes and splendid aspirations, has as yet no basis in objective data. The justification of the contention of those who feel that the spirit of the Yearbook is not progressive will hinge on the definition given to 'progressive.' The changes we have supported are changes which can be made and held, changes based on a sober psychology of learning and of human nature, rather than extravagant changes based on a psychology which in its enthusiasm stubbornly refuses to view all the factors involved. The Committee feels that the treatment of arithmetic in this Yearbook is as progressive as modern thinking, courses of study, textbook construction, and scientific experimentation give it a right to be, and much more progressive than much of present classroom practice.

The spirit in which this Yearbook was written, while not extreme, assumes the desirability of a liberal school in contrast to the lock-step, teacher-driven school of the '90's. It recognizes the child as the center of interest. The final criterion of all values is considered to be the effect any technique of teaching or any content of instruction has upon the child. The Committee has held in mind, however, that it is the whole child, not a part of him, which is the reality to be kept constantly in mind. A child's present life is but a part of himself, and an educational philosophy based upon the assumption that the present interests, needs, strengths, weaknesses, whims of the child comprise the sole or dominating aspect of the child will in practice render but limited service. The child's future is a part of him. In a sense, that the child will soon become an adult is a reality of childhood which must not be forgotten. Further, it is of importance to realize that the child, whose most precious attribute is 'soon to become an adult,' is destined to live in an actual society, a total environment, which will be, roughly, the United States between the years 1940 and 1980. The actualities of this total environment are not likely to be the ideal ones of which we now dream with fondness. In our more realistic moments we see that the child will be an adult living his life in terms of needs, duties, responsibilities, successes, failures, satisfactions, and monotonies very much like our own.

It is not enough to cast education in terms of children's present interests and desires alone. A child's life at the moment is not a thing in itself, nor is it at all self-sufficient and self-contained. His life is a continuum; his future is more real than his present. He is essentially an organism which is becoming something other than a child. Hence the education of the child must be cast in terms of his becoming an adult as well as in terms of his present status. The child must, of course, learn (and be taught) in ways which utilize the principles of child psychology, but the aims of his education must be influenced by two considerations: (a) his real nature, a potent part of which is his rapid leaving of his present status and his constant becoming an adult, and (b) the demands which life will place upon him to-morrow. These demands are not those of our wishing, but those which will exist in the United States in the next generation, many of which can be predicted with reasonable certainty.

Certain educational philosophers seem to slight this reality of the future. Whether or not these philosophers have this intention, their pronouncements are interpreted to mean that childhood (having its own rights as it surely does) should serve the purposes of childhood only or mostly. The fact that a given unit of material is preparation for adult living is to these persons no sufficient defense for its inclusion in a child's curriculum, even if it be adapted to childhood in accord with good psychology. The aims of the school and the aims of childhood can be cut loose from adult aims and can be considered as quite separate from the aims of the future. Aims, as aims, are thus located in the present rather than in the future. Let the child eat, drink, and be merry, for to-morrow he will—become only an adult. A further present tendency which seems to the Committee dubious philosophy is the attitude of helplessness in predicting the demands which life will place upon the adult of the immediate future, say, 1940 to 1980. This helplessness is often alleged to be a necessary consequence of the rapid changes now occurring in society. Present society is changing in its technicalities, but· the fundamentals of competent and useful living are not changing so rapidly that reasonable predictions of demands a generation or two in the future are either impossible or undesirable.

The revolt against the conventional school is a blessing, but it carries with it certain abuses. The Arithmetic Committee feels that a gradual evolution is more desirable than either a revolution or an impatient, extravagant attempt at reform. A temperateness in change may not be quite as thrilling to the philosopher as sweeping radical changes, but it is better sense.

The philosophy of this Yearbook, then, finds aims in the future as well as in the present. It suggests the desirability of preparation for adult living and holds it to be evident that a prediction of the demands of the future is feasible to a reasonable and useful degree of certainty. We should teach, then, those skills, informations, judgments, attitudes, habits, ideals, and ambitions which the child will find adequate and satisfying to the most important part of his whole self; that is, to his future adulthood as well as to his present childhood. How to teach the child can be separated, in discussion, from what to teach—and how to teach is fundamentally more a matter of psychology based on research and investigation than a matter of philosophy.

IV. THE PSYCHOLOGY OF LEARNING ASSUMED IN THE YEARBOOK

Theoretically, the main psychological basis is a behavioristic one, viewing skills and habits as fabrics of connections. This is in contrast, on the one hand, to the older structural psychology which has still to make direct contributions to classroom procedure, and on the other hand, to the more recent *Gestalt* psychology, which, though promising, is not yet ready to function as a basis of elementary education.

The psychological point of view pervading this Yearbook emphasizes the fact that teaching based upon felt needs and interest only is inadequate. Not that felt needs and interest are lacking in vitality and importance, but that neglect of other matters (even if the neglect is only by way of inference) weakens effective teaching and learning to an intolerable degree. Use of all the dynamics of learning, rather than a use of some and a neglect of others, is the position taken. In the older school there was an overconfidence in drill—too often so stupidly administered that it could not possibly effect learning—and a corresponding neglect of interest and of the significance of the work to the worker. In short, there was a failure to capitalize the energy-releasing power of felt needs, together with a very naïve view of the psychological nature of the curriculum. One might suspect that today we are being led by our laudable attention to interest, significance, and the creation or discovery of felt needs to a neglect of other dynamics of human learning. We are in danger of slighting the contributions of properly organized practice; we may allow felt needs to degenerate into whims (often requiring less effort); we may continue (through neglect) to teach subject matter with but a superficial view of its psychological nature. A pedagogy based on a use of all the dynamics of learning in proper proportion is highly preferable to overemphasis upon a single aspect of learning in one generation followed by a corresponding neglect of it in the next generation.

In some quarters it seems the fashion to think that anything that at all resembles conventional practices is necessarily wrong and vicious. There is almost an emotional antipathy to anything that in any way reminds us of the kind of schools we attended as children. The assumption that children must be unhappy and will develop frightful personalities if exposed to a pedagogy which uses the principles upon which the older schools were based is a sort of inverted old-oaken-bucket delusion. Many aspects of the older school are, after all, distinctly good psychology; they are based on correct theorems relating to human nature. Two instances will illustrate the caution against a lopsided psychology of learning based solely on interest and the felt needs of the child:

(a) A very modern teacher, sure that anything which is conventional is wrong, decided to allow the curriculum of her first-grade class to be guided by the wisdom of her pupils. "Now to-day," she said, "we can do anything we like to do." She suggested several possible projects which were *anything but* customary school work. Silence followed this attempt to discover felt needs. Finally a child summoned up courage and said: "I want to learn to read just as older people do." Should this teacher keep on trying to find something else to do or should she follow her philosophy and assist the youngster in his learning to read with a use of the best techniques of learning at her command?

(b) A third-grade teacher told her class on a certain morning that they could do anything they wished to do—at the same time waving some raffia in her hand and having previously laid in conspicuous places equipment for activities of various kinds. A hand promptly went up, followed by this suggestion: "Let's do some more drill in long division, so that it will not be so hard." What should this teacher do?

The notion that regular school work is or must be essentially intolerable to children is not true. Even skill subjects can be taught, and often are taught, in ways which are even more than tolerable to children. A curriculum laid down before the child enters school can be lived through with zest and enthusiasm. The 'going to school' may, in itself, be an abiding and sufficient project. When an adequate psychology underlies the daily work, many of the criticisms directed against the 'orthodox' school lose their force. Many of the attacks on the 'conventional' school so describe it that the attack is against a straw man.

Much may be said for the following point of view: What to teach should be decided by as wise adults as are available for the task, who will base their decisions as far as possible upon the available body of objective scientific data. How to teach should be based upon a virile psychology of learning which uses all the dynamics of learning—not on the one hand, running to seed, as in the case of the older school, on dead tasks for the tasks' sake; and not, on the other hand, declaring a Roman holiday, and becoming concerned only with the factor of interest. The actualities are such that until we are much more skillful than we are, the interest value of many moments in school is not particularly high. But, in spite of this, a total psychology of learning would, on occasion, defend such moments as moments to keep on doing the same thing while improving the interest in it, rather than to avoid doing it altogether. There must be no retreat from the position that felt needs be utilized, that the tasks be made significant, that the sustaining effects of interest be earnestly sought and capitalized. Further, we must continue to seek both increased knowledge of the psychology of the subject matter taught (a field quite neglected by the left wing) and increased skill in the use of such aspects of learning as are suggested by the phrases: drill, continued effort, ability to withstand distraction, persistence though momentarily bored, effort sustained not by rewards at hand but by confidence in values forthcoming in the future, and the intent to master the matter in hand as a permanent possession rather than as a temporary accomplishment.

For the Committee,
F. B. KNIGHT.

GUIDE TO CHAPTER IV

	PAGE
Introduction	145
I. Principles of Curriculum Construction	145
1. A Useful Content	145
2. Present Research Tentative	146
3. Willingness to Change	148
4. A Critical Attitude	148
5. The Influence of Method	150
6. Respect for Possibilities	151
7. The Sources of Method	152
II. Absence of Scientific Information an Embarrassment	153
1. Interference Factors	153
2. Data on Difficulty	156
3. Fitting Methods to Abilities	159
4. Control of Motivation	159
5. Precise Histories of Learning	161
III. Mathematical Knowledge versus Pedagogical Knowledge	162
1. An Analysis of Long Division, arising from Stressing the Mathematical versus the Pedagogical Point of View	167
2. Characteristic Inadequacies Arising from Stressing the Mathematical	174
IV. A Process Is an Organization	177
V. Addition of Whole Numbers	183
VI. Analyses of Actual Instructional Material	184
1. The Uses of Analyses	185
2. Limitations of Analyses of Text Material	187
VII. An Analysis of Instructional Material in the Analysis	187
1. General Methods Employed in the Analysis	188
2. Data Presented Are Medians	188
3. The Identification of the Fundamental Addition Combinations	192
4. The Identification of Higher-Decade Addition Combinations	195
5. Summary on the Teaching of Addition Combinations	195
6. Instruction on the Units of Skill Used in Addition	200
7. Instruction in the Abilities Used in Addition	202
8. Massed versus Distributed Instruction in Addition	204
9. The General Status of Instruction in Addition	205
10. The Problem of Qualitative Merit, or Effectiveness	206
11. A Few Applications to Method in General	207
VIII. Analyses of Instructional Material in Subtraction, Multiplication, and Division	207
IX. Analyses of Instructional Units in Common Fractions	207
1. The Meaning of Fractions	208
2. The Total Amount of Instruction	211
3. Instruction on the Several Units of Skill	211
4. Summary of Instruction in Common Fractions	212
X. Analyses of Instruction in Percentage	212
1. Methods of Analyzing Instructional Material in Percentage	212
2. Instruction in Ideas of Percentage	213
3. Instruction in Ideas of Wholes and Parts	214
4. Instruction in Changing Decimals to Percents	216
5. Instruction in Other and Related Changes	217
6. Instruction in the Three Cases of Percentage	217
7. Summary of Instruction in Percentage	218
8. The Specific Material Used in Instruction in Percentage	219
9. The Technical Vocabulary of Percentage	220
10. The Gross Amount of Instruction in Percentage	221
11. The General Adequacy of Instruction in Percentage	221
XI. Summary on Instructional Materials	222
XII. Method in Drill: Some General Considerations	223
1. Two Purposes of Drill	224
2. Typical Alternatives in Drill	224
3. Should Drill Be Distributed or Non-Distributed?	226
4. Should Drill Be of the Isolated or Mixed Form?	227
5. Standards and Tests in Drill Material	232
6. Drill Material and the Supervisor's Needs	233
7. Summary	238
XIII. Analyses of Provisions for Drill	239
1. Drill in Whole Numbers	239
2. Drill in Common Fractions and Small Mixed Numbers	240
3. Drill in Percentage	245
4. Summary of Method in Drill	255
XIV. In Review: Some Points of View on Method	260

CHAPTER IV

Some Considerations of Method

.
.
.

III. MATHEMATICAL KNOWLEDGE VERSUS PEDAGOGICAL KNOWLEDGE

Anyone at all acquainted with the personnel of workers in the field knows the distrust that many mathematicians, as mathematicians, feel concerning pedagogues, as pedagogues. It has been asserted in many quarters that only trained mathematicians should be responsible for the view of arithmetic given teachers in their professional training. What can a pedagogue know about arithmetic?

It is just possible that the amount of pure mathematics needed for competent work in arithmetic is far less than that needed in the teaching of advanced algebra, solid geometry, and college mathematics. A somewhat assiduous search of the literature fails to discover just how a mastery of advanced mathematics functions in the teaching of arithmetic. On the other hand, it is interesting to inquire into the possibility of several types of knowledge of arithmetic which may be useful. Let us assume for the moment that there is a useful distinction between a knowledge of arithmetic from the standpoint of mathematics as mathematics and knowledge of arithmetic from the standpoint of its teaching. This latter type of knowledge implies that when arithmetic is studied from the standpoint of children learning it, a somewhat different set of criteria might be used in judging one's mastery of it.

An example of teaching knowledge vs. mathematical knowledge of arithmetic may be found in the case of long division. From the mathematical point of view, the accompanying examples are the same. They are all long division examples, and that is all there is to be said.

$$
\begin{array}{llll}
\text{(a)} \quad 42\overline{)8946} & \text{(b)} \quad 26\overline{)598} & \text{(c)} \quad 53\overline{)1219} & \text{(d)} \quad 93\overline{)5301} \\[2mm]
\text{(e)} \quad 93\overline{)5303} & \text{(f)} \quad 93\overline{)5332} & \text{(g)} \quad 46\overline{)27738} & \text{(h)} \quad 74\overline{)27385} \\[2mm]
\text{(i)} \quad 306\overline{)23256} & \text{(j)} \quad 78\overline{)4551} & \text{(k)} \quad 29\overline{)17835} & \text{(l)} \quad 17\overline{)714}
\end{array}
$$

(a) quotient 213; (b) quotient 23; (c) quotient 23; (d) quotient 57; (e) quotient $57\frac{2}{93}$; (f) quotient $57\frac{1}{3}$; (g) quotient 593; (h) quotient $370\frac{5}{74}$; (i) quotient 76; (j) quotient $58\frac{27}{78}$; (k) quotient 615; (l) quotient 42.

From the standpoint of teaching, however, there are important differences between them. Mathematical knowledge is not enough nor is it of the right kind to exhaust the information needed for a good basis for the teaching of this process. Thus in computation:

Ex. (a) requires no carrying in the multiplication and contains no borrowing or carrying difficulty in the subtraction.

Ex. (b) contains a carrying difficulty in multiplication but no difficulty in subtraction.

Ex. (c) contains no carrying difficulty in multiplication but a subtraction difficulty.

Ex. (d) contains both multiplication and subtraction difficulties.

Ex. (e) contains a remainder which, if written in fraction form, cannot be reduced.

Ex. (f) contains a remainder which, if written in fraction form, can be reduced.

Ex. (g) contains a 'middle' zero in the quotient.

Ex. (h) contains a final zero and a remainder in the quotient.

Ex. (i) contains a three-digit divisor.

Ex. (j) contains difficulty in finding the correct quotient figures which does not appear in examples before (j). In estimating the first quotient figure it seems that 6 would be the correct digit since 7 is contained in 45 six times, yet the correct quotient figure is 5.

Ex. (k) contains an aggravated form of quotient difficulty. By estimating, it would seem that 8 would be the correct first quotient figure, since 2 is contained in 17 eight times. However, the correct figure is 6, which is two digits away from the estimated 8.

Ex. (l) contains an even higher level of quotient difficulty. By estimating, the first quotient figure 7 would seem to be correct. The number 4, which is quite a distance away from 7, is the correct figure.

These examples of long-division difficulties are not complete, but sufficient to illustrate a very important point of view. *A mathematical description of an arithmetical process does not yield the kind of information about that process which is an essential basis for its instruction to children. Analysis in terms of learning difficulty is essential.* The literature of arithmetic is somewhat incomplete because in many processes such learning analyses are conspicuously absent. Too often vigorous sermons about things in general are given, when decisions about method need precise and quantitative data. A discussion of the uses of analyses in terms of learning difficulties will be postponed until representative analyses of various types can be presented.

1. AN ANALYSIS OF LONG DIVISION

The following analysis of a section of long division is of no particular importance from the standpoint of mathematics but from the standpoint of teaching it possesses real merit. It shows levels of complexity and difficulty which have bearing upon problems of teaching.

Table III [1] accounts for all long-division examples with double-digit

1. This table was first printed in the *Fourth Yearbook of the Department of Superintendence* and is the work of H. A. Jeep.

TABLE III.—CLASSIFICATION OF ALL POSSIBLE TWO-DIGIT DIVISOR, SINGLE-DIGIT QUOTIENT LONG-DIVISION EXAMPLES*

Examples Which Involve No Quotient Difficulties			Examples Which Involve Quotient Difficulties—Other Difficulties Neglected		
Number	Percent	Nature of Difficulties†	Number	Percent	Nature of Difficulties
171	0.4	ND-I-NC-NB-NR	2489	6.2	ND- I
4238	10.6	ND-I-NC-NB- R	14,202	35.4	D-NI
4681	11.7	ND-I-NC- B- R	1454	3.6	D- I
186	0.5	ND-I- C-NB-NR	——	——	
6391	15.9	ND-I- C-NB- R	18,145	44.6	
6283	15.7	ND-I- C- B- R			
——	——		40,095—Grand Total		
21,950	55.4				

* Examples in which the units' digit of the divisor is zero are not included in this study. See Footnote 2.

†C means there is carrying in the multiplication.
NC means there is no carrying in the multiplication.
B means there is borrowing in the subtraction.
NB means there is no borrowing in the subtraction.
R means there is a remainder.
NR means there is no remainder.
ND means there is no quotient difficulty when the first digit of the divisor is used as the trial divisor.
D means there is a quotient difficulty when the first digit of the divisor is used as the trial divisor.
NI means there is no quotient difficulty when the first digit of the divisor increased by one is used as the trial divisor.
I means there is a quotient difficulty when the first digit of the divisor increased by one is used as the trial divisor.

divisors and single-digit quotients (other than zero) with the exception of those examples [2] with divisors in which the units' digit is zero. There are a total of 40,095 such division examples. It is not contended that this table accounts for all the skills which go to make up the total long-division ability. It does provide, however, for a sufficient number of the total skills to make possible a clear picture of the distribution and classification of many of the skills of long division. The following comments will make this more clear.

The classification in Table III is on the basis of carrying, borrowing,[3] remainder, and quotient skills. Examples in which there are quotient diffi-

2. Double-digit divisor examples in which the units' digit of the divisor is zero are omitted from Table III because of the similarity of such examples, speaking from the psychological point of view, to single-digit divisor examples. Zero as a quotient is omitted since its difficulty is not the type of quotient difficulty here considered.
3. When the additive method of subtraction is used, this would refer to the bridging in such subtraction.

culties are grouped according to the type of quotient difficulty, regardless of the carrying, borrowing, and remainder difficulties they may or may not involve. The following illustrations are given for the purpose of clearing up any questions as to the nature of this classification.

$$\begin{array}{r} 21 \\ 42\overline{)882} \\ 84 \\ \hline 42 \\ 42 \end{array}$$

This example involves no carrying, no borrowing,[4] no remainder, and no quotient difficulty.

$$\begin{array}{r} 7 \\ 85\overline{)595} \\ 595 \end{array}$$

This example involves *carrying,* but no borrowing, no remainder, and no quotient difficulty.

$$\begin{array}{r} 7 \\ 85\overline{)597} \\ 595 \\ \hline 2 \end{array}$$

This example involves *carrying,* a *remainder,* but no borrowing and no quotient difficulty.

$$\begin{array}{r} 7 \\ 85\overline{)603} \\ 595 \\ \hline 8 \end{array}$$

This example involves *carrying, borrowing,* a *remainder,* but no quotient difficulty.

$$\begin{array}{r} 2 \\ 39\overline{)106} \\ 78 \\ \hline 28 \end{array}$$

This example involves a *quotient difficulty.* The correct quotient is not obtained when the first digit of the divisor is used as the trial divisor.

    3 is the trial divisor

    $10 \div 3 = 3$

    3 is not the correct quotient.

$$\begin{array}{r} 6 \\ 59\overline{)359} \\ 354 \\ \hline 5 \end{array}$$

Some authorities advise the use of the increase-by-one rule[5] for such examples; i.e., the using of the first digit of the divisor increased by one as the trial divisor. There is a *quotient difficulty* in this example even though the increase-by-one rule is used.

    $5 + 1 = 6 =$ the trial divisor

    $35 \div 6 = 5$

    But 6, not 5 is the correct quotient.

4. See Footnote 3.

5. There are two rules for estimating the quotient in long division. First, by using the first digit of the divisor as it stands as the trial divisor.

    $63\overline{)294}$ $6 =$ trial divisor
             $29 \div 6 = 4 =$ true quotient

Second, for those examples in which the second digit of the divisor is large it has been found that many errors in estimating quotients can be avoided by use of the increase-by-one rule. When this rule is used in estimating quotients the first digit of the divisor increased by one is used as the trial divisor.

    $28\overline{)193}$ $2 + 1 = 3 =$ trial divisor
             $19 \div 3 = 6 =$ true quotient

In this study the increase-by-one rule is considered for only those examples in which the second digit of the divisor is 6 or larger.

It is apparent that such examples as $24\overline{)48}$, $76\overline{)161}$, and $27\overline{)172}$ are the direct concern of Table III. Each of them is a double-digit divisor, single-digit quotient example, and therefore each is accounted for in Table III on the basis of the carrying, borrowing, remainder, and quotient skills practiced in it. For instance:

$24\overline{)48}$ Practices: No carrying
No borrowing
No remainder
No quotient difficulty

$76\overline{)161}$ Practices: No carrying
Borrowing
Remainder
No quotient difficulty

$27\overline{)172}$ Practices: Carrying
Borrowing
Remainder
A quotient difficulty

For purposes of this study a two or more digit quotient example is considered as a complex of two or more single-digit quotient examples. For instance, such an example as $23\overline{)483}$ is accounted for by the examples $23\overline{)48}$ and $23\overline{)23}$. Likewise, $41\overline{)861}$ is accounted for by the examples $41\overline{)86}$ and $41\overline{)41}$.[6]

It will be seen from a study of Table III that as far as finding quotients is concerned there are 21,950 which cause no especial difficulty where the apparent-quotient or the increase-by-one rule is used. There are 18,145 divisor-dividend combinations in which there is a conflict of interest between the apparent-quotient and the increase-by-one rule. Of these, 2489 cause no difficulty if the apparent-quotient rule is used, but do cause difficulty if the increase-by-one rule is used. There are 14,202 divisor-dividend combinations which give difficulty with the apparent-quotient rule but not with the increase-by-one rule. But a considerable number of these 14,202 combinations have divisors with unit digits of 2, 3, 4, or 5, so that the increase-by-one rule would not ordinarily be used. There are 1454 divisor-dividend combinations with difficulties with either rule. There is disagreement on the economy of teaching the increase-by-one rule. There is by no means a clear case for it. For a further discussion of the pros and cons of the increase-by-

6. It is obvious that when a two-digit quotient example is broken down into two single-digit divisor examples, psychologically the sum of the two latter examples is not exactly equal to the one two-digit example. For instance, the situation $23\overline{)23}$ is not exactly the same situation as the second division in the example $23\overline{)483}$.

one rule, see pages 41-48 of the *Second Yearbook of the National Council of Teachers of Mathematics.*

The question can justly be raised as to the possible use of an analysis of the divisor-dividend combinations as reported in Table III. An analysis seems warranted by such considerations as these:

It is always safer to know the facts than to be ignorant of them. A teacher or textbook writer who is not impressed with the vastness of the number of divisor-dividend combinations may very well underestimate the sheer extent of the field concerned. Such underestimation leads to compression and terseness in initial instruction. Furthermore, a clear picture of the possible combinations, ordered by presence or absence of varying combinations of computational difficulties, increases the chances of giving a better sampling of difficulties in drill work. It is easy to construct drill work in long division which consciously or unconsciously avoids certain combinations of computational difficulties common in long-division examples. If, however, examples are to be selected in accordance with the relative frequency of combinations of difficulties contained in the total field, analysis alone will give us the needed facts. Obviously, if division, rather than only the easy section of the total possibilities, is to be taught, a table such as Table III is almost necessary—first to show what relative emphasis should be given, and then to check drill work to ascertain whether it is provided. In addition, until some analysis lays out the total function in an orderly fashion, prudent sequence of instruction as well as wise sequence in drill is rendered haphazard and uncertain. That such an analysis is useful will be apparent to one who compares the drill and instructional material printed before this analysis was first published (or before similar unpublished analyses were made) with instructional and drill material appearing subsequent to 1924. It is, of course, obvious that a listing of the 40,095 combinations, indexed for types of difficulties present, is the true source of material for drill material made to specifications. Table III is but a statistical summary of such a list. The important thing to hold in mind at the moment, however, is that such an analysis is not mathematical but pedagogical in nature. It is offered here to support the point of view that mathematics, as such, is not a sufficient basis for the teaching of arithmetic.

2. CHARACTERISTIC INADEQUACIES ARISING FROM STRESSING THE MATHEMATICAL VERSUS THE PEDAGOGICAL POINT OF VIEW

Addition, subtraction, multiplication, and division which involve the use of whole numbers only are relatively simple affairs from the standpoint of mathematics. When their teaching is dominated by the mathematical point of view in contrast to the learning point of view, the instruction given them is built on a general assumption that the rapid presentation of the procedures as a whole, with a few cautions here and there, is sufficient. Such presentations are models of preciseness in definition and dignity in composition. Instruction so dominated seems to treat children as if they were miniature adults. Printed instructional material is presented in great compactness. It is highly economical of space, and an adult who is already familiar with the topic is prone to judge it to be economical of the pupil's time. An instructor dominated solely by the mathematical point of view often gives the impression of being more familiar with the subject than with the pupil. Unfairness to teaching procedures dominated by the mathematical point of view must be avoided. They have been somewhat influenced by notions that children were not instantaneous and perfect learners, yet the mathematical view has yet to deal seriously and persistently with learning difficulties. This failure is evidenced in several ways. As just mentioned, the criteria of good instructional material have been compactness, a dictionary type of terseness, and an ungrounded faith in the efficacy of rules and definitions. Such instructional material is very meaningful to the adult—who brings to its reading a mastery of the process. But what it looks like to the child, who with an immature mind is learning something he does not yet know, is quite another question.

Instruction dominated by the mathematical point of view almost always has assumed large amounts of transfer between processes and parts of them which are closely allied in the mind of the adult. Such instructional units have been summaries of procedures rather than learning explanations, and they have given little attention to the exact nature of the difficulties which children actually do encounter in their learning.

Some examples of unfortunate assumptions relative to the learning difficulties inherent in the four processes using whole numbers are presented in the next few pages. These are probably the result of slighting the learning point of view in favor of the mathematical point of view.

a. Omissions of Fact.—Instruction and drill which are faulty because of omissions of facts useful in learning fairly permeate present teaching. These faults in method seem traceable to erroneous theory which assumes that the learning of certain facts will cause the mastery of others—extra booty, as it were—by way of transfer. This assumption presupposes amounts of inferential thinking which typical pupils may not possess. It is obvious that the products of inferential thinking should not be assumed until such thinking is known to exist.

(1) An example of Fact Omissions is the assumption that a child who knows that $4 + 6 = 10$ will thereby know that $6 + 4 = 10$. Specific instruction on $7 + 9$ is assumed to carry over to $9 + 7$. If we speak of $4 + 5$ as an addition fact and $5 + 4$ as its reverse, there are forty-five primary addition facts and forty-five reverses. Ten combinations have no reverses. If we neglect the idea of transfer, there are one hundred primary addition combinations.

Until quite recently, practically all work in beginning addition has been based on teaching the forty-five primary addition facts and rather trusting to luck or transfer for the mastery of their reverses. Now, logically and mathematically, a real identity may exist between $4 + 5$ and $5 + 4$, and similarly between the other forty-four facts and their reverses. However, that these facts and their reverses possess psychological and learning equivalence is a gratuitous assumption which is flatly contradicted by substantial evidence. To-day we teach the one hundred combinations. Satisfactory transfer from an addition fact to its reverse is not assumed. Of course, teachers for many years have taught all the one hundred combinations, but in doing so they exceeded the provisions in method books and in printed material.

(2) A careful examination of theoretical discussions of method will show that instruction in addition has frequently been based on the assumption that if a child knows that $4 + 5 = 9$, he will also know that $14 + 5 = 19$, $24 + 5 = 29$, $34 + 5 = 39$, and so on (presumably through inferential thinking). That the possibilities of such inferential thinking on the part of children can be easily overestimated need not be argued.

(3) Zero in mathematics may not trouble the adult, but to the learner it is a veritable demon. Even to-day one is rather 'modern' if he teaches with care the combinations involving zero. An example of rather widespread neglect of zero in instruction is the case of a well-known text which tells the child, in its reference to a block of drill which deals with the primary subtraction facts, that the material in question contains all the subtraction facts that the learner needs to know. Still the following combinations do not appear in the material: 0-0, 9-0, 8-0, 7-0, 6-0, 5-0, 4-0, 3-0, 2-0, 1-0. Probably from the standpoint of mathematics, zero in subtraction can be omitted, but in second- and third-grade classrooms keen attention to such combinations is not omitted except by quite inexcusable oversight.

Assuming that reverses of combinations in addition, higher decade addition combinations, and combinations involving zero can be omitted as unnecessary elaboration of the obvious, are but chance illustrations of many instances of fact omissions.

[The remainder of this section continues the same theme, pointing out that the "mathematical viewpoint" is inadequate in teaching algorithms.]

A New Approach to Elementary Geometry

BY George D. Birkhoff and Ralph Beatley

Purpose of Demonstrative Geometry.—In demonstrative geometry the emphasis is on reasoning. This is all the more important because it deepens geometric insight. To the extent that the subject fails to develop the power to reason and to yield an appreciation of scientific method in reasoning, its fundamental value for purposes of instruction is lessened.

There are, to be sure, many geometric facts of importance quite apart from the logical structure. The bulk of these belong properly in the intuitive geometry of Grades 7 and 8 and are not the chief end of our instruction in demonstrative geometry in the senior high school.

If, then, we find that some of our pupils in demonstrative geometry make little if any gain in the power to reason as a result of our instruction and find, moreover, that other pupils of equal intelligence and schooling—except that they have had no demonstrative geometry—show very marked improvement in their ability to reason, our position is certainly open to attack. We cannot blame the pupils entirely. Perhaps there is something wrong with the subject; or perhaps the teaching could be improved.

Undefined Terms.—If we are to give our pupils an appreciation of scientific method in reasoning, we ought to insist on a few undefined terms at the outset. Why pretend to define everything? The words "straight line" mean more to most people than Euclid's definition, or later paraphrases of it. Then why not call "straight line" an undefined term? If we cannot define "point," "surface," "angle," without involving the concept we are defining, why not take them as undefined?

Need of Certain Assumptions.—Do our students appreciate the need of certain assumptions as fundamental in our logical system? Do we not allow them to infer that in geometry we can prove everything and that we assume certain elementary propositions not because we have to, but because we are in a hurry to get on to more important matters? Should we not rather seize the opportunity to impress on them the need of certain assumptions and show that this need is not peculiar to geometry, but is inherent in all logical

Reprinted from *The Teaching of Geometry,* Fifth Yearbook of the National Council of Teachers of Mathematics (New York: Bureau of Publications, Teachers College, Columbia University, 1930), pp. 86–95.

systems? Could anything but good come from our indicating the possibility of some latitude in the choice of assumptions for geometry and showing that each such choice leads to a slightly different approach to geometry, each valid with respect to its own group of assumptions and to no other? It is neither necessary nor desirable, perhaps, to mention non-Euclidean geometries in this connection.

What is the point in telling beginners that we shall assume certain "self-evident truths" and then asking them to *prove* certain other propositions which they regard as equally self-evident truths? Would they not come to a quicker understanding of the nature of a proof through the effort to prove easy "originals" which are not too plausible and which seem therefore to require justification?

The Method of Proof by Superposition.—If we can possibly avoid it, should we continue to demoralize our classes at the outset by asking them to prove the obvious by the method of superposition, a method so out of harmony with the larger aim of our instruction that even though we recognize its validity we restrict its use to those few cases for which we can find no better method?

The Incommensurable Case.—Euclid developed the arithmetic and algebra he needed purely geometric methods and made no reference to number. Confronted by "the incommensurable case," he was able to circumvent it only by means of inequalities and an exceedingly shrewd definition of proportion. Our instruction in arithmetic and algebra employs concepts developed since Euclid's time and takes number as its starting point. Our pupils are not troubled by irrationals and see no need of the incommensurable case. Our present practice is to pay but scant attention to it; but that hardly removes the difficulty, because it still stands in print before us. With more effective use of our irrationals we could get along without any mention of incommensurable cases; but for Euclid they were of fundamental importance. If we mention the incommensurable case at all, we can hardly dismiss it as exceptional, for the incommensurable is of relatively common occurrence: the commensurable is the exception.

Texts in Geometry.—In short, many pupils get little good from their study of geometry because at certain critical points the text is quite inadequate. This is of course no disparagement of Euclid; his audience knew more about logic and less about number than do our pupils in school today. From our point of view his text should say much more about the foundations of logical method, connecting these with situations outside geometry by appropriate exercises, and should start with the real-number system as we have it today and gain the power and simplicity which such an approach can yield.

Possible Changes in Teaching Geometry.—Perhaps if we are to rewrite Euclid we should consider other questions too. Congruence and parallelism are fundamental in Euclid's geometry; and from parallelism is derived the concept of similarity. We can express this symbolically as follows: $=, || \rightarrow \sim$. But in our demonstrations we refer chiefly to similarity and less often to those aspects of parallelism not comprised in similarity. Moreover, congruence and similarity have much in common. The British report on *The Teaching of Geometry in Schools* (G. Bell and Sons, London, 1923, p. 35) makes the interesting suggestion that we replace the parallel postulate by a postulate of similarity and derive the idea of parallels from similarity. This arrangement can be shown symbolically as follows: $=, \sim \rightarrow ||$.

Whether we make such a change or not, our pupils should see that the parallel postulate can be replaced by some other assumption—for example, a proposition concerning equal corresponding angles formed by a transversal and two other lines—and that the erstwhile parallel postulate is now a theorem depending on the new assumption. The pupils should also discover the effect on geometry of omitting the parallel postulate, or its equivalent, and all the theorems dependent on it.

Plane and Solid Geometry Combined.—Inasmuch as most students of demonstrative geometry devote but one year to the subject, it will probably be worthwhile to make as many allusions as possible to related propositions in three dimensions. This three-dimensional material would have to be based on intuition and find expression mainly in the exercises. The principle of duality and certain other modern concepts should be included also.

An Approach Based on Number.—Let us give further consideration to an approach to geometry based directly on number.

Within the last century Riemann devised an approach to geometry, not intended for elementary purposes and quite unsuited to them, but nevertheless very suggestive. In this geometry the notion of *distance* between two points is regarded as the primary geometric relation. A little thought will make it plain that most geometric conceptions can readily be defined in terms of distance. For example, the line segment AB may be defined as the collection of points P such that the distance from A to P plus the distance from P to B is equal to the distance from A to B. Again, the circle may be defined as the plane figure consisting of all the points P at a given distance r from a fixed point O called the center. From the Riemannian point of view geometry then appears as the theory of the interrelation of various distances between points, and the formula which expresses the distance between any two points is regarded as the basic element.

In the case of Euclidean geometry this formula may be written

$$P_1P_2 = \sqrt{(x_2 - x_1)^2 + (y_2 - y_1)^2},$$

where the pairs of numbers x and y are the labels which identify the point in question. This asserts that the distance between any two points P_1 and P_2 whose number pairs are $x_1, y_1,$ and x_2, y_2 is given by the square root of the sum of the squares of the differences of the x's and y's corresponding to these two points. Here we are not to think of the formula in itself as having geometric significance; instead we must think of a vast collection of points, the distance of any two of them being given to us by tabular entries, for instance, and then we must think of the above formula as giving a particularly simple rule by which the various points could be identified and the distances between them found as given in the fundamental table by short numerical reckoning.

Advantages of Such a Method.—Now with this Riemannian method of approach intuitive processes which are fundamental for Euclidean geometry have no place. That indeed is the fundamental difficulty with the method from a pedagogical point of view. But from a logical point of view it has several advantages which ought to be pointed out. In the first place, whereas Euclidean geometry takes for granted that there exist such things as points, lines, and planes, although as a matter of fact none actually correspond to physical objects, in this new method the whole construction is based upon the number system. For example, a point is defined to be a pair of numbers x, y, and the distance between any two points is defined as in the above rule. Consequently we know at the outset that we are dealing with entities which exist in the same sense that numbers do, so that our conclusions about them are bound to be as consistent as our rules of reckoning with numbers. In the second place, when we employ this method of approach we build up at the same time the elementary ideas which belong to analytic geometry and thus introduce the student not only to the ordinary geometric theorems but also to their formulation in terms of concepts of analytic geometry.

Illustrative Examples.—A simple illustration will bring out both of these points. Suppose that we are seeking the points on the line segments which join point A $(0, 0)$ to the point B $(1, 1)$. If P (x, y) represents any point of this segment, then, by the definition above, $AP + PB = AB$ and

$$\sqrt{x^2 + y^2} + \sqrt{(1-x)^2 + (1-y)^2} = \sqrt{2}.$$

If now we transpose one of the terms on the left, square, and simplify, we find by a little easy algebra that

$$x + y = \sqrt{2}\sqrt{x^2 + y^2}.$$

If both members of this equation are squared again, we obtain the equation

$$x = y,$$

which defines the line upon which all points of the segment must lie. It is then easy to show that only those points are to be taken for which $x(= y)$ is numerically less than 1 and positive. Here, then, we have illustrated how the natural definition in terms of distance leads to the formulation of the equation of a line in a simple case. From this point of view questions concerning intersecting lines and nonintersecting or parallel lines reduce themselves to algebraic questions as to whether or not certain pairs of linear equations in two unknowns x and y have or have not a solution.

The Pythagorean Theorem.—As another illustration we might refer to the Pythagorean theorem. How does the Pythagorean theorem appear from the Riemannian point of view? In the first place, we may regard the elementary formula itself as a formulation of the Pythagorean theorem, at least when the triangle in question has two of its sides parallel to the x and y axes. But more generally, we should first have to define two perpendicular lines. To this end we could define the perpendicular PM dropped from P to the line l and meeting l at the point M as that line for which the distance PM is as small as possible. By purely algebraic manipulation it turns out that given any two line segments AC and CB such that AC and CB are perpendicular, then $(AB)^2 = (AC)^2 + (CB)^2$.

The Euclidean Method.—Considering, then, these two contrasting methods of approach to elementary geometry, we may say that the Euclidean method proceeds from qualitative propositions called postulates, not involving number at all (to which we therefore attach the symbol 0), to other propositions involving linear and angular measurement (to which we accordingly attach the number 1), and finally to propositions which involve number in a two-dimensional way (to which we therefore attach the number 2). Of this last class the Pythagorean proposition and the theorem that the sum of the three angles of a triangle is 180° may be regarded as the typical and most important instances. Thus the processes of development in the Euclidean approach may be indicated schematically by the following diagram:

$$0 \to 1 \to 2.$$

The Riemannian Approach.—In the Riemannian approach we start with a formula which involves number in a two-dimensional way at the outset, for the fundamental formula really embodies the Pythagorean theorem. Then from this formula, by means of suitable definitions and the use of algebraic methods, we deduce other propositions, such as those dealing with linear and angular measure and also the qualitative propositions with which we started in the Euclidean case. For example, the proposition that two points determine a straight line would involve first the definition of the straight line as indicated above, second the proof that any equation of the first degree in x and y represents a straight line, and finally that one and essentially only one equation can be found which is satisfied by two given distinct pairs of numbers, x_1, y_1 and x_2, y_2. In consequence the diagram which we use to characterize this method of approach is the following:

$$2 \to 1 \to 0.$$

Disadvantages of Each Method.—The disadvantages of both methods are obvious. Euclid's method is circuitous and does not take advantage of well-known facts concerning number and linear and angular measurement in terms of number. These facts, which appear absolutely self-evident at an

499

early age under present conditions of training, must in this scheme be regarded as things to be demonstrated, at least if a purely logical point of view is adopted. The method of Riemann, on the other hand, is totally devoid of intuitive significance and involves fairly difficult algebraic manipulations at the outset.

Each method has, however, its advantages, which have been referred to above.

A New Approach to Elementary Geometry.—With these preliminaries let us attempt to formulate a method of approach which may possibly eliminate most of these disadvantages and at the same time embody the fundamental advantages of both methods. This method may in brief be characterized by this diagram:

$$0 \leftarrow 1 \rightarrow 2.$$

In this case we take for granted at the outset the notion of number and assume that the student is capable of making simple computations by means of number. Also we admit the self-evident fact of linear and angular mensuration and scale drawing; that is to say, we accept the simple facts familiar to any boy or girl who knows how to use ruler and protractor. On the basis, then, of four or five simple postulates of this type, the most important geometric conclusions which are not self-evident can be rapidly developed. Among these would be the Pythagorean proposition and the theorem that the sum of the angles of a triangle is 180°. Furthermore, on the basis of these postulates and these fundamental theorems all other theorems in geometry can be derived easily and naturally.

Fundamental Principles.—The fundamental principles necessary to such a development may be taken as follows:

 I. The Principle of Line Measure.—*The points on any straight line can be numbered so that number differences measure distances.*

 II. *There can be only one straight line through two given points.*

 III. The Principle of Angle Measure.—*All half lines having the same end point can be numbered so that number differences measure angles.*

 IV. *All straight angles have the same measure, 180°.*

 V. The Principle of Similarity[1] (Part I).—*Two triangles are similar if an angle of one equals an angle of the other and the sides including these angles are proportional.*

Basic Theorems.—By means of these five assumptions we can prove the following six basic theorems:

1. Principle V is very powerful. Though stated in terms of similarity and proportion, it evidently includes the case of two congruent triangles with two sides and included angle respectively equal. It is apparent from the content of these five fundamental principles what terms we must define, or take as undefined.

VI. The Principle of Similarity (Part II).—*Two triangles are similar if two angles of one are equal to two angles of the other.*

VII. *If two sides of a triangle are equal, the angles opposite these sides are equal; and conversely.*

VIII. The Principle of Similarity (Part III).—*Two triangles are similar if their sides are respectively proportional.*

IX. *The sum of the three angles of a triangle is 180°.*

X. *Through a point on a line there exists one and only one perpendicular to the line.*[2]

XI. The Pythagorean Theorem.—*In any right triangle, the square of the hypotenuse is equal to the sum of the squares of the other two sides; and conversely.*

Corollaries.—As corollaries of XI we have the following:

XI*a*. *The altitude on the hypotenuse of a right triangle is the mean proportional between the segments of the hypotenuse.*

XI*b*. *If the hypotenuse and side of two right triangles are in proportion, the two triangles are similar.*

XI*c*. *The sum of two sides of a triangle is greater than the third side.*

XI*d*. *The shortest distance from a point to a line is measured along the perpendicular from the point to the line.*

XI*e*. *Of two oblique lines drawn from a point to a line, the more remote is the greater; and conversely.*

Treatment of Parallels.—The treatment of parallels can be derived from the principle of similarity. By means of this principle also we can show that any two perpendicular lines (coordinate axes), together with all the lines at right angles to them, form a rectangular network; and that all the lines perpendicular to an axis are parallel.[3] The concept "slope of a line with respect to a network" follows also from the principle of similarity and leads at once to the equation of the straight line.

Area of a Triangle.—The area of a triangle is a number, constant for the triangle and equal to k times the product of a side and the altitude upon it. We may assign any value we like to k; so we choose such a value as will

---

2. Theorem X should be taken for granted at the outset; for although it can be derived from the basic principles, most beginners would hardly care to question it. At the end of the course they can return to a consideration of the basic principles underlying their geometry and can prove this proposition which formerly they took for granted. This same procedure should be applied to one or two other theorems whose content seems obvious to the beginner. He should make a list of all the propositions he takes for granted and compare it at the end of the course with the minimum list on which the geometry is based.

3. See George D. Birkhoff, *The Origin, Nature, and Influence of Relativity* (New York: Macmillan Co., 1925), p. 36.

make the area of the unit square equal 1. This means that k must equal ½.

Advantage of Pythagorean Theorem.—It is a tremendous advantage to use the Pythagorean theorem from the very beginning, especially in connection with early propositions concerning the circle.

Possible Constructions.—It is interesting to see what constructions were possible for Euclid with only unmarked straight edge and compasses; but it is comforting also to have scale and protractor always at hand and to know that it is good form to use them.

Advantages of the New Approach.—Let us see how this program stands in comparison with the Euclidean and Riemannian programs, from the standpoint not only of mathematical importance but of pedagogical usefulness. In the first place, it is severely logical. In this respect it offers as satisfactory training as that of Euclid and is much more direct. It lends itself admirably to explicit consideration of the place of undefined terms, definitions, and assumptions in any chain of logical reasoning and leads to the development of those same habits, attitudes, and appreciations which all teachers of geometry claim for their subject. In the second place, it takes advantage of the knowledge of number and of linear and angular mensuration which the student possesses, and so does away with the feeling of artificiality which is inevitable when seemingly self-evident propositions are "proved." In the third place, it leads very naturally to the elementary facts of analytic geometry and makes it apparent in this way that geometry is really a self-consistent discipline whether or not such things as points, lines, and planes really exist.

Value of Study of Geometry.—It is true that some of our pupils seem to derive little or no profit from their study of geometry. Perhaps some teachers take comfort in the notion that their subject possesses a disciplinary something capable of "transfer" to situations outside geometry and forget that they must do their share to encourage the transfer. The text usually fails in the same respect and has other shortcomings, as we have been at pains to point out. But the remedy for these ills is not the present popular mode, complete abolition of the subject in question, or an almost equally dire emasculation. For although it is difficult to prove that the study of geometry necessarily leads in large measure to those habits, attitudes, and appreciations which its advocates so eagerly claim for it, it is even harder to prove that under proper conditions it cannot be made to yield these outcomes, and more readily than other subjects of instruction. Should we then abolish geometry from the secondary school, or should we try first to reform it?

It is often said that the Euclidean approach to elementary geometry was designed for thoroughgoing scholars and was not intended for the immature youth of today. That is of course true; but it should not be taken to mean that geometry is beyond the ken of pupils in secondary schools simply because it was not written with them in mind. Youngsters in the grades today grapple with arithmetic and algebraic intricacies, many of which were subjects of debate among adult Greeks of Euclid's time, and some of which it was reserved for adults of relatively recent times to discover. Later discoveries often shed light on earlier revelation and render easy what once was hard. That has been true of algebra and could be equally true of geometry if we but dared to take the step.

We have suggested a modification of Euclid in accord with psychological and mathematical ideas which, though commonplace to us today, were not available to Euclid. This modification would at once simplify the subject and give it greater significance.

In an age when the amount of material of scientific importance which the student ought to learn has become very large and the demands upon his time are numerous, it would seem that the possibilities of this new method of approach should be thoroughly investigated.

Psychological Considerations in the Learning and the Teaching of Arithmetic

BY WILLIAM A. BROWNELL
Duke University

Arithmetic is singularly unfortunate in the language which has come to be used to describe the processes by which its subject matter is to be learned and to be taught. One continually encounters such terms as "the number facts," "skills," "consumers' arithmetic," "incidental learning," "automatic associations," "fixed habits," "bonds," "100% accuracy," "crutches," "meaningful experiences," "drills," etc., etc. These terms have a significance which is seldom sufficiently recognized, for in one way or another they imply certain theories regarding the psychology and pedagogy of arithmetic. More important, perhaps, they lead directly to the adoption of instructional practices of varying degrees of merit.

Analysis of ambiguous and misleading terms would repay the time required. Since space limitations forbid, however, another method is employed to get before the reader some of the crucial psychological aspects of learning and teaching arithmetic. This method consists in examining critically the psychological bases of the three commonest theories with respect to arithmetic instruction. To this examination the remainder of this chapter is devoted. The reader should be warned that a theory of arithmetic instruction is rarely, if ever, practiced in pure form. The theory held to predominantly by a teacher will determine the points of emphasis in her teaching practice, but the practice itself will reveal the influence of other and perhaps conflicting theories. The three theories, as they are here isolated for analysis, are not so isolated in practice. While it is probable that a particular teacher can be classified as adhering in general to one theory, she will not be found to be a one-hundred-per-cent practitioner of that theory. Rather, she

Reprinted from *The Teaching of Arithmetic,* Tenth Yearbook of the National Council of Teachers of Mathematics (New York: Bureau of Publications, Teachers College, Columbia University, 1935), pp. 1–31.

tends, wittingly or unwittingly, to employ various features of two or even three of the theories. To examine the psychological foundation of the three theories, however, it is necessary to consider these theories separately—in purest state, as it were.

I. THE DRILL[1] THEORY OF ARITHMETIC

Exposition of the theory. The drill conception of arithmetic may be outlined as follows: Arithmetic consists of a vast host of unrelated facts and relatively independent skills. The pupil acquires the facts by repeating them over and over again until he is able to recall them immediately and correctly. He develops the skills by going through the processes in question until he can perform the required operations automatically and accurately. The teacher need give little time to instructing the pupil in the meaning of what he is learning: the ideas and skills involved are either so simple as to be obvious even to the beginner, or else they are so abstruse as to suggest the postponement of explanations until the child is older and is better able to grasp their meaning. The main points in the theory are: (1) arithmetic, for the purposes of learning and teaching, may be analyzed into a great many units or elements of knowledge and skill which are comparatively separate and unconnected; (2) the pupil is to master these almost innumerable elements whether he understands them or not; (3) the pupil is to learn these elements in the form in whic hhe will subsequently use them; and (4) the pupil will attain these ends most economically and most completely through formal repetition.

Example of drill organization. The nature of the drill theory and of the four component aspects of the theory which have just been outlined may be made clearer by means of an illustration. The following section occurs in a textbook for the third grade. It was intended apparently to supply the child all he would need in order to learn the new topic, "Written Subtraction with Carrying." Following the section quoted from this book is a page of problems, none of which is analyzed, designed to provide drill on the new process.

---

1. The term "drill" is loosely used in discussion relating to arithmetic instruction. Sometimes it is employed in a sense which makes it cover all forms of instruction. Sometimes it refers inly to practice and the maintenance exercises which follow initial instruction. And at still other times it signifies only maintenance activities. The reader should note carefully that in this chapter the term "drill" is used to characterize a theory of arithmetic instruction which makes repetition on the part of the pupil the essential feature of learning. In other chapters of the *Yearbook* the word "drill" will probably be used with a different signification.

1. Mary wants a doll that costs 42 cents. She has 28 cents. How much more does she need?

42	Think, "8 and 4 are 12." Write 4. Carry 1 to 2.
28	Think, "3 and 1 are 4." Write 1.
14	

Prove the answer by finding the sum of 14 and 28.
Think, "4 and 8 are 12." Carry 1 to 1.
Think, "2 and 2 are 4." 42 is the sum of 14 and 28.

When the number in any column is less than the one below it, think what added to the lower number will make a sum that ends in the number above, and carry 1.

It will be observed (1) that the process of carrying in subtraction has been isolated as one of the elements to be learned; (2) that meaning and understanding are neglected (with respect both to the problem as requiring subtraction and to the method of the process by which the subtraction is to be performed); (3) that the pupil is expected at once, without question, to take on a type of thinking characteristic of the expert adult who in meeting his practical need for subtraction performs the operation without thought of its underlying logic; and (4) that the pupil is to acquire the new skills by repetition—by working the examples and problems which follow without any assistance other than that provided by the mechanical model in the above quotation.

Popularity of the drill theory. Of the three conceptions of arithmetic instruction which will receive attention in this chapter the drill theory is by far the most popular. In the classroom its popularity is manifest in the common extreme reliance upon flash cards and other types of rapid drill exercises, in the widespread use of workbooks and other forms of unsupervised practice, and in the greater concern of the teacher with the pupil's speedy computation and correct answer than with the processes which lead to that computation and that answer.

But the popularity of the drill theory is by no means revealed only by the prevalence of certain practices in classroom instruction. On the contrary, its popularity is evident, as well, in the organization of arithmetic textbooks, in much of the research in arithmetic, in current practices in measuring achievement in arithmetic, and in treatises on the teaching of arithmetic.

The makers and publishers of arithmetic textbooks are prone to direct attention to the extraordinary care they have exercised with respect to drill provisions, as if the provision of adequate drill (that is, adequate according to certain criteria) were the crucial problem in the preparation of basic instructional matter. Research workers report laborious "evaluations" of textbooks in which, too frequently, differences in drill organization are divorced from differences in instructional theory which give significance to discovered variations in drill provisions. In commercial arithmetic tests and in treatises on educational measurement importance is given to set standards in terms of rate and of accuracy of computation, at the expense of growth in fundamental understanding, in orderly quantitative thinking, and the like. Last of all, few textbooks on methods of teaching arithmetic treat such matters as how children develop their number concepts or how they come to apprehend the rationale of the number system and the arithmetical processes it makes possible, preferring rather to deal with the selection of instructional items, the distribution of practice thereon, and the like.

Reason for popularity. The popularity of the drill theory is by no means to be understood as the result of a careful and intelligent judgment between the merits of the possible types of arithmetic instruction. More commonly the drill theory is adopted and practiced, one may conjecture, without any clear comprehension of its assumptions and implications. Wide acceptance of the theory seems to be due to two misleading approaches to a definition of arithmetic ability: (a) analysis of adults' uses of arithmetic and (b) the "bond" theory of learning.

(a) The theory draws support (or seems at first glance to draw support) from the adult's everyday use of arithmetic. Thus, in making a purchase of a loaf of bread for six cents and of five pounds of sugar for twenty-five cents, an adult seldom, if ever, hesitates in finding the total. Much less does he inquire into the reason why 6 and 25 are 31, or into the methods of the thinking by which he secures the sum. The arithmetic teacher, performing daily many such computations, is struck by the automatic, the instantaneous quality of her reactions. From this observation of her own conduct it is but a step to the conclusion that since she *uses* number so, so the child should *learn* it. She has quite forgotten her own trials in learning arithmetic. She probably does not even realize that she never did learn "25 and 6 are 31" as a number fact.

(b) Nor does the teacher who looks beyond her own present number experience find much assistance in the typical psychological treatments of arithmetic instruction. As a matter of fact, the drill theory of arithmetic has become popular largely because of the popularity of that system of psychology which has been most influential in education in the last two decades. According to this school of psychology *all* learning consists in the establishment of connections or bonds between specific stimuli and specific responses. This view of learning in general seems to be of particular value in describing the learning process in the case of number. Thus, one connects the response "6" with the stimuli "4 and 2," the response "9" with stimuli "3 × 3," and so on. Each arithmetic fact represents such a bond, and all skills likewise are reducible in last analysis to similar bonds. It seems to follow, therefore, that the way to teach arithmetic is to teach immediately and directly the bonds which are to be established. Drill then becomes the instructional method best adapted to this end, and repetition becomes the essential mode of learning.

In view of the prominent place given to repetition by the drill theory, the rest of this section is given over to a consideration of the rôle of repetition, first, in learning in general and, second, in arithmetical learning.

Repetition in learning in general. As contained in certain formulations and interpretations of the Law of Exercise, repetition was for many years regarded not only as a factor but as the important factor in promoting learning. To repeat a reaction was to learn it. To acquire a form of behavior, one had to repeat it. To the extent that one repeated, one learned. More recently, under pressure alike from critical theoretical discussion and from research findings, the Law of Exercise has been restated by many psychologists and has been entirely discarded by others. Now other factors than repetition have come to be viewed as the vital determinants of learning.

An example from ordinary experience will reveal the place and function of repetition in learning. Suppose Mr. B. undertakes to improve his "drive" in golf. He is observed to set up his ball, to grasp his club, to take a position with respect to ball and line of flight, and to swing. Suppose further that the result of the first swing is not very successful. Does Mr. B. "repeat" his first performance on his second try? Does he set up the ball exactly the same height, does he stand the same distance from the ball, does he place his hands precisely as he did the first time, and so on? Hardly: certainly not if he can help it. Instead of attempting to "repeat," he does his best to avoid repetition. He varies, changes, modifies—all with a view to securing a new combination of reactions which will produce more satisfactory results. Suppose, however, he does repeat his first unsuccessful performance. He stands, holds the club, and swings exactly as before. The result is the same poor shot, but made a little more proficiently. If he continues to repeat, he becomes steadily more expert in poor golf. If he would improve his game, he must cease repetition and adopt variation. The point of the illustration is that repetition can at most increase only the speed and the accuracy of a reaction, good or poor; it cannot furnish a new way, a better way, of doing anything.

Criticism of the drill theory in arithmetic. Three major objections may be raised to drill as the sole, or even the principal method of arithmetic instruction. The first objection is that the drill theory sets for the child a learning task the magnitude of which predetermines him to failure. The second objection is that drill does not generally produce in children the kinds of reaction it is supposed to produce. The third objection is that, even if under conditions of drill the proposed kinds of reaction were implanted, these reactions would constitute an inadequate basis for later arithmetical learning.

(a) *Magnitude of the task.* No one can define the limits of the learning task in arithmetic when that task is described in terms of the drill theory. Each item of knowledge or skill must, according to the theory, be isolated and specifically taught. The objectives of arithmetic set by this theory become utterly unattainable. Consider, as a case in point, the situation with regard to the number of addition combinations which must be taught. Years ago there were assumed to be 45 simple addition facts, the mastery of which, accompanied by an understanding of addition by endings, was regarded as sufficient preparation for all phases of this process. Later, research established the fact that children who knew $4 + 5 = 9$, for example, might not know $5 + 4 = 9$ equally well. The reverse combinations had, therefore, to be taught, and 36 new combinations were added to give a total of 81 facts. Investigation then demonstrated peculiar difficulties in the zero-combinations, and the addition combinations to be taught grew from 81 to 100 to accommodate the nineteen zero-facts. More recently it has been shown that the knowledge of $5 + 4 = 9$ does not guarantee the knowledge of $15 + 4 = 19$, $25 + 4 = 29$, or $45 + 4 = 49$, etc. To the 100 simple addition combinations there now have been added, at Osburn's[2] suggestion, the 225 combinations required by higher-decade addition with sums to 39 and the 87 combinations required for carrying in multiplication. The original 45 addition combinations have now become 412.

Similar analyses of other phases of arithmetic have resulted in item-totals equally staggering. Thus, Knight demonstrates the presence of 55 "unit skills" in the one process of division of common fractions, and Brueckner finds 53 "types" of examples (exclusive of "freak types") in the subtraction of common fractions alone. In problem-solving Judd reports, on the basis of an examination of only three sets of textbooks, approximately 1,900 different ways of expressing the fundamental operations in one-step verbal problems, and Monroe and Clark are able to differentiate 333 kinds of verbal problems (52 kinds of "operative problems" and 281 kinds of "activity problems") with which children must eventually be able to deal. These figures, large as they are, can be regarded only as typical of what would be found if the many other aspects of arithmetic were dissected as have been the relatively few reviewed above.

The statement that the drill theory in its extreme form sets an impossible

---

2. The reader will understand, of course, that the citation of these analyses does not classify their makers as exponents of the drill theory.

learning task for the child would seem to be justified by the results of the analyses mentioned above. If the child must learn separately and independently, through repetition, in the form in which he is later to use them, all these items of knowledge and skill (and tens of thousands as yet untabulated), what are his chances of success in arithmetic? Suppose the reader were faced by the necessity of mastering an equivalent number of unrelated meaningless items—not only to master them, but to remember them, to retain order among them, and to use them intelligently when and as they should be used. Assume such a condition—what chance of success would the reader have in this learning? Would he even be willing knowingly to undertake the task?

Now manifestly, no one actually carries the drill theory to the extremes suggested in the foregoing paragraphs. The teacher, with or without aid from textbook and manual, does supply something of a sensible basis for learning, and thereby breaks with the logical requirements of the drill theory.[3] Even the theoretical writer on arithmetic, who advocates repetition as the basis of arithmetic learning, is in the end forced to be inconsistent with his own view. Soon or late he must call to his assistance the factor in learning which his theory in effect denies. At the last he too recognizes the impossibility of training children in all the separate skills required in the total which he knows as arithmetical ability. In his dilemma the theorist finally finds himself invoking transfer of training to guarantee that children will be able to deal adequately with skills they have had no time to learn as such.

(b) *Reactions produced by drill.* When the teacher provides drill in arithmetical skills, she does so on the assumption that pupils will exactly practice certain prescribed reactions. Thus, for example, when she administers flash-card drill on such number combinations as $4 + 3 = 7, 8 - 6 = 2$, etc., she expects all pupils to think silently or to say aloud, "4 and 3 are 7," "8 less 6 are 2," and so on. It is her belief that by such repetition the children will come eventually to respond only and always "7," "2," etc., on presentation of the corresponding combination items. To express the idea differently, the administration of drill by the teacher presupposes repetition by the pupil. That this presupposition, this assumption, is not warranted by the facts is well shown by the results secured in a recent investigation.[4]

---

3. Here is, by the way, a good example of the distortion against which a warning was given on page 1. Such a discussion as this must exaggerate conditions in order to make clear important differences.

4. Chazal, Charlotte B., "The Effects of Premature Drill in Third-Grade Arithmetic." Unpublished A.M. thesis, Department of Education, Duke University, 1935. An abstract of the thesis under the same title is to appear shortly in the *Journal of Educational Research*.

About a week after the beginning of the school year fifty-seven third grade children were given a written test in the 100 simple addition combinations. They had been taught these combinations in Grades 1 and 2 by methods which agree closely with the drill theory of instruction.[5] On the basis of their showing on this group test thirty-two children were selected for individual study. Those chosen were ten who had the highest scores, thirteen who had average scores, and nine who had very poor scores. An interview was held privately with each child. In these interviews an attempt was made to discover how each child secured his sums, that is, how he thought of the numbers, what processes he employed. For the interview sixteen combinations were used. These sixteen consisted of the ten of greatest difficulty and the six of average difficulty on the group test. There were, therefore, a total of 512 responses in the interviews—the responses of each of the thirty-two children to sixteen combinations.

The interview revealed that 116 combinations (22.7% of the 512) were *counted*; that 72 (14.1%) were *solved indirectly* (e.g., "6 and 4 are 10 because 5 and 5 are 10"); that 122 (23.8%) were incorrectly *guessed;* and that only 202 (39.5%) were *known* as memorized associations. These facts can be interpreted only as meaning that the instructional procedure of drill had missed its mark in Grades 1 and 2. It had utterly failed to produce the 100% of "automatic responses" for which it was designed, and it had failed by the wide margin of 60%. After two years of drill these pupils counted and solved nearly as many combinations (36.7%) as they knew directly as combinations (39.5%). The evidence is that, expected to repeat the formulas, these pupils had not repeated at all. Unknown to the teacher who assumed they were repeating, they had trained themselves in other ways of thinking of combinations. Drills by the teacher had not resulted in repetition by the pupils.

The investigation did not stop here. In the month following the first group test and the first interview five minutes of the arithmetic period were each day set aside for drill on the addition combinations. The drill,

5. Specifically, the facts were taught as facts from the outset. Experience with concrete numbers was kept at a minimum. The facts were not developed for the child or discovered by him. They were given to him, that is to say, he was told that 3 + 4 are 7, and was then drilled on this fact along with similarly presented facts. The usual variety of drill activities was provided: there was repetition by the class as a whole, and repetition by individual children. There were oral drills and silent drills and written drills. Packs of cards were handled, the one side containing the combinations, the other side, to be consulted only if the sum was unknown, containing the answer. There were games to motivate drill, etc., etc. In all the activities, be it noted, the essential requirement on the part of the child was that of *repetition,* however much variation there may have been in the form of the response or in the number presentations which evoked that response.

which called for oral, silent, and written practice, was so organized that, on the average, each combination was presented at least twice a day. Then came the second administration of the group test on the 100 addition combinations and the second interview with the same thirty-two children on the same sixteen combinations. At this time 48.8% of the combinations, as compared with 39.5% on the first interview, were *known*, that is to say, were responded to as they are supposed to be responded to under drill conditions. On the other hand, *counting* and *indirect solution* still accounted for 37% of the answers (as compared with 36.7% on the first interview). The evidence from the second phase of the investigation agrees closely with that from the first phase: drill was provided by the teacher, but repetition was *not* provided by the children. Instead, the children continued throughout the month of drill to employ substantially the same procedures in thinking of the combinations as they had developed in Grades 1 and 2 and as they brought with them into Grade 3. If at the time of the first interview they counted their combinations they persisted in *counting* a month later, in spite of the daily drill which was designed to require repetition. If at the time of the first interview, they *solved* the combinations, they *solved* them a month later. Drill failed signally to produce in these children the desired types of mastery.

The study just described deals, it is true, with drill in connection with but a single phase of primary grade arithmetic. There is, however, no reason to doubt that the weakness here ascribed to repetition as a method of learning and to drill as a method of teaching holds with any less validity for more advanced phases of arithmetic.

(*c*) *Preparation through drill inadequate.* The third criticism of the drill theory arises from a consideration of the nature of arithmetic itself. Arithmetic is best viewed as a system of quantitative thinking. To describe arithmetic in this way is to set up a criterion by which to judge the adequacy of any system of arithmetic instruction. If tried by this criterion, the drill theory is found wanting: instruction through drill does not prepare children for quantitative thinking.

If one is to be successful in quantitative thinking one needs a fund of meanings, not a myriad of "automatic responses." If one is to adjust economically and satisfactorily to quantitative situations, one must be equipped to understand these situations and to react to them rationally. Specific responses to equally specific stimuli will not serve one's ends. It may be granted (in spite of the evidence to the contrary in the preceding section of this chapter) that drill may furnish to the child a number of fixed modes of response. Even so, its claim to preëminence as a method of instruction in arithmetic would have to be denied. Drill does not develop meanings. Repetition does not lead to understandings.

This limitation of drill may be illustrated by citing again the learning of the number combinations. Suppose that a pupil, through repeating the formula, has memorized "12" as the answer to "How many are 7 and 5?" Suppose, further, that in the absence of other types of experience than repetition, the pupil is asked, "What does it mean to say that 7 and 5 are 12?" His reply must be, "I don't know—just that 12 is the answer to 7 and 5." The meaning of "7 and 5 are 12" is for him restricted to merely making the appropriate noises and to reading and writing the symbols which stand for the combination.

The psychological fact is that meanings are dependent upon reactions. It is not too much to say that the meanings *are* the reactions. Meanings are therefore rich and full and useful to the degree to which the corresponding reactions have been numerous and varied. To repeat "7 and 5 are 12" is to practice but a *single* reaction. No matter how long continued or how frequent the repetition the effect is only to increase the efficiency (the rate and the accuracy) with which that reaction is made. Increased efficiency in making a small number of reactions is no substitute for rich meanings. If there are to be meanings and understandings (and there must be these if children are to be capable of quantitative thinking), there is but one way to engender them. That way is to lead children to react variously and often to the item of knowledge or skill which is to be acquired.

As stated above, drill and repetition are ill-adapted to the building of meanings. In them the pupil finds no suggestion of a variety of reactions, no help and no encouragement to discard primitive and clumsy ways of thinking (immature reactions) for steadily more refined and efficient thought processes (mature reactions). On occasion, drill may, it is true, be given credit for accomplishing just this end. Such seemed to be the case, for example, in the investigation referred to in the foregoing section.[6] The month of drill on the combinations which followed the first group test brought a reduction of approximately 35% in the amount of time required to write the sums for the 100 addition combinations and a reduction of 75% in the number of errors made. The interview data, however, contained the real explanation. Drill had not developed improved procedures: it had merely afforded opportunity for practice and increased efficiency with undesirable procedures. Under other circumstances, too, drill may be given undeserved credit for a different reason. Children may despair of ever mastering by repetition all the subject matter of arithmetic. In the end, quite without the knowledge of the teacher who continues to prescribe drill, they may desert the repetition of verbalisms in the effort to put order and sense into what they are learning. They may discover or adopt from others modes of response which actually do increase the number of ways in which they may

6. Chazal, *op. cit.*

react to the items to be learned. Under such conditions if arithmetic becomes meaningful, it is absurd to assign the credit to drill. It is much nearer the truth to say that if under these conditions arithmetic becomes meaningful, it becomes so in spite of drill.

II. THE INCIDENTAL LEARNING THEORY

Nature of the theory. At least partly as a reaction against the forcing and driving classroom tactics of teachers who are zealous advocates of the drill theory, a second theory, or group of theories, has become increasingly popular in the last fifteen years or more. According to these theories, which differ chiefly in detail, children will learn as much arithmetic as they need, and will learn it better, if they are not systematically taught arithmetic. The assumption is that children will themselves, through "natural" behavior in situations which are only in part arithmetical, develop adequate number concepts, achieve respectable skill in the fundamental operations, discover vital uses for the arithmetic they learn, and attain real proficiency in adjusting to quantitative situations. The learning is through incidental experience. The theory is accordingly here designated the "incidental learning theory."

Some who hold to the theory of incidental learning would postpone systematic arithmetic instruction until the third or fourth grade and would concern themselves not at all with the kind of number usages, if any, which children encounter before that time. Others differ from this position only in that they would postpone arithmetic instruction much longer (one investigator reports the omission of "formal" arithmetic through the seventh grade without "harmful" consequences in the eighth grade). And still others, distrusting somewhat the wholly hit-or-miss number contacts which would result from the first two variations of the theory, would select arithmetical activities for children, but would arrange them in such a way that the arithmetic is only a minor part of the total situations in which children might find themselves. Exponents of this last plan are those who prepare "integrated units" of activity, in which the different subject-matter fields, including arithmetic, of course, lose their identity.

Criticism of the theory.—Critical comment here must be confined to two points which are common to the different variants of the theory of incidental learning. The first of these points involves the place of interest in learning. The second involves the assumption that children will themselves isolate the arithmetical aspects in general situations and that through purely incidental number experiences will attain whatever arithmetic ends and outcomes are set for them.

(a) *Place of interest in learning arithmetic.* The theory of education through the process of incidental learning probably had its origin in the discussion attendant upon the emergence of the "child-centered school." Some years ago the more radical leaders in this reform movement did not hesitate to insist that all education must be derived from, and must be organized and directed with respect to, children's self-determined interests and needs. This extreme position, which is held less widely now than formerly, rested upon a faulty psychological basis. Interests and needs were supposed to arise spontaneously, as the product of some kind of inner compulsion which made their appearance more or less automatic at a predictable time. Viewed thus, interests are sacred; they are not to be altered, for alteration amounts to profanation. To disregard these natively fixed indices of growth, or, worse yet, to go against them, is to "violate the child's nature."

It is now rather generally recognized as a fact that children's interests are socially determined. The reason why children of a given age manifest certain interests is found, not in heredity, but in growth under conditions which are relatively alike for all children. Stated differently, children's interests and needs are but the products of experience. As such they reflect the useful, the valueless, and the harmful in that experience. Viewed thus, interests and needs lose much of their sacred quality. Modification and direction are no longer to be denied. On the contrary, they must be exercised if growth and development are to be sound and healthful.

The foregoing paragraphs may seem to dispose of a still debatable issue in a manner which is overly abrupt and summary. If so, this has been done only to clear the way for a more fundamental criticism of the place accorded interest by the incidental theory of arithmetic instruction.

Probably no one today doubts the virtues of interest as a factor which facilitates learning. On the contrary, all agree that children learn best when they want to learn. So far as effects on learning are concerned, the source of that interest, whether it be heredity or society, is of little consequence. Even the ardent practitioner of the drill theory seeks to have his pupils interested. (Witness his attempt to discover races, games, and other means for motivation.) Be that as it may, it is to the credit of those who have expounded the theory of incidental learning that the importance of interest in learning is now more generally recognized. These theorists have consistently and vigorously preached that pupils should want to learn what they are given to learn. And they have made real headway with their gospel.

Two objections may be entered, however, to the part assigned to interest by the incidental theory of teaching arithmetic. The first objection is that from the standpoint of learning arithmetic the pupil's interest is apt to be in the wrong place. When number is observed only as it functions in situations which are predominantly non-arithmetical, there is little likelihood of the child's being interested in number. That is to say, he is interested in the learning situation, but, for the purpose of arithmetic learning, he is interested in the unimportant part of it. He is primarily concerned with the successful completion of his unit of activity or of his project. If he is interested in the arithmetic at all, the interest is secondary and derived. He gives his attention to the arithmetic only because of the extrinsic motivation furnished by the situation. Under these conditions his interest in arithmetic as such is apt to be as superficial as is his interest when it is stimulated in drill through games and similar devices. The pupil learns as the adult learns—where his interest lies. His interest lies in the larger activity as such, and consequently he acquires, first of all, types of behavior which relate most closely to that activity. What interest is left over may or may not attach itself to arithmetic.

The second objection to the place of drill in the incidental theory is the implication that interest aroused in any way other than through large units of purposeful activity is somehow unworthy. There seems to be the notion that the desire to learn arithmetic for its own sake, that is, through intrinsic motivation, is somehow unnatural and something to be discouraged as being in some way undesirable. Admittedly, such an interest is hardly apt to appear under conditions of incidental learning, but this fact cannot be argued to mean that the interest is, on that account, unfortunate or any the less effective as a factor in learning. The contrary is the truth. It is a wholesome situation, if not a common one, for children to want to learn arithmetic because they like it. Under the stimulation of such a motive, moreover, it is highly probable that the learning will be economical and thorough. And, last of all, this happy state of affairs can be brought about through a direct instructional attack upon arithmetic as a subject for learning, fully as well, if not better, than by the indirect and uncertain experiences prescribed by the incidental theory.

(b) *The product of incidental experience.* When an individual reacts to some general situation in which there is a quantitative element, the form of his response to that quantitative element will depend upon many things. Chiefly, perhaps, it will depend (1) upon his preparation for reacting to such elements and (2) upon his disposition with regard to the element at that time. In the case of the educated adult, who has *learned* his arithmetic, the quantitative element may be readily isolated, correctly apprehended, and promptly dealt with. The adult is only momentarily distracted from his major objective, to which he returns at once upon solution of the quantitative problem. He has learned no new mathematical ideas or operations; he has merely applied previously acquired ability in a new connection.

The experience of the child as he engages in an assigned "integrated unit" or in his self-chosen and self-controlled activities may be quite different from that of the adult. If the general situation which he faces requires no *new* arithmetical skill or knowledge, his experience may be quite like that of the adult. Like the adult, too, he will apply to the situation only what he has already learned; he will learn nothing new in arithmetic from his experience. If, on the other hand, the situation involves some unknown arithmetical skill or knowledge his experience will be quite unlike that of the adult. The child's concern is with the attainment of some end beyond the intermediate arithmetical task. Too long delay in mastering the novel arithmetical skill is to him unthinkable—it may be ruinous to his plans. At best he gives to the arithmetical aspect of the situation only enough attention to remove it as an obstacle to the realization of his purpose. Furthermore, he deals with that quantitative element with whatever habitual response he may possess or with a response altered as little as may be.

It is at this point that the teacher who relies upon the incidental theory comes, curiously enough, very close to one of the fallacies of the drill theory which, as part of that theory, she would oppose. That is to say, she is very apt to make the error of assuming that mere contact with number teaches all that the child needs to know about number. She may easily overlook the fact that the quantitative aspects of general situations represent only possibilities for learning but not guarantees of learning. The child in the first three of four grades has few "natural" needs for arithmetic which he cannot meet by counting. Left to himself he will solve his problem by counting. Consider, for example, the following situation: the child is constructing a boat. He must fasten an irregularly shaped board to the side of the boat. He needs four nails for one end and three nails for the other end. To the adult the situation calls for the use of the fact "4 and 3 are 7." To the child the situation merely calls for "4, 5, 6, 7," or even "1, 2, 3, 4, 5, 6, 7." He does not see the situation as involving "4 + 3" at all. Counting is to him a wholly satisfactory method of dealing with the number need. So he counts, regardless of what his teacher thinks he should do.

Unquestionably, opportunities for arithmetical learning abound both in the practical affairs of children and in "integrated units," just as the supporters of the theory of incidental learning insist. If, however, these opportunities are to be utilized for the development of sound skill and knowledge, the new arithmetical elements must be abstracted from general situations and must become the objects of direct teaching. In this way provision can be made for supplementary experiences which, by introducing variety and number of reactions, guarantee the meaningful concepts and the intelligent skills requisite to real arithmetical ability.

There is a second way in which instruction based upon the incidental theory is likely to disregard the peculiar nature of arithmetic learning. To a far greater extent than is true in the case of any of the other school subjects (at least as these subjects are now known) arithmetic must be taught with due regard to its logic, its internal order and organization. By contrast, there seems to be no compelling reason why in history, for example, Topic A must be taught before Topic B. Justifiable violations even of chronological sequence are frequent, and events and personages may be omitted or treated in detail without serious consequences which are discernible. Similar illustrations could be drawn from geography and others of the content subjects. But in the case of arithmetic the number of changes which can safely be made are comparatively few. Integers must be taught before fractions, and the combinations must be taught before complicated operations which make use of them. This internal organization must be observed not merely with respect to the relatively fixed order of topics but also with respect to the sequence within the topics. Thus, within the process of addition the various skills and sub-skills must be arranged so that mastery of a late step is made possible by mastery of preliminary steps. This internal coherence and organization are determined on the one hand by the nature of the subject matter and on the other hand by the psychology of the learner.

It is just this organization which is difficult to maintain when the learning of arithmetic is left to the incidental experiences of children. This statement holds even when these experiences are prescribed in "integrated units."[7] When, however, there is no attempt thus to select number experience, the likelihood that children will learn in what is psychologically and logically the most economical fashion is extremely small. As a consequence, arithmetic can hardly be learned as it should be learned; relationships, dependencies, mathematical principles may easily escape the notice of the teacher, and so of the learner.

Impracticability of the theory. All that has been said in the above section helps to explain why arithmetic instruction based upon the incidental theory of learning is impracticable. Incidental learning, whether through "units" or through unrestricted experiences, is slow and time-consuming. Interest of teacher and pupil alike in the non-arithmetical aspects of general situations tends to reduce the occasions on which the arithmetical aspects are called to the learner's attention. Such arithmetic ability as may be developed in these circumstances is apt to be fragmentary, superficial, and mechanical.

However successful an occasional teacher may be in teaching arithmetic through incidental experience, general attainment of this success is not possible. The discriminating selection and orderly arrangement of vital and helpful learning situations involving number is no simple task. On the con-

---

7. This statement does not imply that number needs *appear* in the life of children with due respect to the order prescribed by mathematical logic. Such is not the case. The statement applies to *learning*. Even though a desirable mathematical sequence is disregarded in the time when number uses appear, that mathematical sequence must be, in large measure, honored in the instruction given in connection with these uses.

trary, it calls for unusual insight into the mathematical and psychological nature of arithmetic on the one hand and into the psychology of childhood and of the learning process on the other hand. In a word, it calls for a degree and kind of insight which is, without aspersion of teachers as individuals, quite outside the equipment of the average teacher. Until teachers are differently selected and differently trained, it is fruitless to expect them adequately to teach children arithmetic through incidental experience. In the meantime it is far safer to base arithmetic instruction upon a judicious use of textbooks in the preparation of which the kind of insight just described has been exercised.

Values of the theory. Like the drill theory of arithmetic instruction, the theory of incidental learning is not without certain advantages and merits which should be recognized and utilized to the full. These special values are at least three in number.

In the first place, the experiences of children in situations which are only incidentally arithmetical (whether in "units" or otherwise) may serve as powerful motives for the learning of new arithmetical ideas and processes by revealing the need for such abilities. In the second place, the opportunities for practice afforded in the general situations which children face both in and out of school may have the effect of increasing the meaning of number ideas and skills which have already been acquired and of maintaining them at a high level of efficiency. In the third place, perhaps the most important contribution of the theory of incidental learning has been to oppose the common practice of teaching arithmetic narrowly as an isolated subject. The incidentalists have rightly argued that arithmetic so taught cannot perform its full or, indeed, its most valuable function, for number is a real socializing agency.[8] Arithmetic provides an exact method of interpreting practical quantitative problems which otherwise are confused and unintelligible. On this account instruction in arithmetic must lead children to discover and to use the number they learn, not merely in order that they may know it better but in order that they may attain ends which are largely outside of arithmetic. It is at least an implication of the theory of incidental learning that children do not know arithmetic as they should until they are better able to prosecute their own designs and to understand the quantitative aspects of the society in which they live.[9]

---

8. That this view of arithmetic is by no means original with the advocates of incidental learning is clear from a perusal of the writings of Charles H. Judd who, as long ago as 1903 in his *Genetic Psychology for Teachers* (Chapter IX, especially) was expounding this wider interpretation of arithmetic.

9. In this chapter not much attention is given to the social phases of arithmetic. The brevity of this treatment does not imply any doubt as to their importance, which cannot be questioned. Fuller discussions will be found in the third and fourth articles, the presence of which in this *Yearbook* constitutes the reason for omission in this article.

III. THE "MEANING" THEORY OF ARITHMETIC INSTRUCTION

The third theory of arithmetic is not readily named. It can hardly be termed the "eclectic" theory because, while it does contain features of other theories, it also contains features which are peculiarly its own. Furthermore, this third theory is too coherent and unified to justify the implication of looseness and forced relationships which is associated with the word "eclectic." With this acknowledgment that no name would be without objectionable connotations, the third theory is here designated as the "meaning" theory. This name is selected for the reason that, more than any other, this theory makes meaning, the fact that children shall see sense in what they learn, the central issue in the arithmetic instruction.

Relation to other theories. Within the "meaning" theory the virtues of drill are frankly recognized. There is no hesitation to recommend drill when those virtues are the ones needed in instruction. Thus, drill is recommended when ideas and processes, already understood, are to be practiced to increase proficiency, to be fixed for retention, or to be rehabilitated after disuse. But within the "meaning" theory there is absolutely no place for the view of arithmetic as a heterogeneous mass of unrelated elements to be trained through repetition. The "meaning" theory conceives of arithmetic as a closely knit system of understandable ideas, principles, and processes. According to this theory, the test of learning is not mere mechanical facility in "figuring." The true test is an intelligent grasp upon number relations and the ability to deal with arithmetical situations with proper comprehension of their mathematical as well as their practical significance.

There is room, also, in the "meaning" theory for certain features of the theory of incidental learning. The "meaning" theory allows full recognition of the value of children's experiences as means of enriching number ideas, of motivating the learning of new arithmetical abilities, and especially of extending the application of number knowledge and skill beyond the confines of the textbook. But the efficacy of incidental learning for developing all the types of ability which should be developed in arithmetic is held to be highly doubtful by advocates of the "meaning" theory.[10]

Encouragement of understanding. It has been said that the "meaning" theory is designed especially to encourage the understanding of arithmetic. It does this in at least three ways.

(a) *Complexity of arithmetical learning.* First of all, it takes full account of the complexity of arithmetical learning. The significance of this

---

10. These statements should make it clear that the "meaning" theory is no compromise. It does not represent an attempt to harmonize differences in the drill and the incidental theories. The "meaning" theory is a separate theory, which stands or falls on its own merits or weaknesses.

statement may best be appreciated by contrasting various ways in which certain arithmetical ideas and skills may be taught. In the following paragraphs the "meaning" approach to number concepts and to the number combinations is presented in some detail.

Arithmetic, when viewed as a system of quantitative thinking, is probably the most complicated subject children face in the elementary school. Number is hard to understand because it is abstract. No special "arithmetic instinct" fits the child directly to learn arithmetic. Neither does nature provide the child with tangible evidence of number which he can apprehend immediately and thus come easily to know through sense perception. There is no concrete quality of "five-ness" in five dogs which may be seen, heard, and handled. Color, barking, weight, and shape may be grasped through the senses, but the "five-ness" is not thus open to immediate observation. Neither is there any "five-ness" in $\vdots$, or in "five," or in "5." In each case the "five-ness" is the creation of the observer; it is a concept or an idea which the observer imposes upon the objective data. Furthermore, it should be clear that the observer cannot impose the number idea "five" upon objects unless he has that idea—unless he has acquired the thought pattern which stands for "five." Such considerations as these with regard to the nature of arithmetic reveal the fact that from the very start, in the earliest as well as the later grades, number is complex.

One way of putting "five-ness," "seven-ness," "ten-ness," etc., into objective representations of number is to enumerate. The ability to count objects the school does develop, but it does little more than this by way of providing children with other, and more advanced, ways of thinking of concrete numbers. Too commonly instruction in counting is immediately followed by drill on the addition and subtraction combinations.

This approach to primary number almost totally neglects the element of meaning and the complexity of the first stages in arithmetical learning. It even disregards the evidence provided by children themselves that they do not understand what they are learning and that they are in trouble. When children know a combination one day and do not know it the next, there is something wrong in the learning. So is there something wrong when, told that their sums and remainders are wrong, children complacently make other errors. Likewise, there is evidence of difficulty and of faulty learning when children's written responses reveal such situations as this $\begin{array}{r} 3 \\ +\,2 \\ \hline \end{array}$ $\vdots$, and when their oral responses are delayed while resort is made to counting and to other undesirable procedures. According to the "meaning" theory these evidences of difficulty must not go unheeded.

The truth is that training in counting alone is insufficient to develop number ideas. Assume that the child has correctly counted five given objects. What has he found out? Perhaps very little indeed. It is true that he has employed the sequence of number names accurately in a one-to-one correspondence with the objects, but the "five" he announces at the end may mean merely that he has run out of objects and that consequently he has no more verbal responses to make. There is no quantitative significance in such counting; the child might as well be saying, "a, b, c, d, e," as "1, 2, 3, 4, 5." Or the child may mean by the "five," not the group but the last object, the fifth one. Or again, if he means by "five" to indicate a total, that total is constituted only of discrete ones; "five" is thus one, and one more, and one more, and one more, and one more. The "five" in such a case stands for no *group,* for no *unit,* for no single pattern in his thinking. It is but a conglomeration, a loose organization, of ones. Before this child is ready to deal understandingly with situations involving grouping, he must learn to see numbers as groups.

Accordingly, the "meaning" theory interposes a definite period of instruction between counting and the number combinations. The purpose of this period of instruction is to provide for the child activities and experiences which will carry him by easy stages from enumeration to meaningful ideas of numbers as groups. The child begins with concrete number—with objects which he can see and handle. He makes groups of objects, compares groups of objects, estimates the total in given groups of objects, learns to recognize at a glance the number of objects in small groups and in larger groups when the latter are in regular patterns.[11] Eventually he comes to think of concrete numbers in terms which are essentially abstract. At the conclusion of this period of learning, "5" is as much a unit in his thought processes as is "1." The "5" does not need to be broken down into five 1's. It is a meaningful concept and is available for use as such in new relationships. Equipped with this and other like number concepts, the child is ready for the number combinations.

If the number combinations were "number *facts*" as they are frequently said to be, children would encounter little difficulty in learning them. They can easily learn "two dogs and three dogs are five dogs," for this is a fact. But "2 and 3 are 5" is not a fact; it is a generalization. If it were a fact, children could, as drill advocates desire them to do, memorize it as they would a fact in history. Since, however, it is a generalization, the learning is much more arduous and much more time-consuming. One learns the number combinations as he learns other generalizations, not all at once by some stroke of will or mind, but slowly, by abstracting likenesses and differences in many situations, by reacting to the number aspects of situations

---

11. For an example of the kind of primary number instruction which is here described in general terms, see: Deans, Edwina, "The Effect of the Meaning Method of Instruction on the Teaching of Second-Grade Number." Unpublished A.M. thesis, Department of Education, Duke University, 1934.

in steadily more mature ways.

As stated in the criticism of the incidental theory, the presence of three objects and of five other objects in the same situation does not automatically suggest to the child " 3 + 5 = 8." If the child is to think of the "3" and the "5" in the form of an abstract combination, he must be taught to see it so. It does little good to tell him that 3 and 5 are 8. He will have to be told the same thing again the next time the situation, or one like it, occurs, or else he will memorize the statement. Memorization at this time should by all means be prevented. Instead of telling the child "3 + 5 = 8" and of urging him to memorize it, the teacher should lead the child to *discover* it. Furthermore, one discovery is not enough. He must discover it many times and in connection with many situations. At the beginning he will need to make the discovery with concrete materials. Eventually he will rediscover the same relation in abstract numbers. Too, his method of discovering the fact will change. He may have to count at first. This type of reaction should not be forbidden if it is necessary to the child, for it may be his only means of relating the numbers. As fast as may be, however, he should be helped to eliminate counting in favor of some more mature method of dealing with the numbers. Thus, he may see that 3 and 5 are 8 because the objects may be repatterned as 4 + 4, or as 2 + 6, or what not. Finally, he should come (and under skillful teaching he will come) to the point where he reaches the generalization, 3 + 5 = 8. Now is the time for him to memorize the fact, if, indeed, he needs to memorize it. It is far more likely that his numerous and varying experiences with these number relations will have been enough to fix the fact for him without memorization. Drill will, however, be of service in increasing facility of recall and in assuring permanence to the learned fact.

(*b*) *Pace of instruction.* In the second place, understanding of arithmetic is encouraged, in the "meaning" theory, through adapting the pace of instruction to the difficulty of the learning. At first when the new ideas and processes are unfamiliar the pace is kept slow. Time is allowed for meanings to develop before children are expected to employ the given item of knowledge or skill as a highly habituated reaction. To some extent this feature (adaptation of instructional pace to learning difficulty) has been illustrated in the case of the simple number combinations. It may be further illustrated by considering instruction in the case of the addition combinations with sums above 10.

The common practice in teaching 7 + 5 = 12, for example, is to provide the child with a single picture of two groups of objects, seven and five in number. He is then asked how many objects there are in all. Not being given any way of securing the total, he probably counts the parts. He is then informed that his answer "twelve" is correct, and the fact is written for him as $\begin{array}{r} 7 \\ +\,5 \\ \hline 12 \end{array}$ or as $7 + 5 = 12$. He then proceeds to "learn" it, that is, to repeat it, until it has taken its place among the dozens of similarly memorized items.

The "meaning" theory outlines quite a different kind and pace of instruction. The child's difficulty in attempting finally to habituate the combination is recognized as due to causes which relate to the initial stages of learning. Accordingly, the rate of instruction at first is kept slow. Activities and experiences containing the new fact $7 + 5 = 12$ are multiplied. Furthermore, the child is not left at the primitive level of counting as his only means of understanding the relationship. Instead, he is soon shown how to complete the first number (7) to 10 by taking from the second number (5), and thus to translate the new fact into a familiar one ($10 + 2 = 12$). He first discovers the identity of $7 + 5$ and $10 + 2$ by using concrete objects. He rediscovers them with other concrete objects and later with pictures, with semi-concrete objects (such as pencil marks), and with easily imagined objects in described situations. Ultimately he comes to a confident knowledge of $7 + 5 = 12$, a knowledge full of meaning because of its frequent verification. By this time, the difficult stages of learning will long since have been passed, and habituation occurs rapidly and easily.

It is impossible to illustrate at such length all the implications of the "meaning" theory for relating instructional pace to learning difficulty. It will be possible here only to refer to one type of change in practice which has possibilities not yet fully appreciated. This change is to "spread" instruction in various arithmetic topics over a wider span of the grades than is now the custom. Material progress along this line has been made in recent years, but much more can be done. To illustrate, many of the characteristics of common fractions are well within the intellectual grasp of primary grade children and are properly taught in these grades. Others of the easier learned aspects of fractions may well be "teased out" and taught through Grades 2 and 4, and the most difficult ones, when located, could be left for Grade 6, and even 7. There would seem to be little justification for the common instructional organization which concentrates so much of teaching of fractions into a single grade. The proposed changes would utilize the earlier years for a slow, painstaking development of the basic meanings of fractions. The child would thus be prepared to understand better the systematic treatment of fractions assigned to Grade 5 and the more difficult features of the topic reserved for Grades 6 and 7.

Experience in the attempt to make arithmetic meaningful to children may some day demonstrate the wisdom of "spreading" in a similar manner instruction on other topics. Thus, some of the simplest multiplications and division combinations may well be learned in Grades 1 and 2, and the most difficult of these combinations (with 8 and 9 as multiplier and divisor) may be postponed to Grade 4. The division of integers by a digit may be introduced through the long division form, which would be employed in Grade 4 to teach as many as possible of the difficult features of the process; two-digit divisors could then be withheld until Grade 5, and some of the most difficult (and most unusual) types of division, until Grade 6. Decimals, denominate numbers and measurement, and even per cent and ratio might readily be made more intelligible and significant by adapting instructional pace to learning rate through "spreading" the teaching of these topics. Not the least of the advantages of these changes is that "spreading" would help to remove a large part of the burden of uninspired "maintenance drill" which now seems to have made itself an integral part of arithmetic instruction.

(c) *Emphasis upon relationships.*[12] The third way in which arithmetic instruction according to the "meaning" theory helps to make number sensible is by emphasizing relationships within the subject. Five illustrations are all that can be offered at this point.

According to the drill theory "6 and 5 are 11" should not be taught in close temporal proximity to "7 and 4 are 11," for fear that children will use the one to solve the other instead of establishing independent bonds for the two. According to the "meaning" theory, children's recognition of the relation between the two statements not only is not harmful—it is a distinct gain. In fact, it could even be insisted that unless the relationships were understood neither fact would be adequately learned. After all, the number system *is* a system, a fact which for some curious reason is withheld from children when they study arithmetic. As a system it contains relationships and connections which, if mastered, should enable children to make progress much more readily in their learning.

It has been said that the number system is a system. Our number system is a decimal system; its unit is 10. That is to say, our system is organized around 10.[13] A second way, then, in which the "meaning" theory would emphasize relationships is to make much more use of the unit 10

12. Let the reader not be disturbed by what may seem to be the resurrection of a well-laid ghost. It is true that nearly a half-century ago (following Grube) the attempt to systematize arithmetic instruction came to grief and was abandoned in favor of what has become, in some instances, almost an absence of logical organization. The "meaning" theory is no revival of the Grube ideas. If the emphasis here given to meanings, understandings, and rationalizations seems to bear a close resemblance to discarded practices, a closer scrutiny will reveal the resemblance to be less real than fancied. The mere fact that failure attended one plan of teaching which, though it did aim at understanding, was nevertheless psychologically and socially unsound, is slight reason to disapprove all other such instructional plans.

13. For a valuable and stimulating discussion of certain ones of the points made in this section see: Wheat, Harry C., *The Psychology of the Elementary School*, Silver Burdett Co., 1931, pp. 135-142, or, better yet, all of Chapter IV.

than is common—for example, in teaching children the meaning of numbers above 10, in teaching them to read and write such numbers, and in teaching them the addition and subtraction combinations with sums and minuends of 11–18. The principle of adding and subtracting by endings and the procedure in higher-decade addition and subtraction would be far more intelligible to children if developed in terms of the basic unit 10. The unit 10 also could be employed not merely to explain "carrying" in addition and in subtraction but also to introduce some of the earlier types of multiplication and division. Decimal fractions, their notation, and operations with decimals should be much more easily understood if familiarity has been acquired with 10 as the unit in whole numbers.

A third illustration of the way in which the "meaning" theory emphasizes relationships is found in connection with the topics, common fractions, decimal fractions, and per cent. As these topics are now taught, they commonly impress the child as three essentially unlike mathematical forms, which can, by certain mechanical methods, be changed back and forth as required by the textbook. Actually these mathematics forms are but three different ways of expressing the same ideas. It may be inferred that they will be better understood if their relationships rather than their differences are stressed in teaching.

A fourth place in which the "meaning" theory requires attention to relationships is in the matter of the mathematical operations themselves—addition, subtraction, multiplication, and division. Each of these processes stands for a special type of relationship: in addition, that of "putting together"; in subtraction, that of "taking away"; etc. That children do not understand the meaning of the relationships thus contained in these operations is only too frequently demonstrated in problem-solving. Children and when they should subtract, multiply when they should add, and so on. There is little reason why they should not be expected to make these errors. What is done in instruction to forestall the errors? A child learns "2 'n 3 're 5" and is supposed to understand that he has added. He learns "8 take away 2 're 6" and is supposed to know that he has subtracted. The nature of the operation is hardly indicated by these verbal statements. Even if it were, the use would be associated only with the signs "add," "$+$," "sum," etc.; understanding would not be complete enough to set off the appropriate activity in verbal problems in which, in place of a few specific symbols, hundreds of language forms are employed to express it. If the operations are to be understood properly, the mathematical relationships for which the operations stand must be definitely taught.

The fifth illustration of relationships which would be stressed in instruction according to the "meaning" theory is that of the forms used in arithmetic—the column in addition and subtraction, the placement of partial products in multiplication, the method of writing the quotient figures in division with respect to the figures in the dividend, and so on. These forms are frequently taught as tools, only the mechanics of which need to be known; and yet each one of these forms contains its own logic which adapts it perfectly to its function. This purpose can be taught to children. If children understand it, they will have acquired another valuable relationship, namely, the relationship of form of expression to the thought to be expressed. The need of keeping numbers in their proper order place (1's at the right, 10's next, etc.) is usually demonstrated in the case of column addition, too often, however, with the hope merely of securing thereby a greater number of correct answers. The form used in multiplication can likewise be explained. Consider the series of teaching steps given on the following page.

Example: $\begin{array}{r} 42 \\ \times\ 2 \\ \hline \end{array}$

(1) $42 = 4$ tens, 2 ones (2) $\begin{array}{r} 2 \\ \times\ 2 \\ \hline 4 \end{array}$ (3) $\begin{array}{r} 4 \text{ tens} \\ \times\ 2 \\ \hline 8 \text{ tens} \end{array}$ *or* $\begin{array}{r} 40 \\ \times\ 2 \\ \hline 80 \end{array}$

(4) answer $=$ (5) $\begin{array}{r} 42 \\ \times\ 2 \\ \hline 4 \\ 80 \\ \hline 84 \end{array}$ (6) $\begin{array}{r} 42 \\ \times\ 2 \\ \hline 4 \\ 8 \\ \hline 84 \end{array}$ (7) $\begin{array}{r} 42 \\ \times\ 2 \\ \hline 84 \end{array}$
   $80 \times 4 = 84$

Steps (1) to (4) offer no difficulty to the child, for he has long since learned the ideas and procedures involved. They are included in the presentation, however, because they review the multiplication of 10's and of 1's and, more important, they yield the answer of the new example *before* the new form is to be taught. Steps (5), (6), and (7) simply translate the known operations and answers into the new form, which then takes on the meaning which is associated with steps (1) to (4). Thereafter, the form is not a senseless device—it is an intelligible instrument for expressing a relation.

Development of quantitative thinking. According to the "meaning" theory the ultimate purpose of arithmetic instruction is the development of the ability to *think* in quantitative situations. The word "think" is used advisedly: the ability merely to perform certain operations mechanically and automatically is not enough. Children must be able to analyze real or described quantitative situations, to isolate and to treat adequately the arithmetical elements therein, and to make whatever adjustments are required by their solutions. When the purpose of arithmetic instruction is defined in the above terms, true arithmetical learning is seen to be a matter of growth which needs to be carefully checked, controlled, and guided at every stage. It cannot safely be presumed that children can themselves find and follow the most advantageous course of development. On the contrary, the responsibility for sound and economical growth rests squarely upon the teacher.

In meeting this responsibility the teacher is unwise who measures progress purely in terms of the rate and accuracy with which the child secures his answers. These are measures of efficiency alone, not of growth. It is possible for the child to furnish correct answers quickly, but to do so by undesirable processes. The true measure of status and of development is therefore to be found in the level of the thought process employed. If the teacher is to check, control, and direct growth, she must do so in terms of the child's methods of thinking. If the child tends to rest content with a type of process which is low in the scale of meaning, she will lead him to discover and adopt more mature processes. If she asks him to "explain" an exercise written on the blackboard or on his paper, she will not be satisfied merely to have him read what he has written; she will insist upon an interpretation and upon a defense of his solution. She will make the question, "Why did you do that?" her commonest one in the arithmetic period. Exposed repeatedly to this searching question, the child will come soon to appreciate arithmetic as a mode of precise thinking which derives its rules from the principles of the number system.

Possible criticism of the "meaning" theory. Those who subscribe to the "meaning" theory must expect criticism. The objections of the exponents of the drill theory and of the theory of incidental learning may be easily imagined. But there is another type of criticism which comes from a different quarter. To some writers in the field of arithmetic the "meaning" theory is but an attempt to restore dignity to the discredited faculty psychology and to revive the dead issue of formal discipline. These writers insist that the term "quantitative thinking" is but a vague if lovely phrase —gibberish—which, if it makes sense at all, is misleading in these practical days when teachers need to think concretely and specifically about arithmetic instruction.

There are two answers to this criticism. The first is to show that "quantitative thinking" is not pure fiction, but an actuality commonly within the experience of those who understand number—even of those who maintain that there is no such thing as "quantitative thinking." The lecturer who has strayed somewhat from his prepared remarks happens to draw out his watch. His response comes almost immediately: "Here! Here! I must hurry." An artificial analysis of his behavior would reveal the following reactions to have taken place: telling the time, noting the amount of time left in the hour, estimating the ratio of elapsed to available time, determining the amount of the lecture already given, the same for the amount yet to be given, computing the ratio between the two, comparing the two ratios, and arriving at a judgment. Only, of course, the lecturer experiences nothing whatsoever of this sort. The numerous complicated computations isolated above never take place at all—certainly the lecturer is unaware of any such operations. Instead of making this analysis and this series of separate computations, the lecturer engages in a bit of instantaneous "quantitative thinking," and his adjustment following upon the thinking is as real and as adaptive as any other activity in his life. His behavior is inexplicable except as the result of a highly organized system of thought processes. It resembles the operation of a group of mechanical units only in that the individual does not *seem* to be actively the director of the behavior, as certainly he is, however. His behavior is purposive and extraordinarily intelligent. It would be impossible to an individual who had not developed the most mature types of quantitative thought processes. To say that the lecturer engaged in a skillful bit of "quantitative thinking" is, then, merely to *describe* his behavior—it is not to *explain* it; least of all is it to ascribe that behavior to the operation of some obscure "faculty." Mental organization does not imply "faculties."

The criticism of the "meaning" theory as requiring impossible mental feats and nonexistent mental faculties is, in the second place, founded upon an inadequate conception of the learning process and of transfer of training in particular. To set as the end of arithmetic instruction the development of the ability to think precisely in quantitative situations is not to call upon magic; it is simply to insist that the greatest possible advantage be taken of the capacity of mind to generalize. It is incorrect to say (though the statement is still frequently enough made) that experimental research has disproved the fact of transfer of experience. Research has done nothing of the kind. It has, however, demonstrated that if transfer is desired from one learning situation to another, then the training must be such as to assure transfer. No one who writes about "quantitative thinking" assumes that transfer is to be assured in any way except through arithmetic instruction designed to secure it. The nature of this instruction has already been described in the foregoing pages.

IV. CONCLUDING STATEMENT

The record of arithmetic in the school is an unenviable one. The position taken in this chapter is that the fault lies in the type of instruction generally given. Arithmetic instruction has for a number of years inclined much too far in the direction of the drill theory of teaching. The trend now seems to be in the direction of the incidental theory of instruction. While this change in instructional theory represents distinct improvement, it does not, for reasons given in the foregoing pages, promise the kind and amount of reform needed. An attempt has been made in this chapter[14] to outline a general shift in instructional emphasis and an altered view of the nature and purpose of arithmetical learning which may bring about the desired consequences. The basic tenet in the proposed instructional reorganization is to make arithmetic less a challenge to the pupil's memory and more a challenge to his intelligence.

14. Most of the illustrations of, and arguments for, the "meaning" theory have been drawn from the field of primary number. This fact should not, however, be interpreted to mean that the theory holds only for the first three grades. On the contrary, meaning affords the soundest foundation for arithmetical learning throughout the elementary school. Primary numbers has been most often cited for another reason. Almost everyone agrees that children in Grades 5, 6, 7, and 8 have to be able to "think" in arithmetic. That ability to "think" in these grades is conditioned by "thinking" in the primary grades is a fact which is much less commonly recognized. No one has shown how it is possible for children suddenly to become intelligent in upper-grade arithmetic when they have been allowed no exercise of intelligence in lower-grade arithmetic. In spite of the unreasonableness of such an expectation, primary number is taught as if skills acquired mechanically would later surely take on meaning, and verbalizations memorized unintelligently would later inevitably become well-rounded concepts. It is the thesis of the "meaning" theory that children must from the start see arithmetic as an intelligible system if they are ever to be intelligent in arithmetic. Hence, in this chapter, the implications of the "meaning" theory for the primary number have been especially stressed.

PART FOUR: 1938–1959
Prewar and Postwar Reforms

The depression of the 1930s had a substantial impact on the secondary school mathematics program. Because of the lack of employment more students stayed in school; at the same time, fewer students enrolled in college. Since mathematics was an elective subject, enrollments in traditional courses decreased. A new, hybrid general mathematics course developed which is difficult to define and more difficult to justify. This kind of course is still with us. Mathematics was in disfavor.

The Progressive Education Association (PEA) reacted to the situation with the publication of *Mathematics in General Education* in 1938. This report concentrated on developing a mathematics curriculum to meet the needs of students and to develop personal characteristics essential to democratic living. The report pointed to generalized problem solving as a crucial need in a democracy. The emphasis on meeting needs and social requirements led to an emphasis on incidental teaching—that is, mathematical material was to be taught only if a need for it arose in a nonmathematical situation. In the 1930s much experimentation tested the feasibility of this approach.

One educator who endeavored to relate social goals to other goals of the arithmetic curriculum was Leo J. Brueckner. He also led in applying child development psychology to arithmetic in attempting to determine optimum developmental levels for learning arithmetic concepts. The general effect of these efforts was to postpone many topics and teach them to students at a later age than formerly. Brueckner's analysis is included in this section, as is Carleton Washburne's report of the recommendations for grade placement of topics made by the influential Committee of Seven of the Northern Illinois Conference of Supervision.

The Joint Commission report of 1940, *The Place of Mathematics in Secondary Education,* tried to reduce the unpopularity of mathematics by stressing the goals of mathematics and the role of individual differences among students. Mathematics was advocated as useful because it developed clear thinking, because formulas were needed in modern society, and because mathematics was a necessary part of one's cultural background.

The advent of World War II immediately after publication of the 1938 PEA and 1940 Joint Commission reports curtailed the influence these statements might have had. The need to defend mathematics instruction vanished with the need for trained manpower. This technical need also defeated the argument of felt social needs. The war and the concomitant development of industrial and scientific technology created a need for the mathematical reform that is still evolving. World War II was probably a greater stimulus for reform than the launching of Sputnik in 1957.

Toward the end of the war the board of directors of the National Council of Teachers of Mathematics appointed a commission on postwar plans. The commission's second report (1945) essentially eliminated incidental teaching. It stressed functional competence for all, suggesting a track program and abandonment of mathematics as a tool subject. This report was more in keeping with the "1923 Report" than with the reports of the late 1930s. Significantly, its chairman was Raleigh Schorling, a member of the committee responsible for the "1923 Report." The report of the Commission on Post-War Plans started a surge toward reform in secondary education.

Following the war, the need for skilled, college-trained manpower and the changing complexion of pure mathematics research made the college preparatory program of the high school not only inadequate but also out of touch with mathematics itself. These deficiencies led in 1951 to the establishment of the University of Illinois Committee on School Mathematics (UICSM), the first major reform group to incorporate modern views into its experimental materials. Its history as an innovating group is well known. The selection included here is an early report of the work and philosophy of the UICSM program.

Differing committee reports and the disparagement of college entrance examinations led to formation in 1955 of the Commission on Mathematics of the College Entrance Examination Board (CEEB). Its report, *Program for College Preparatory Mathematics,* issued in 1959, was the last major national commisson report to suggest a specfic curriculum for secondary schools. This report has had a major impact on teacher training. Textbooks and the curricula of secondary schools have been revised nationally in an attempt to present a point of view similar to that of the CEEB *Program.* The resulting emphasis on college-bound students left unreformed the mathematics for other tracks in the secondary school. Only recently have significant attempts been made to correct the "general mathematics" malaise.

MATHEMATICS
IN GENERAL EDUCATION

A REPORT OF THE COMMITTEE ON
THE FUNCTION OF MATHEMATICS IN
GENERAL EDUCATION

for the

COMMISSION ON SECONDARY SCHOOL CURRICULUM

D. APPLETON–CENTURY COMPANY
INCORPORATED

NEW YORK   LONDON

Albert A. Bennett, *Professor of Mathematics, Brown University.*

Cuthbert Daniel, *Editorial Consultant, Radio Research Project, Princeton University.*

Harold Fawcett, *Associate Director and Teacher of Mathematics, Ohio State University School.*

Maurice L. Hartung, *Assistant Professor of the Teaching of Mathematics, University of Chicago.*

Robert J. Havighurst, *Director for General Education, General Education Board.*

Joseph Jablonower, *Member Board of Examiners, New York City, and formerly Head of the Department of Mathematics, Fieldston School.*

Ruth Kotinsky, *Secretary of the Commission on Secondary School Curriculum, Progressive Education Association.*

V. T. Thayer, *Chairman of the Commission on Secondary School Curriculum, Progressive Education Association, and Educational Director of the Ethical Culture Schools.*

[Members of the Committee on the Function of Mathematics in General Education were listed as shown above.]

CONTENTS

PAGE v

PART I
THE TEACHING OF MATHEMATICS IN RELATION TO GENERAL EDUCATION

CHAPTER

I. INTRODUCTION 3
  Reasons for a Reëxamination of the Aims and Content of Mathematics Instruction 3
  The Persistence of Disciplinary, Practical, and Cultural Aims: An Historical Sketch 5
  Changing Social and Economic Conditions Affecting Secondary Education 6
  New Psychological Theories Affecting the Educational Values of Mathematics 8
  A Loss of Confidence in the Report 9
  A Brief Description of the Report 12
  To Whom This Report Is Addressed 14

II. MATHEMATICS IN RELATION TO THE PURPOSES OF GENERAL EDUCATION 16
  Needs as the Basis of Educational Planning . . 17
  The Concept of Educational Needs 20
  Classification of Educational Needs 21
    Personal Living 22
    Immediate Personal-Social Relationships . . 22
    Social-Civic Relationships 22
    Economic Relationship as the Basis of Educational 24
  The Major Ideals of Democracy as the Basis of Educational Values 27
    Optimum Development of Personality . . . 28
    Reciprocal Individual and Group Responsibility for Promoting Common Intelligence . . . 29
    The Free Play of Intelligence Essential to Democratic Living 31
    Personal Characteristics ix

CHAPTER   PAGE

    Social Sensitivity 32
    Esthetic Appreciation 33
    Tolerance 35
    Coöperativeness 36
    Self-Direction 36
    Creativeness 37
    The Disposition and Ability to Use Reflective Thinking in the Analysis and Solution of Problem Situations 39
  Summary Formulation of the Purpose of General Education 42
  The Role of Mathematics in Achieving the Purpose of General Education 43
    The Role of Mathematics in Meeting the Needs of Students 44
    The Role of Mathematics in Developing Personal Characteristics Essential to Democratic Living 48
    Social Sensitivity 48
    Esthetic Appreciation 49
    Tolerance, Coöperativeness, Self-Direction, and Creativeness 50
    The Disposition and Ability to Use Reflective Thinking in the Solution of Problems . . . 52

PART II
MAJOR UNDERSTANDINGS GROWING OUT OF MATHEMATICAL EXPERIENCE

III. INTRODUCTION TO PART II: SOME CONCEPTS BASIC TO PROBLEM-SOLVING, CRUCIAL IN DEMOCRACY, AND PERVASIVE IN MATHEMATICS 59
  The Relation of These Concepts to the Problem-Solving Process 59
  The Relation of These Concepts to Democracy . . 63
  The Relation of These Concepts to the Development of an Understanding of Mathematics as a Unified Field 69
  The Relation of These Concepts to the Organization of the Curriculum 71

IV. FORMULATION AND SOLUTION 75
  Focusing Students' Attention on the Process and Nature of Formulation 77
    Restricting and Idealizing the Problem . . . 77
    The Statement of the Problem: The Choice of Helpful Concepts 82
    Explicitness and Clarity of the Premises . . 82

CHAPTER   PAGE

  The Relation of the Formulation to the Possibility of Solution 83
  Focusing Students' Attention on the Nature of Acceptable Solutions 84
    Types of Solutions and the Possibility of Solution 84
    Criteria for the Acceptability of Solutions . . 87

V. DATA 90
  Building Students' Understanding of the Nature of Data 90
    Characteristics 91
    The Variety of Acceptable Data 91
  Focusing Students' Attention on the Processes of Collecting and Recording Data 92
    The Question of Accessibility 95
    The Choice of Accessibility 96
    The Use of Units 96
    The Choice of Measuring and Recording Devices 97
  Focusing Students' Attention on the Processes of Organizing Data 100
    The Construction and Use of Tables . . . 101
    The Construction and Use of Graphs . . . 102

VI. APPROXIMATION 103
  Building Students' Understanding of the Nature of Approximation in Measurement and Computation 109
    Approximations Originating in Measurement . . 112
  Building Students' Understanding in Mathematical Theory 115
    Measures of Central Tendency 115
    Measures of Dispersion 119
    Approximate Relations Among Associated Variables 121

VII. FUNCTION 122
  Developing Students' Understanding of the Functions of one Variable 127
    Fundamental Notation 130
    Common Types of Mathematical Functions . . 139
  Developing Students' Understanding Related to the Function Concept 141
    Independent Variables 141
  Developing Students' Understanding of Functions of Several 148
    Function Concept 159
    Generality as to Arguments 161
    Propositional Functions 162
    Relations 163

CHAPTER PAGE

VIII. OPERATIONS
Building Students' Understanding of Concepts Basic to Operations . 168
Concepts Basic to Counting and the Fundamental Operations . 170
Concepts Basic to Comparisons: Difference, Ratio, Proportionality . 170
Helping Students Develop the Necessary Skills and Techniques . 177
A Point of View on Drill . 180
A Point of View on Correctness in Computation . 181

IX. PROOF . 181
Developing Students' Understanding of the Nature of Proof in the Broad Sense . 183
Cases in Which Proof of Any Kind Is Unnecessary, Impossible, or Premature . 187
Inductive Proof . 190
Developing Students' Understanding of the Nature of Proof in the Narrower Sense . 191
The If-Then Principle . 192
The Interplay of Deduction . 195
Logical Deduction, Truth, and Fact . 203
Four Stages of Abstraction with Regard to Definitions and Assumptions . 204

X. SYMBOLISM . 205
Improving Students' Understanding of Symbols Through Study of Mathematical Usage . 214
Mathematical Usage and Comparison with Non-Mathematical Usage . 216
Some Uses of Symbols in Mathematics . 217
Distinctions Between M and NM Uses of Symbols . 225
The Social Origins of Symbols . 232
Some Broader Aspects of Symbolism . 234

PART III

THE DEVELOPMENT AND NATURE OF MATHEMATICS

XI. THE DEVELOPMENT AND NATURE OF MATHEMATICS . 241
Understandings Related to the Development of Mathematics . 241
Mathematics as a Direct Response to the Spirit and Needs of the Times . 242

CHAPTER PAGE

The Insufficiency of the Needs and Spirit of the Times as an Explanation of All Mathematical Development . 245
Understandings Related to the Development of Mathematics as a Science . 248
The Cumulative Character of Mathematical Development . 248
Some Non-Cumulative Aspects of Mathematical Development . 254
Light Thrown on the Nature of Mathematics by Certain Aspects of Its Development . 256
Approaches to the Development of These Understandings . 258
Some Connections in Which Historical Materials May Be Introduced . 258
Adaptation to the Maturity of Students . 261
Adaptation to the Special Interests of Individual Students . 262

PART IV

UNDERSTANDING THE STUDENT AND EVALUATING HIS GROWTH

XII. UNDERSTANDING THE STUDENT . 269
The Adolescent as the Teacher Observes Him . 273
The Adolescent as the Teacher Understands Him . 275
The Strains and Conflicts of Adolescence . 275
Typical Adolescent Behavior in Response to Strain . 280
The Influence of Early Experience in the Family . 286
The Study of Personality . 292
The Developmental Approach . 292
An Illustrative Case: Paul . 293
Introduction . 293
Identifying Data: Family and School . 294
As the School Sees Paul . 295
As the Parents See Paul . 303
As Paul Sees Himself . 305
Reconstructing Paul's Social and Intellectual Development . 305
The Rôle of Mathematics in Paul's Personality . 314
The Significance of the Individual Case . 324
The Implications for Teaching . 325

XIII. THE EVALUATION OF STUDENT ACHIEVEMENT . 329
General Characteristics and Methods of Evaluation . 338
Some Characteristics of a Satisfactory Evaluation Program . 340
Major Steps in the Process of Evaluation . 345

CHAPTER PAGE

Sample Evaluation Techniques . 354
The Ability to Recognize Quantitative Factors in Problem Situations . 355
Understanding of Some of the Qualities of Good Data . 357
Understanding of Data in Tabular Form . 357
The Proper Use of Approximate Numbers . 359
Choosing a Form of Graphical Representation and Drawing a Graph . 360
The Interpretation of Data . 366
The Ability to Apply Several Rather General Principles of Variation . 368
The Nature of Proof . 372
Evaluation of Qualities of Personality Other than Reflective Thinking . 375
Sample Interpretations Based on a Single Test . 375
Interpretations Based on Several Tests . 378

APPENDICES

I. A SOURCE UNIT ON NORMAL VARIABILITY . 385
II. ILLUSTRATIVE SHORT ACTIVITIES . 403

INDEX . 413

I

Introduction

The purposes of this Introduction are, first, to explain the factors that have led to a reconsideration of the aims and content of mathematical instruction and, second, to provide a descriptive survey of the Report as a whole.

REASONS FOR A REEXAMINATION OF THE AIMS AND CONTENT OF MATHEMATICS INSTRUCTION

Attention is usually focused on the modification or fundamental reconstruction of education when school practices and procedures, appropriate to the past, are carried into a period of changed social conditions and revised theories of learning. This introductory discussion makes clear that the reconsideration of mathematics instruction represented in this Report was undertaken because of precisely such a situation.

The Persistence of Disciplinary, Practical, and Cultural Aims: An Historical Sketch

Until very recent times, mathematics instruction was accepted almost without question by most educators as an essential part of a secondary education. This was reflected both in college-entrance requirements and in state legislation. A Massachusetts law[1] of 1827, for instance, required the teaching of algebra, geometry, and surveying in every high school in towns of 500 families or more. Similar legislation was passed in other states and remained in force for decades.

One of the reasons for the compulsory inclusion of mathematics in the curriculum during this period was the disciplinary effect it was presumed to have upon the adolescent mind. When called upon to defend mathematics beyond this, educators cited, on the one hand, its traditional standing as an element of a cultural education, and, on the other, its usefulness in the practical affairs of life. Since 1890 mathematical education has been subjected to repeated scrutiny both by individual reformers and by committees representing various national organizations. Yet these three conceptions of the

---

1. *An Act of the Commonwealth of Massachusetts, A.D., 1827, To Provide for the Instruction of Youth* (Boston, Christian Register Office, 1828), pp. 1-2.

purpose and value of the study of mathematics—disciplinary, utilitarian, and cultural—continue to influence practice and content to the present day.

The first comprehensive survey of the program and purpose of secondary education in the United States, made by the Committee of Ten[2] in 1893, assumed that mathematics has a general disciplinary value. This assumption freed the Committee from the necessity of examining critically the traditional content of courses or considering the degree to which this content might be helpful to young people in solving their problems. Its recommendations[3] for the mathematics curriculum dealt primarily with the placement of traditional subject-matter. The Committee suggested, for example, that some algebra and what is now called intuitional geometry should be taught much earlier than had been previously customary.

As an outgrowth of the work of the Committee of Ten, the College Entrance Examination Board[4] was established and began to function in 1900. The requirements set by this Board (and by its counterparts in regional accrediting agencies) have continued to exert a profound influence on the content of courses of study, and have reflected, in modified though clearly recognizable form, the faith in the disciplinary aim that characterized the nineteenth century.

The first stimulating criticism of mathematical work being done at the secondary-school level came from influential teachers of mathematics. At the turn of the century Felix Klein in Germany,[5] John Perry in England,[6] and E. H. Moore in the United States[7] suggested certain changes in methods and in the organization of materials. The proposed changes were designed to make the subject function more effectively in the thinking of students.

2. The official title of this Committee was "The Committee on Secondary School Studies of the National Education Association."

3. *Report of the Committee of Ten on Secondary School Studies* (New York, Published for the National Education Association by the American Book Co., 1894), pp. 104–116.

4. The report of the Committee of Ten led in 1895 to the appointment of the joint Committee of the Secondary Department and the Department of Higher Education of the National Education Association. This Committee evolved into the Committee on College Entrance Requirements, which, after four years of work with associations of teachers in secondary schools and colleges, formulated plans for the College Entrance Examination Board.

5. Felix Klein, *Elementary Mathematics from an Advanced Standpoint,* translated from the 3rd German ed. by E. H. Hedrick and C. A. Noble (New York, The Macmillan Co., 1932), *passim.*

6. John Perry, Editor, *Discussion on the Teaching of Mathematics,* British Association Meeting, Glasgow (New York, The Macmillan Co., 1901).

7. Eliakim Hastings Moore, "On the Foundations of Mathematics," *Bulletin* of the American Mathematical Society, Vol. 9, May, 1903, pp. 402–424; reprinted in *A General Survey of Progress in the Last Twenty-five Years, The First Yearbook* of the National Council of Teachers of Mathematics, 1926, pp. 32–57.

The recommendations of these men are noteworthy in that they made little mention of disciplinary aims and brought practical aims to the fore. The organization they proposed foreshadowed what is now sometimes called an integrated course. The integration, however, was to take place upon the basis of the logical interconnections among a number of subjects, rather than primarily with reference to students' needs and interests. Essentially similar goals and the "fusion" of various divisions of elementary mathematics—for example, algebra and trigonometry—were also recommended in 1914 by T. Percy Nunn,[8] a leader in mathematical education in England.

In recent years, the Report of the National Committee on Mathematical Requirements of the Mathematical Association of America,[9] published in 1923, has been widely recognized as authoritative. Accepting the customary classification of aims into practical or utilitarian, disciplinary, and cultural, the Committee gave a more satisfactory statement of them than had previously been available. The influence of this report on point of view and practice of teachers can hardly be overestimated. Authors of mathematics texts have almost invariably claimed that their books conform with its recommendations. Teachers in training have studied it as they have studied no other pronouncement in the field, and writers on methods of teaching continue to devote many of their pages to a discussion of its views.

This historical sketch indicates that successive recommendations in regard to the aims, content, and method of mathematics instruction have not deviated significantly from traditional doctrine. Thus the question is raised as to whether or not purposes and procedures characteristic of the past have not been carried into the present without sufficiently fundamental reconstruction. In order to answer this question it is necessary to consider certain changes in the social structure and in psychological theory as these affect secondary education.

Changing Social and Economic Conditions Affecting Secondary Education

The economic readjustments and social changes of recent years call for a reconsideration of the aims and purposes of secondary education as a whole. Changing social and economic conditions have, in the first place, brought about a gradual postponement of gainful occupation until now most young people of secondary-school age are virtually excluded from employment. This situation has resulted in part from a general reduction in economic opportunity for all, and in part from the fact that modern business and industry employ relatively fewer youthful workers than formerly. Re-

8. T. Percy Nunn, *The Teaching of Algebra (Including Trigonometry)* (New York, Longmans, Green and Co., 1914), pp. 16–21.

9. *The Reorganization of Mathematics in Secondary Education,* A Report by the National Committee on Mathematical Requirements under the Auspices of The Mathematical Association of America, Inc., 1923.

duction in employment opportunities for youth has contributed to an unprecedented increase in secondary-school enrolments, and has set certain new problems in the education of adolescents.

Whereas in 1900 only 11.4 per cent of the appropriate age group were enrolled in the secondary schools, 64 per cent were enrolled in 1934. This change in size of enrolments entailed changes in the characteristics of the secondary-school population. The student body now includes a far wider range of academic ability and of types of interests, talents, and life goals than ever before. Furthermore, a generation ago almost all high-school students came seeking preparation either for skilled jobs or for college—which, it was assumed, would eventually lead to professional employment. The schools served them by helping them meet college-entrance requirements or by equipping them with requisite vocational skills. With the growing limitations on individual economic opportunity and the increasing recognition of the unethical quality of mere "getting ahead" as an ideal, preparation solely for successful vocational performance is seriously to be questioned. Instead, adolescents must be helped to profit from a prolonged period of nonparticipation in the world's work by learning to manage the problems with which the conditions of their lives now confront them—much as younger children profit from childhood by living fully and richly on their own level.

Economic and social changes are bringing about profound changes in the adolescent's immediate social relationships in the family and in other face-to-face groups. They are making his effective participation in wider social and economic life more and more difficult. And they call for a new system of values by which he may endow his personal life with worth. Problems in these areas perplex all adolescents, and it is in these areas that social readjustment is now necessary.

Thus social and economic changes have given rise to the necessity that aims and methods of secondary education designed to equip a fairly homogeneous and relatively restricted group for individual success be reconstructed so as to equip all adolescents for creative participation in a wider social life. But there is an additional way in which these changes are giving a new turn to educational planning. A period of profound economic readjustment and uncertainty has been followed by mounting threats to the democratic way of life. Adolescents not only need help in reformulating their personal, social, and economic relationships in response to the new conditions that influence them; it is increasingly recognized that they must also be helped to do this in ways which harmonize with democratic ideals and conserve democratic values.

New Psychological Theories Affecting Secondary Education

Though many teachers continue to justify the study of mathematics in terms of its disciplinary values, methods of instruction have been based more generally upon the theory of specific-habit responses than upon the training of supposed "faculties of the mind." But just as the specific-habit theory of learning superseded faculty psychology, more recent theories are now superseding habit formation as the key to learning.

Evidence is accumulating to the effect that the individual responds as a whole to whole situations which confront him, and is to some degree re-made as a person in the course of his experience. This means that in planning educational experience for students, the school must take into account the whole personality, emotional as well as intellectual—what it is now, how it changes, and what it would best become. Furthermore, it means that such factors as teacher, classmates, method, and school atmosphere constitute a part of the learning situation; they influence what the student learns—how he changes as a person. Methods themselves must be such that the student deals with whole situations rather than practices upon specific skills.

When education overlooks the importance of the wholeness of the personality of the learner and the wholeness to which he responds, any specific habit learned in school may fail to function when it is called for in out-of-school situations, or when it does function, may be put to questionable uses. The ability to compute a percentage, for example, may fail to come into play when it would facilitate making a personal budget, or it may be used to mislead the public in a newspaper article.

The inadequacy and inappropriateness of preëstablished specific habits are emphasized by the unprecedented complexity and novelty of the problems which a scientific age and its social and economic consequences have brought in their wake. The newer conception of the individual and the way he learns is particularly important from a social point of view: it gives hope of personalities capable of dealing constructively with ever new environmental conditions—changing them in desirable directions, and being changed themselves in the process.

A Loss of Confidence in the Educational Values of Mathematics

Changes in mathematics instruction have not kept pace with the changing interests and concerns of the student body or with emerging conceptions of the proper aims and purposes of secondary education. The teacher has been made increasingly aware of the inappropriateness of traditional courses by the indifference of many students to the subject, or their outspoken dislike for it. He has also been disturbed by criticism of the mathematics curriculum voiced by specialists in education, many of whom are known to understand mathematics and to prize it for what it has meant to them.

Loss of confidence in the educational values of mathematics is strikingly evidenced by a decrease in the per cent of the total high-school population enrolled in mathematics courses. The great increase in the total number of enrolled students has partially concealed this fact, since the schools are filled and many teachers are overwhelmed with large classes. The situation is made clear, however, by the following table showing the total registrations in the secondary schools of ten states across the country for 1928 and 1934, and the per cents of these students who were registered during the same years in certain mathematics courses.

THE NUMBER OF STUDENTS IN SECONDARY SCHOOLS AND THE PER CENT REGISTERED
IN CERTAIN MATHEMATICS COURSES FOR TEN REPRESENTATIVE STATES* IN
1928 AND 1934

Region	Years	Total No. of Pupils in Secondary Schools (to nearest thousand)	% Registered in General Mathematics	% Registered in Elementary Algebra	% Registered in Plane Geometry
United States	1928	2,897,000	5.4	27	18
	1934	5,402,000	2.4	19	12
1. Massachusetts ...	1928	119,000	4.8	19	15
	1934	246,000	4.1	13	9
2. New York	1928	363,000	1.1	26	18
	1934	531,000	1.8	12	8
3. Ohio	1928	177.000	5.8	26	14
	1934	412,000	3.1	18	10
4. Illinois	1928	194,000	3.3	29	20
	1934	340,000	0.6	24	18
5. Tennessee	1928	31.000	6.0	34	20
	1934	62,000	0.9	29	16
6. Wisconsin	1928	77,000	3.4	28	19
	1934	149,000	0.6	20	17
7. Missouri	1928	82,000	4.9	27	18
	1934	112,000	1.7	23	15
8. Oklahoma	1928	50,000	5.8	29	22
	1934	106,000	1.3	24	18
9. Colorado	1928	33,000	3.0	28	20
	1934	59,000	1.8	18	12
10. California	1928	190,000	3.6	21	14
	1934	347,000	3.1	12	9

* See Carl A. Jessen, "Registrations in Mathematics," *School Life*, Vol. 22, No. 7, pp. 211-212.

In each of the states listed the per cent of the school population registered in both elementary algebra and plane geometry was less in 1934 than it was in 1928. The situation in the State of New York, where about 10 per cent of the high-school students of the country were enrolled in 1934, deserves special attention. Not only did the per cent of students registered in mathematics decrease, but the actual number of them thus registered also declined.[10] Yet during this short period the total school population in New York State increased about 46 per cent. These data reveal in quantitative terms a situation which many mathematics teachers have sensed but have not fully realized.

Some of the underlying causes for a decline in the per cent of students enrolled in mathematics courses have already been suggested. As the total number of failures in these courses mounted owing to changes in the interests and capacities of the growing student body, educational administrators, many of whom had small confidence in mathematics as taught, sought to meet the situation by making these courses elective. Under the new conditions many students availed themselves of the privilege of omitting mathematics from their programs, and their course advisers acquiesced, seeing no reason to urge them to study the subject except for the sake of meeting college entrance requirements. Eventually colleges were pressed to admit students who had not taken these courses. As more and more colleges have yielded, even this compulsion upon secondary-school students to elect algebra and geometry is losing its force. As a result, the education of a large portion of the high-school population involves no more than incidental experience with mathematics.

Yet mathematicians and teachers of mathematics are convinced of the value of their field in the education of youth. The Committee shares the conviction that, divested of much of its conventional content and formal organization, mathematics as a mode of thought and an instrument of analysis has an indispensable function in general education. It has much to contribute in meeting the needs of students—both as these are felt by students themselves and as they are defined by educators. This Report therefore attempts to present an acceptable statement of the aims and purposes of general education under modern conditions, to interpret the function of mathematics in serving these purposes, and to suggest appropriate content and method.

A BRIEF DESCRIPTION OF THE REPORT

Part I of this Report outlines the basic educational philosophy that has guided the thinking of the Committee and includes a discussion of the rôle

---

10. In 1928 New York State had about 96,000 students studying elementary algebra and about 64,000 studying plane geometry; in 1934 the figures were 65,000 and 43,000 respectively. This is a decrease of about one-third in each case.

of the teacher of mathematics in the achievement of the aims of general education.

Part II is devoted to a discussion of certain broad concepts and related abilities that are involved in problem-solving: Formulation and Solution, Data, Approximation, Function, Operation, Proof, and Symbolism. The discussion of these concepts centers on the special contribution the mathematics teacher can make in their development.

Part III consists of a chapter on helping students appreciate the development and nature of mathematics.

Part IV contains two chapters that are intended to help the teacher clarify his views concerning, first, the student as a human being whose development is influenced by a variety of potent factors, including his family, social background, friends, and the school; and second, the problem of evaluating the growth of the student toward the objectives of general education.

An Appendix contains an illustrative "source unit" and some activities that should help the teacher in the effort to apply the general principles discussed in the other parts of the Report.

This outline indicates that the Report discusses mathematics teaching within the context of general education. By definition, general education is not primarily concerned with preparation for specific vocations or for college. It is not specialized or restricted to any particular group. It emphasizes meeting the educational needs of each student, and the group with which it is concerned is the secondary-school population as a whole.

In such a program the curriculum for a given school or group must, in the last analysis, be determined in the light of the needs of the particular individuals who make up the group to be taught. Since students differ widely as to their needs, capacities, and interests, it would not be consistent with the purpose of this Report to outline a detailed course of study to be followed by all, or even to propose a number of alternative courses. Furthermore, teachers also differ in their capacities and interests, and in general do more effective work under conditions that allow them some freedom in planning their own programs. For these reasons, instead of recommending a single more or less formal course of study, the report outlines a set of fundamental concepts and guiding principles designed to serve as a basis upon which teachers may so organize their own work as to make it appropriate to the possibilities and limitations of individual schools, or classes, or, ideally, individual students.

In seeking to meet the needs of the large group who constitute the bulk of the school population, the more specialized needs of certain students must not be neglected. Some of the concepts and skills mentioned in this Report should doubtless be developed only with those secondary-school students who show special aptitude, or whose definite vocational interest calls for more mathematics than may reasonably be given to all. Prospective engineers and scientists fall into these classes. The range of topics discussed thus becomes large in order to make possible the selection necessary to care for the wide range of needs, abilities, and interests to be served.

In formulating the outlines of a program through which mathematical education may advance during the next few years, the Committee had of necessity to be idealistic. To make the proposed program effective and to supply innumerable details of possible content and organization will require experimentation, both extensive and intensive, over a period of years.[11] In the light of such experimentation certain suggestions of this Report will almost certainly need to be modified or even rejected. But without making such recommendations the Committee could hardly hope to outline a forward-looking program, and without such a program mathematics for general education is not likely to become consonant with the needs of times.

TO WHOM THE REPORT IS ADDRESSED

This report is addressed primarily to the growing group of well-trained teachers who are dissatisfied with the mathematics curriculum in their schools and are seeking a basis for a fundamental reconstruction consistent with modern educational theory. Convinced that the curriculum should be reorganized, some of them are already moving forward along lines proposed here. It is hoped that in this discussion they will find helpful suggestions and from it gain greater confidence when they discover ideas of their own coinciding with those which have survived the gauntlet of Committee deliberation.

It is hoped that the Report will be helpful to administrators and curriculum experts who are interested in bringing about changes in the curriculum and are seeking clues as to the proper rôle of mathematics in the program of secondary education.

The Report is also addressed to teachers in training and those who guide them. Although the literature appropriate to courses on the teaching of mathematics is becoming extensive, much of it is devoted to special methods of teaching particular topics. By focusing attention upon broader aspects of teaching mathematics, the discussion in this volume is intended

---

11. It is with respect to this point that the task undertaken by this Committee differed from that of the Joint Commission of the Mathematical Association of America and the National Council of Teachers of Mathematics. In preparing its report on *The Place of Mathematics in Secondary Education,* the Joint Commission, after discussing the general aims of education, sought to outline a program of the sort being offered at the moment by some schools in advance of the great majority. Most of its suggestions have been tested to some extent in practice, and the Joint Commission took a practical rather than experimental point of view.

to help future teachers see such details in proper perspective.

Parts of the Report will be of interest to all teachers of mathematics at the secondary level. Those who, for one reason or another, find it impossible to embark upon the major reorganization recommended may nevertheless become acquainted with the point of view and find certain suggestions they can put into effect. Every effort of this sort, if successful, will in the long run serve to promote the purpose of the Committee—to help teachers of mathematics better meet the needs of boys and girls.

II

Mathematics in Relation to the Purpose of General Education

[Only the summary portions of Chapter II have been selected. These portions adequately cover the content of the chapter.]

SUMMARY FORMULATION OF THE PURPOSE OF GENERAL EDUCATION

A brief statement of the purpose of general education may now be formulated. General education is designed to help the individual meet his needs in ways that are consistent with and promote social welfare. A fourfold classification of the basic aspects of living facilitates the identification of these needs and of the experiences through which they may be met. In this process education should strive to achieve the values of the democratic way of life and to develop related desirable qualities of personality. The purpose of general education may, then, be summarized as follows:

THE PURPOSE OF GENERAL EDUCATION IS TO PROVIDE RICH AND SIGNIFICANT EXPERIENCES IN THE MAJOR ASPECTS OF LIVING, SO DIRECTED AS TO PROMOTE THE FULLEST POSSIBLE REALIZATION OF PERSONAL POTENTIALITIES, AND THE MOST EFFECTIVE PARTICIPATION IN A DEMOCRATIC SOCIETY.

THE RÔLE OF MATHEMATICS IN ACHIEVING THE PURPOSE OF GENERAL EDUCATION

The teacher of mathematics can make certain indispensable and distinctive contributions to the attainment of the broad purposes of general education. He can also make certain contributions that are similar in nature to those made by teachers in other fields. This section seeks to define both of these types of contribution in the large, and so to foreshadow detailed discussion of the special resources of mathematics in subsequent chapters.

Any field of study deserves a place in the curriculum only insofar as it has a unique rôle to play in meeting the educational needs of students. Although teachers in all departments of the school share the major purposes of education and can unite in discussing their common objectives and common difficulties, the teacher who by taste and training is especially well equipped along some one line may be expected to have his own particular contribution to make.

But in investigating the rôle of a particular field of study it is necessary to examine the tracery of its interconnections with other fields. In the past this necessity has escaped the attention of many, largely because of their continuing faith in pure discipline. As a result, the resources peculiar to each field have seldom been properly focused upon attaining common aims, and students have neither recognized the mutually reënforcing rôles of the concepts, methods, and techniques of the various areas of human knowledge nor have they profited from this reenforcement in meeting their needs.

Furthermore, the experience of the student in the school has all too seldom been designed as experience in democratic living. The teacher of each subject, preoccupied with imparting his own particular knowledges and skills, has failed to devise classroom methods with this larger aim in view. The development of desirable characteristics of personality has been largely left to chance through lack both of insight on the part of teachers in the different fields and of coöperative planning and action on the part of the staff as a whole.

The generality of the educational aims formulated in the first part of this chapter makes further discussion necessary in order to clarify the common and differential provinces of the various areas of instruction. The present discussion therefore attempts to make explicit the interconnections of mathematics with other fields in meeting the educational needs of students and developing personalities capable of creative participation in the democratic way of life.

The Rôle of Mathematics in Meeting the Needs of Students

Adolescents encounter certain problems[16] as they strive to meet their needs in the basic aspects of living. The "wise selection and use of goods," a need in the area of economic relationships, for example, may find a specific instance in the problem of purchasing a new suit of clothes. The function of the school is obviously not to select and buy the suit for the student. But school experience should enable him to make his own selection more wisely —not only in this instance but in others. Helping him to solve this problem is one way of helping him to meet his needs.

But the wise selection of any article involves a number of considerations. What style is appropriate for the individual and the occasions on which he intends to wear the suit? What are the wearing qualities of various fabrics? What determines their relative warmth or coolness? What factors are to be weighed in deciding how much to pay for a suit? Should one buy only union-made clothes?

16. "Problem" is here to be interpreted not as an exercise of the traditional sort assigned for solution in mathematics classes, but as a difficulty appreciated by the student and awakening in him a desire for its solution.

These questions illustrate the fact that a need cannot be adequately met without the coöperation of teachers of home economics, art, natural and social science, as well as teachers of mathematics. On the one hand, some essential consideration in the wise selection of goods would be lacking without the pooling of their separate and distinct points of view, sensitivities, techniques, methods, concepts, and backgrounds of knowledge. And on the other hand, all fields of human study and knowledge rely upon reflective thinking, and all teachers should be concerned with improving the student's ability in problem-solving, as well as in developing other desirable characteristics of the personality. Only by coöperative work and planning can they reënforce one another's efforts to these ends.

The rôle of the mathematics teacher in this process is analogous to that of any other teacher. Just as the art teacher may be concerned with the problem of taste, and the teacher of natural science brings his specialized knowledges and techniques to bear in analyzing and solving some particular aspects of a problem, the mathematics teacher makes his special contribution whenever quantitative data and relationships or the facts and relationships of space and form are encountered. The highly effective special symbolism and methods of mathematics have been developed in order to treat just such aspects of experience, and the actual problems of living involve them to an extent that should not be underestimated. The teacher of mathematics bears the responsibility of equipping students to solve such problems with the aid of mathematical concepts and methods as they seek to meet their needs throughout life. In this process he also has the responsibility of throwing light on the nature of problem-solving.

The mathematics teacher also has a rôle to play in meeting certain needs that do not involve problems of quantitative and spatial relationships. Like other teachers, he is the representative in the school of a special field of human activity of inestimable social significance to all. For some persons in the world outside the school—engineers, scientists, actuaries, statisticians—mathematical activities are a means of livelihood, and to some they are a source of intense personal satisfaction. Adolescents need to feel the social bearings and import of their activities as students, and the teacher of mathematics may acquaint them with persons, groups, and institutions using mathematics in furthering the advance of human knowledge or in solving community and social problems. In this same process he helps them meet their need to understand the vocational reference of their school interests. And he may help them to estimate the value of mathematics as a personal interest on a basis sounder than either its promise of pecuniary rewards or the public esteem in which it is held. In meeting needs of this kind the teacher of mathematics uses his field precisely as the teacher of art, or English, or science, or any other field uses his, but it is his own special field, and he alone is fully sensitive to its personal and social values.

The importance of mathematics in contemporary culture raises the question of the extent to which students in general should be urged to study advanced mathematics. The professional mathematician not engaged in research at a university, or in teaching, has not many lines of occupation open to him. But some writers, enthusiastic over the value of mathematical information and discipline, would seek to show that practically every worth-while activity calls for advanced training in mathematics either directly or indirectly. Nor is supposedly expert evidence lacking. For example, a jurist perhaps attributes most of his critical acumen to early training along mathematical lines. Some surgeon may believe his powers of analytical diagnosis due to algebraic training, and credit the study of geometry for much of his essential spatial intuition and sense of form. A minister may find in mathematics evidence of the Infinite Mind of God and see in the invariance of mathematical relations a promise of an everlasting future of perfect harmony. Despite the sincerity of such views, one may wonder whether those who enjoy mathematics may not attirbute to thinking in this subject what may more properly be said to characterize thinking in general. Similar encomiums indeed have been voiced for classical training, for a godly mother, and for the incentive due to a childhood of privation. Where one algebraist finds the finger of the Lord in a algebraic identity, another no less eminent admits that as for the existence of God, he has found no need to make such an hypothesis.

In brief, the citing of selected examples as contrasted with the technique of statistical sampling and the use of controls is poor reasoning even if used in a noble cause. One could by such methods make out a strong case for the advantage to one's future career of being born, say, on a Thursday. An impressive list of distinguished persons may be cited who have been born on any desired preassigned day of the week—namely, approximately one-seventh of all famous people whose birthday is known. And the chief warning to teachers to be content with more modest claims for the values of mathematical training lies in the number of those who dislike mathematics and still have found success in some chosen line of work.

Yet it seems true that to a rapidly increasing extent specialists are being called for in all lines of adult enterprise, and with specialization comes a steadily increasing mathematization of all fields. For example, business administration, psychology, education, and biology all invoke mathematical statistics of an advanced sort where but a few years ago mathematics would have been regarded as an impertinent intrusion. Furthermore, in an enlightened community it might be reasonable to expect, for every practising specialist, many intelligent alert citizens who understand the nature of the problems being tackled by the specialists who serve them.

The rôle of the mathematics teacher in meeting needs that involve problems in quantitative and spatial relationships is illustrated in the

Appendix of this report. His rôle in developing desirable characteristics of personality is discussed in the section below, and the whole of Part II is devoted to an exploration of his very special contribution in the common task of developing a high order of ability in reflective thinking and problem-solving.

THE RÔLE OF MATHEMATICS IN DEVELOPING
PERSONAL CHARACTERISTICS ESSENTIAL
TO DEMOCRATIC LIVING

In stating objectives for mathematics instruction it has not been customary to stress the development of such qualities of personality as tolerance, coöperativesness, self-direction, creativeness, social sensitivity, and esthetic appreciativeness. Yet teachers of mathematics can share with other teachers in this task, in some instances through the choice of problems on which students work, in others through the special resources of mathematics, and in still others through the way they guide the conduct of the class as a social group.

Social Sensitivity

Social sensitivity is a quality of personality that may be increased through the proper choice of problems to be studied. If these problems are socially significant, students may not only learn proper techniques for presenting and interpreting data, but may also at the same time become increasingly familiar with and sensitive to important social facts and concepts. For maximum effectiveness in this respect teachers of mathematics should coöperate with teachers of the social studies and other fields in choosing the problems and related data to be analyzed and studied. It should also be noted that without mathematical concepts and methods, chiefly statistical in nature, it is impossible to be fully sensitive to many dynamic social factors and their interplay. Thus the teacher of mathematics has a unique contribution to make in equipping the students with methods for understanding wider social problems and relationships.

Esthetic Appreciation

The teacher of mathematics may contribute to growth in sensitivity to the esthetic quality of experience through appropriate use of the unique content and methods of his own field. Many people respond favorably to quantitative facts and relations. They enjoy statistical comparisons, economic estimates, and mathematical formulations of physical principles. Arithmetic and algebra are for them natural and highly prized means for interpreting their environment; through them they may find ways of manifesting their personality. The recognition of familiar elements in new contexts, which contributes to the satisfaction of the successful student in mathematical courses, also influences his appreciation of geometric form as seen in the world around him. Mathematical instruction may enhance appreciation of geometric form as it occurs in nature, art, industry, and architecture. In the application of geometric construction to artistic design, the student has an opportunity to exhibit his esthetic taste and to create new combinations more or less expressive of some aspect of his personality.

Mathematical exposition, which involves the choice and arrangement of words as well as of mathematical symbols, has esthetic overtones. On reading an artistic piece of mathematical exposition, many mathematicians feel pleasure akin to that experienced on reading a selection of good poetry or on seeing a well-painted picture. Under superior teaching secondary-school students may have similar experiences at their own level of appreciation. A taste for strict logical deduction, a hearty respect for the power of reasoning, a confident faith in the value of sound inference, all these aspects of an appreciation for logical thinking are particularly appropriate objectives of mathematical study. Finally, an understanding of the rôle that mathematics has played in the drama of civilization has appreciational qualities which appeal to many students.

Tolerance, Coöperativeness, Self-Direction, and Creativeness

Such qualities of the personality as tolerance, coöperativeness, self-direction, and creativeness may be developed no matter what may be the content of the problems to which students are giving their attention, provided only that it is a problem real to them. Furthermore, the development of these characteristics is not dependent upon the peculiar methods and concepts of mathematics. But the mathematics class, like any other class, is a social group, and its experiences or activities may provide experience in either desirable or undesirable social living.

If the mathematics teacher is fully aware of the meaning and desirability of tolerance and coöperativeness, he can foster their development by consciously adjusting classroom activities to this end. This is especially true when the class undertakes work on a comprehensive problem which requires coöperative activity in the collection of data, for example, or even in the formulation of the problem. Again, individuals or small groups, taking their departure from tenable but different basic assumptions, may on occasion present conflicting conclusions on the same problem. In a case like this properly guided class discussion may contribute to growth in intelligent tolerance. These examples serve to show how certain types of class activity offer a means of developing characteristics of personality appropriate to democratic group life.

In addition, mathematics, like other fields, can contribute to an appreciation of the values of tolerance and coöperation through developing insight into its own history and development as a science. The following quotation clarifies this type of contribution.[17]

The . . . teacher can use his subject-matter in several ways to foster attitudes of coöperativeness in his students. . . . He can show them how the sciences themselves offer striking evidence of coöperation. A science, they can see, is seldom nationalistic or race conscious; it is the product of the collective activity of men who are widely separated in space and time, linked in many cases only by their common interests and attempts to understand and control nature. Even the geniuses of science have depended upon their fellow-workers—Newton himself said, "If I have seen a little farther than others, it is because I have stood on the shoulders of giants." The increasingly rapid progress of science in modern times may be attributed to coöperative attack by many men upon more difficult and complicated problems; to no small extent it has been due to the fact that scientists publish their work widely and look for help from other scientists throughout the world.

In the same way the general classroom methods used in teaching mathematics may lead to growth in intelligent self-direction and creativeness, or they may retard such growth. Responsibility for planning and carrying through individual projects and for evaluating one's performance in them is useful in this connection. Teachers of mathematics can encourage young people to "reach out beyond present experience into uncharted seas," rather than confine them to routine activities. A simple illustration relates to geometric exericses of the traditional sort. Here the opportunities for creative activity could be greatly increased if, instead of giving both the assumptions about the figure and the conclusion, the teacher returned at least occasionally to the practice of an earlier day and presented the figure only,[18] suggesting to students that they attempt to discover all the facts and relationships which appear to hold true about it. If the figure is not too simple this constitutes a stimulating creative exercise.[19] Creativeness may also be encouraged in discovering and formulating problems, in devising methods of attack, in recognizing relationships among data, in discovering methods of proof, and in presenting conclusions in expositional or other forms. But if mathematics is to be a field for creative activity, the approach to problems must involve a type of investigational experience which is an adventure into the unknown—it must provide constant opportunity for discovery.

Mere moralistic precepts are of course futile in the development of any of these characteristics. All aspects of classroom activity have to be intelligently guided with reference to their effects upon the personalities of students

17. *Science in General Education,* p. 284.
18. It is said that when an ancient geometer had discovered a new theorem, he presented only the figure and the word "Behold " to his colleagues.
19. Perhaps one reason why the Theorem of Pythagoras is so famous is that it has been a rich field for creative activity of this kind. No less than 167 different proofs are known, one of these having been discovered by President James A. Garfield!

if growth in this respect is to be achieved. The personality of the teacher, the pattern of student-teacher and group relationships, and the atmosphere of the school are also highly influential. The mathematics teacher must have insight into dynamic factors in the personality development of adolescents if his part in their education is to be fully effective.[20]

The Disposition and Ability to Use Reflective Thinking in the Solution of Problems

The development of intelligence in analyzing problem situations, otherwise referred to as reflective thinking, although but a part of the purpose of general education, is so essential a part as to be given a major place in this Report. But reflective thinking is not the special province of any single subject-matter course. Rather, after one fashion or another, it is the concern of all departments of the school, for it stands at the heart of the method of scientific inquiry—not only within the special fields of natural science, nor only within science so interpreted as to cover the activities concerned with developing all organized knowledge, but in every case where intelligent postponed decision is called for. Whether one considers the military officer planning a campaign, the lawyer drawing up a brief, the merchant analyzing the sources of his overhead expenses, the child deciding which parent is most likely to grant a special privilege and just how and when the subject be broached, there one meets a problem situation demanding analysis, a call for reflective thinking.

Although sharing with others the task of developing the disposition and ability to use reflective thinking as well as other characteristics of personality, nevertheless it is here that teachers of mathematics can make their major unique contribution. Part II of the Report discusses a number of major concepts which are involved in problem solving and shows how mathematics viewed from this angle often plays a fundamental rôle in the process.

[*The chapter ends with two pages of bibliography.*]

20. See Chapter XII, "Understanding the Student."

III

Introduction to Part II: Some Concepts Basic to Problem-Solving, Crucial in Democracy, Pervasive in Mathematics

Part II of this report is devoted to a discussion of the following major concepts, with special reference to their mathematical aspects:

Chapter IV. Formulation and Solution
Chapter V. Data
Chapter VI. Approximation
Chapter VII. Function
Chapter VIII. Operation
Chapter IX. Proof
Chapter X. Symbolism

In the judgment of the Committee, an understanding of these concepts is of inestimable value to the teacher in helping the student to learn the nature of both mathematics and the problem-solving process, and to appreciate the values of a democratic society. It is also the belief of the Committee that the student should gradually develop an always more mature understanding of the meanings of these concepts and that they should acquire richer and more discriminating content for him as his study of mathematics progresses.

THE RELATION OF THESE CONCEPTS TO THE PROBLEM-SOLVING PROCESS

As intimated at the conclusion of the previous chapter, the major rôle of mathematics in developing desirable characteristics of personality lies in the contribution it can make to growth in the abilities involved in reflective thinking, or problem-solving. In the opinion of the Committee the study of mathematics is of educational value because mathematics can be made to throw the problem-solving process into sharp relief, and so offers opportunity to improve students' thinking in all fields. As one traces the biography of any problem situation from its inception in perplexity and conflict through to its mastery by means of human intelligence, those places in which mathematics has a special contribution (which for some problems means throughout) may be seen to come under one or more of the headings of the chapters in Part II.

Formulation and solution are discussed first among the concepts related to problem-solving because they are central to the process and in a way primary. To solve problems successfully, one must have a clear notion of what it means to formulate a problem, and also of what is meant by a solution. Before one can lay out an intelligent plan of campaign in the resolution of a difficulty, identify significant factors, make hypotheses, define terms, make assumptions, know where to look for information, or what to use in the way of technique, both the impelling problem and the aim sought must be reasonably clear. Formulation and solution are discussed together because the foreseen end affects the formulation of the problem, and the way the problem is formulated affects both the final solution and the process by which it is secured. In the course of solving a problem the more specific purpose originally laid down may be redefined or even rejected, but some end is always kept in view, and this end-in-view directs all steps in the process.

When a problem has been formulated, the next step is usually to collect the *data* necessary for arriving at a solution. But not all data are equally relevant, representative, accurate, and reliable. In order to solve many problems competently, it is necessary to be discriminating about the acceptability of data in these terms, and to collect, record, and organize them in ways appropriate to the problem.

Acceptable data ordinarily must not only be collected and organized, but analyzed and interpreted before it is possible to draw conclusions from them. In order to analyze and interpret many types of data it is necessary to understand *approximation*. Approximation is always inherent in any problem that involves data collected by measurement. It is also usually inherent in the solution of problems that require the description of groups of data or the discovery of trends and relationships. In the latter case the analysis and interpretation call for the use of statistical concepts and methods. The attempt to analyze approximate quantitative data without a clear understanding of appropriate méthods is likely to be futile. Moreover, many qualitative statements implicitly involve some degree of quantitative approximation, and without recognition and understanding of this fact conclusions drawn from such statements are likely to prove misleading. Some examples of statements of this kind are: "Americans enjoy a better standard of living than any other people in the world"; "Germans are sentimental and given to regimentation"; "Diabetes is inherited"; "Normal boys are not interested in marriage."

In the solution of many problems the notion of *function*—of some sort of determinate correspondence between two (or more) sets of data—underlies the entire process. The particular correspondence may in some cases rest upon definition (as in a table of squares) or on arbitrary assignments (as in the listing of telephone numbers to correspond to the names of subscribers). In other problems the correspondence is not arbitrary but is like the relationship between distance covered and elapsed time in the case of a falling body. In analyzing and interpreting data the investigator seeks to discover a determinate correspondence of this kind; he hopes to find such relationships among the variables that knowledge of the values of one or more of them serves to determine uniquely the values of some one other variable. If such relations can be shown to exist, more precise and often more far-reaching conclusions can be drawn; sometimes formulas can be constructed that serve to facilitate and extend the analysis and to summarize relationships in compact symbolic form. Understanding of the concept of function as an ideal toward which the investigator strives in his work lends guidance in the attack on quantitative problems. Furthermore, some aspects of the concept of approximation can be completely understood and appreciated only in the light of comparison or contrast with the concept of function.

Problems cannot be solved without some degree and kind of "doing"— hypotheses must be tested by actual experiments, by "imaginary experiments," by computation, or some other *operation*. Each field of study has developed relatively unique kinds of operations appropriate to the analysis and interpretation of its own particular type of data. Mathematical operations are the active processes—techniques and methods—by which mathematical symbols, representative of data, are manipulated. The concepts of approximation and function serve primarily to guide the selection of procedure and methods, but the actual carrying out of the process requires the performance of operations upon the data.

In order to judge the validity of the solution of a problem it is necessary to understand the nature of *proof*, the basic principles of inductive and deductive reasoning. Without insight into the relation of conclusions to initial assumptions and to defined and undefined terms it is impossible either to work through to a solution upon which one can rely with assurance, cr to accept or reject with confidence the solutions proposed by others.

Finally, the process of problem-solving involves *symbolism* of some sort. Without symbols—mhich may be words or may be other signs or marks representing concepts—many forms of reflective thinking are hardly possible. The use of symbols facilitates the manipulation of ideas and is essential for the communication of ideas to others.

The student's growth in understanding of these concepts as related to problem-solving means no mere superficial extension of his vocabulary, no mere contact with undigested information. Instead it should result in more effective and mature ability to resolve complex problems, and be manifested through more appropriate behavior in the face of problem situations in all the aspects of living. The development of such ability is not the task of teachers of mathematics exclusively. Teachers of many fields share this responsibility and can contribute toward students' well-rounded growth in the ability to solve problems.[1] Thus this constitutes a common ground for coöperative development of an essential characteristic of personalities equipped to function creatively in a democracy.

THE RELATION OF THESE CONCEPTS TO DEMOCRACY

But what, it may be asked, have the formulation and solution of problems, data, approximation, and the like, to do with "fostering the ideals of democracy"? In the judgment of the Committee the connections are immediate as well as fundamental. They become clear when the ways in which problems are formulated and solved in countries where there is less democracy (as in Germany, 1939) are contrasted with the formulation and solution of problems in a country where there is more democracy (as in the United States, 1939).

In the first place, the difference lies in the very possibility of formulating problems at all. In dictatorships like Germany (in 1939) the man on the street is not permitted even to formulate many problems, such as the following, which directly concern him: We Germans are told we have got rid of unemployment, but are we really better off? How does it go with the Russian worker and with the American worker? Is all this rearmament and military drill really for peace? Is it possible to believe that Jews are actually in control in all the countries that are against us, or that the Jews were trying to poison us? With one victory after another achieved by our Leader, why are we still so miserable? Secondly, in Germany the Leader, having permitted some problems to be formulated after a fashion, takes upon himself the right to provide the only acceptable answers. Finally, in dictatorships these problems are so formulated that they cannot be solved by the use of reflective thinking, and only mystical answers are possible to the questions raised. If the Leader is asked his opinion on an important issue, he replies, "No one can prevent me from fulfilling the mission entrusted me by Destiny." If asked what his mission is, he replies, "My mission is to save the country, the country must and will be saved. Nothing will prevent me from saving my country. No one can oppose Destiny. That, brothers, is my mission." Objective formulation, the need for checking apparent results, emphasis on method of formulation and solution stressed in Chapter

1. Teachers of English, science, and the social studies are also turning their attention to aspects of this objective. See the Report of the Language Section of the Committee on the Function of English in General Education, *Language in General Education;* the Report of the Committee on the Function of Science in General Education, *Science in General Education,* Ch. VII; The Report of the Committee on the Function of the Social Studies in General Education, the *Social Studies in General Education.* All are published or forthcoming reports of Committees of the Commission on the Secondary School Curriculum of the Progressive Education Association, published by D. Appleton-Century Company, New York.

IV, are all negated as completely as possible in anti-democratic countries.

The United States is called more democratic at least partly because in this country the situation with reference to the formulation and solution of problems is different. In far fewer instances is the possibility of formulating our pressing problems restricted. True, there are groups that do not wish certain questions to be asked, and these groups are sometimes powerful (advertisers exert a large measure of control over all the widely circulated media of expression, for example, and so-called "patriotic" groups try to forbid the objective study of Marxist theories of society). But there is still a considerable area of freedom for the asking of important questions and for the demand that answers be reliably and responsibly supplied. There is more respect for experts who are judged by their previous success, and less for those who solve problems by revelation. More questions that concern actual living are asked, and they are so formulated that objective answers are possible. And one of the most important privileges accorded the individual in the democratic countries is that of being allowed to check apparent facts, at least in some important areas. What Ford says is happening in his plants can be checked against what others say. There is no way of checking on the statements of industrialists in Germany (1939).

The United States and the other democracies will increase their measures of democracy when there is organized and widespread demand for it. The teacher of mathematics who helps his students realize the necessity of the types of freedom discussed above is building their allegiance to democratic ideals and at the same time fostering the fuller realization of these ideals in the future. If the child, accustomed to rely on the judgment and decisions of adults, is to achieve a status of mature independence, he must learn to identify his difficulties for what they are, to state his problems, and to describe clearly the nature of appropriate solutions. Questions such as "Exactly what is the problem that I am facing? What am I hoping to do? What sort of results should I seek?" must become habitual and fruitful, not only in relation to the more immediate aspects of the adolescent's life, but in his wider social relationships. It goes almost without saying that the teacher who does not permit his students to raise questions which are susceptible to mathematical treatment and which also seem important to them will not be able to make clear that mathematics has these direct connections with the ideals of a democratic society. Nor will he be able to develop in his students the allegiance to these ideals which alone assures their preservation.

A comparable analysis holds in regard to Chapter V on "Data." The very possibility of merely gathering and organizing data in many important areas is precluded in antidemocratic societies. Neither authoritarian societies nor authoritarian groups within more democratic societies can permit the collecting of certain kinds of data about themselves or about subjects on which reliable data would impede the attainment of their ends. It is a striking fact that the availability of reliable statistical data on the standards of living of a country are a direct measure of the degree of democracy prevailing in that country as judged by other standards. The difficulty of securing data, however, applies not only in relation to such problems as the objective comparison of standards of living in Germany, Russia, France, and the United States, but also in relation to so-called business secrets, hidden accountancy, and advertising methods of certain groups within this country. Clearly, the path toward increased democracy lies in the direction of insisting on the right to collect and organize data for analysis and interpretation.

The crucial importance of widespread understanding of the concept of "Approximation" (Chapter VI) in a democracy is clarified when it is recognized that the word *statistics* originally meant "facts about the state." Without certain basic statistical notions, judgments concerning social phenomena are impossible, for social phenomena are group phenomena, and study of them necessarily involves approximations. The maintenance of democracy today is predicated upon the ability of large numbers of people to think clearly about probelms that are essentially statistical in character. There is, in addition, a more specialized way in which understanding of basic notions may serve to stem the inroads of antidemocratic forces. Such forces tend to create a spurious group divisiveness—mutual suspicion and mistrust among persons of various social, economic, or racial backgrounds. Valid reasoning about any characteristic of a group (a school class, an income group, a social class, or a race) depends upon knowledge of how this characteristic is distributed both through the group under discussion and through the total population. The facts of wide variability among individuals and of the wide range of every so-called distinguishing character in every group that has been called a race establish the invalidity of prevailing concepts of race, and so point to the importance of developing widespread understanding of statistical concepts. Those who propound theories of racial superiority, of course, need more than a requisite knowledge of statistics to induce them to renounce their theories. It is likely, however, that the number of adherents they recruit will be diminished when more young people understand how to check their claims from a statistical point of view.

The concepts discussed in Chapters VII and VIII on "Function" and "Operation" are perhaps too specifically mathematical in reference to have an identifiable specialized bearing on democracy, aside from the contribution they may make to the common man's ability to think for himself in all areas of experience. But the ideas and concepts treated in Chapter IX on "Proof" are again typically related to democratic living. The notion of proof, as discussed there, is one that could not be encouraged in an antidemocratic country, and it would be well if students were to realize this fact at the time that they are learning something about the nature of proof.

The emphases of Chapter X on "Symbolism" are particularly important at a time when democracy is threatened by those who would consciously undermine it through the use of flamboyant symbols and specious phrases to delude and mislead the public, obfuscating its attempts to think clearly for itself. In order to offset the effects of propaganda, advertising, and special pleading, the man on the street must learn to test the soundness of what is proposed in words, numbers, and graphs by what these proposals mean—their antecedents and probable consequences in action. He must learn to be wary, too, of the symbols he uses in his own thinking, lest they undermine his intellectual integrity and leave him a ready instrument for anti-democratic forces.

It may be noted that the bearing of each of these concepts on democracy and its maintenance under contemporary conditions is related more closely to "the free play of intelligence" than to either of the other two strands of the democratic tradition outlined in Chapter II—"optimum development of personality" and "reciprocal individual and group responsibility for promoting common concerns." Nor is this surprising, in view of the fact that the concepts themselves were chosen for emphasis partly on the basis of their relevance to reflective thinking and problem solving. Yet it must be clear from the above discussion that the maintenance of these other two strands of the tradition is dependent upon facilitating the free play of ideas among the people at large, and hence that the teaching of mathematics may be so conducted that it contributes to the enhancement of democracy in all of its aspects.

The contention of the argument above might be summarized in this way: The fruits of scientific (and mathematical) thinking in terms of application to the problems of human living require democratic societies for their full development. More important still, the kind of scientific and mathematical thinking that the Committee advocates developing in students—that is, thinking applied to the real problems in the basic relationships of living— provides a valuable tool for the preservation of a democratic way of life. Students who are in the habit of formulating real problems, and of insisting on genuine solutions, who know how to judge, collect, and interpret data, who are not misled by inaccurate or misleading statistics, and who know how to recognize valid proof, will not so easily be misled by propaganda, suppression of evidence, systematic calumny, demagoguery, or mystical symbols.

It may be remarked in conclusion that the fundamental operations of arithmetic, the formal solution of algebraic equations, the memorization of Euclidean propositions are taught in Germany (in 1939) possibly as well as they are taught anywhere. It is clear that mathematics taught as an abstract science contains little that is anti-authoritarian or pro-democratic; the same is not true for the kind of teaching of mathematics urged in this Report.

THE RELATION OF THESE CONCEPTS TO THE DEVELOPMENT OF AN UNDERSTANDING OF MATHEMATICS AS A UNIFIED FIELD

A set of major concepts worthy of special emphasis in the mathematics curriculum should serve to unify instruction in mathematics regarded not only as a tool for problem-solving, but as a science considered apart from possible applications as well. The number of concepts should be small in order that the list may be readily held in mind, and the concepts should have the property of systematic recurrence in diverse problems—or, stated negatively, they should not be the sort of concepts which, while necessary or at least useful in treating some problems, are not needed at all in many others.

If asked to state the major mathematical concepts involved in problem-solving many teachers might think first of labels appropriate only to some special aspect of mathematics, and might speak of equations, fractions, congruence, similarity, area, and the like. Important as such ideas are, they fail singly and as a group to meet the conditions stated above. They are not particularly helpful in the process of problem-solving in general; they are useful in some problems but not in others; they do not serve to unify instruction in mathematics; and finally, an inventory of concepts of this type results in an unwieldy list of items ranging in significance from the trivial to the profound. Thus the unquestionable usefulness of some of these concepts in many problem situations is in itself not enough to make them major concepts in the sense intended here.

Most of the objections that hold against the use of ideas like "congruence" or "equation" as major concepts also hold against the use of the fields into which they are commonly classified—the subject-matter divisions of arithmetic, algebra, geometry, trigonometry, and so on. This classification reduces the number of concepts, but fails to assure the unification of instruction. The essential interdependence of arithmetic, algebra, geometry, and trigonometry that becomes obvious to advanced students easily escapes the perception of students pursuing these subjects separately and for the first time. Differences in special techniques are often allowed to hide the common aspects which alone justify applying the single name *mathematics* to all these seemingly diverse studies. Even within a single subject, such as algebra, the unity is easily forgotten amid a multiplicity of topics. When these special subjects are emphasized as such, not only does the student frequently fail to gain a sense of unity in mathematics as a science, but the unity in its methods of approach to problem-solving is also obscured.

Recognizing these difficulties, many teachers have sought eagerly for unifying principles. For several years the function concept has seemed to enjoy special popularity. Yet certainly this concept, viewed narrowly and treated rigorously, does not unify all of mathematics. Distinguished writers have been cited as authoritative sponsors for other unifying ideas such as that of logical implication, of group properties, of relations, of quantitative variation, and so forth. Undoubtedly some among these might be stretched to cover by devious extensions most of the important concepts of mathematics, but in the judgment of the Committee none of them is adequate for the purposes of the teacher. To the teacher one all-inclusive concept is less important than a few important ones permeating mathematics irrespective of special topic and reasonably comprehensive of what is involved in problem-solving.

The list of unifying concepts to be emphasized in this Report might be altered in several respects without departing essentially from the conditions stated above, but in a general way these concepts seem to cover the subject and yet to deal with aspects so separate that a student with sound training in lines concerned with one may be deficient in his understanding of others. All are involved in dealing with mathematical questions that arise in analyzing many problem situations, and almost all (even all, by extension of meaning) are important in the solution of every problem whether or not it calls for characteristically mathematical treatment.

THE RELATION OF THESE CONCEPTS TO THE ORGANIZATION OF THE CURRICULUM

The Committee does not mean to suggest that these unifying concepts are to be considered separately or are to be made the basis of organization of separate groups of units devoted to each. The arrangement here adopted is intended to be, in the main, logical for anyone who surveys the field in retrospect. The order is not inteded to represent psychological steps in learning to parallel stages of adolescent growth.

In the ideal program these concepts would be employed repeatedly in the course of solving different problems. From time to time the emphasis would necessarily shift from one to another, since it would probably not be expedient for teachers to attempt to dwell simultaneously upon more than a few fundamental concepts. But it does seem possible to develop more than one at a time, and it is highly important that at least one be continually kept in mind. It is also to be remembered that the nature of these fundamental concepts is such that the power to give them formal expression and full appreciation comes only as the crowning step in a process that may be lifelong. Some of the more abstruse ideas here mentioned in elaborating one or another of the concepts should perhaps never constitute explicit foci of attention for most students at the secondary-school level. They are included here because the teacher should understand all these ideas and should consciously direct his own teaching practice in accordance with them.

The mathematician seeks to obtain generalizations and rules of procedure that are applicable to a wide variety of specific situations. This characteristic of mathematics has influenced the Committee to organize the chapters of Part II in such a way as to show eventually how certain concepts apply in the various aspects of living rather than organizing about the latter and showing the concepts that apply to each. Although the Committee subscribes to the view that mathematics has something to contribute to the meeting of needs in every aspect of living, presentation of these contributions built around the basic aspects of living would have entailed considerable repetition in the Report. Thus, for example, the ability to interpret data expressed in graphical form is useful in relation to needs in each area; the specific abilities involved are essentially the same whether the data to be interpreted have to do with personal living, immediate personal-social relationships, social-civic relationships, or economic relationships.

It should perhaps be made doubly clear at this point that the Committee advocates planning curricular sequences primarily on the basis of concrete problems encountered in meeting educational needs in these four areas, rather than on the basis of logical sequences of the familiar sort, or separate subjects like algebra, plane geometry, solid geometry, and so on, or unifying concepts presented here or elsewhere. Secondary-school mathematics has been criticized as being "too general and too abstract" for secondary-school students. This criticism is justified less by the nature of mathematics itself than by the tendency to impose certain general and abstract concepts upon the student—without his having had any responsible part in the gradual process of generalization and abstraction from concrete and specific instances arising in problems real to him.

The position of the Committee, briefly stated, is essentially this: A mathematics curriculum may be built by locating and studying concrete problem situations which arise in connection with meeting needs in the basic aspects of living. The major concepts here emphasized play a fundamental rôle in the analysis of these problems. They help to clarify the method of attack, and they tend to recur systematically in diverse problems. This recurrence in itself provides for the development of a sense of unity in mathematics as a method of dealing with problems. But in addition these major concepts serve to unify sub-concepts and related abilities customarily classified in separate subject fields—such as algebra and geometry. These sub-concepts, encountered first in concrete situations, should eventually be abstracted and generalized, and, in similar fashion, the major concepts should eventually serve to throw light on the analysis of problems arising in many different fields of thought.

In conclusion, it should be hardly necessary to remind the teacher that his contributions to the achievement of the major purposes of education are not confined to the development of the concepts and abilities particularly emphasized in the material of Part II. This Part is intended to supplement rather than to supplant Part I. The discussion is confined primarily to a detailed analysis of the specific contribution of mathematics to the development of ability in reflective thinking or problem-solving—indispensable both in meeting needs and in conserving democratic values. But the teacher of mathematics must build his total program toward an affirmative answer to such questions as the following:

Does it help the adolescent meet his needs in the major aspects of living (personal living, immediate personal-social relationships, social-civic relationships, and economic relationships)?

Does it promote, enrich, and refine democratic ideals through the development of related desirable qualities of personality?

The next two selections come from successive chapters of a year-book. The later chapter, by Carleton Washburne, describes the extensive experimental work done by the Committee of Seven to determine developmental levels at which arithmetic concepts are best learned. The preceding chapter, by Leo J. Brueckner, analyzes the study made by this committee, and similar experimental work, for the sake of application. Brueckner's application is important because the widely used arithmetic texts he wrote were in the forefront of the trend to postpone many topics, that is, to teach them to students at a later age than had earlier been the practice. Also of interest is Brueckner's stress on social arithmetic, an emphasis compatible with the report of the Progressive Education Association's Committee on the Function of Mathematics in General Education.

Both selections contain lists of the topics seen to be appropriate at various levels. They are of interest in comparison with current practice, which tends to reverse the postponement trend here found.

THE
THIRTY-EIGHTH YEARBOOK
OF THE

NATIONAL SOCIETY FOR THE STUDY OF EDUCATION

PART I
CHILD DEVELOPMENT AND THE CURRICULUM

Prepared by the Society's Committee on Maturity
CARLETON WASHBURNE (Chairman), JOHN E. ANDERSON, FOWLER D. BROOKS,
LEO J. BRUECKNER, KAI JENSEN, ARTHUR T. JERSILD,
HAROLD E. JONES, and RALPH W. TYLER
Assisted by Members of the Society and Others

Edited by
GUY MONTROSE WHIPPLE

THIS PART OF THE YEARBOOK WILL BE DISCUSSED AT THE CLEVELAND MEETING OF
THE NATIONAL SOCIETY, SATURDAY, FEBRUARY 25, 1939, 8:00 P.M.

PUBLIC SCHOOL PUBLISHING COMPANY
BLOOMINGTON, ILLINOIS
1939

TABLE OF CONTENTS

	Page
PREFACE	iii
OFFICERS OF THE SOCIETY FOR 1938-1939	iv
MEMBERSHIP OF THE SOCIETY'S COMMITTEE ON MATURITY	ix
EDITOR'S PREFACE	3

INTRODUCTION

INTRODUCTION ..... CARLETON WASHBURNE

SECTION I.—THE DEVELOPMENT OF THE CHILD

Chapter	Page
I. CHILD DEVELOPMENT AND THE GROWTH PROCESS ..... JOHN E. ANDERSON	15

SECTION II.—DATA ON THE RELATION BETWEEN THE CURRICULUM AND CHILD DEVELOPMENT

	Page
PREFATORY NOTE ON THE USE OF A CLASSIFICATION BY SUBJECT MATTER ..... CARLETON WASHBURNE	53
II. EDUCATION IN MOTOR ACTIVITIES ..... CARLETON WASHBURNE	57
III. HEALTH AND SAFETY EDUCATION ..... ARTHUR T. JERSILD	85
IV. EARLY TRAINING IN ROUTINE PHYSICAL HABITS ..... RUTH STRANG	97
V. THE PRACTICAL ARTS ..... ARTHUR T. JERSILD AND FRANCES MARKEY DWYER	109
VI. MUSIC ..... FOWLER D. BROOKS AND PAUL J. FAY	135
..... ARTHUR T. JERSILD	

v

CONTENTS

Chapter	Page
VII. RADIO AND MOTION PICTURES ..... ARTHUR T. JERSILD	153
VIII. THE GRAPHIC AND ALLIED ARTS ..... NORMAN C. MEIER	175
IX. READING ..... WILLIAM S. GRAY	185
X. THE DEVELOPMENT OF SPOKEN LANGUAGE ..... JOHN E. ANDERSON	211
XI. LANGUAGE: THE DEVELOPMENT OF ABILITY IN ORAL AND WRITTEN COMPOSITION ..... LEO J. BRUECKNER	225
XII. LANGUAGE: THE DEVELOPMENT OF ABILITY IN SPELLING ..... ERNEST HORN AND PAUL MCKEE	241
XIII. LANGUAGE: THE DEVELOPMENT OF ABILITY IN HANDWRITING ..... FRANK N. FREEMAN	255
XIV. FOREIGN LANGUAGE ..... FOWLER D. BROOKS AND C. O. ARNDT	261
XV. THE DEVELOPMENT OF ABILITY IN ARITHMETIC ..... LEO J. BRUECKNER	275
XVI. THE WORK OF THE COMMITTEE OF SEVEN ON GRADE-PLACEMENT IN ARITHMETIC ..... CARLETON WASHBURNE	299
XVII. THE SOCIAL STUDIES ..... KAI JENSEN	325
XVIII. EMOTIONAL AND SOCIAL DEVELOPMENT AND THE EDUCATIVE PROCESS ..... HAROLD E. JONES, HERBERT S. CONRAD, AND LOIS BARCLAY MURPHY	361
XIX. SOME THEORETICAL AND PRACTICAL IMPLICATIONS OF THE DATA ON DEVELOPMENT ..... CARLETON WASHBURNE	391

CONTENTS

vii

SECTION III.—APPRAISAL OF OUR KNOWLEDGE OF THE RELATION OF THE CURRICULUM TO CHILD DEVELOPMENT AND OF OUR METHODS OF INVESTIGATING THE PROBLEM

Chapter	Page
XX. PROBLEMS OF METHOD IN MATURITY AND CURRICULAR STUDIES ..... JOHN E. ANDERSON	397
XXI. NEEDED RESEARCH ..... KAI JENSEN	423
XXII. A CRITIQUE ..... ERNEST O. MELBY	439

Information Concerning the National Society for the Study of Education

List of the Publications of the Society

For Constitution of the Society, Minutes of the Atlantic City Meeting, Proceedings of the Board of Directors, Report of the Treasurer, and List of Members, see Part II of this Yearbook.

CHAPTER XV

The Development of Ability in Arithmetic

Leo J. Brueckner
Professor of Elementary Education
University of Minnesota, Minneapolis, Minnesota

I. THE SOCIAL SIGNIFICANCE OF ARITHMETIC

In the modern curriculum, arithmetic has much broader functions than were commonly recognized in the traditional school. Present thinking emphasizes four major functions of arithmetic: (a) the computational function, which deals with the development of essential computational skills; (b) the informational function, which deals with the development of an understanding of the history, evolution, and present status of institutions, such as banks, insurance, and taxation, that have been created by society to deal with social uses of number; (c) the sociological function, which deals with the development of an awareness of the problems faced by these institutions and of the means, current and proposed, for solving those problems; and (d) the psychological function, which deals with the development of the power to do quantitative thinking and of an appreciation of the value and significance of quantitative data and methods in dealing with the affairs of life (16).

Computational arithmetic may be differentiated from social arithmetic. The latter may be regarded as including the informational, sociological, and psychological functions listed above. Computational arithmetic consists of a hierarchy of knowledge, skills, and abilities to be mastered. The logic of the number system has in the past to a large extent determined the order in which the computational skills have been taught, since it is true that each of the major skills requires the use of more basic skills that must be mastered before the more difficult processes can be learned. It is also commonly recognized that there are points below which it is not advisable to attempt to teach a particular process. For example, no one would think seriously of teaching long division in the second grade or calculus at the junior-high-school level. In recent years a number of investigations have attempted to determine with some precision the optimal points at which to present each of the processes. These studies will be reviewed later in this section.

Social arithmetic does not consist of such a definite hierarchy of skills to be mastered, but rather includes a variety of abilities, insights, generalizations, and ideas that in a sense develop and change throughout the life of the individual. These ideas are encountered in the affairs of daily life and have meaning to the extent that they are directly related to the common experiences of people. The growth of the quantitative elements of ·the vocabulary is a gradual process, beginning at a very early age and continuing at varying rates throughout life. The meaning a particular word may have is the by-product of experience. Similarly, appreciation of the social significance of money, measurement, business practices, taxes, and geometric design is the outcome of a more or less continuous process of growth and development to which all experience contributes and that can at all times be facilitated by well-planned instruction. Of course it is true that different individuals at any given level of schooling will not have the same breadth of appreciation and understanding of such topics as those listed. However, it is evident that for each individual these values will become richer, broader, and more vital as he proceeds through successive stages of a well-planned curriculum that emphasizes the social functions of arithmetic, and that these concepts will take on added meaning and significance throughout life.

II. PROCEDURES IN COMPUTATIONAL AND IN SOCIAL ARITHMETIC

It thus appears that arithmetic instruction must recognize two different kinds of outcomes, each of which requires an essentially different kind of teaching procedure to insure its achievement. Computational arithmetic requires the use of systematic, carefully graded learning materials that will insure easy effective learning of number processes. In these materials the steps in learning will be from easy processes to more difficult ones, with systematic diagnostic testing at all points to locate difficulties. Research has conclusively demonstrated that no new process should be taught until the pupil is 'ready' for it; that is, until he has the mental ability to learn the process, until the essential basic skills are established, and until the process has meaning for him as the result of experiences that show him its social value.

In so far as social arthmetic is concerned, the chief instructional problem is to utilize a rich, well-planned series of social experiences that will give the learner many-sided contacts with the important applications and uses of number in the affairs of daily life. As far as we now know, there is no particular sequence in which these units of instruction need appear. The order of their appearance can vary from class to class as the occasion may warrant. Nor need these activities be the same in all classes. In these experiences the need of computational arithematic will be clearly demonstrated. Many maintain that drill on number processes should be assigned only after pupils have sensed their need of these processes to carry on their activities. The outcomes of these rich social units will be valuable knowledge, insight, appreciation, and ability, to which the work at successive levels will add its contribution.

In so far as the curriculum related to social arithmetic is concerned, it is regarded as necessary that the teacher select social units adapted to the level of development, interests, and needs of the pupils in the group that will at the same time apply concretely the computational processes most readily learned at that level. As will be shown later in this chapter, a number of investigators have made studies of the kinds of units suitable for various levels of the school. However, these are not as definite in suggestions as to sequential arrangement of materials as are the studies of computational arithmetic. This lack of specificity is largely due to the fact that the outcomes of social arithmetic are of a cumulative developmental kind, constantly being enriched and altered as the result of social experiences, whereas skill in a computational process may in fact be mastered at one level of the school and be used substantially as originally learned at higher levels—save that rate of work in the particular skill will increase as the pupil progresses through the school.

It should be pointed out that there is some evidence to indicate that there is not so much need of systematic, logically organized instruction in computational processes as has sometimes been thought necessary. Harap (22, 23), for example, has shown that processes in whole numbers, fractions, and decimals can be learned through their practical use in carefully selected activities adapted to the level of development and interests of the pupils, in which the need of performing computations involving these processes arises. No further organized practice or supplementary drill appears to be necessary, he reports. These findings are extremely important for those who wish to utilize the 'activity' approach in instruction. They demonstrate the desirability of presenting number processes in connection with meaningful experiences, even though it is planned to carry on subsequently a program of systematic practice with prepared materials (14). Harap unfortunately did not determine the optimal level at which these skills could be taught through activities such as were used in his experiments; indeed, he taught them in only one grade in each case. No data are available in his studies as to the relative ease of learning these processes at other grade levels under the same conditions or under variations of these conditions.

III. INDIVIDUAL DIFFERENCES IN ARITHMETIC

The fact of individual differences is of great significance, both in the organization of the curriculum and in the selection of methods of instruction.

Investigations have made it clear that the curriculum should be kept flexible because of differences in the rates at which children learn. These differences have been revealed by many studies (13). Failure to recognize them has been one of the major factors contributing to the difficulty such large numbers of children have had with arithmetic. To provide for these differences in the rate of learning number processes, materials have been devised that make it possible for pupils to progress at different rates in the mastery of computational skills. Such drill materials as those devised by Courtis, Studebaker, Washburne, and others illustrate the point. Several workbooks are available that provide effectively for adapting instruction in computational arithmetic to individual differences in rates of learning. There is no longer any reason why all pupils in a group should be at work on the same computational skill at the same time, regardless of the differences existing in their readiness for this work. The curriculum should not be organized as a set body of materials for each grade that all pupils are required to master before promotion to the next grade. Ideally instruction in computation should be adapted to the level of progress of each learner and to his rate of learning.

Individual differences in learning social arithmetic are probably as great as in computational arithmetic, but the method of dealing with them is not the same. The fact that probably no two persons learn the same things from any social experience in which both may participate should be recognized. Instead, therefore, of providing a systematic series of exercises in social arithmetic with certain definite outcomes so organized that pupils may progress at different rates, as can be done in computational arithmetic, the teacher should provide a variety of rich group experiences that introduce aspects of social arithmetic to the class and enable the pupils to explore their different interests and to relate what is being learned to their varied backgrounds of experiences. Applications of number in all school subjects furnish many opportunities for this kind of activity. The outcomes of these formal and incidental experiences will vary widely among the members of the group.

The method of organizing instruction dealing with social arthmetic therefore differs considerably from that of organizing instruction in the computational aspects of the subject. The former may be organized as a class or group activity, the latter should be individualized. However, in both instances the teacher should be concerned with the selection of those procedures and experiences that will facilitate learning and that are adapted to the level of development of the individual. Both phases of arithmetic must be definitely provided for, since investigations have shown that under present conditions there is a low correlation between the scores on tests of social and computational arithmetic (17). The problems involved that are related to the issue of this Yearbook may be stated as follows:

In relation to computational arithmetic:

1. What is the optimal sequence of steps in presenting the number facts and processes?
2. Are there points in the child's development before which it is not advisable to teach the various number processes if efficient learning is to take place?
3. In what ways can instruction provide adequately for individual differences in rates of learning number processes?

In relation to social arithmetic:

1. What types of quantitative social concepts should be presented at various stages in the curriculum?
2. Are there definite stages in the child's development at which they can be most suitably introduced?
3. What are the most satisfactory means of developing meaningful social concepts in the field of arithmetic?
4. How can units of social arithmetic be selected so as to contribute effectively at the same time to the vitalizing of instruction in computational arithmetic?

IV. DEVELOPMENTAL LEVELS IN ARITHMETIC

So far as can be discovered, no one has published a defintion of developmental levels in either computational or social arithmetic that is based on extensive studies of the growth process, such as are available for language, reading, and physical development. For purposes of discussion the following developmental levels, the bases of which will be elaborated in this chapter, may be distinguished:

Stage 1

The stage at which readiness for formal number work is attained. During this period the child acquires a considerable variety of simple quantitative concepts and a small quantitative vocabulary through incidental contact with number in his daily informal experiences, and through guided experiences and training in school that promote number readiness. This level comprises the preschool years, the kindergarten, and usually at least part of Grade I.

Stage 2

The initial stage in learning arithmetic. This usually comprises Grades I and II, during which the child acquires the ability to read numbers, to count systematically, and to group and compare objects. He also learns easily the basic number facts of addition and subtraction, either through organized teaching or through informal procedures. Through well-chosen social activities involving simple applications of number in measurements and social practices, the pupil can readily be led to acquire a rich background of meaning, which will facilitate more formal learning at the next stage. There is a rapid increase in his arithmetical vocabulary. Usually there is considerable interest in number work.

Stage 3

The stage of rapid progress in fundamental arithmetic habits and attitudes. This stage includes in general Grades III and IV, during which the pupil masters the simpler processes with whole numbers readily, his knowledge and understanding of social arithmetic is expanded, and he develops the ability to apply simple quantitative methods in his affairs. At the end of this stage the pupils should have mastered the addition and subtraction facts, the easier multiplication and division facts, and the simpler computational processes involving whole numbers. He should also have an understanding of the meaning and uses of the more common fractions.

Stage 4

The stage during which social experience extends rapidly and increased power, efficiency, and skill in arithmetic computation are developed. This stage includes Grades V to VIII, during which occurs the learning of generalized number concepts, more difficult processes in fractions of various kinds, long division, and more difficult social applications of number, and during which there is rapid growth in power to think quantitatively.

Stage 5

The stage at which special aptitudes appear and broader interests are developed. This stage is at the high-school and college level, at which point special aptitudes are recognized, interests are developed and broadened, and a high level of efficiency in the uses of number is secured.

It should be recognized that these stages of development cannot be sharply differentiated and that they merge gradually as parts of a continuous process of growth. While approximate grade limits are given for each stage, these designations should serve merely as guides to teachers, since pupils will not all reach the various stages at the same time.

[*Section V, "Investigations Dealing with Arithmetic Development," not given here, details research, including that of the Committee of Seven.*]

VI. CONCLUSIONS

First, the arithmetic curriculum should place much greater emphasis of social arithmetic than has been the practice in the past. The acceptance of this position should result in a radical change in the character of the arithmetic work in the primary grades, a recognition of stages one and two in the development of arithmetic. Here it is essential that stress be placed on the development of number meanings and an appreciation of the functional uses of number in the affairs of children. This readiness program should have as its major purpose the development of readiness on the part of pupils for the more formal number work to be begun at the third stage of instruction.

Second, the core of the curriculum should consist of a series of carefully selected units of social arithmetic of demonstrated value adapted to the needs, interests, and level of progress of the pupils. The purpose of these units should be to give the pupils a rich social insight and an understanding of the functions of number in daily life and to enable them to praticipate more effectively in the affairs of a changing industrial democratic society. The units should vary from locality to locality, but the basic principles underlying their selection should be the same in all places. Emphasis is placed by the Yearbook Committee on the planned approach to be made to this work, since it is held that an unplanned, incidental approach to the subject will not produce the desired results. Much experimental work must be done before we can be sure that the elements of a planned program of arithmetic that gives due consideration to child development are validly established.

Third, through these units of work the pupil should also be led to see the functional value of the various number processes and be given ample opportunity to apply them in a meaningful way. It is essential that the work in social and computational arithmetic be carefully integrated. This can be accomplished by selecting units of work for the different grade levels that will give the best opportunity to present the number processes most suitably taught at each level. The information concerning the learning difficulty of the several number processes produced by such investigations as those of the Committee of Seven, as outlined in Chapter XVI, should be of great value in determining the proper arrangement and gradation of the number processes. Further study is needed of the relations between the apparent learning difficulty of the elements of the different number processes and the nature of methods and materials of instruction. Data that are now available on these points are based on results secured under existing conditions. It is obvious that somewhat different results may be secured under improved methods of teaching, with improved materials of instruction, or when a different approach to the teaching of number is used; for example, through a socialized approach.

Fourth, whatever the plan may be that is finally selected for organizing the curriculum, careful consideration must be given to the question of individual differences. Pupils do not all earn at the same rate, nor do they learn the same body of information from any single experience. It is clear, therefore, that it is desirable to provide a plan of practice on the number processes that will enable each pupil to practice on materials adjusted to his level of development and rate of growth. It is desirable, likewise, that every effort be made to adapt the rate of progress of the class work to the ability of the pupil. To this end it is necessary that the teacher have information concerning the pupil's level of mental development, and reliable information as to his readiness to undertake the work on the new step or process, including not only his ability in basic skills essential to the process to be presented but also his understanding of the concepts that are involved.

CHAPTER XVI

The Work of the Committee of Seven on Grade-Placement in Arithmetic

CARLETON WASHBURNE
Superintendent of Schools, Winnetka, Illinois
and
Chairman of the Yearbook Committee

Reasonably full treatment is given in this chapter to the work of the Committee of Seven of the Northern Illinois Conference on Supervision[1] for the following reasons: The experiments in placement conducted by the Committee of Seven have been directly in line with the general purpose of the Yearbook and have been the first and most extensive investigations in this field. They began in 1926 and are still continuing. They have consisted of controlled, coöperative experiments in 255 cities and towns in 16 states, involving 1190 teachers and 30,744 children. They have been reported repeatedly in educational literature and have had a direct effect upon courses of study in both the United States and Canada and upon textbook construction. They are suggestive as to techniques that might well be used in fields other than arithmetic in determining the relation of the curriculum to levels of child development, and they have indicated the nature of further research needed both on the problem· of arithmetic placement and on the problem of placement in general. While the conclusions of the Committee of Seven are tentative and subject to well-recognized limitations, they nevertheless point to definite practical procedures in regard to the placement of

---

1. The Committee of Seven has consisted, during the period covered by most of this report, of the following persons: Orville T. Bright, Superintendent of Schools, Flossmoor; Turner C. Chandler, Principal of the Burnside School, Chicago; Harry O. Gillet, Principal of the University of Chicago Elementary School; J. R. Harper, Superintendent of Schools, Wilmette; Raymond Osborne, while Principal of the Francis W. Parker School, Chicago; O. E. Peterson, Head of the Department of Education, Northern Illinois State Teachers College, DeKalb; Howard C. Storm, Superintendent of Schools, Batavia; and Carleton Washburne, Superintendent of Schools, Winnetka, *Chairman.* Mabel Vogel Morphett, Director of Research in the Winnetka Public Schools, and William H. Voas, Psychologist in the Winnetka Public Schools, have been associates of the Committee.

arithmetic topics and are therefore usable by classroom teachers, textbook-makers, and curriculum-revisers who prefer even tentative and limited recommendations based upon research to a purely traditional or subjective plan of curriculum construction.

[*Sections I and II, not given here, detail the experimental procedures used by the Committee of Seven.*]

III. A SUMMARY OF THE FINDINGS AND RECOMMENDATIONS OF THE COMMITTEE OF SEVEN TO DATE

A summary of all the findings of the Committee of Seven to date is appropriate for this Yearbook. It should be emphasized that these findings are tentative, that they are subject to the limitations outlined later in this chapter, that the research suggesed later in this chapter may materially modify some of the recommendations, and that teachers who are willing to spend more time, or accept lower standards of achievement, or to present a subject before three-fourths of the children can master it may legitimately attempt the subject at a lower level, while those whose standards are higher or whose time is more limited may legitimately postpone a given item until a higher level. It should also be pointed out that there are, except as otherwise indicated, *terminal* placements; *i.e.*, the placements at which the topics can be learned to completion. How much earlier the topics may legitimately be introduced, the Committee's data do not show. Finally, it should be borne in mind that all recommendations as to mental-age placement presuppose reasonable mastery of foundations; *i.e.*, possession of the knowledge and skill pertaining to prerequisite topics.

DATA AND RECOMMENDATIONS FOR PLACEMENT

Mental Age 6–7

While children at this mental age can learn the addition facts with sums of 10 and under and the easy subtraction facts, there is much doubt whether systematic instruction in arithmetic should begin so early. Even these two elements are better learned a year later. Experimental evidence is beginning to accumulate to indicate that this year, and possibly the next, should be devoted largely to informal experience and activities to give children real concepts of numbers and space relations, without any systematic drills.

Mental Age 7–8

The addition facts with sums of 10 and under are well learned at this level, and there is little gain in further postponement. The harder addition facts and the easy subtraction facts can be successfully learned at this age, but there is a definite gain in postponing them to the next level. The desirability of systematic drill in these facts at this level is open to question, in spite of the fact that it produces satisfactory results. Many persons feel, and there is some evidence to justify the feeling, that the informal experiences and activities of mental level 6–7 should be continued and extended at this level and that systematic drill of all sorts should be postponed to the next one.

Simple comparisons of length, height, thickness, width, and the like, including the recognition that one object is two, three, or four times as high, wide, long, thick, or deep as another, are well learned. Children can also readily learn to measure lines in even inches, and, with more difficulty, to draw lines an even number of inches long. They can learn how many inches there are in a foot and in two feet.

Children can learn to read the clock on the even hour, to distinguish between morning and atfernoon, and to understand the symbols *a.m.* and *p.m.*

Mental Age 8–9

The elements assigned to the previous level can be postponed to this level with advantage. Children can also learn the more difficult subtraction facts, although there is some gain in postponing these another year. They can learn to subtract three-digit numbers from three-digit numbers as far as the handling of the mechanics is concerned, but there is reasonable ground for doubt whether such numbers have any real meaning to them.

The easy multiplication facts can be taught at this level very effectively. Multiplication facts fall, with a few exceptions, into two categories, those with products of 20 and less, and those with products of more than 20. The former belong definitely at this level; the latter about three years later. An exception is 5×5, which was correctly retained by 89 percent of children of mental age 8. An exception in the other direction 4×3 (with the 3 written above the 4). This was correctly retained by only 68 percent of 8-year-olds. In general, however, this is the obvious level for the multiplication facts with products of 20 and less, provided children have an adequate foundation in the addition facts.

The simplest forms of square measure belong here, involving a recognition of areas two, three, or four times as large as a given area, when either the height or the base is held constant. Under the same conditions the children can recognize whether a rectangular area is half as large as a given one, and, using a square inch of cardboard as a measuring device, can learn to compare areas where both height and base differ in such problems as, "Is this picture three times, four times, or six times as large as the square inch of cardboard?"

In time measure, children can learn to distinguish standardized units, such as minutes, hours, and days, from unstandardized units, such as length of time to walk a block. They can learn to read clocks to the half and quarter hour and to read the calendar. On the calendar they can count the elapsed days within the same month. They can learn a simple table of time, including minutes, hours, days, and weeks.

Mental Age 9–10

Column addition with columns not more than three digits high and three digits wide can be learned at this level as far as accuracy of computation is concerned. Question may legitimately be raised as to the meaning and use of such columns at this level, but research on the point is lacking.

It is probable that simple multiplication involving no partial products over 20 should be introduced at this level. The Committee is carrying on research now to investigate this hypothesis. It is highly probable that the easy division facts (dividends of 20 and less) can be introduced here or even at the level below, since there is a very high correlation between the learning of the division facts and the learning of the multiplication facts. The Committee is analyzing the division facts one by one to verify this. Similarly, there is some ground for supposing that short division in which no partial dividends exceed 20 may belong here. Again, research is in progress to determine this finally.

The meaning of simple fractions of a whole object definitely belongs at this level. Children can learn to recognize and distinguish half of an object, a third, a fourth, three-fourths, and so forth. ('Half' can be learned much earlier.)

In linear measure children can learn the relation of inches, feet, and yards, the number of feet in one yard and two yards, and the number of inches in a yard. They can compare length, height, width, and so forth, involving the practical concepts of one-half, one-third, and one-fourth—again, the concept of one-half can be taught earlier.

In square measure, likewise, children can recognize that a given rectangle is a half, a third, a fourth, or an eighth as large as a specified one when either height or base is held constant. They can learn to get areas of rectangles by dividing them up into square inches with a ruler, and do this with very little instruction. They can learn to recognize a square foot drawn on a blackboard as distinguished from a six-inch square or a square $18'' \times 18''$ or larger—indeed, they can do this in many cases without systematic instruction. Using a ruler and pencil, they can learn how many square inches there are in a square foot; one may well question, however, the value of learning this here—it may develop a concept which has later use, but it is probably not related to any need, interest, or use of children at this level.

Mental Age 10–11

Column addition four digits high and three digits wide can be done accurately at this mental age. Children can understand the meaning of simple decimals and can learn to add and subtract them. Common observation indicates that where the adding and subtracting of decimals involves only dollars and cents and does not require the supplying of naughts, children can learn these earlier. If the very doubtful procedure of adding and subtracting 'ragged' decimals is to be taught, the optimal age is considerably higher than this, and even the minimal age is one level higher.

The addition and subtraction of fractions and mixed numbers with like denominators, if confined to the ones commonly used in life, can be successfully learned at this level. If fractions are kept simple enough and mixed numbers are not included, this unit can go even into the preceding level.

Simple bar graphs not involving computation and fractional estimates can be learned very successfully, including both the reading of such graphs and the making of them.

In linear measure children can effectively measure in feet and inches and measure and draw lines accurately as to the quarter of an inch. They can learn to estimate roughly such lengths as that of the classroom, although this ability bears very little relation to mental age and can be taught almost equally well from a mental level of 9 to a mental level of 12 or 13. Similarly, the 10-year level is as good as any, but not much better, for teaching children to recognize what units of measure are used to express the distance between cities, the length of a piece of cloth, the height of a building, the length of a farm.

When dimensions are given in whole feet, children can learn, with systematic instruction, to get perimeters. Likewise, very simple problems in subtraction of feet and inches, involving no borrowing and well within the children's experience, can be taught at this mental age. Even the muliplication of feet and inches in such a problem as the following can be taught here very successfully: "The table Ralph is making needs four legs, each one 2 feet, 1 inch, long. How long a piece of lumber must he have to make all four legs?"

In time measure, children can now complete the table of time from seconds up to leap years, including days in a year and weeks in a year. They can learn to read clocks accurately to the minute and to express time accurately to the minute in the form '10:22 P.M.' They can learn to recognize the difference between arbitrary and natural time units, such as hours and minutes *versus* days and years. They can calculate time elapsed in even quarter hours within a given hour. Those who have the necessary ability in division can even calculate the number of minutes required, for instance, to walk one block if 30 minutes are required to walk 15 blocks, or the number of days to make one poster if 72 days are needed to make 9 posters.

Mental Age 11–12

Multiplication facts with products over 20 are not adequately learned at a mental age of 10 years, 9 months; only 56 percent of the children of this mental age make scores of 76 percent or more, even when they have an adequate foundation of addition facts. The Committee's data do not go above mental age 10–9 for multiplication facts, but the simple multiplication foundations test for long division would indicate that by a mental level of about 11 more satisfactory learning of all the multiplication facts is entirely possible.

Just as soon as the multiplication facts are all learned, simple multiplication with multiplicands up to four digits can be learned, and compound multiplication, with multiplicands as high as four digits and multipliers as high as three digits, can be learned from the standpoint of technical mastery. Again serious question may be raised whether such large numbers as are involved in the products of this type of multiplication are within the child's experience and whether the process therefore has either meaning or use to him.

Either before or after the learning of simple and compound multiplication, as soon as children know all the multiplication facts, they readily learn the division facts. Shortly thereafter they are reasonably successful with short division,[2] although there is a gain in postponing this until the next level.

Long division with a two-place divisor and a one-place quotient is successfully

---

2. 'Short division' is used throughout this report to mean 'division by a one-place divisor.' Although the Committee's teaching materials used the traditional short division form rather than the probably superior long division form, the placement would not be changed had the long division form been used, since it is knowledge of the multiplication facts that is crucial, and either short division or the simpler forms of long division can be taught as soon as these facts are mastered.

learned at this level by children who know their multiplication and division facts—indeed, for the relatively smaller percentage of children who know their multiplication and division facts at a lower mental age, such long division problems can be acquired at that lower level. While the elements of remainder and trial divisor increase the difficulty of the examples, they do not raise this unit of long division above this level. As in the case of short division, long division with one-place quotient is somewhat more successfully taught at the next level higher. If the standard of success is two problems right out of three, long division with a two-place quotient (and two-place divisor) can also be successfully learned here. Further discussion appears under the next mental level.

Children can memorize the 'aliquot parts' (*i.e.*, fractional and decimal equivalents). They can divide decimals by integers and can multiply decimals by decimals.

This is the level at which square measure as a regular topic can be best introduced in its simpler form. For the first time children can recognize that an area is a certain number of times larger than another area when the height and base both differ and when the relationship is simple. They can recognize a square inch drawn on the blackboard as distinct from a half-inch square or a two-inch square—although this last is not clearly a function of mental age, as the curve for it is nearly flat. They can calculate the number of square feet or inches in a given area when the dimensions are given in even feet or inches. They can memorize the number of square inches in a square foot and both calculate and memorize the number of square feet in a square yard.

Mental Age 12–13

Long division with a two-place quotient involving naughts, remainder, and trial-divisor difficulties probably belongs at this level. The data available do not, unfortunately, show any standard of success between 67 percent and 100 percent. But a problem-by-problem analysis of the test data clearly puts the more difficult two-place quotient problems at a mental level of 12 years, 9 months.

The meaning of fractions of a group of objects belongs here, such as the recognition that three objects is a third of nine objects. Following this, children can learn the multiplication and division of fractions satisfactorily. To this level belong also Case I percentage and Case II percentage involving only simple division of decimals; *i.e.*, division of a decimal by a whole number.

Three distinct new elements of linear measure can satisfactorily be taught at this level, although all of them give better results if postponed to the following year. Children can draw and measure lines accurately to the eighth of an inch; can calculate the number of inches in a fraction of a yard; and can measure distances on maps with a scale of miles.

It is not until this mental level that children are successful in learning to recognize squares and oblongs as rectangles, distinguished from triangles, trapezoids, and the like. It is hard to believe, however, that with longer teaching and practice on this element it could not be taught earlier if there was any object in doing so.

Children can learn to recognize the relative sizes of rectangles marked off into squares—seeing that one is one-sixth as large as another, for example—with both base and height differing. With some difficulty they can learn how many small cards can be cut from a larger card when they are in readily divisible units, like the number of 3″ × 5″ cards that can be cut from a sheet 9″ × 10″. This unit is taught more economically at the next level higher.

Measure of volume is still being investigated.

In time measure, children can solve simple problems in the multiplication of hours and minutes, even involving the change of a product like 7 hours and 70 minutes to 8 hours and 10 minutes. This could even be taught at the preceding level were there other time units indicated therefor. It is not until the 12-year level that children can successfully count the elapsed weeks on a calendar from one month into the next and the elapsed days from one month into the next, and the elapsed hours and minutes from one hour to another hour, such as 8:45 to 10:30 or 8:45 A.M. to 4:15 P.M.

Mental Age 13–14

Long division with a three-place quotient, with or without the difficulties of naughts, remainders, and trial divisors, but still using a two-place divisor, is not taught successfully before this level. This is true whether tests are graded in terms of accuracy or in terms of correct process, disregarding mechanical errors. It should be remembered that the Committee's standard for successful teaching requires that three-fourths of the children retain the knowledge six weeks after teaching sufficiently well to make a satisfactory score [3] in a test involving all difficulties. Even at mental age 13–3, the Committee's standard is not quite reached; only 70 percent of the children score 67 percent or higher. Children at this level can learn to divide decimals or whole numbers by decimals and can complete Case II percentage.

In linear measure, children can learn to divide feet and inches by a whole number when both feet and inches are evenly divisible, and to divide yards by inches, making the necessary change in denomination in such problems as "Barbara is putting blue paper on her cupboard shelves. She has three yards of blue paper; the shelves are 27 inches long. How many shelves will this cover?"

In square measure children can learn to draw rectangles of a given number of square inches with varying bases given, such as drawing a 4-square-inch rectangle 2 inches wide. As a matter of fact, this particular problem can be learned at the level below, but when the problem involves a fraction, such as a base one-half inch wide, it is better learned at the level above.

While there is some doubt as to the children's realistic concept of the size of an acre and a square mile (see next level), they can get the area of a tract of land in square miles when the dimensions are given, even at the level below this. At this level they can learn how many acres there are in a square mile and calculate from a diagram the acres in half a section. Smaller fractions of a section, however, belong in the next level higher.

Mental Age 14–15

The usual textbook problems in addition and subtraction of unlike fractions involving the finding of common denominators and, in the case of the subtraction

---

3. Because the long-division test used by the Committee of Seven included only three examples of this type, children getting either two or three of the three examples right were considered to have satisfactory achievement.

of mixed numbers, involving borrowing are not successfully learned below a mental age of 14. Much of this textbook material, however, is of very doubtful social use, so that it is possible that the lack of reality to the child is a factor in his failure to learn, as when, for example, he is asked to add 48$\frac{5}{12}$ plus 76$\frac{4}{5}$.

The manipulation of denominate numbers, involving the more complicated forms of applying the four fundamental processes to them and involving the changing of denominations, apparently cannot be effectively taught and retained until this level. Now, however, all practical forms of applying the fundamental operations of linear measure can be taught, although some of the more difficult ones, such as dividing 10 feet, 1 inch, by 2 feet, 7 inches, either require more practice than the Committee's experiment gave, or belong to a higher level.[4] In dividing feet and inches there is a marked contrast between the problems that 'come out even' and those that require more arithmetical manipulation. There is a three-year gap between the ability to learn to do such problems as the first and the second of the following samples: (1) "Paul has several pieces of lumber 3 feet, 2 inches, long. He wants to fill in a gap in the sidewalk 12 feet, 8 inches, long. How many pieces of his lumber would he need to fill the gap?" (2) "How long will each piece be if a 13-foot, 4 inch, plank is cut into four equal pieces?" The former belongs at the 14-year mental level and can be taught with reasonable success a year earlier; the latter is not satisfactorily learned until the 16-year mental level! In problems of this sort the type of division involved makes no difference; *i.e.*, whether it be finding the size of a given part of a whole, finding how many parts of a given size are contained in a whole, or finding by what number a part must be multiplied in order to give a whole—all are equal in difficulty.

A table of linear measure can be completed at this time, including feet in a rod and feet in a mile.

Square measure involving the finding of the number of acres in the usual fractions of a section belongs here. The familiar schoolroom problems of finding the number of square yards of linoleum needed to cover a floor, the dimensions of which are given in feet, is not successfully learned until this level. And it is not until somewhat later that city children are able, even with teaching, to estimate the number of acres in their school grounds or to diagram a square mile of land in the neighborhood by indicating street or road names. Yet it will be remembered that children's ability to manipulate acres and square miles, whether or not they understand them, comes earlier.

In time measure, as in linear measure, children can solve problems involving the fundamental operations applied to hours and minutes, and involving changes of denomination. Some of these problems, however, are apparently too difficult at this mental age.

The foregoing recommendations, as already said, must not be taken rigidly. Often it is advantageous to teach a unit at a level higher than that recommended. Occasionally one may teach it at a level lower with very little loss in efficiency. In some cases the placement is very definitely indi-

---

4. The method taught was that of changing feet and inches to inches before dividing if division before changing did not come out even.

cated by the Committee's data. In some cases it is a matter of judgment as to which of two levels is the proper one — the smoothed graph may place the topic at one level, the unsmoothed one at the next one higher or lower. The general sequence and approximate placements as a whole, however, are thoroughly workable in a public school system and produce, according to the teachers who have used them, gratifying results. Actual research data as to the total results of such placements in comparison with the traditional placements are entirely lacking and should certainly be obtained.

[*The chapter ends with criticisms of the committee's techniques and recommendations.*]

The National Council of Teachers of Mathematics

FIFTEENTH YEARBOOK

The
Place of Mathematics
in
Secondary Education

THE FINAL REPORT OF
THE JOINT COMMISSION OF
THE MATHEMATICAL ASSOCIATION
OF AMERICA AND
THE NATIONAL COUNCIL OF
TEACHERS OF
MATHEMATICS

BUREAU OF PUBLICATIONS
TEACHERS COLLEGE, COLUMBIA UNIVERSITY
NEW YORK
1940

Commission on the Place of Mathematics in the Secondary Schools of the Mathematical Association of America and the National Council of Teachers of Mathematics

Representing the Association

K. P. Williams, Chairman
Indiana University
Bloomington, Ind.

A. A. Bennett
Brown University
Providence, R. I.

H. E. Buchanan
Tulane University
New Orleans, La.

F. L. Griffin
Reed College
Portland, Ore.

C. A. Hutchinson
University of Colorado
Boulder, Col.

H. F. MacNeish
Brooklyn College
Brooklyn, N. Y.

U. G. Mitchell
University of Kansas
Lawrence, Kan.

Representing the Council

William Betz
Rochester Public Schools
Rochester, N. Y.

M. L. Hartung
University of Chicago
Chicago, Ill.

G. H. Jamison
State Teachers College
Kirksville, Mo.

Ruth Lane
State University of Iowa
Iowa City, Ia.

J. A. Nyberg
Hyde Park High School
Chicago, Ill.

Mary A. Potter
Supervisor of Mathematics
Racine, Wis.

W. D. Reeve
Teachers College
Columbia University

CONTENTS

Introduction: THE ROLE OF MATHEMATICS IN
CIVILIZATION 1
Historical Perspective 1
Mathematics an Outgrowth of Fundamental Human
Needs 2
Arithmetic and Geometry 3
The Greek Achievement 4
Other Branches of Classical Mathematics 5
The Service Values of Mathematics 6
The Newer Uses 8
Mathematics as a Mode of Thinking 8
The Significance of Accurate Thinking 10
Mathematics as Relational Thinking 11
Influence of Mathematics on Our Philosophical
Outlook 11

I. LOOKING AT MODERN EDUCATION AND ITS GENERAL AIMS . 14
Our Faith in Education 14
A More Comprehensive View of Education 15
Need of a More Comprehensive View of Education . . 17
The Dual Aspect of the Curriculum 19
Enduring Educational Concerns 21

II. GENERAL OBJECTIVES FOR SECONDARY EDUCATION . . . 22
Ability to Think Clearly 25
Ability to Use Information, Concepts, and General
Principles 25
Ability to Use Fundamental Skills 26
Desirable Attitudes 30
Interests and Appreciations 33
Other Objectives 35

III. THE PLACE OF MATHEMATICS IN EDUCATION 37
Mathematical Study as Training in Clear Thinking . . 41
Mathematical Information, Concepts, and Principles . . 42
Mathematical Skills 45
Mathematics and Desirable Attitudes 45

Mathematical Appreciations 48
Remarks 50

IV. THE MATHEMATICS CURRICULUM 52
Basic Considerations 52
A Tentative List of Guiding Principles
Mathematical Categories as a Basis of Organization
of the Curriculum 55
Essentials of a General Program in Secondary
Mathematics 58
Habits and Appreciations in the Mathematics
Classroom 62

V. ONE DISTRIBUTION AND ORGANIZATION OF THE MATERIALS
OF INSTRUCTION, GRADES 7-12 68
Introduction, Grades 7-12
Considerations Relative to Time Allotment 72
The Problem of the Retarded Pupil 72
Suggested Grade Placement Chart, Grades 7-12 . . . 73
The Work of the Seventh and Eighth Grades . . . 75
The Work of the Ninth Grade 76
The Work of the Tenth Grade 78
The Work of the Eleventh Grade 86
The Work of the Twelfth Grade 91

VI. A SECOND CURRICULUM PLAN 94
Introduction 96
The Work of the Seventh and Eighth Grades . . . 99
The Course in General Mathematics for the Ninth
Grade 99
The Course in Algebra for the Ninth Grade . . . 100
The Work of the Tenth Grade 101
The Work of the Eleventh Grade 107
The Work of the Twelfth Grade 109

VII. THE PROBLEMS OF RETARDATION AND ACCELERATION . . 111
Varying Capacities of People 112
Function of Intelligence Tests 120
Recent Changes in High School Population 120
Present Grade Groupings 121
Ability Grouping 123
Other Methods of Caring for Ability Differences . . 124
Characteristics of Backward Children 126

Contents

III. TERMS, SYMBOLS, AND ABBREVIATIONS IN ELEMENTARY MATHEMATICS . . . 223
    Vocabulary . . . 223
    Symbols . . . 231
    Verbal Abbreviations . . . 236
IV. EQUIPMENT OF THE MATHEMATICS CLASSROOM . . . 238
    Instruments . . . 241
    Models . . . 241
    Showcase and Wall Displays . . . 241
    Supplies . . . 241
    Teacher's File . . . 242
    Mathematical Books and Periodicals for the High School Library . . . 242
V. GRADE PLACEMENT CHART FOR PLAN OF CHAPTER V, GRADES 7–12 . . . 246
VI. ONE POSSIBLE SELECTION AND ARRANGEMENT OF INSTRUCTIONAL TOPICS FOR SLOW PUPILS . . . 252

Contents

    Characteristics of Bright Children . . . 135
    Teachers for Backward and Superior Groups . . . 136
    Teaching Procedure . . . 138
    The Mathematics for Backward Pupils . . . 141
    The Mathematics for Superior Pupils . . . 144
    Mathematics . . . 147
    Bibliography . . . 149
VIII. MATHEMATICS IN THE JUNIOR COLLEGE . . . 149
    Development of the Junior College . . . 151
    Function of the Junior College . . . 153
    Present Junior College Mathematics . . . 154
    Different Mathematical Programs Needed . . . 155
    Courses for Semi-Professional Groups . . . 157
    Mathematics for the Academic Group . . . 162
IX. EVALUATION OF THE PROGRESS OF PUPILS . . . 164
    The Purposes of Evaluation . . . 171
    The Limitations of Current Testing Practices . . . 176
    Some Limitations of Recent Years . . . 181
    Some Advances for the Future . . . 186
    A Program for the Future . . . 187
    Conclusion . . . 187
X. THE EDUCATION OF TEACHERS . . . 188
    General Considerations . . . 189
    Social and Civic Attributes . . . 190
    General Culture . . . 193
    Professional Education . . . 200
    Training in Mathematics . . . 200
    Specific Programs of Mathematics and a Second Subject . . . 202
    High School Teachers of Mathematics Alone . . . 203
    High School Teachers of Mathematics and a Second Subject . . . 207
    Junior College Teachers . . . 207
Appendix
I. ANALYSIS OF MATHEMATICAL NEEDS . . . 210
    For Ordinary Life . . . 211
    For Leadership and Higher Culture . . . 217
    For Specialized Use . . . 222
II. THE TRANSFER OF TRAINING
    General References

CHAPTER III

The Place of Mathematics in Education

"I shall on with my story of praise, and then show you the heart of my message."

—VIOLA IN TWELFTH NIGHT

The influence that mathematics has long had in our civilization and its growing importance indicate in a general way the place it should occupy in education. Since the function of the schools is to equip boys and girls not only to be effective members of our society but also to be appreciative of our culture, schools must especially provide contacts with a study which has done so much toward both "controlling our environment" and forming our intellectual background. Though such a general statement is easy to make, difficulties arise when its consequences are sought in such specific things as curricula. For illustration one needs merely to call attention to the divergent views now expressed. On the one hand there are those who urge that only a small amount of mathematics be universally required, and who say that we should expect only pupils with special inclinations to go further. On the other hand we have the thesis of Hogben, not a teacher of mathematics but a social biologist, that there are urgent social and individual reasons for a large number of persons to become proficient over a wider range of mathematics than they have covered in the past.

One point should be disposed of at the beginning. There are many persons occupying important places in society who to all appearances have negligible mathematical appreciations yet live rich cultural lives. In some cases their study of mathematics evokes unpleasant memories, tempered only by recollection of the joy that accompanied ultimate release. What does the Commission make of this? In many cases the dislike for mathematics may have been created either by the ineffectiveness or the personality of a teacher or by the unsuitability of the material that a competent teacher had been required to present. This, howevr, cannot b offered as a universal explanation. If mathematics is to be given the prominence in education which this Commission believes should be given it, every effort should naturally be made to reduce the number of those who carry on the subject in secondary years with a feeling of unhappiness and with a belief that no substantial benefit is being obtained. Better courses of study and

590

better teachers can do much to bring this about. It can be said here, however, that the Commission is prepared to accept the possibility of conditioned antipathy in some individuals, and would not force mathematics beyond the elements of arithmetic either upon a pupil whose rebellious distaste toward the subject seems firmly entrenched or upon one whose genius or legitimate absorptions leave little leisure for mathematical development.

As to the complaint that there are too many cases where mathematics has been unsuccessfully studied, the following needs also to be said. Similar criticism is made of the teaching of other subjects, so the complaint is only a part of the popular criticism of current efforts at educating. We "teach" English, and there is still much bad grammar and an apparently increased reading of cheap and vulgar writing. We dwell upon the social studies, and their lessons are left within the classroom by many who succumb to the lure of economic panaceas. We instruct in health, but the rules are disobeyed not infrequently by the teachers themselves as well as by the physicians who devise them. These are discouraging facts about human nature, but they are not reasons for lowering our educational standards. The Commission believes strongly that educators should not resign themselves to the doctrine of "minimum education" as the norm. It believes that we should by all means require as ideals and standards something definitely superior to the small amounts of this or that subject which some people "get along with." Constant reasonableness should be used in meeting the difficult special situations that grow out of mass education; but the schools should certainly be unremitting in their efforts to raise the general standard of American culture. We should never be content with a "high standard of living" only in the material sense.

There is a positive answer to the question as well as the somewhat negative answer just set forth. The Commission believes that under proper teaching, supported by discriminating and sympathetic guidance, a fairly large proportion of boys and girls can realize that man has lived so long, accomplished so much, and learned so many things, that they cannot reasonably isolate themselves from traditions which strongly condition the present. The conviction will come to them that they can hope to deal effectively with the future only by paying attention to the past. In view, therefore, of the increasing importance of mathematics to civilization, because of the techniques it has perfected as well as its methods of reasoning, the Commission believes that ample opportunity and encouragement should be given to all individuals to continue their mathematical training as far as their powers allow and as other conditions permit. Such instruction should be in definitely organized mathematics courses, for incidental learning of mathematical fragments in connection with other studies cannot give either the general understanding or the appreciation of the subject that is here advocated.

The manner in which mathematics as a school subject contributes to the objectives discussed in Chapter II will now be discussed.

MATHEMATICAL STUDY AS TRAINING IN CLEAR THINKING

It is unfortunate that for a long time it was maintained that mathematics furnished a general training of the "reasoning faculties," as if a certain power might thereby be developed to function in all situations. The problem of "transfer," however, need not be gone into here more than to note that it is now generally accepted that transfer is possible. It is to be observed, moreover, that nothing was said regarding the training of a general "reasoning faculty" when in Chapter II the ability to think clearly was discussed.

What was said about *gathering and organizing data, presenting data,* and *drawing conclusions* shows at once how important mathematics may be in giving instructive experience in these procedures. If, as was stated before, mathematical teaching in the past has not paid sufficient attention to the first point, gathering and organizing data, this was partly due to the fact that scholars in other fields were not always cooperative. They shut themselves away from mathematical methods. But this has now changed, and the development and the wide use of statistical methods have greatly increased the area in which significant quantitative work is possible. A certain knowledge of basic mathematics is required in these areas. A fair competence in algebra is needed if one is to understand concepts and procedures beyond the most elementary ones. In a way algebra may be a "tool" for statistical work but a tool in a very fundamental sense, since it is woven closely into the texture of the subject and into the thinking which is involved. That something far more than routine skill is required becomes apparent when the subject is carried into the range of *probabilities,* a field into which it inevitably moves as soon as measures of reliability are introduced.

The truth of what has just been said is being constantly demonstrated by individuals attempting to do statistical work without adequate preparation. The difficulties which so frequently take them to a mathematician for aid usually center around the *meaning* of things. Actual use of formulas may have caused no trouble, but neither the ideas from which the formulas were derived nor their implications are understood. The person in distress has usually obtained a number of whose accuracy he is sure, but whose meaning quite confounds him. Such a situation is evidence not of lack of numerical adroitness but of comprehension. The person may be bewildered solely because he does not have at his command the only language which will allow one to "think through" the subject he is trying to handle. Such unhappy situations as this will be corrected only when mathematics is rightly viewed as essential to clear thinking in certain domains, and all talk of it as only a "tool subject" has ceased.

Portions of mathematics can be made especially effective in developing habits and traits discussed under the heading "Establishing and Judging Claims of Proof." Geometry has always been regarded as presenting unusually impressive instances of deductive reasoning. In a formal course in the subject a pupil almost daily has an assignment involving "proofs," and in no other study is this likely to be the case. The nature of the material with which the proofs deal is indeed quite different from the "life situations" which he will encounter later as an adult and a citizen. It is altogether probable that, in the past, mathematics teachers did not do all they should to make the experiences of the geometry class as broadly significant as they may well be.

Geometry has been treated solely as geometry and not as a subject, which in addition to being a splendid example of deductive reasoning, important and interesting in itself, can also serve the purpose of creating a critical attitude of mind toward deduction and thinking in general. It is essential to have the theorems of the text understood and the problems worked, and to place the main emphasis of the study upon geometry itself; but it is important also for mathematics teachers to make geometry yield all the educational benefits it can. Teachers who have experimented have found that, without lessening seriously the amount of geometry taught, the course can be made the means of establishing a general critical attitude on the part of pupils, an attitude that they recognize and value. Especially at the high school level, principles of deductive thinking can be most effectively taught in connection with a well-organized, substantial subject such as geometry, which, being logical itself and free from personal prejudice, can serve as a yardstick. It is clear that little can be accomplished merely by announcing principles and criteria of good thinking and calling attention to the danger of their violation by illustrations of good and bad thinking taken from "life situations." In a miscellany of such illustrations there would be neither coherence, growth, nor any body of knowledge significant in itself. Furthermore, abstract principles of reasoning are not designed to arouse response, particularly in young people. On the other hand it is not strange, when one pauses to reflect about it, that geometry, with its origin in mensuration constantly kept before us by its very name, with its employment of figures and its superb logical structure, often has been a favorite study and has even stirred those gifted with literary expression, though not pursuers of mathematics, to affectionate praise of its satisfying truth and its serene beauty.

Until recently there has been little inductive thinking in elementary mathematics. Comprehensive books on algebra have frequently contained a chapter with the austere title "mathematical induction," probably poorly understood and productive of little result unless the pupil went considerably beyond algebra. Mathematicians have disagreed with the statement of Huxley that mathematics knows nothing of observation, of experimentation, or of induction. Though definitely untrue, if one is thinking of the way in which the subject has developed, the criticism has been valid when applied to methods employed in its teaching. There is now, however, a definite trend toward leading pupils into new topics through their own experiences. Especially is such procedure possible in geometry, and the appearance of informal geometry, including intuitive and experimental procedures, in the seventh and eighth grades is a distinct and significant step in this direction. The possibilities are certainly numerous, and it is to be hoped that mathematics will emerge finally as the vehicle through which may be obtained impressive experiences in inductive as well as deductive reasoning.

MATHEMATICAL INFORMATION, CONCEPTS, AND PRINCIPLES

A large body of mathematical knowledge is of unquestioned utility and involves no intricate techniques. For example, theorems of geometry are merely facts about figures, of either a descriptive or a metric character. Necessary for certain trades or technical occupations, they may be universally desirable. Undoubtedly a very large number of Americans can find the area of a rectangle. To find the area of a circle, however, would lead many to ask aid, although some would be quick to claim, "I could solve such a problem once." However, just as one need not inventory the mathematical requirements of trades and technologies, he need not enumerate all instances in which mathematical information may profitably be used, in order that the place the subject deserves in our school curricula, on the score of information alone, may be recognized.

On a somewhat different level, insofar as they affect mental activities of educated persons, come the concepts and principles with which one has contact in mathematical instruction. When well impressed upon the mind, they are more permanent possessions than facts or even skills, which are likely to be impaired through disuse. In a society which draws so heavily upon mathematics, as does our own, mathematical principles and concepts should affect the manner in which the individual thinks and should color the appraisals he makes. The signed numbers of algebra, the similarity, the congruence, and the parallels of geometry, the rates of change of elementary calculus should be so taught that they leave lasting impressions. The ambition to make mathematical instruction more broadly significant through emphasis on concepts has led to stressing the *function concept* as a unifying element. Inasmuch as it deals with relationships, it is quite true that few concepts have greater universality or importance. A society, all members of which while in school have been given persistent and effective contact

594

with this concept, should view problems and situations more intelligently than a society which has only a certain number of mathematical specialists. But the great importance of the function idea should not lead to an over-emphasis upon its significance, nor should it lead to slighting mathematics which does not come under its scope, for very important and very interesting parts of the subject are unrelated to it.

MATHEMATICAL SKILLS

An effort has been made to describe the fundamental ways in which mathematics is embedded in thinking and to discuss its concepts in such a way that they will not be confused with skills. But a precise dividing line cannot be drawn. Mathematical technique is a very real thing. Its extensiveness and the difficulty of mastering it will always be a source of discouragement to some pupils and a perplexity to some teachers. Unless one has facility with its processes, however, mathematics cannot be used effectively. Its techniques must be so well acquired that, in a sense, they take care of themselves, leaving all of one's powers available for other purposes, especially the higher ones of analyzing and directing. If the handling of fractions or the solution of simple equations taxes the pupil's ability, there is little chance that he will deal satisfactorily with situations in which these processes enter. If there is, on the other hand, such command of the processes that there is true fluency in their use, there is likelihood that mathematics may be justly appraised and effectively used.

The character of the techniques of mathematics is in part responsible for the fact that it is necessary to study the subject for some time before it pays extensive returns. A pupil may attend one class in first aid, learn how to apply a tourniquet, and later save a life. But it is hard to conceive of much benefit from one lesson in algebra or geometry. The deep-seated desire for quick returns, however, will always arise in connection with mathematical study as in other situations, and should be honestly faced. Of course every effort should be made to make mathematics pay returns as promptly as possible; even the very prudent investor with his eye chiefly on the future is pleased with early dividends, for they support his faith in large ultimate profit. The recent efforts to make mathematics, especially algebra, yield more of interest in its early stages are both laudable and notable. They make the study resemble an insurance policy with a good surrender value in early years.

Though techniques should be regarded as means and not as ends, those of mathematics have certain virtues on account of the broad educational processes involved. Some teachers, unsettled by attacks upon mathematics, have sought to turn these attacks aside by fleeing from techniques as though they were evil, or have pretended that they could be learned, to the extent necessary, without conscious or serious effort. The actual educational value of the techniques, which makes such a retreat unnecessary, will be touched upon later.

It is not difficult to draw up a list of situations in which one can profitably use algebra, and such a list assists in a realization of its importance. One is confronted, however, with the question whether the mathematics that could be used actually will be used even when the person is competent. Certainly not always by any one person; even the accomplished mathematician may not employ his knowledge in all situations where he could use mathematics. It is to be expected that in actual life mathematics will be used according to the individual's taste and the extent to which he is actually stimulated by some problem. Neither mathematics nor any other subject can make the horse drink. The mathematics teacher is as powerless to make a pupil use mathematics as is the teacher of health to make him follow its well-established laws. But education, which must not shirk the responsibility of developing capacities, at the same time must enable persons to realize the meaning of intelligent living in a scientific age and urge them not to slump into a state of mental indolence, after having been potentially brought to a rather high level of understanding.

Comparatively few pupils during the secondary years know what their later activities and studies will be. In the absence of required courses or suitable advice, many erroneously assume that they will need no extensive work in secondary mathematics. On entering college they often find doors closed to desired fields of study because of the lack of adequate mathematical preparation. For example, they are unable to take work of substantial character in the physical sciences, or in those parts of the social and biological sciences that employ statistical methods. To be sure, special courses are sometimes offered for poorly prepared students, but such weak or emasculated studies are poor substitutes for standard courses that employ mathematics where it is naturally needed. To postpone until college years basic preparatory studies that experience has convincingly shown can profitably be pursued in the secondary school, gravely handicaps the pupil in his later effort to make a program of real collegiate studies. The doctrine of "postponement," like the doctrine of "incidental learning," however alluring to the shortsighted person and however valid in certain subjects, is indefensible in the case of mathematics. The subject is so extensive and so difficult, requiring systematic and protracted study, as to be unsuitable for the general application of either of these doctrines.

Administrators should feel deep concern over the large number of pupils who find themselves without adequate preparation for the activities, professions, or additional studies which they later wish to undertake but which presuppose substantial foundations. In their solution of this problem lies the test of their educational statesmanship. A strong and corrective influence should be exerted upon those boys and girls who are capable of doing fair work with secondary mathematics but who, although they have no serious dislike for the subject, and insufficient knowledge to form a sound opinion, think it unnecessary and yield to what is easiest or most glamorous at the moment. It is for the good of society that each year there should go forth from the secondary schools a large number of young people with marked proficiency in the technical skills of mathematics, together with a fundamental understanding of some of its concepts. The steady flow of such a group into our democracy is a major responsibility of school administrators.

MATHEMATICS AND DESIRABLE ATTITUDES

It is often asserted that as a people we have high regard for the specialist, the claim seeming to indicate a respect for knowledge and competence. However prevalent such a regard may be, it is not a discriminating one. Our people are, in fact, frequently and badly victimized by pseudo-specialists and pseudo-experts, simply because they are unable to recognize important fundamentals. In the future years, as in the past, revolutionary programs of an economic and social nature will be urged upon our country. After the partisan and political character of a proposal has been scrutinized, there will still remain the question whether the proposal is based on a broad knowledge of facts and an intelligent analysis of their relationship, or on little more than wishful thinking.

Now no subject excels mathematics and those sciences that draw heavily upon it for ability to set up high standards of knowledge, of analysis, and of techniques for arriving at accurate conclusions. Since mathematics and kindred sciences undertake to construct systematic bodies of doctrine, they stimulate thinking, analysis, discovery, and growth. When the pupil is studying them, he finds himself unable to advance merely by using his memory or his fluency of speech. He uses books whose first chapters *must be understood* in order to advance to the last. Only by comprehending each step in the progressive development of these sciences can he finally attain the understanding of the things that are being studied, things that are permanent and significant. From this contact with ideal knowledge, he gains an experience that furnishes a background for accurate discriminations and distinctions. We are at present confronted by so many social problems for which it is impossible to "know the answer" that it is especially important for society to acquire the steadying and careful habit of procedure which may come through the discipline of mathematical study. Good will and a warm heart are not enough to furnish us with the protection of life insurance; the formulas and the tables of the actuary are in some ways more necessary. This Commission believes, in short, that mathematics can be so taught that it will help reveal the meaning of knowledge, as distinguished, on the one hand, from opinion and conjectures, and, on the other hand, from trivial and commonplace facts.

It is probably true in certain respects that pupils are held to a higher level of achievement in mathematics classes than elsewhere by the nature of the subject itself, for here the standard of accurate definitions, of logical coherent statements in demonstration, and of precise results must necessarily be stressed. In a broad sense, all this is merely claiming that mathematical methods furnish examples of good workmanship. The possibilities of giving discipline of universal significance are not lessened by the fact that not all the situations in which it may be used have the general characteristics of mathematics. The question is one of creating an ideal and of setting up standards of excellence, not one of whether mathematics resembles other subjects. First the ideal must be glimpsed; then it must be so lived with that it will become a part of our lives. This practice can most likely be accomplished through formal educational experience in which the ideal is constantly emphasized. This Commission believes that some teachers of mathematics have been indifferent to their full opportunity to hold up to their pupils high ideals of workmanship. College students, showing very clearly that they have been allowed to "get by" in mathematical work as well as elsewhere, will unblushingly hand in papers whose careless appearance should give shame to any student. Neat, well-arranged work can have a sensory appeal, and should stimulate accuracy and precision. All these qualities, neatness, accuracy, and precision, are merely attributes of "taking pains," a thing that is essential to good work in any field. It is not to be expected that mathematics will maintain the place its teachers desire, unless teachers are willing to meet the insistence of administrators and educators that their subject yield all possible contributions to the varied goals of education.

Intimately related to good workmanship is the ideal of thorough understanding, and certainly here even the techniques of mathematics can be made to contribute wholesome lessons. Something as non-essential as a change of letters will often cause confusion for the beginner. Though a pupil may think he understands the identity $(a + b)(a - b) = a^2 - b^2$, he is not likely to argue the case if he did not see its application to 84×76 until it was pointed out to him. A pupil's progress in mathematics depends largely upon his grasp of the full implication of both the concepts and the powerful techniques. When he fails to understand some point, his teacher frequently can trace the difficulty back step by step to something the pupil believed he understood but which in reality he grasped only imperfectly. The lesson to be learned from such an experience is much broader than the mathematics involved. Many parts of the subject can be so presented that mathematics will help to build up in pupils the desirable habit of questioning the clarity and the fullness of all their knowledge. The desire to look into things a little more deeply can be stimulated by frequent illustrations in mathematics of the profitableness of such a search.

It might seem at a first glance that mathematics has little to do with developing social-mindedness, which was set down in Chapter II as one of the attitudes much in favor at present. The "social studies" are currently urged as the cure for maladies which we know afflict us, but which we cannot describe except in vague terms. It is, however, to be remembered that mathematics sprang from elementary human needs, from problems of feeding, clothing, and shelter; and today, although it embraces a great deal more, it still has intimate connections with such primary questions. Thus, when properly taught, mathematics surely should appear as one of the chief instruments of "social progress."

Open-mindedness, the last attitude discussed in Chapter II, is related to willingness to admit one's self wrong, but it is an attitude that should be carefully distinguished from mere mental instability. In mathematics a person cannot long deceive either himself or another, for arguments that arise must end by the admission of one disputant that he had been wrong. This may cause the discomfort that some pupils experience in the mathematics classroom, where it is difficult to cover up a weakness. Even if one's error is honestly come by at the expense of considerable toil, it must be laid aside without prejudice or resentment. Every pupil in geometry has had the experience of seeing what he believed was a valid proof of an "original" explode under the questioning of his teacher. Even in studying his lessons, he repeatedly finds it necessary to abandon a thought that for a few moments held the prospect of being the key to working a problem or proving a proposition. Such a situation may look somewhat grim, but though the discipline may be too unpleasant for a few, an actual laboratory in open-mindedness, where one receives training in admitting an error endeared to him by the effort expended in seeking to establish it, may be more valuable in forming a social attitude than rhetorical exhortations.

MATHEMATICAL APPRECIATIONS

The schools must teach mathematics beyond its elements not only to equip those who need it as a tool, but also to make people appreciate in a forthright and intelligent way how basic is its place in our culture. The artist who depicted the "tree of knowledge" for the Hall of Science at Chicago placed mathematics at the very roots, with other subjects growing and flowering from it, thus implanting in the minds of many people the idea of its important cultural value. But such a mode of instruction is not sufficient, nor is it sufficient for teachers of mathematics, animated by enthusiasm and pride, to display their trees of knowledge in their classrooms. The goal should ever be to create such understandings and appreciations that pupils in their own right become competent appraisers of mathematics. The position of mathematics in the "tree of knowledge" is a challenge to teachers of mathematics as well as an assertion of the value of their subject, and, repeated in our classrooms, it is a challenge to pupils, showing them not only what they may need in order to succeed, but what they must know if they are to comprehend certain essential elements of the civilization they are to share. The "tree of knowledge" is suggestive of a library with the names of poets, dramatists, essayists, and novelists cut into its walls. Assuredly the highest purpose here is not to give merited honor to those who cannot profit from it, nor to elevate ourselves a little by the act of honoring them, but rather to encourage those who see the names to learn why these names merit the honor shown them, and to share in a feeling of appropriateness.

In the past mathematics has enjoyed such an appreciation, shown by the honors paid it in our literature and philosophy, and it still finds honor in contemporary literature. The fact that there are people who study mathematics and then assert that their time was wasted does not affect the matter at all. The cultural tastes, appreciations, and accomplishments of the critic should be appraised before weight is given his opinion, though naturally in practice charity frequently intervenes. The Commission has stated at the beginning of his chapter that only the bare elements of mathematics need be required of a pupil thoroughly rebellious against the subject or of a pupil with a strong talent, wishing to devote his time to other subjects. The Commission believes, however, that appreciation of mathematics should be even more extensive than it now is, and it strongly urges upon administrators the wisdom and importance of using as a general guide the ideas so well expressed by Professor Snedden in the lines quoted in Chapter II.

There is evidence of some interest in mathematics among adults for reasons other than narrow utility; for example, newspapers and magazines from time to time carry mathematical problems. Although these problems sometimes have the nature of a puzzle, they reveal an inclination toward mathematical thinking. One would hardly care to venture the prediction that mathematics will ever be a serious leisure-time activity for adults to any extensive degree, but we have no knowledge of what the actual possibilities are. Encouraging success has attended some notable efforts to popularize the subject, and a thorough consideration of the problem of adult education may well show that the mathematics taught in the secondary school is necessary for desirable work in later years.

600

REMARKS

The Commission believes that what has been said indicates that mathematics should have a prominent place in secondary education. There should be ample provision for courses beyond the ones that are required, conscientious efforts being made to influence pupils to continue mathematical study. Boys and girls should be informed as to number of subjects that employ mathematics, and they should be led to see that an acquaintance with it helps one to live more intelligently in an age as scientific and as technical as our own. They should also be informed that in addition to its great helpfulness to man, mathematics has peculiar qualities, representing a form of perfection so striking that many persons, although not following it in any professional way, have considered their study of it one of their most valued experiences. Nor should there be withheld from them the noteworthy fact that the greatest tributes to the subject have come not from mathematicians but from dramatists, poets, and novelists. Finally, they should be protected against becoming victims of the doctrine of incidental learning or the doctrine of postponement.

The effort to make mathematics a prominent feature of education implies the desire to keep secondary education on a high level, with respect to both the ideals that inspire it and the standards of achievement that are expected The Commission supports such a general educational position, in opposition to the movement toward minimum education. It is true that our attempts at universal education will bring into the schools many a case of Johnnie Lowique and Winnie Barely-pass, as well as delightful Huck Finns who "take no stock in mathematics." Unless the American temper changes completely there is little danger that such boys and girls will be dealt with unsympathetically while we continue our efforts to devise studies and activities really suitable for them. But they should not be allowed to set the general pattern for education, any more than their tastes should be allowed too much weight in determining the pleasures and diversions available for educated people. A survey of movies and radio might indicate, however, that such a surrender is being made. In concluding, one might say that the statement of Hogben that the history of mathematics is the mirror of civilization suggests that its position in the schools may reveal something not only about our conception of education but about our national philosophy and ideals.

CHAPTER IV

The Mathematics Curriculum

"We shall make one or two postulates, deduce rules, and give examples."

—FOWLER, THE KING'S ENGLISH

BASIC CONSIDERATIONS

The Importance of Continuity and Organic Growth. For many years American educators have urged the creation of curricula based on the view that formal educational process extends from the pupil's infancy through his adolescent years, or even further. This idea is now receiving uniform emphasis in all the major subject matter fields. Mathematics, by virtue of its highly cumulative nature, cannot yield the cultural returns of which it is capable if it is offered as a disconnected sequence of isolated units. On the contrary, the major objectives of mathematics, its central themes and its broad life values, must be given an opportunity to unfold gradually and continuously, in harmony with known facts of mental growth.

The Importance of Flexibility. Secondary education in America has not yet achieved relatively stable, clearly defined lines of demarcation that set it off from the domain of elementary education on the one hand and from that of collegiate education on the other.[1] We have, and may continue to have, a diversity of administrative divisions that are due to a variety of considerations. Thus, in certain communities, the traditional 8–4 plan has been replaced by the 6–3–3 plan, the 7–5 plan, the 6–6 plan, or the 6–2–4 plan, either specifically for curricular purposes or because of a problem of building accommodations.[2]

At this point we are merely interested in the fact that because of this

---

1. In this report the junior college is regarded as belonging to the secondary field.
2. Data concerning the growth or the relative frequency of these administrative types of organization may be obtained from the publications of educational research bureaus, and from educational yearbooks and statistical abstracts. See, for example, the monographs comprising the *National Survey of Secondary Education*, Bulletin, 1932, No. 17, U. S. Office of Education.

variety of types of administrative organization in the field of secondary education it has been extremely difficult, even if it were desirable, to arrive at anything approximating general agreement as to curricular offerings at any stage of the educational process. No national commission can prescribe, or should even attempt to suggest, such a rigid organization of the materials of instruction that there would be no further opportunity for individual initiative and constructive experimentation. On the other hand, there is need at the moment to elaborate as carefully as possible a group of guiding principles that may offer a definite step toward educational harmony. A tentative list of such principles will be outlined in the following pages. The second step is that of describing the curricular offerings, as far as possible, in terms of broad fields rather than in terms of specific units of work.

It is the opinion of this Commission that the obvious difficulty of providing for both continuity and flexibility has been the great stumbling block in the development of a nation-wide mathematical program of instruction. Accordingly, in this Report is described a program for mathematics in grades 7 to 14 that definitely aims to provide for continuity of development, and that at the same time respects the reasonable demands for flexibility on the part of school administrators and teachers.

The Work of the Elementary Schools. The Commission has not attempted to suggest mathematics curricula for the first six grades. That responsibility has been assumed by the National Council Committee on Arithmetic,[3] which will issue a separate report dealing with this problem.

The mathematics program of the elementary schools is the indispensable foundation of all the pupil's later mathematics work. If that foundation is weak, the pupil's subsequent progress is likely to be permanently handicapped.

In the following pages, it is assumed that a pupil who is adequately prepared for the work of the seventh grade has acquired a working knowledge of the arithmetic commonly taught in the primary schools. An increasing number of representative syllabi also assign to the elementary grades some preliminary work in the field of space intuition and a knowledge of geometric forms. Hence the following attainments may be regarded as the normal mathematical equipment of the American pupil who has satisfactorily completed the work of the sixth grade:[4]

3. Sponsored by the National Council of Teachers of Mathematics, under the chairmanship of Professor R. L. Morton, Ohio University.

4. For a synopsis of present tendencies in arithmetic, the reader may be referred to the *Tenth Yearbook* of the National Council of Teachers of Mathematics. See also Norton and Norton. *Foundations of Curriculum Building,* Chapter XI. Ginn and Co., 1936. For the work of the primary grades, see especially, Morton, Robert Lee. *Teaching Arithmetic in the Elementary School.* Silver, Burdett Co., 1937.

(*1*) A familiarity with the basic concepts, the processes, and the vocabulary of arithmetic.

(*2*) Understanding of the significance of the different positions that a given digit may occupy in a number, including the case of a decimal fraction.

(*3*) A mastery of the basic number combinations in addition, subtraction, multiplication, and division.

(*4*) Reasonable skill in computing with integers, common fractions, and decimal fractions.

(*5*) An acquaintance with the principal units of measurement, and their use in everyday life situations.

(*6*) The ability to solve simple problems involving computation and units of measurement.

(*7*) The ability to recognize, to name, and to sketch such common geometric figures as the rectangle, the square, the circle, the triangle, the rectangular solid, the sphere, the cylinder, and the cube.

(*8*) The habit of estimating and checking results.

A TENTATIVE LIST OF GUIDING PRINCIPLES

Considerations Governing the Selection of the Materials of Instruction, Grades 7-12. Among the considerations governing the selection of material in building a curriculum, the following may be mentioned:

(*1*) Since there has been general agreement that the learning of mathematics rests upon acquiring a knowledge of a certain body of concepts, principles, processes, and facts that are essentially the same for all pupils, there can remain little freedom of choice as to the inclusion in the curriculum of these fundamental elements. The curriculum should include the basic elements of arithmetic, algebra, geometry, graphic representation, and trigonometry.

(*2*) In contrast with this permanent foundation, we have the equally important fact that mathematics has had a remarkable growth and has been extended to widely varied fields of application.

For every type of pupil, a mathematical course of study must give constant attention to the "foundations," while at the same time it stresses significant applications within the learner's potential range of understanding and interest.

(*3*) The selection of the fundamental mathematical units of work, especially in grades 7-9, is a highly technical task.

In particular, the fundamental concepts, principles, and skills of mathematics must be introduced and developed in a carefully organized pattern. Due attention must be given at all times not only to logical considerations, but also to psychological and pedagogical principles.

(*4*) Extensive experience has led to the conviction that in the case of retarded pupils, modifications are needed in the rate of progress and the degree of comprehension, rather than in the choice of the basic mathematical units. (See also Chapter VII.)

(*5*) The precise scope and degree of emphasis to be given to each major type of work, in a particular school, cannot be stated with finality in any general discussion. On the contrary, these items must be regarded as subject to further local experimentation, in the light of actual time schedules and of desired or possible types of application and of training.

(*6*) Psychological considerations such as those having to do with the problem of understanding, with motivation, rates of learning, and with degrees of mastery, are also of great significance in connection with the construction of modern curricula. These questions must certainly be kept in mind when one wishes to determine the amount of work which may safely be accomplished during a certain period of time. They are furthermore of primary importance in the preparation of detailed instructions for the teaching of each unit or topic.

(*7*) Mathematics is often described as a "hard" subject. It has acquired this reputation (i) because it is composed of a relatively large body of closely related abstract ideas often presented too abruptly; (ii) because its fundamental facts and principles must be learned as an organized sequence; (iii) because only constant attention and real understanding will lead to success in this field; and (iv) because only considerable practice, over a period of months or years, will insure mastery and the ability to apply with ease the results of mathematical training. While these features of mathematics cannot be denied, it is also true that each forward step in the subject is, as a rule, a very simple one. Hence, by safeguarding each day's progress, and by following a teaching practice based on the laws of learning, the teacher can eliminate, to a large extent, the painful and futile struggle that is only too evident in some mathematics classrooms. In particular, the following considerations are significant:

(*a*) Early in each year the mathematical maturity of each pupil should be determined. In case the required information is not available from reports, inventory tests may be needed to determine the amount of ground that may be covered during the semester, as well as the necessary amount of reteaching.

(*b*) Since mathematics is a cumulative subject, pupils should be made to realize that each day's work counts toward success or failure.

(*c*) An understanding of the concepts and principles of mathematics is the key to its successful study. To teach in such a way that the concepts become clear is the hardest and the most significant task confronting the teacher of mathematics. By way of illustration, a definition should usually be the outgrowth, not the beginning, of a learning process.

(*d*) "Overviews" and motivating discussions are valuabel as directing guides, while summaries and organic reviews are effective means of creating perspective and confidence. A properly constructed curriculum will give adequate attention to such considerations.

(*e*) In the past, much dependence was placed on mere drill. Recent psychological investigations suggest that all techniques should be based on insight. This implies that adequate practice is to be provided, not mere drill, to lead the pupil to proper assimilation and mastery.

(*f*) Modern psychology has proved the effectiveness of "spaced learning." That is, "bunched learning" is not so productive of lasting values as "spaced learning." With slow pupils, especially, the idea of a periodic return to the same topic, providing for its growing mastery and enlarged application, is of the utmost importance. Experience shows that we cannot expect "one hundred per cent mastery" after a single, brief exposure.

(*g*) The slow learner profits by at least the same degree of motivation, of cultural enrichment and interest, as do other pupils. But interest is primarily a means of stimulating effort, not a substitute for effort.

Principles of Arrangement. The following principles refer primarily to the *sequence* of the topics to be included in the curriculum.

(*1*) The sequence in the curriculum should be such that each topic will contribute definitely toward an ever-growing and more significant organization of the basic concepts, principles, skills, facts, relationships, types of appreciation, and fields of application, resulting in the development of a unified mathematical picture.

(*2*) Even in a reduced program, the study should emphasize problem solving and modes of thinking, and should not become a mere sequence of formal and relatively abstract drills.

(*3*) If a unit organization is followed, it is not always advisable to attempt in each of the units a complete or exhaustive treatment of the central theme or topic under discussion. On the other hand a unit should not include unrelated "odds and ends."

(*4*) In general, a new topic should not be introduced unless there is a sufficient background of prerequisite concepts and skills to permit unhindered concentration upon the new elements.

(*5*) A new idea or principle should not, as a rule, be introduced prior to the time at which it is needed or may be effectively applied.

MATHEMATICAL CATEGORIES AS A BASIS OF ORGANIZATION OF THE CURRICULUM

The Doctrine of "Centers of Interest." Elementary and secondary school systems are operating in many cases under different conceptions as to the best way to carry on the "educative process." One can with some propriety speak of the "old education" and the "new education" although such descriptions tend to over-simplify the problem. Not all schools of fifty or seventy-five years ago were alike; many of them were not so narrow in offerings or as restricted in points of view as is asserted in some present-day writing. In education, as elsewhere, one must remember that a careful study of the past reveals not only faults unsuspected by some people but virtues associated by others only with the present. On the other hand, what is called the "new education" may have more conservative elements than is sometimes realized. This much, however, it seems safe to say by way of generalization. The "old education" interpreted teaching as a process of transmitting or inculcating a relatively fixed body of skills, information, facts, behaviors, and habits that were considered necessary or useful to a person, both in "making a living" and in living with satisfaction. It tended to employ fixed curricula, though not without giving attention in varying degrees to the interests and abilities of its clientele through the use of electives or different curricula. The "new education," in contrast, tends to be much more "child-centered." It questions fixed curricula, even when provision is made for electives, and seeks to induce the pupil to reach out for such elements of information or training as may be in harmony with his own "needs and interest," both felt and unfelt.

Under the "new education" an effort is being made in some schools to build the curriculum primarily around significant "centers of interest" or "areas of experience," so broad in character as to anticipate potentially a large number of the educational needs of children. By this means it is hoped to insure both a set of desirable practical and cultural backgrounds and the possibility of favorable subjective reactions. Furthermore, it is hoped that through sufficiently expert handling of these backgrounds the school will succeed in transmitting the skills, facts, habits, and attitudes necessary to a successful life and well-rounded development. Under the "old education" many of the most important of these facts and skills have been isolated, logically organized, and systematically taught. Under the "new education," however, they are to be acquired much more informally in the course of experiences selected, at least in part, for reasons other than their fruitfulness as a means of transmitting predetermined skills, facts, and habits.

In the elementary school the "new education" has secured widespread endorsement. The secondary school is being subjected to great pressure to follow a similar course; that is, it is being asked to give up its "adult-organized," sequential subject matter courses in favor of broad, flexible "areas of experience" that are assumed to appeal to the individual student. In this Report the concern is mainly with the question of the extent to which such a conception is feasible in the field of mathematics.

Unsettled Status of This Educational Issue. The fact has been stressed that the mathematics of the elementary school is a comparatively closely organized and cumulative system of concepts, skills, facts, and relationships. A pupil cannot master a given unit in most branches of mathematics until he has acquired some understanding of and reasonable skill in the related earlier steps involved. If the basic equipment in mathematics is to be acquired by means of "centers of interest," as these are commonly understood, such as the farm, transportation, and consumption of goods and services, mathematics becomes only one aspect of such study. Today a crucial question of curricular theory centers around the extent to which the methods of the "new education" lead to mastery or understanding of fundamental subjects such as mathematics.

The evidence accumulated on the relative merits of curricula organized according to the newer and the older theories is far from conclusive, at least with respect to instruction in mathematics. The "new education" is still definitely in the experimental stage in the secondary school. There can hardly be any doubt that an exclusive dependence upon "centers of interest" as a basis for organizing the curriculum makes very difficult the application of the guiding principles discussed in this Report. In the absence of more convincing evidence in favor of one point of view over the other, this Commission has sought a basis of organization that adheres to accepted principles, yet incorporates modern views on the way the mathematics curriculum should be organized. The Commission recognizes the desirability of correlated activities and a reasonable utilization of centers of interest pertaining to important aspects of modern life, but under present conditions it recommends that for other than experimental classes the curriculum be organized in conformity with principles outlined above and later in this Report.

Expressing the Mathematics Curriculum in Terms of Broad Categories. For the reasons suggested above, this Commission has found it desirable to outline a general plan of organizing the materials of instruction in secondary mathematics, for grades 7–12, in terms of two principles of classification. *First*, there is the subdivision according to major subject fields: I. The field of number and of computation. II. The field of geometric form and space perception. III. The field of graphic representation. IV. The field of elementary analysis (algebra and trigonometry). V. The field of logical (or "straight") thinking. VI. The field of relational thinking. VII. The field of symbolic representation and thinking. *Second*, there is the subdivision of the fields into categories such as the following: I. Basic concepts, principles, and terms. II. Fundamental processes. III. Fundamental relations. IV. Skills and techniques. V. Applications.

A curriculum that is constructed in conformity with such a plan has the following merits:

(*1*) It consists of parts which, separately and in combination, for many years have constituted the essential elements of successful mathematics work in the grades considered.

(*2*) It is flexible enough to make possible its use in schools representing virtually all the principal administrative types of organization, such as the 8–4 plan, the 6–3–3 plan, the 6–6 plan, and so on.

(*3*) It is sufficiently adaptable to meet a large variety of local conditions and special needs.

(*4*) It provides definitely for continuity of training with respect to the central objectives of secondary mathematics.

(*5*) It suggests and makes possible extensive correlation with related fields.

In later chapters of this Report two such curricula are described, without any implication that other satisfactory programs are not possible. Indeed other well-considered and tested plans have appeared which seem to the Commission to be basically in agreement with those described here. The plans do not restrict the freedom of the teachers as to methods of teaching, or types of motivation, or lesson organization.

ESSENTIALS OF A GENERAL PROGRAM IN SECONDARY MATHEMATICS

In the following pages there is submitted in broad outline a summary of those mathematical fields and types of training and of appreciation that are necessary in order that the pupil may meet the demands of modern life and may realize the desirable cultural contributions that have been discussed. It is the opinion of this Commission that the mathematics program of our secondary schools, in grades 7-12, should be built substantially on abilities and outcomes such as those suggested below.

I. The Field of Number and of Computation

(A Continuation of the Work of the Elementary Grades)

Basic Concepts and Principles. There should be a growing familiarity with the basic vocabulary and working principles of arithmetic. This involves (*1*) naming or identifying a concept when encountered, (*2*) giving an example or an informal explanation of the meaning of given terms, and, at a higher level, (*3*) developing formal definitions of terms that have a broad operational significance. Examples of such terms are the following:

(*a*) Operations: addition, subtraction, multiplication, division, rounding off numbers.

(*b*) Results: sum, product, difference, quotient, per cent.

(*c*) Relations: ratio, proportion, equality, increase, decrease.

(*d*) Applications: interest, discount, commission, rate, premium, profit, loss, average.

In all teaching of secondary mathematics much attention should be given to a conscious grasp of the *principles* which underlie the fundamental processes of arithmetic. Examples of such principles are the following:

(*a*) The numerator and the denominator of a common fraction may be multiplied or divided by the same (non-zero) number, without changing the value of the fraction.

(*b*) The order of the factors in a product does not affect the result.

Fundamental Skills. The pupils should develop such skills as the following:

(*a*) The ability to use the four fundamental operations with integers, common fractions, and decimal fractions, due regard being given to the learner's maturity.[5]

(*b*) The ability to use the principal units of measure in everyday life situations.

(*c*) The ability to read simple numerical tables in connection with the educational program as a whole.

Application.[6] There should be a gradual and continuous development of the ability to recognize and use arithmetical facts, concepts, and principles in everyday life situations, wherever encountered, not merely for the study of pertinent numerical problems, but also for purposes of explanation and prediction.

This ability should be stressed constantly until its use becomes a habit.

Further Topics. There should be a gradual growth in the pupil's understanding of the extended number system (negative numbers, irrational numbers, and so on). Attention may also well be given to:

(*a*) The ability to perform addition, subtraction, multiplication, and division by use of a computing machine.

(*b*) The ability to multiply, divide, square, and find square roots by a slide rule.

(*c*) The ability to exercise judgment in presenting numerical results of measurement or of computations based upon measurements. Due regard being paid to the learner's level of maturity, there should be developed gradually the habit of retaining an appropriate number of significant digits and using appropriate accuracy in computation.

II. The Field of Geometric Form and of Space Perception

Basic Concepts. The ability to recognize at least the elementary geometric figures and terms involves (*1*) naming a figure when seen or presented, (*2*) sketching or drawing a figure to illustrate a term, and, at a higher level, (*3*) developing a formal definition of the basic terms. The following list suggests types of terms that

---

5. It is understood that these processes are to be considered not merely in an abstract way, but in many concrete problem situations such as those involving percentage and other business and social applications. Accuracy should receive the main consideration, but a reasonable degree of speed must also be regarded as essential.

6. The description given here will apply with appropriate and rather obvious modifications to fields II, III, and IV, and reference will be made back to it on later pages.

should receive attention:

(*a*) Entire figures: rectangle, circle, triangle, square, trapezoid, parallelogram, rectangular solid, cube, cone, pyramid, sphere.

(*b*) Parts of figures: radius, diameter, diagonal, vertex, sides, chord, arc.

(*c*) Mensurational terms: length, area, volume, perimeter, and such units as inch, foot, square inch, cubic foot, centimeter, meter, degree.

(*d*) Positional relationships: parallel, perpendicular, vertical, horizonal, oblique.

(*e*) Terms involving comparison: greater, less, equal, congruence, similarity, symmetry.

(*f*) Incidence relationships: intersection, tangency, coincidence.

Fundamental Skills. The drawing, the measuring, and the basic construction of the common geometric figures are skills, the development of which should represent a continuous program accompanying the study of the fundamental geometric relationships.

Among the skills to be stressed are the following:

(*a*) The ability to use such common instruments as the ruler, graduated or ungraduated, the compasses, the protractor, and squared paper.

(*b*) The sketching, or drawing, and the construction of common geometric figures, either full size or to scale.

(*c*) The direct measurement of lengths and of angles.

(*d*) The determination by formula of such common areas as those of the rectangle, the square, the triangle, the circle, and the trapezoid.

(*e*) The determination by formula of such common volumes as those of the prism, especially the rectangular solid and the cube, and the cylinder.

(*f*) A use of the technique of indirect measurement in simple field work.

Elementary Geometric Facts, Properties, and Relations. The pupil should acquire such abilities as the following:

(*a*) The ability to recall and to apply habitually fundamental metric relations or propositions, such as the following: The sum of the angles of any triangle is 180°; the Pythagorean relation.

(*b*) The recognition of relations resulting from varying positions of geometric figures, such as the possible intersection of lines, of circles and lines.

(*c*) The ability to recognize and to state simple functional relations resulting from changes in dimension or position, such as the change in the area of a square whose side is doubled.

Discovery and Verification. There should be a gradual and increasing development of the ability to discover and to seek means of testing important geometric relationships. An acquaintance with the major propositions resulting from this training should become a definite part of the student's mathematical equipment.

Application. See [under "I"].

III. The Field of Graphic Representation

Basic Terms and Concepts. There should be a growing familiarity with the basic vocabulary of graphic representation. As in other fields this involves (*1*) naming or identifying a concept when encountered, (*2*) giving an example or informal explanation of the meaning of given terms, and at a higher level, (*3*) developing formal definitions of the more important terms. Examples of such terms are the following: ordinate, abscissa, axis, coordinate, distance, tangent, line, slope, locus, graph, symmetry, table, formula, scale, bar chart.

Fundamental Skills. The pupil should be able to:

(*a*) Take tabular data and construct therefrom a graph with a suitable scale, properly titled and of appropriate type.

(*b*) Read a given graph, recognizing not only values at intermediate points, but also rates of rise and fall, and maximum and minimum values.

(*c*) (Optional) Draw a line to "fit" data approximately linear.

Application. See [under "I"].

Further Topics. Some schools may find it feasible to extend the work in graphic representation into the field of elementary statistics, including the use of alignment charts (nomograms).

IV. The Field of Elementary Analysis

The Basic Vocabulary and Working Concepts of Elementary Analysis. The pupil should be able to: (*1*) name or identify a concept when encountered, (*2*) give an example or an informal explanation of the meaning of the basic terms, and, at a higher level, (*3*) develop formal definitions of such terms as have a broad operational significance. Among these are the following:

(*a*) Types of number: positive and negative numbers, fractions, irrational numbers.

(*b*) Operations: addition, subtraction, multiplication, division, reducing to lower terms, finding square root, raising to a power.

(*c*) Structural terms: monomial, binomial, polynomial, coefficient, exponent, radical, similar terms.

(*d*) Functional terms: equation, formula, variable, dependence, table, correspondence, sine, cosine, tangent.

(*e*) Applications: average, rate of motion or of work, evaluation of a formula, approximation, per cent of error.

Fundamental Principles and Techniques. The pupil should be able to use the fundamental principles of algebra and elementary analysis involved in basic techniques and in related pertinent applications. Examples of such principles are: the rule for the addition of similar terms, the rule for reducing fractions to lower terms, the laws of exponents. Illustrations of these techniques follow:

(*a*) The fundamental manipulative techniques.

(*b*) The ability to solve equations.

(*c*) The ability to make trigonometric reductions.

(*d*) The ability to solve triangles.

Application. See [under "I"].

Further Topics. Some schools may find it desirable to extend this field of work to include in the later years some work in the technique of differentiation, together with applications that are within the comprehension of the pupil.

V. The Field of Logical (or "Straight") Thinking [7]

While it has always been recognized that mathematics is essentially a mode of *thinking*, it has not been equally clear precisely how the types of thinking characteristic of mathematics are to be stressed in connection with the customary materials of instruction. Nor is there general agreement as to the degree of emphasis that should be given to training in mathematical thinking. Recent psychological investigations tend to prove, however, that the "transfer" value of any given school subject is largely a result of a conscious and persistent application, in everyday situations, of *generalized* concepts, procedures, and types of thinking. The ability to apply widely and habitually such potentially broad areas of training is not acquired suddenly, but is the result of a gradual process of growth. Hence every opportunity must be used in the classroom, throughout the entire mathematics program, to cultivate the active interest of the pupil in the modes of thinking which we are here discussing. These considerations suggest the need of analyses of the kind given below. That is, in this field of work we are concerned with aspects such as the following:

Basic Terms and Concepts. A clear understanding of the meaning of the basic terms and the ability to recognize their actual occurrences and their bearings in life situations. Examples of such concepts are: assumption or postulate, proposition, converse, conclusion.

Fundamental Principles. A clear grasp and appreciation of the assumptions and principles on which the structure of mathematics rests. This involves considerations such as the following:

(*a*) A knowledge of the principles underlying the manipulative techniques of mathematics, such as those relating to order, grouping, distribution, and the like.

(*b*) The realization of the logical implications of related propositions, such as those involving a given theorem, its converse, its opposite.

(*c*) The realization of the economy resulting from such an organizing principle or assumption as that of *continuity*.

Fundamental Abilities. Such abilities as the following should be gradually developed:

(*a*) To recognize and formulate the assumptions underlying an argument.

(*b*) To recognize terms that require precise definition.

(*c*) To organize statements in a coherent logical sequence.

(*d*) To recognize the proposition under discussion and to realize when a conclusion has been reached.

---

7. In connection with this topic reference can be made to Keyser, C. J., *Thinking about Thinking*, E. P. Dutton and Co., New York, 1926, and Fawcett, H. P., *The Nature of Proof*, Thirteenth Yearbook of the National Council of Teachers of Mathematics, Bureau of Publications, Teachers College, Columbia University, 1938.

(*e*) To discover common flaws not only in reasoning in mathematical and related fields, but also in areas inviting emotional bias or requiring propaganda analysis.

(*f*) To recognize the logical structure or plan of an extended series of propositions, or of a related group of discussions.

Application. A gradual and increasing development of the ability to manifest coherent, logical thinking in everyday life situations.

VI. THE FIELD OF RELATIONAL THINKING

Here we are concerned with the development of a growing ability to recognize, in everyday life situations, cases of quantitative relationships and of functional dependence. The importance of this type of training was stressed as follows in the Report of the National Committee on Mathematical Requirements (p. 12):

"The primary and underlying principle of the course should be the idea of relationship between variables, including the methods of determining and expressing such relationships. The teacher should have this idea constantly in mind, and the pupil's advancement should be consciously directed along the lines which will present first one and then another of the ideas upon which finally the formulation of the general concept of functionality depends." [8]

Basic Concepts. The ability to recognize, to name, and in simple cases to define fundamental terms should be gradually developed. Such fundamental terms include: constant, variable, independent variable, dependent variable, one-to-one correspondence, function, formula, table, value of a function, invariant relation, increasing, decreasing, maximum, minimum, associated data, ordered list, interpolation.

Fundamental Skills and Abilities. Among these skills and abilities are the following:

(*a*) To read tables of related values, including trigonometric and logarithmic tables.

(*b*) To evaluate formulas for assigned values of the independent variables.

(*c*) To interpolate in tables and graphs.

(*d*) To construct simple tables, such as frequency tables, from raw data, and numerical tables from given formulas.

(*e*) To construct appropriate formulas from verbal statements.

(*f*) To determine the constants (in very simple cases) for empirical formulas to fit approximately a set of given data.

(*g*) To recognize functional dependence, and to select variables pertinent to a given problem.

Application. There should be a gradual and increasing development of the ability to recognize functional dependence as well as statistical associations which fall short of functional correspondence.

---

8. Such strong emphasis was quite justified at that time, but the present Commission has already commented upon the possibility of over-emphasis. (See p. 42.)

VII. The Field of Symbolic Representation and Thinking

The aim here is a gradual development of the ability to translate quantitative statements into symbolic form and conversely, and an increasing appreciation of the economy and the power resulting from the correct use of symbolic techniques.

HABITS AND APPRECIATIONS IN THE MATHEMATICS CLASSROOM

The development of desirable attitudes, habits, and appreciations is an outcome of the procedures employed by the teacher and of the resulting classroom atmosphere. Lasting results of this type, however, depend largely on continued attention to their growth, and cooperation throughout the school.

Every phase of the mathematics curriculum, as well as all classroom procedures, should be scrutinized for the opportunities to develop a growing appreciation of the immense power of mathematics, of its record as a universal servant of mankind, of its cultural significance, and of its permanent place in the study of nature, in the sciences, in the practical arts, in business, engineering, and everyday life.

Types of Motivation; Supplementary Projects and Activities. In recent years encouraging progress has been made in the direction of stressing the appreciational and cultural aspects of mathematics. Many mathematics classrooms are being equipped with illustrative visual aids and interesting charts and pictures giving evidence of the important place which mathematics occupies in the modern world. The literature bearing on this phase of mathematical instruction is being extended. The *Yearbooks* of the National Council of Teachers of Mathematics, monographs published by *Scripta Mathematica*, numerous articles in such journals as *The Mathematics Teacher* and *School Science and Mathematics*, and a growing list of special treatises, all furnish valuable assistance to teachers who desire to enrich their usual programs by contacts with motivating backgrounds. Some effective modes of interesting pupils in this domain are suggested in the following paragraphs.

Nature as a Museum of Form. In the Introduction, attention was called to the great influence of nature upon mathematics. Many geometric forms are either clearly seen in or suggested by what man observes about him, and a constant mindfulness of this fact is to be recommended to all classroom teachers.

Historical References. The history of mathematics should not supersede mathematics; it should supplement its study. It is especially effective in increasing the cultural value of the subject, and a carefully developed account of parts of the history of this old enterprise will give more meaning

615

to both elementary and secondary curricula in mathematics. Furthermore, it is to be recalled that historical considerations often increase a purely abstract interest that one finds in some topic or some problem that has a special appeal to him.

Dramatizing the Role of Mathematics in Modern Life. Every effort should be used to make pupils conscious of the contributions of mathematics to human progress and to individual and public welfare. The close connection of mathematics with the practical arts, with technology, industry, business, commerce, science, and other important enterprises, should receive attention. Among the methods that may be suggested for this work the following have proved successful:

(*a*) *School exhibits.* A periodic display, in classrooms and school corridors, of materials that will stimulate interest in present-day uses of mathematics can be recommended as a helpful device, particularly if the pupils themselves have furnished the materials.

(*b*) *Assembly programs.* Some mathematical units or topics are suitable for presentation before the entire school, in a dramatized form. Brief plays, especially when prepared by the pupils themselves, seldom fail to arouse enthusiasm and sustained interest.

(*c*) *Mathematical films.* The number of commercially available films that have a bearing on mathematics, while still very small, will gradually become larger; and such visual aids assist instruction in mathematics as they have already helped in the field of science. Schools should be encouraged to make simple mathematical films as classroom projects.

(*d*) *Source books.* Pupils should be encouraged to collect and to preserve, in individual source books, items that have a bearing on mathematics. Those who are not acquainted with this device are always surprised to discover how very wide is the range of the source book materials that can be assembled in the course of a single year by any class of normal ability.

(*e*) *A permanent mathematical museum.* In some schools a good beginning has been made in the direction of creating permanent mathematical exhibits. The ideal plan is that of assembling these collections in a central building, preferably in a special "Hall of Mathematics."

(*f*) *Supplementary mathematical projects.* Many enrichment projects based on local interests and showing local uses of mathematics will suggest themselves to a resourceful teacher. Among these might be mentioned scheduled talks by leading members of the community who find daily use for specialized mathematical training, such as engineers, actuaries, and bankers. Sometimes trips to large industrial plants, or for the purpose of engaging in elementary surveying, will add interest and vitality to the subject.

Mathematical Clubs. In many schools it is possible, among other extracurricular activities, to organize at least one flourishing mathematical club. It may be advisable to have a club for the earlier years of the high school as well as one for the later years. Such clubs serve the important purpose of giving a suitable forum to particularly superior or enthusiastic pupils. The study of mathematical recreations, of advanced topics, of historical backgrounds, as well as discussions, reports, competitive tests, and debates will influence noticeably the daily classroom routine. If awards are offered for outstanding work done by members of the club, an effective incentive is often given to the entire mathematics program of the school.

Mathematical Bulletins or School Papers. Another extracurricular activity which has created enthusiasm and has stimulated effort, is that of enabling the strongest mathematics pupils of a school or of the community to edit a school paper devoted entirely to mathematics. Such a publication may also be utilized by the teachers and the pupils as a medium for the collection of community problems, for book reviews and abstracts of important articles, and for important announcements. It may also contain the programs of local or regional mathematical clubs, and may explain and discuss the mathematical equipment demanded by typical vocations or professions. In short, the mathematical paper of a school or a group of schools can attempt to show in what way mathematics is indeed a "mirror of civilization."

The Second Report of The Commission [1] on Post-War Plans

The Improvement of Mathematics in Grades 1 to 14

INTRODUCTION

This report presents suggestions for improving mathematical instruction from the beginning of the elementary school through the last year of junior college. The program throughout these grades is in need of a thoroughgoing reorganization. The arithmetic of the elementary school can be and must be improved. The high school needs to come to grips with its dual responsibility, (1) to provide sound mathematical training for our future leaders of science, mathematics, and other learned fields, and (2) to insure mathematical competence for the ordinary affairs of life to the extent that this can be done for all citizens as a part of a general education appropriate for the major fraction of the high school population. Then, too, the junior college, which has grown up without a well considered design, should now take stock of its valid functions before it enters its second period of rapid expansion. It is reasonable to believe that the greatest advance can be made if teachers of mathematics in the elementary school, in the secondary school, and in the junior college, attack the problem together. At any rate it is sensible because of the essential continuity of mathematical instruction to plan the improvements in any one grade in terms of the total program.

The report presents a series of constructive theses which in spite of appearances are not offered in dogmatic finality. It is hoped that these tentative guides will be widely discussed in order that desirable modifications may be made in a later report. The Commission is seeking, through the cooperative thinking of teachers of mathematics in these grades, to arrive at a set of principles (a blueprint) for building a stronger program in mathematical education. Although the theses are tentative, it should be noted that they stem from the collective experience and thinking of the whole Commission and from a considerable body of pedagogical literature and

1. Created by the Board of Directors of the National Council of Teachers of Mathematics. The first report of the Commission appeared in the May 1944 issue of THE MATHEMATICS TEACHER, pages 226–232.

[This article is reprinted from the *Mathematics Teacher* 38 (May 1945): 195–221.]

investigation. Some have, of course, long been advocated by many leaders. The mental climate with respect to mathematics is at the moment very favorable. Now is the time to put our house in order by making the improvements that have been postponed for too long. In the postwar period we should be ready to provide the very finest mathematics program for every type of youngster in our schools. It is to that end that the Commission submits the following theses for careful study.[2] The first one is of vital concern to every teacher of mathematics from grade one through junior college.

Thesis 1. *The school should guarantee functional* [3] *competence in mathematics to all who can possibly achieve it.*

Competence in mathematics in many respects parallels literacy in communication. The legal specification of literacy is fulfilled by the ability to write and to speak one's own language. In pioneer days, no doubt this ability was adequate. Today the U.S. Army uses the phrase "functional literacy" to imply fourth-grade ability. Though no one knows exactly what functional literacy means, except by arbitrary definition, it is clear that modern technology has stepped up the minimum requirements of literacy in communication.

In great-grandfather's day, when life was relatively simple, the ability to compute accurately when dealing with whole numbers, common fractions, decimals, and per cent was adequate for the ordinary affairs of life. There are good reasons for believing that the minimum requirement in mathematics for effective citizenship is moving upward and that it is already a big step higher than control of the four fundamental processes of arithmetic. Functional competence in mathematics in modern affairs seems almost as crucial as functional literacy in communications. Life in the armed forces today, for a boy who is merely a good computer, is decidedly limited—even the road to the rating as a sergeant is likely to be long and difficult if the candidate has not had some training in simple practical physics and the related mathematics. On the other hand, there is strenuous competition among the services to secure the boy who comes with this bit of mathematical training. Then, too, industry now provides a vast training program which usually includes mathematics in order to get what it needs for a great variety of jobs. The same increasing demand for higher mathematical competence is to be noted in changes in the nonvocational aspects of life today. Certain widely read magazines, the Sunday editions of newspapers of

2. The Commission will at all times welcome critical reactions to its published reports. It is suggested that teachers of mathematics and mathematical clubs and associations examine the theses critically. Comments may be sent to any member of the Commission.

3. Obviously the word *functional* here is used in the sense that the educationist uses the word, not in its mathematical sense.

our larger cities, and even occasional radio programs all assume an understanding of certain basic mathematical ideas which are not fully understood by all of our citizens.

It is fair to ask, "Does anyone know what we mean by functional competence in mathematics, or is the phrase as vague as the word 'literacy'?" The answer is that the meaning has been fairly clear for over twenty years —the most authentic analysis having been given in the 1923 Report of the National Committee on Mathematical Requirements on *The Reorganization of Mathematics in Secondary Education,* which for the first time listed in considerable detail the specific mathematical objectives for citizenship. Moreover, we can now define functional competence in mathematics more concretely by utilizing the experiences of the armed forces. This source of information has already been investigated and the findings have been published in two committee reports.[4] These reports list basic concepts and useful skills that may safely be presumed to include the mathematical materials of functional competence in mathematics for the armed services. But the reader will ask, Does the list of essentials in mathematics for minimum army needs apply to civilian life as well?

The mathematical phase of the training program in military schools, at least for the simpler tasks, came largely from industry. A glance at the list of approximately six hundred jobs in the army is sufficient to convince one that a very high percentage of these jobs have their counterparts in civilian life. Pending further investigation, it will be sensible to assume that the mathematics for minimum army needs, with only slight modification,[5] should be part of the general education of all our citizens. In the terminology of the educationist we can now outline with a good deal of assurance the mathematics of the *core curriculum.* Although the phrase "core curriculum" may disappear from pedagogical literature, there will persist the need for a common mathematical foundation for intelligent citizenship that will at the same time serve as a key to many "families of jobs." We need to make certain that the essentials for functional competence in mathematics are achieved by all who can learn them so that the proper guidance of the pupil may not be an impossible task.

The essentials for functional competence in mathematics are put as questions in the following Check List:

4. See the report of the Committee on "Preinduction Courses in Mathematics," THE MATHEMATICS TEACHER, March, 1943. Pages 114–124; and the report of the committee on "Essential Mathematics for Minimum Army Needs," THE MATHEMATICS TEACHER, October, 1943. Pages 243–282.

5. It is not implied that the mathematics needed by the enlisted man and by the citizen in civilian life are *identical.* There are a few important differences. For example, as regards the mathematics of consumer education the enlisted man has in general little choice as to what he eats and what he wears, his budget problems are obviously not the same as one meets in civilian life.

1. Can the pupil operate [6] effectively with whole numbers, common fractions, decimals, and per cents?

2. Has he fixed the habit of estimating an answer before he does the computation and of verifying the answer afterward?

3. Does he have a clear understanding of ratio?

4. Is he skillful in the use of tables (including simple interpolation) as, for example: interest tables, tables of roots and powers, trigonometric functions, income tax tables, etc.?

5. Does he know how to use rounded numbers?

6. Can he find the square root of a number by table or by division?

7. Does he know the main guides that one should follow in collecting and interpreting data; can he use averages (mean, median, mode); can he make and interpret a graph (bar, line, circle, the graph of a formula, and of a linear equation)?

8. Does he have adequate ideas of point, line, angle, parallel lines, perpendicular lines, triangle (right, scalene, isosceles, and equilateral), parallelogram (including square and rectangle), trapezoid, circle, regular polygon, prism, cylinder, cone, and sphere?

9. Can he estimate, read, and construct an angle?

10. Can he use the Pythagorean relationship in a right triangle?

11. Can he with ruler and compasses construct a circle, a square, and a rectangle, transfer a line segment and an angle, bisect a line segment and an angle, copy a triangle, divide a line segment into more than two equal parts, draw a tangent to a circle, and draw a geometric figure to scale.

12. Does he know the meaning of a measurement, of a standard unit, of the largest possible error, of tolerance, and of the statement "a measurement is an approximation"?

13. Can he use certain measuring devices, such as an ordinary ruler, other rulers (graduated to thirty-seconds, to tenths of an inch, and to millimeters), compasses, protractor, graph paper, tape, calipers, micrometer?

14. Can he make a scale drawing and use a map intelligently—know the various forms employed in showing what scale is used—and is he able to find the distance between two points?

15. Does he understand the meaning of vector, and can he find the resultant of two forces?

16. Does he know how to use the most important metric units (meter, centimeter, millimeter, kilometer, gram, kilogram)?

17. In measuring length, area, volume, weight, time, temperature, angle, and speed, can he convert from one commonly used standard unit to another

6. It is assumed that this item will be held to the needs stated in the two commission reports. For example, as regards operating with common fractions it is there suggested that the drill for mastery be limited to the denominators that people use in practical affairs.

widely used standard unit; e.g., does he know the relation between yard and foot, inch and centimeter, etc.?

18. Can he use letters to represent numbers; i.e., does he understand the symbolism of algebra—does he know the meaning of exponent and coefficient?

19. Does he know the meaning of a formula—can he, for example, write an arithmetic rule as a formula, and can he substitute given values in order to find the value for a required unknown?

20. Does he understand signed numbers, and can he use them?

21. Does he understand what he is doing when he uses the axioms to change the form of a formula or when he finds the value of an unknown in a simple equation?

22. Does he know by memory certain widely used formulas relating to areas, volumes, and interest, and to distance, rate, and time?

23. Does he understand the meaning of similar triangles, and does he know how to use the fact that in similar triangles the ratios of corresponding sides are equal?

24. Can he, by means of a scale drawing, develop the meaning of tangent, sine, and cosine, and can he use a three- or four-place table of these ratios to solve a right triangle?

25. Can he solve simple verbal problems (in arithmetic, algebra, geometry, and trigonometry)?

26. Does he have the information useful in personal affairs, home, and community; e.g., planned spending, the argument for thrift, understanding necessary dealings with a bank, and keeping an expense account?

27. Is he mathematically conditioned for satisfactory adjustment to a first job in business; e.g., has he a start in understanding the keeping of a simple account, making change, and the arithmetic that illustrates the most common problems of communications, travel, and transportation?

28. Does he have a basis for dealing intelligently with the main problems of the consumer;[7] e.g., the cost of borrowing money, insurance to secure adequate protection against the numerous hazards of life, the wise management of money, and buying with a given income so as to get good values as regards both quantity and quality?

[*This check list was used in the "Guidance Report" of the commission, published in November 1947. The following twenty-ninth item was included at that time, after considerable debate by the commission.*]

29. Can he analyze a statement in a newspaper and determine what is assumed, and whether the suggested conclusions really follow from the given

---

7. For a more detailed and definite statement see *The Role of Mathematics in Consumer Education;* single copies may be secured without cost from the National Association of Secondary School Principals, 1201 16th St. N.W., Washington, D. C.

facts or assumptions?

As has been suggested earlier, this thesis is a main goal for every teacher of mathematics throughout grades 1–14. Item No. 1 in the Check List is obviously the major part of the work of grades 1 to 6; the courses for grades 7 and 8 can and should make a substantial beginning in teaching most of the remaining items. General mathematics, commonly offered in the larger schools as an alternative to first year algebra in grade nine, should be constructed around these key concepts. The traditional sequential courses cannot be taught on the assumption that these basic matters have been learned well enough in earlier grades for effective use. Finally, it may well turn out that the subject matter suggested in the Check List is of more importance to many poorly prepared students in the junior college than some of the mathematical topics that they now are attempting to learn.

In our effort to insure functional competence in mathematics we need to keep the following in mind. (1) To an educated person the basic ideas are absurdly simple; typical examples are ratio, the nature of a measurement including degrees of accuracy, dependence, scale drawing, interpolation, the formula, tolerance, etc. (2) Although the basic ideas are simple, they are nevertheless very difficult for many persons to learn, and therefore require a long period of systematic teaching—instructors in the schools of the armed services, when they had to scrape the bottom of the barrel for human material, discovered that it took time and lots of it to teach a few simple mathematical ideas to *all* the boys of all the people. (3) While in general a good student who completes the traditional sequential courses will attain a mathematical maturity or power that exceeds the essentials, it is also true that a good student may complete the traditional courses (as they are now organized) without achieving functional competence; for example, there will almost certainly be gaps of the type revealed by tests in the armed services, and in any case, many students will not have as clear an understanding of some of the basic ideas as they should have. (4) A good student may become functionally competent in mathematics without taking any of the usual traditional sequential courses in high school, and he certainly can achieve the needed competence, as defined in the Check List, in less than four years, as for example, by taking one or two years of general mathematics. (5) Although the ability to compute effectively with whole numbers, common fractions, decimals, and per cents is still the crux of functional competence, this ability is achieved by only a fraction of the school's total population during the first eight grades, and is more likely to deteriorate than to improve in later grades unless something definite is done about it. (6) Although many of these ideas should be taught in earlier grades, this list of essentials for functional competence in mathematics should constitute the main goals of the work in grades 7 and 8. It is not to be inferred that all the essentials needed for functional competence in mathematics should be taught in grades seven and eight, nor that very many of these ideas can be completely taught to all pupils enrolled in these grades. However, grades 7 and 8 provide a golden opportunity for the mathematics teacher.

I. MATHEMATICS IN GRADES 1–6

If in the years to come arithmetic is to serve its proper function in the elementary curriculum, important changes need to be made both in the theory and in the practical procedures of instruction.

Thesis 2. *We must discard once for all the conception of arithmetic as a mere tool subject.*

For decades arithmetic has been classified as a tool subject.[8] Indeed, it is still so classified in many current courses of study. As a consequence, the tool conception of arithmetic has dominated instruction for a long time; indeed, for a time long enough to produce results by which the worth of that conception may be assessed. It is needless here to canvass all the evidence which has been accumulated. It must suffice to say that arithmetic taught purely as a tool subject has not achieved its purpose. It has failed to contribute its part in equipping our citizenry with the kind of mathematical competence which is required for effective and intelligent living in our culture.

The notion that arithmetic is nothing more than a tool subject is then condemned by its record in the schools. It can be condemned as well on theoretical grounds. It is said that arithmetic is just a tool subject because we never use it as an end in itself, but only as a means of dealing with the quantitative aspects of situations which are largely nonquantitative. By the same criterion history is also a tool subject and so is geography. We seldom think about history and geography just to be thinking about them. Rather, we employ them, as we employ arithmetic, in order to solve problems which transcend subject matter lines.

If it be pointed out that history and geography involve concepts, understandings, generalizations, and relationships, the same claim can be made for arithmetic. And by this same criterion arithmetic, like history and geography, becomes a content subject. As such, it has a body of knowledge which calls for the same kind of painstaking instruction that has always been accorded other traditional subjects.

It is possible, below, only to suggest the general character of this instruction. An account in greater detail appears in the published report of

8. Judd, Chas. H., "The Fallacy of Treating School Subjects as 'Tool Subjects'." *Selected Topics in the Teaching of Mathematics,* Third Yearbook of the National Council of Teachers of Mathematics. Pages 1–10. Bureau of Publications, Teachers College, 525 West 120th Street, New York 27, N. Y.

an earlier committee.[9]

Thesis 3. *We must conceive of arithmetic as having both a mathematical aim and a social aim.*

The fundamental reason for teaching arithmetic is represented in the social aim. No one can argue convincingly for an arithmetic which is sterile and functionless. If arithmetic does not contribute to more effective living, it has no place in the elementary curriculum. To achieve the social aim of arithmetic children must be led to see its worth and usefulness. In this connection "natural" as well as planned classroom and extra-classroom uses of number are especially serviceable. Children appreciate the value of arithmetic when it helps them to meet needs of vital importance to them. In meeting their needs through arithmetic they become sensitive to other possible uses, and they acquire the habit of using arithmetic as a perfectly normal way of adjusting to life situations. Children who have developed this sensitivity and this habit of use are well on the way to the attainment of the social aim of arithmetic.

We may grant the paramount importance of the social aim, and yet insist that it can be achieved only to a limited extent if the mathematical aim is neglected. The latter aim relates to the acquisition of the content of arithmetic, to the learning of arithmetical skills and ideas (concepts, principles, generalizations, and the like). Both skills and ideas should be made sensible to children through their mathematical relationships. This means that children must understand whole numbers, the number system, common fractions, decimal fractions, per cents, units of measure, etc.; that they must understand the functions of the basic operations, and that they must understand the rationale of our methods of computation. To teach well these understandings and the essential skills is to achieve the mathematical aim.

It is not a matter of having to choose between the mathematical aim and the social aim—we must realize both aims through our teaching. The next five theses are intended to show how this goal may be realized.

Thesis 4. *We must give more emphasis and much more careful attention to the development of meanings.*

In the discussion of the foregoing thesis "understand" is the key word. The purposes of arithmetic cannot be fully attained unless children understand what they learn and know when and how to use it. We face here the

9. "Essential Mathematics for Minimum Army Needs." Report of a joint committee sponsored by the Civilian Pre-Induction Training Branch of the A. S. F. and by the U. S. Office of Education. THE MATHEMATICS TEACHER, XXXVI (October, 1943), 243–282.

problem of developing meanings, both mathematical and social meanings; and meanings have not customarily received their share of attention in classroom instruction.

Consider as a case in point the common practice of giving children rules instead of *developing* them; for example, of telling children where to write quotient figures in division, instead of helping them to see that their positions are predetermined by the principles of place value; or, of telling children to invert and multiply (a short cut) when they divide by a fraction, instead of developing, first, a rational explanation through the use of the common denominator.

Consider also how relatively empty of meaning are children's concepts of common and decimal fractions when in grades 5 and 6 they come to use them in abstract computation and in problem solving. There is small wonder that such children make absurd mistakes and still are utterly complacent about them. Nothing else should be expected. Not possessing the basic understandings, they can do little more than to acquire skills in a mechanical fashion. And when skills are acquired unintelligently, they can be used only unintelligently.

And, last of all, consider what is too frequently done in teaching the process of measurement and the units used in measuring. Traditionally children have been required to master various tables. This they have done with varying degrees of success, the more capable of them being able to recite the tables confidently and accurately. Yet, their learning may be exceedingly superficial, for they may have only the haziest ideas of the units involved (e.g., the length represented by a yard or the distance represented by a mile). And their learning may be without value, save in enabling them to make the abstract computations of classroom problems. Faced by practical situations, they may not be able to employ in an intelligent manner the units whose names they have memorized. Here, as elsewhere in arithmetic and in other subject matter areas, it is a mistake to accept glib verbalism as evidence of sound learning.

(a) Meanings do not just happen. Nor can they be imparted directly from teacher to pupils, as by having them memorize the language patterns in which meanings are couched. Instead, meanings grow out of experience, as that experience is analyzed and progressively re-organized in the thinking of the learner. In a word, each child creates his own meanings, accordingly teacher activities are perforce restricted to those of guidance. It is the function of the teacher to provide an abundance of relevant experiences and to assist the child to isolate the critical elements and to build them into the desired understandings.

(b) Meanings are not all-or-none affairs: they are relative matters. It is incorrect to say that a child either does or does not have an understanding. He may understand something well enough for one purpose but not well enough for another. The problem therefore is to help him extend and enrich his understandings to the needed limits.

(c) Experiences to develop meanings need to be arranged and ordered as carefully as are the experiences by which we develop computational skills. The first encounters with meanings should ordinarily occur in concrete situations of large personal significance to the learner. At first, and for some time, children should actually use the ruler to determine the length of objects and should find volumes by using cups and quart measures. In these activities their attention should be repeatedly called to the units which they are using, the purpose being to have them acquire an understanding of these units. Next they can be led to estimate lengths and capacities, the estimates being checked by actual measurement. When they can estimate with reasonable accuracy, it is time enough to have them move on to the next level of abstractness and to learn the relationships among inches, feet, and yards, and among cups, quarts, and gallons, as these are summarized in the corresponding tables. As a matter of fact, having themselves (under guidance) discovered these relationships in connection with real measuring experiences, they may already have formulated the relationships and need only to complete their learning by organizing them into the standard tables.

What has been said about the development of meanings relating to measurement and units of measure is not limited, of course, to these ideas. It holds equally well for all the meanings commonly taught in arithmetic, or in any phase of mathematics, for that matter. It holds not only for mathematical meanings, but also for the social meanings of mathematics. In the latter connection it is imperative that teachers know how and when arithmetical skills and concepts are used, or may profitably be used, in the lives of children and of adults alike. In the absence of such knowledge it is improbable that children will have real experiences in employing the arithmetic they learn or that they will come to a rich appreciation of the significance of arithmetic in our culture.

Thesis 5. *We must abandon the idea that arithmetic can be taught incidentally or informally.*

It has been a popular notion in the last fifteen or twenty years that arithmetic can be satisfactorily taught in terms of pupils' "interests and needs" which result spontaneously from casual happenings or which are intentionally stimulated through planned units of work. The limitations of this instructional program have been pointed out many times.

(a) It is unlikely that children left to themselves will have enough number experiences or an adequate variety of experiences to develop a feeling of need for any but the simplest of arithmetical ideas and skills (e.g., counting). (b) Few teachers are sufficiently sensitive to the quantitative aspects of events to recognize them and to call attention to their presence in ordinary situations or to arrange for their presence in activity units. (c) When an effort is made to infuse arithmetic into activity units, not all children profit equally. Usually the more capable children "run away" with the project, and the less capable gain little if anything. (d) Number ideas and skills are not *learned* as such when they occur only as parts of larger experiences. True, these larger experiences may arouse a feeling of need for a new idea or skill, and so motivate learning; true, also, they may provide excellent opportunities to apply ideas and skills that have been already acquired. But they cannot produce or guarantee the learning. One learns little about the chemical nature of sea water by being immersed in it, or about the mechanical principles of a machine by operating it. (e) Mathematics, including arithmetic, has an inherent organization. This organization must be respected in learning. Teaching, to be effective, must be orderly and systematic; hence, arithmetic cannot be taught informally and incidentally.

Thesis 6. *We must realize that readiness for learning arithmetical ideas and skills is primarily the product of relevant experience, not the effect of merely becoming older.*

Of late, the so-called stepped-up curriculum has been rather generally accepted. Systematic instruction in arithmetic is deferred to Grade 3; the multiplication and division combinations are postponed a year or two, until Grade 4 or 5 or 6; the last computations with common fractions appear in Grade 6 or 7, instead of in Grade 5, and so on. The assumption is that children, by reason of their greater "maturity" in later grades, will easily learn ideas and skills which present undue difficulty when taught in the traditional grades.

(a) There is no magic in birthdays. So far as learning the school subjects is concerned, increase in age makes for readiness only (or at least predominantly) to the extent that extra time gives opportunity for relevant experience. Postponement of arithmetical topics can by itself be only a questionable device for removing learning difficulties. (b) The earlier years are wasted. Children are deprived of ideas and skills which could give them surer control over their environment and their activities. (c) Not only this, but unless we are prepared to shift much of the traditional arithmetic of Grades 7 and 8 into the high school, there must inevitably be a jamming of content in Grades 3, 4, 5, and 6, with consequent superficiality in learning. (d) When children are adequately prepared (i.e., when they have been provided with relevant experiences), the traditional placement *for mastery* is not far from wrong. Admittedly, the more troublesome phases of topics may well be postponed; but a movement of the easier phases to earlier grades may be justified equally as well. In any case, the fundamental requirement is that children's number experiences be ordered so as best to assure progression in sound learning. (e) The research on readiness which is supposed to establish the need for postponement is exceedingly shaky, and does not warrant the conclusions which have been drawn. Certainly it does not justify the notion that the teacher's function is one of custodial care while waiting for the day of readiness to make learning possible. This idea is naïve in its psychological basis, and impracticable in operation.

Thesis 7. *We must learn to administer drill (repetitive practice) much more wisely.*

The pendulum swings from one extreme of excessive drill to the other extreme of no drill. It is possible to expect from drill both too much and too little. Drill—having children do essentially the same thing over and over again—cannot develop understanding. For this purpose varied experiences are called for. But once the desired degree of meaning has been generated, repetitive practice reduces the meaning to an easily managed thought pattern, it gives the learner confidence in what he does, and it protects the meaning against forgetting. In the case of skills it makes for efficiency of performance and leaves a basis for the building of later mastery. It may do even more than this. It may help to forestall the feelings of insecurity, frustration, and fear which too many children now experience in the arithmetic of the upper grades because of their lack of confident mastery.

From all this it follows that drill is to be prescribed, not in this or that grade, but at the critical time with respect to each separate idea and skill. This critical time comes in the last stage of learning, when earlier steps have been completed and when mastery is the goal.

Thesis 8. *We must evaluate learning in arithmetic more comprehensively than is common practice.*

Evaluation, like teaching, starts with a consideration of the outcomes, *all* the outcomes, which are to be achieved. In arithmetic these outcomes include more than skill in abstract computation and in problem solving. They include mathematical understandings, mathematical judgments, the ability to estimate and approximate, habits of use, and the like. If these outcomes are important for teaching, they are equally important from the standpoint of evaluation. And no program of evaluation which disregards these outcomes is adequately comprehensive.

Recognizing these facts, we shall use paper-and-pencil tests for what they are worth; but we must supplement these tests with other procedures, such as those of the interview, observation, the examination of work products, and the like. The spontaneous use of arithmetical ideas and skills in the ordinary happenings of the classroom and in planned activity units is, for example, the best kind of evidence that children are realizing the social aim of arithmetic.

II. THE MATHEMATICS OF GRADES SEVEN AND EIGHT

The theses which follow apply in essence to *all* seventh-grade and eighth-grade pupils of normal intelligence, irrespective of the type of school in which they are enrolled. The mathematical program of grades 7 and 8 should not be viewed as a problem by itself, but as an integral part of the total program as suggested in this Report.

Thesis 9. *The mathematical program of grades 7 and 8 should be essentially the same for all normal pupils.*

This is not the place to begin differentiated courses. As was pointed out in the opening section of this Report, "we need to make certain that the essentials for functional competence are achieved by all who can learn them, in order that the proper guidance of the pupil may not be an impossible task." The seventh and eighth grades are crucial years in the attainment of that objective. Departure from these essentials will not only jeopardize the attainment of functional competence, but also result in large-scale retardation that is so difficult to correct later.

Regardless of the type of school or the community, the mathematical program of these grades should be designed to do three things:

(a) *Provide an adequate, organic continuation of the work of grades 1–6.*

The seventh-grade teacher must, of course, begin the year's work with pupils "as they are." However, disabilities in arithmetic should not be regarded as an inevitable and permanent feature of the elementary school. On the contrary, the Commission wishes to assert that a fatalistic attitude toward this vexing issue is unwarranted, and that wherever large-scale weaknesses in arithmetic are observed, they should be corrected at the source, namely, in the elementary grades. On the basis of completely trustworthy evidence the claim is warranted that, under competent instruction, American children can and do acquire a satisfactory foundation in arithmetic in the elementary grades, and that the average child, when properly taught, enjoys arithmetic.

Disabilities in arithmetic should be located at the earliest possible moment with the aid of reliable inventory or diagnostic tests. An adequate remedial and maintenance program should be regarded as an integral part of the curriculum. Experience shows that shortages in arithmetic, if not promptly corrected, prevent or retard the pupil's progress in mathematics. In all the basic techniques of arithmetic the goal should be mastery. To attain this goal, extensive re-teaching is necessary in all cases of marked disability. Mere repetitive drill, devoid of real understanding, only aggravates the situation. A remedial program or a refresher course which is not anchored on insight, cannot be expected to produce lasting results. The secret of success in arithmetic is meaningful learning, combined with intelligent practice and functional application.

(b) *Provide a substantial beginning in achieving functional competence.*

It is the clear responsibility of mathematics to provide training that will make the pupil intelligent and efficient in dealing with the problems that he may meet in other school subjects, in the home and in his everyday reading and conversation. Therefore, as has been suggested earlier, many of the items in the Check List should be an important part of the program.

(c) *Provide a dependable foundation for subsequent courses in mathematics.*

Obviously, the mathematical program at any stage should not be determined exclusively by considerations of immediate needs and interests or of direct experience, but should also have regard for possible future needs.

Thesis 10. *The mathematics for grades 7 and 8 should be planned as a unified program and should be built around a few broad categories.*

Before it is possible to consider the grade placement of specific topics, it is necessary to develop a comprehensive plan for these two years. The program should be organized [10] around: (1) number and computation; (2) the geometry of everyday life; (3) graphic representation; (4) an introduction to the essentials of elementary algebra (formula and equation).

It should be pointed out that these four categories are essential not merely for subsequent courses in mathematics, but also for the demands of modern industry, technology, and business, as well as for national defense.

Thesis 11. *The mathematics program of grades 7 and 8 should be so organized as to enable the pupils to achieve mathematical maturity and power.*

The teachers should constantly develop a genuine understanding and appreciation of the fundamental concepts, principles, and modes of thinking, and to develop real proficiency in using the basic techniques of mathematics.

The shortages in the mathematical training of young men entering the armed forces have in some quarters been attributed merely to "forgetting." However, there is convincing evidence that lack of understanding of the key concepts and principles, and of mathematical modes of thinking, is primarily to blame for widespread mathematical incompetence. The remedy is obvious. As Professor Dewey pointed out long ago, skills cannot be used effectively unless intelligence has played a part in their acquisition. Me-

10. See, for example, The Report of the Joint Commission on "The Place of Mathematics in Secondary Education," The Fifteenth Yearbook of the National Council of Teachers of Mathematics, 1940, pp. 62 ff. The Bureau of Publications, Teachers College, 525 W. 120th St., New York, N. Y.

chanical drill is not a substitute for understanding.

At all stages of mathematical instruction, the first concern of the teacher should be that of developing a real understanding of key concepts and principles. The pupil should know the underlying reasons for all the processes he is taught. In building for power the classroom work should involve more than mere theory. It calls for constant and insistent attention to significant applications. This is necessary for the sake both of effective motivation and of effective transfer. The range of possible and desirable mathematical applications is growing from year to year. As science and technology become increasingly important in the modern world, the functional uses of mathematics, likewise, become correspondingly urgent. In fact, throughout the recorded period of human history, mathematics has been a mirror of civilization. It seems destined to continue in that role.

III. MATHEMATICS IN GRADE NINE

Thesis 12. *The large [11] high school should provide in grade 9 a double track in mathematics, algebra for some and general mathematics for the rest.*

In the large high schools, the teacher of mathematics is confronted with a difficult problem, but, fortunately, it is one than can be solved. The range as regards both native ability and acquired competence of pupils is very great. For example, one commonly finds in the same class a few pupils with and I.Q. as low as 75 and several that have an I.Q. higher than 140. Many have not mastered the essentials whereas perhaps a fourth of the class are fully ready to undertake successfully the study of first-year algebra.

Far too often a school resorts to one or more of the following unsatisfactory solutions. (1) Only general mathematics is offered. This policy delays the beginning of the study of algebra for those who plan to take the long road to leadership in science and mathematics. (2) Only algebra is provided. This program inevitably results in a large number of frustrated pupils who fear and dislike mathematics, with a devastating lowering of standards in all algebra classes. In a survey by *Fortune*,[12] mathematics was the best-liked subject in the high school curriculum, but it also received a high vote as the least-liked subject. (3) Only a diluted algebra is taught. This practice is a shot that misses both targets. Algebra cannot fullfil its main purpose if the teacher resorts to a wide use of popular materials in the futile effort to meet the needs of pupils who should not be taking algebra

11. By a large high school the Commission means a school with more than 200 pupils. The special problem of the small high school is discussed in a separate section.

12. *Fortune,* November and December issues, 1942. Free reprints of this material may be secured by writing to the General Manager, *Fortune* Magazine, Time and Life Building, Rockefeller Center, New York, N. Y. See also THE MATHEMATICS TEACHER, February 1943. Page 83.

at their stage of mathematical maturity. (4) Most of the pupils are encouraged to elect commercial arithmetic or consumer mathematics. This plan results in teaching much too early material that might be very worth while if taught several years later. In general, ninth grade pupils do not have the experiences that are needed for dealing with the mathematics of consumer problems in respectable fashion. It is difficult to motivate the arithmetic that may be needed on an unknown job that is still several years in the future. (5) The slowly maturing pupil is discouraged from taking any mathematics. This practice, as the experience of the schools of the armed forces has convincingly demonstrated, is an oversimplification of the problem. Too often this type of pupil leaves school with little control over the essentials needed later on a semitechnical job. (6) Many schools give drill work in arithmetic computation without stopping to teach the meaning of the processes used, without diagnosis, and even without motivation. This is merely giving a larger dose of a medicine that hasn't helped the pupil in earlier grades.

The situation in the ninth grade of the large high school clearly requires a double track in mathematics—algebra only for those whose ability and future outlook indicate to their advisers that they should take it and a good course in general mathematics for the rest. General mathematics for the ninth grade is here defined as a course that includes and emphasizes the elements of functional competence as outlined in the Check List on pages 197–198 of this report. It has been suggested earlier that the task of insuring functional competence cannot be completed for all pupils in the first eight grades. For many, this task must be continued at least through grade 9. The main purpose then of a general mathematics course in the ninth grade is to provide such experiences as will insure growth in understanding of the basic concepts and improvement in the necessary skills.

We come now to the phase of our problem that is difficult for many teachers of mathematics—the administration of general mathematics in a way that will make it respectable and desirable. Here the attitude of the teacher is the determining factor and far too often the teacher is, by training, disposed to propagandize unduly for algebra. As a matter of fact, algebra needs no propaganda—it will always be respected and it will always have great value for the person who should elect it. When, however, a teacher implies that the penalty for failure in algebra is transfer to general mathematics, an unwarranted halo of prestige is given to algebra that implies stigma and disrespect for general mathematics which should not be so if the general mathematics is properly organized and taught.

It should be made clear to pupils that the two parallel courses of the ninth grade are both tremendously worth while, but that they do have very different goals and experiences for pupils with different interests and needs. General mathematics is a more flexible course than algebra; it can more easily be adapted to different backgrounds and levels of ability. The material can and should be offered in such a way as to challenge the pupil to his best effort. Pupils should be told that general mathematics is *organized* differently, that it offers a greater *variety* of topics and that it is related *more directly* with immediate application. They may well be told that good work in general mathematics demands as much time and exertion as algebra. It is a fatal error to imply that in general mathematics anything will do. Shop teachers of the right kind certainly expect accuracy in computation and measurement beyond anything required in the ordinary academic class. General mathematics may seem an easier course than algebra, but that fact alone will not stigmatize the course in the opinion of a student body.

Classification should not be based on ability alone. In a strong mathematics department some of the best pupils in the ninth grade will be studying general mathematics. Differentiation to avoid trouble for either group should, as has been suggested, be based primarily on a difference of goals. A good argument for general mathematics is that a mastery of the essentials, as outlined in the Check List, will remove the feeling of insecurity from many ninth grade pupils who have never had the satisfaction of achievement. The best criterion, obviously, for selecting a pupil for the algebra class is the desire and the ability to do work of a high order of excellence. Therefore, unsatisfactory work in algebra should be tolerated for only a brief trial period—a semester would seem to be much too long. It should be noted that in guiding the pupil into the appropriate course, measures of reading, intelligence, and computation are also very helpful. Teachers should scrutinize critically all materials used in the guidance of pupils to make certain that they do not include statements that prejudice pupils against the general mathematics courses.

One or more general mathematics sections and at least one algebra section should be scheduled at the same hour in order to facilitate the transfer of pupils. The pupil who, at the end of a year of general mathematics, wishes to study algebra, may, if he has provided convincing evidence of adequate ability, be encouraged to elect the second semester of first-year algebra. Finally, it should be noted that the real hazard to general mathematics is the undesirable label unconsciously in the minds of many traditionally trained mathematics teachers. In schools where teachers of mathematics recognize the very great importance of general mathematics in the total offering, it readily becomes a popular course for many pupils. The road to algebra should be open to the pupil who matures slowly in mathematics, and general mathematics will be more highly regarded by pupils if it is made clear that it contributes to the successful pursuit of many things. The goal of a strong mathematics department should be to have every pupil in the appropriate course with no dissatisfied customer in any class.

Thesis 13. *In most schools first-year algebra should be evaluated in terms of good practice.*

Let no one assume that all is well with first-year algebra. There is a wide gap between first-year algebra as it is commonly taught and what good teachers everywhere have long demonstrated. The situation described in the following quotation[13] may still be found in many schools although it was written twenty-five years ago:

The situation that needs to be met may best be illustrated by the case of algebra. Our elementary algebra is, in theory and symbolism, substantially what it was in the seventeenth century. The present standards of drill work, largely on non-essentials, were set up about fifty years ago. A considerable number of teachers, both in the secondary schools and the colleges, believe that the amount of time spent by pupils on abstract work in difficult problems in division, factoring, fractions, simultaneous equations, radicals, etc., is excessive; that such work leads to nothing important in the science, and adds but little to facility in the manipulation of algebraic forms.

However, let us turn to the brighter side of the picture and see what is happening in the classrooms of competent teachers of first-year algebra in some parts of the country. It is likely that there are few, if any, high-school subjects that have been improved as much during the last quarter of a century as has first-year algebra.

The list of desirable trends is a long and impressive one. Today good teachers of algebra (1) reduce the manipulation of symbolism (nests of parentheses, four-story fractions, involved cases of factoring, difficult cases of simultaneous equations, etc.); (2) introduce a unit of from four to six weeks' duration on the trigonometry of the right triangle; (3) emphasize the notion of dependence or function; (4) teach with great care the meaning of a formula; (5) apply graphic techniques widely; (6) use the newer testing procedures for instructional purposes; (7) introduce symbolism gradually and through a variety of geometric and other illustrations; (8) discard the definitional approach and manage materials so that definitions as well as principles, processes and concepts stem from numerous and simple mathematical experiences; (9) make better provision for individual differences by providing problems of graded difficulty; (10) use a more sensible program of "drill" based on the fact that a pupil learns more quickly and remembers longer the things that he understands fully; (11) use a

13. Quoted from a memorandum addressed to the General Education Board by a committee representing the Mathematical Association of America. This memorandum secured generous funds for the support of the National Committee on Mathematical Requirements. It is, therefore, of special interest to the student of mathematical education.

few simple, interesting, and practical applications to motivate each new principle and topic; (12) strive to improve the problem material by selecting functional applications (aviation, the school shop, general science, etc.); (13) make sagacious use of the bulletin board and other visual aids to enrich the subject; (14) utilize whenever possible laboratory or investigational techniques and seek to give the mathematics classroom the furniture, equipment, and atmosphere of a workroom; (15) know that reading ability fixes a low ceiling as to what can be achieved in problem solving in the case of many pupils; (16) recognize that it is far better to teach a few concepts well than to teach many concepts superficially; and (17) do what they can to restrict first-year algebra to those pupils who should study it and provide a course with sufficient rigor and continuity for subsequent courses.

IV. MATHEMATICS IN GRADES TEN TO TWELVE

The traditional sequential courses include the elements of algebra, plane geometry, solid geometry, and trigonometry. In some schools they may also include the elements of statistics, analytic geometry, and the Calculus. While an attempt is often made to correlate these various subjects, in general, they are taught separately. The very fact that the sequential courses are the oldest mathematics courses in the high school makes it difficult to change them. However, there is great opportunity for improvement. Again we might do well to follow the example of the industrialists and go forward with improved materials and more efficient methods.

Thesis 14. *The sequential courses should be reserved for those pupils who, having the requisite ability, desire or need such work.*

All the pupils in the high school need training in quantitative thinking, but it would be a mistake for this reason to require all of them to take the sequential courses in mathematics.

Pupils of ability should be informed that the sequential program in mathematics is a definite prerequisite for many lines of work.

The need for careful training in mathematics for those planning careers in the physical sciences, engineering, architecture, and similar fields is universally recognized. In order to give adequate preparation for these technical fields, the sequential courses must give attention to many phases of mathematics that are more detailed and abstract than is necessary or desirable for most pupils. If the sequential courses are to fulfill the purpose for which they are intended, they cannot be emasculated to fit the needs of those of low ability and weak purpose.

Thesis 15. *Teachers of the traditional sequential courses must emphasize functional competence in mathematics.*

It has been assumed that pupils studying algebra, geometry, and the higher branches of mathematics of the high school not only retain their skills in arithmetic and other important topics of the junior high school but gain further understanding of these topics. This is not always the case. The war has taught us that success in the traditional sequential courses does not guarantee mastery of all the items in the Check List. For this reason the study of the fundamentals of arithmetic and of other phases of elementary mathematics taught in grades 7 and 8 must be continued in the senior school.

Most of these topics can be fitted into the regular sequential work and become an integral part of it. For example, instead of being content with the understanding of principles in algebra and geometry and applications of these principles in numerical exercises with small whole numbers as is often done, good practice in arithmetic can be obtained by using larger numbers, fractions, mixed numbers, and decimals.

It follows that provision should be made for periodical checks on pupils' understanding of these topics. Topics not clearly understood should be retaught and adequate practice provided for those students who need it.

Thesis 16. *The main objective of the sequential courses should be to develop mathematical power.*

Drill on the manipulation of mathematical symbols not accompanied by clear understanding of the underlying concepts and principles is of little value. When such drill is discontinued, the ability is soon lost. Power is attained when the learner understands the relationships involved well enough to apply them in new and varied situations.

Thesis 17. *The work of each year should be organized into a few large units built around key concepts and fundamental principles.*

In a sequential course the major emphasis should be on concepts and principles. It has long been urged that some of the more complex manipulations in algebra be treated lightly or omitted altogether, provided the basic ideas are mastered. For future work in mathematics and the sciences, the basic ideas are more important than complex details. The student who knows the fundamental meanings and has complete mastery over the simpler manipulations in connection with the basic ideas can gain the complex details when and if necessary. For example, in a first course in algebra, one of the large units may well be "algebra as generalized arithmetic." The unit devised on this idea would point two ways, backward to arithmetic already learned, and forward to more advanced algebra. It would carry with it the symbolism of algebra, would bring together and clarify many of the relationships of arithmetic, and give meaning to a host of isolated topics usually considered as merely formal algebra.

Then too, we should not continue to give so much time to continuous logical development in geometry. Once a student has learned what it means to prove a statement deductively, it is not necessary to devote an entire year to deductive proof. Of course, we should continue proofs throughout the year, and in subsequent years, just as we should continue arithmetic. Meanings and skills are not established once for all. Some of the theorems can be postulated after careful laboratory work, while others can be discussed informally.

In solid geometry proofs might be restricted to those theorems which deal with lines and planes in space, and with the geometry of the sphere. The metric properties of solids, including the sphere, may well be developed informally.

A common complaint of teachers is that there are so many topics to teach in any one year that they cannot "finish the book." If we teach in terms of the mastery of key concepts and fundamental ideas, the pages not covered will not matter so much.

While there is considerable continuity in the sequential courses, there is not as much as has been generally believed. As taught, the various topics in algebra and geometry seem, to the pupil at least, to be quite unrelated. The continuity can be seen better in terms of large ideas rather than in terms of details.

Planning a year's work in terms of large units built around key concepts and fundamental principles will also help to solve the problems of integration of the various subjects. It is obvious that natural interrelations between algebra, geometry, and trigonometry should be emphasized.

Thesis 18. *Simple and sensible applications to many fields must appear much more frequently in the sequential courses than they have in the past.*

Applications of mathematics to problems of industry, physical science, aviation and business should be used for purposes of motivation, illustration, and transfer. Mathematics teachers must become sufficiently familiar with these fields so that they can choose the applications wisely. But mathematics cannot be taught solely through its applications. A few simple applications at every advanced step should be used for motivation and as a means of increasing the possibility of transfer. They cannot be an end in themselves.

Thesis 19. *New and better courses should be provided in the high schools for a large fraction of the school's population whose mathematical needs are not well met in the traditional sequential courses.*

As everyone knows, there are pupils—very large groups—who do not elect the sequential courses, and many of whom are maladjusted in case they do. Such pupils as these will never be satisfied with a purely academic program. Many of them have the ability to render valuable services with a bit of mathematical training as is evidenced by the several hundred thousand boys who held important semi-technical jobs in the military activities as a result of mathematics they studied *after* they left the regular schools. The military training program took these boys and taught them a simple technical science and the related mathematics. We must give more attention to the needs of industry, which the traditional mathematics teacher has neglected far too long. We must provide a more realistic curriculum for the large number of persons who will continue to be absorbed fairly early in life by industry, trade, farm, and business. Then, too, we must provide a course that will give them greater mathematical security in practical affairs, such as budgets, insurance, taxation, and the like.

Since there are in our high schools these large groups of pupils whose needs cannot possibly be met by traditional mathematics courses, the sensible thing to do is to provide good courses with very different goals and experiences for groups with different needs. Furthermore, as has been suggested earlier, we must somehow do this in a manner that does not offend any group.

What kind of courses are suggested by these varied needs? It is obvious that a year or even two years of mathematics paralleling the sequential courses, in grades 10 and 11, will serve a useful purpose for a very large part of the total school population. The content of this mathematics would clearly embrace substantial materials from at least several of the following areas: mathematics as related to trades and shop work; commerce and business; industry; agriculture. It is also clear that every pupil is potentially both citizen and consumer; hence all pupils should be given some understanding of the persistent problems that confront most of our families; viz., social security, taxation, insurance against the numerous hazards of life, and ways and means of stretching the dollar in order to buy the maximum of material comforts and values with a given income.

To be sure, this does not preclude the possibility that certain schools in certain areas will deem it advisable to treat these separate areas more extensively and specifically through specialized courses.

In the early months of the war, a refresher course in mathematics was popular among seniors in the high schools. Even though the term "refresher" may disappear, there will probably always be pupils in the late years of the senior high school who have a feeling of insecurity with respect to mathematics. It would seem that there is a place, at least in the large high school, for a course that reteaches the essentials of mathematics with new and fresh materials consisting of practical applications that are simple and interesting.

Then too there will probably always be some pupils who arrive at the eleventh or twelfth grades without having taken any mathematics beyond the eighth grade. These pupils may wish to rectify a mistake, and so will want a course that will make them as competent as possible in a relatively short period of time. The Commission believes that, so long as this need exists, the larger schools, at least, should continue to provide a course for pupils in the eleventh and twelfth grades with a content for the most part as outlined in a report entitled *Preinduction Courses in Mathematics*.[14]

There is here no implication that the traditional sequential courses will be less important in the future than they have been in the past. Since the turn of the century the high school has been facing a double responsibility. It must train for leadership, and it must provide a broad education in terms of effective citizenship, in the home, the community, the state and the world. It is not a question as to whether special attention shall be given to either group; *both jobs must be done*. However, it is the main thesis of the Commission that there are at present large neglected groups of pupils whose needs cannot possibly be met in traditional courses, and for whom new and better courses should now be provided.

Thesis 20. *The small high school can and should provide a better program in mathematics.*

Many persons do not realize that more than two-thirds of all high schools are small, with certainly fewer than 200 students and probably fewer than 8 teachers. Such small high schools enroll in all more than a million pupils. Professional literature dealing with the mathematics of the small high school is meager. For example, the important committee reports on mathematical education devote very little space to this problem. In amazing fashion a considerable fraction of the population of our high schools has been overlooked altogether in formulating programs for the betterment of mathematics.

The mathematical offering of the small school is necessarily limited by the following conditions: (1) the rate of turnover of teachers is high; in a given year, most, indeed all, of the teachers may be new to their positions; (2) the teachers have little experience; in a three-teacher school, all may be beginners; (3) the member of the staff teaching mathematics may have had little or no training in the field; (4) the cost of instruction per pupil is high; (5) the library and the storage space within the classrooms for supplementary materials are inadequate; (6) there is seldom a classroom devoted exclusively to the teaching of mathematics, and (7) the teacher of mathematics may have to teach in two or more other fields.

As a result, the curriculum in mathematics is meager and remote from the pupils' needs. Thus, a small high school with five or six pupils in a class may offer only two years of mathematics. These two years may be

14. See THE MATHEMATICS TEACHER for March 1943.

organized according to any one of many patterns that are in most cases unrealistic when evaluated in terms of the pupils' mathematical needs. For example, a school may offer a year of formal algebra and a year of demonstrative geometry. Presumably the aim in this case is to prepare all pupils for college even though the school may have sent relatively few of its graduates to college in its entire history. At the other extreme a school may offer only one year of commercial arithmetic and a year of agricultural mathematics with little emphasis on basic concepts and fundamental principles. Then too, many schools offer only a year of general mathematics and a year of commercial arithmetic. In such schools the occasional pupil who should be preparing himself for future leadership in science and mathematics, graduates with far less of the sequential mathematics than he should have.

What constructive suggestions can be made for the improvement of mathematics for the small school? Let us assume that we are dealing with a school that has only six pupils in each grade from 9 to 12 inclusive. Let us further assume that we can use only as much of one teacher's time as is represented by one-third of the school day (two periods of an hour each). For this small school the Commission makes the following suggestions.

(a) *Offer two courses simultaneously within the same class period.* Instead of general mathematics or algebra, one or the other, it is proposed that both be taught. The teacher of the one-room rural school has always taught from six to eight groups simultaneously; it seems reasonable that a high school teacher can teach two. In fact, an experiment in Indiana has demonstrated the feasibility of such a procedure. In our hypothetical school, one, or perhaps two, of the six ninth-grade pupils might, under proper guidance, elect algebra and the remainder study general mathematics. A generous fraction of each hour period should be a work-period with an up-to-date textbook. The algebra pupils might not need more than thirty minutes per week for the checking and guidance of their work. There are instances on record where pupils have done a year's work in algebra to prepare themselves for rigorous college entrance examinations without utilizing more than a dozen hours of a teacher's or tutor's time. The notion that a pupil must recite for five hours a week is outmoded.

Our hypothetical school might, in the tenth year, offer both geometry and a course in consumer mathematics to which pupils in the tenth, eleventh, and twelfth grades might be admitted. Thus the mathematics offering of a small high school might well be broadened and made more flexible. If a school can afford instruction in mathematics for three or four periods of the school day, its offerings can, by this plan, be as wide as is now commonly found in much larger high schools.

(b) *Provide correspondence courses in the small high schools.* The small school can extend its mathematics offering by encouraging interested and capable pupils to elect correspondence courses. A great variety of correspondence courses are now provided by commercial organizations. Moreover, it seems reasonable to assume that the many correspondence courses now available to the men and women of the armed services may be made available also to public education in the postwar period. It is gratifying to note that at least one state (Wisconsin) has authorized school boards to buy correspondence courses, and in other states there seem to be no legal obstacles in the way of a school board that desires to pay for correspondence courses. The Wisconsin law reads as follows:

> The board of any school district which operates a high school may contract with the university extension division of the University of Wisconsin for extension courses for pupils enrolled in such high schools. The cost of such contract shall be paid out of school district funds and shall be included in the cost of operation and maintenance of the high school districts which enter into such contract for the purpose of computing tuition costs.

During the war, over a million men have taken correspondence courses under conditions that were often very difficult. It would seem that pupils in the small high school would have a much better chance to succeed in correspondence courses than men in the armed forces for the reason that the local mathematics teacher might service such work in the courses that he happens to be teaching. Under this plan a pupil who wishes to study first year algebra might attend the class in general mathematics or in geometry, and take a correspondence course in algebra under the general supervision of the teacher. Since the teacher of our hypothetical school has only a few regular students, the implementation of a correspondence course for one or two pupils would obviously not be an impossible task.

(c) *Increase the number of courses by cycling.* Our hypothetical school might well offer algebra and general mathematics one year, geometry and general mathematics the next year, and general mathematics and another course consisting of a third semester of algebra and a semester of trigonometry in the following year. Under adequate guidance and by careful planning early in his high school career a pupil can thus get at least two years of general mathematics or even three years of sequential mathematics by the time he graduates from high school. It is assumed that some schools might wish to substitute a course in related mathematics, commercial arithmetic, consumer mathematics, and the like, for any one of the courses used in the preceding illustrations. However, in cycling, careful planning and adequate guidance are necessary in order to avoid a situation in which a prerequisite course has been offered in the wrong year for a group of students.

From the foregoing, it becomes obvious that the offerings of the small high school do not need to be as limited as they so often are. Incidentally, by this plan classes will be approximately doubled in enrollment with the cost of mathematical instruction per pupil sharply reduced. Finally, it is suggested that the superintendent and the board of education employ at least one teacher with a respectable minor or major in mathematics in order that the extended offering may be properly taught.

V. MATHEMATICS IN THE JUNIOR COLLEGE

It is now rather generally agreed that one of the main functions of the junior college is to serve as somewhat of a "community institute" providing educational opportunities, which otherwise might be inaccessible, to a large number of educable youth. The curriculum of each junior college, therefore, becomes something of a local enterprise in that it needs to be organized and administered in relation to the pattern of living in its community. This statement does not restrict the curriculum within the narrow limits for living always in that community; rather it calls attention to the perspective needed for a really functional educational program.

From the point of view of interest in mathematics, the student body of the junior college will divide itself into three major groups: *Group I*—those students who desire some knowledge of mathematics merely as a part of their cultural background; *Group II*—those students who need a minimum of certain mathematical prerequisites because of their desire to follow specific vocational interests; *Group III*—those students who have major mathematical needs because they plan a career in some field such as engineering, natural science, or pure mathematics.

Thesis 21. *The junior college should offer at least one year of mathematics which is general in appeal, flexible in purpose, challenging in content, and functional in service.*

In any junior college there is likely to be a group of students who feel that they do not care to take a traditional course in mathematics (Group I). They are not interested in intricate calculations and excessive manipulation. Many of them do not have, at least they think they do not have, the special aptitude necessary for understanding such work. It does not follow, however, that these students would elect to by-pass all mathematics courses. Many of them might find interesting challenge in courses containing those mathematical ideas and experiences which are an essential part of a liberal education. A basic general course in mathematics might offer these individuals opportunities for development which the traditional courses in freshman mathematics do not offer.

A course such as the one suggested above could also have definite cultural content. This would be particularly true if the mathematical concepts and techniques developed were presented as an important part of the history of thought, and were interpreted in terms of social usefulness. Such a presentation of materials would enhance the opportunities for richer significance, deeper appreciation, and clearer understanding of all mathematical concepts and techniques. Those students who have an interest in mathematics only as a part of their liberal education would learn from such a course something of the vital significance of mathematics as an integral element of the cultures of the world.

Thesis 22. *The junior college program should provide for a one-year pre-vocational course in mathematics.*

There is a wide range of vocations which require that mathematics in varying amounts be given a significant place in the program of preliminary training, and the number is likely to increase in the post-war period. It, therefore, follows that the students of Group II will very likely be one of the largest and most important groups in any junior college program. The mathematical requirements of many of these vocations will be such that they can be satisfied by a one-year program in basic mathematical concepts and techniques. It is the responsibility of teachers of mathematics to determine this body of basic mathematics and to organize it into a general one-year program which will take care of the pre-professional requirements which this group of students will need to meet. For example, there are many prospective teachers of other school subjects who are not prepared for, and who, therefore, cannot be expected to become interested in conventional courses in college algebra and trigonometry. There is, however, an abundant reservoir of mathematical information of rich cultural value and essential educational significance to all who aspire to teach in our nation's schools. Similarly, there are many students preparing for pharmacy, medicine, business, agriculture, industry, and many other fields of service, who are forced to elect traditional freshman mathematics instead of being challenged by a more functional program of mathematical training.

There is a great need for a basic one-year program in mathematics at the junior college level such as has been outlined by the Joint Commission.[15] Needless to say, in a movement so young as the junior college, considerable experimentation will be necessary to determine the desirable content of such a course. The function of such a course will indeed vary from time to time, and from one community to another.

Thesis 23. *The junior college program should make ample provision for the student with a major interest in mathematics.*

One of the important functions of the junior college is that of preparing its students for subsequent work at a more advanced level of instruction. The third group of students, namely, those who have a major interest in mathematics, should be provided with the opportunity for becoming more

15. Report of the Joint Commission, *op. cit.*, p. 159.

proficient in fundamental mathematical techniques and for broadening their contacts with basic mathematical concepts and skills. Their horizon of mathematical needs will vary considerably from the more modest demands of the less technical phases of biology to the maximum prescriptions of a major in mathematics. The program for this group of students should be characterized by a clear current of challenging mathematical thought and meaningful practice.

A program allowing for such flexibility of mathematical training as is suggested in this report will greatly enhance the opportunities of the junior college for effective educational service. It should be of particular significance in the immediate post-war period, when the varying demands of the returning war veterans will tend to make the planning and administering of educational programs very difficult.

VI. THE EDUCATION OF TEACHERS OF MATHEMATICS

A. In Grades 1–8

Most mathematics courses in the elementary school are taught by teachers who have responsibilities with respect to other bodies of subject matter. On this account the proposals to be advanced below are offered with full recognition of the necessity to prepare teachers for duties in addition to those relating to arithmetic (elementary mathematics).

Thesis 24. *All students who are likely to teach mathematics in Grades 1–8 should, as a minimum, demonstrate competence over the whole range of subject matter which may be taught in these grades.*

It is a mistake to assume that teachers need to know only the subject matter which they will teach. In the first place, they should be expected to have more mathematical competence than we should insist upon for the average adult. In the second place, they cannot orient their instruction properly if they do not recognize the potential consequences of their instruction for successful accomplishment on the part of their pupils in later grades. For example, primary-grade teachers may see little sense in teaching the nature of our number system if they do not understand how this knowledge facilitates the meaningful learning of computation in Grades 3 to 6.

Each prospective teacher should be expected to achieve and to demonstrate mathematical competence. Teachers of Grades 1 to 6 should do this on their own responsibility, without course credit for whatever special study they may need to make. Instead, with or without coaching, such students should prepare themselves until they can make a satisfactory score on an acceptable examination. It is suggested that this score might be equivalent to the tenth grade norms in computation and problem solving on some comprehensive and reliable standard test. For teachers of Grades 7 and 8 this criterion is wholly inadequate, for competence needs to be assured over a much wider range of subject matter, to include something beyond the elements of algebra, geometry, and trigonometry which are involved in the courses for Grades 7 and 8.

Thesis 25. *Teachers of mathematics in Grades 1–8 should have special course work relating to subject matter as well as to the teaching process, as detailed below.*

Thesis 24 above merely assures mathematical competence as such competence has traditionally been conceived. An earlier section of this report made clear the shortcomings of this conception, at least as far as arithmetic is concerned. It therefore becomes necessary to outline other aspects of mathematical preparation, now too commonly neglected, which are nevertheless indispensable parts of the equipment for effective teaching. As will be evident, the provision of this professional equipment places heavy responsibilities upon instructors in the college courses which are called for. This is particularly true in the case of courses for teachers in Grades 7 and 8. In such courses the instructors might well be mathematicians who, besides their interest in the improvement of instruction, have rich backgrounds of experience in the social, vocational, and industrial uses of mathematics.

(*a*) *Theory and background of elementary mathematics.*—To live effectively and intelligently in our culture we must of course be able to compute and to solve verbal problems quickly, accurately, and confidently. But we must also be equipped with meanings, generalizations, appreciations of relationships, and the like. In a word, we need to know something of the theory and background of elementary mathematics.

Important as this knowledge is for the average citizen, it is vastly more important for teachers. Lacking it, teachers will scarcely be qualified to help their pupils to acquire it. Hence, at some point in their education, prospective teachers of Grades 1 to 6 need to learn a good deal about the nature of our decimal number system and the story of its development, the evolution of fractional notation, the theory and history of measurement, the functions of the fundamental operations with whole numbers, fractions, and decimals, and the rationale and history of computation. Teachers of Grades 7 and 8 need all this, but they obviously need much more than this. Their course work in algebra, geometry, and trigonometry should be correspondingly extended to include the social and historical background of these more advanced mathematical subjects.

(*b*) *Important applications.*—The foregoing paragraphs are intended to suggest the type of preparation teachers should have in order to realize as fully as possible the mathematical aim of their subject matter. But steps need also to be taken to assure equivalent preparation in order that they may realize the social aim as well. It is possible to know mathematics as a closed system of ideas and skills without being able to apply it.

Teachers of Grades 1–6 who know arithmetic in this narrow way are insensitive to the contribution of arithmetic to social progress and to sound and effective individual adjustment in our present culture. The course in the teaching of arithmetic should remove this deficiency. It can do so if the topics mentioned in the preceding section are treated with respect to their social implications and if students are encouraged to note systematically the applications of mathematical concepts and processes to everyday life. The same generalization applies in the case of teachers in Grades 7 and 8, of course with due recognition of the expanded area of their mathematical subject matter. Beyond the material which they will teach they need backgrounds in the social and economic uses of mathematics. Thus, to be able to teach with confidence and assurance such topics as buying a home, the cost of running an automobile, making provision for the future (savings, insurance, social security, and investments), protection against large losses (fire and liability insurance), the prospective teacher needs course work and real experiences in these economic applications of mathematics.

(c) *Supplementary instructional equipment.*—Prospective teachers should have access to new textbook and workbook series, to some of the better courses of study, to standard tests, and to the newer devices and aids for teaching, such as models, films, film strips, slides, and the like. They should have access to a reasonable amount of this equipment; but, more than this, they should have opportunity to examine it critically and to note special advantages and limitations. No single textbook or workbook series, for example, has a monopoly on good systems of organization, on superior methods of meeting individual differences, on ingenious testing devices, and on commendable developmental explanations. And teachers should not expect to find all that is good and all that is important in the series which they happen to teach. Moreover, they should know and understand the value of the many excellent multi-sensory aids which are being made available in increasing numbers. (See Section VII of this report.)

(d) *Methods of teaching.*—In courses in the teaching of mathematics, the methods which are most commonly described and exemplified are those which relate to facts and to mechanical skills. With new emphasis on the mathematical aim of arithmetic, prospective teachers must learn how to develop meanings, understandings, generalizations, a sure grasp of relationships, and the like. And with the new emphasis on the social aim, they must know how to engender in their pupils sensitivity to the usefulness of number and of measurement in life.

(e) *Student teaching.*—Provision should be made for adequate experience in student teaching. In considering this need, see Thesis 32.

(f) *Procedures for comprehensive evaluation.*—It was stated above that prospective teachers should know about the better standard tests in mathematics. But, good as they are for some purposes, these instruments are inadequate for comprehensive evaluation. Almost without exception they measure skill in computation and ability in problem solving and these outcomes only. If the other outcomes which are inherent in the mathematical and social aims are to be evaluated at all, they must be evaluated by means other than published tests.

For comprehensive evaluation prospective teachers need, first of all, to have a clear conception of the purposes of mathematics. They need, second, to know and to be able to identify the kinds of behavior which will be exhibited both by their pupils who are achieving these purposes and by those who are not. Third, they must have considerable ingenuity in devising situations for testing, observing, and interviewing, in order to elicit critical types of behavior. And, fourth, they must have confidence in their judgment, however subjective it may be, as a basis for evaluating progress in learning.

(*g*) *Research literature.*—In the end, it will be through competent research that we shall arrive at greatly improved teaching procedures. There are at present more than two thousand published reports of quantitative investigations, some good, some bad, on the teaching of mathematics. Yet, many teachers are unaware of this large body of information, and still fewer make use of it. This condition should be remedied.

Only a few teachers will become producers of research, but all of them can and should become intelligent consumers of research. This latter purpose can be achieved if at some time in their education they can be brought into contact with a few selected research reports. These reports they should study under guidance, with the view to developing habits of critical analysis. When they are possessed of these habits, they can profit immediately from the findings of new studies rather than have to wait, as is now the case, for these findings to work their way slowly into textbooks and courses of study. In this connection the Yearbooks of The National Council of Teachers of Mathematics should be helpful.

B. In Grades 9–12

The *optimum* training of mathematics teachers for grades 9–12 should be based on the functions they should be able to perform and on the objectives they should seek for their pupils. A well-prepared teacher of mathematics should have adequate training so that he can meet all classroom situations with that assurance which can be based only on wide knowledge and rich background. The following theses, based on this optimum training, suggest course work and study in mathematics, education, and related fields over a period of five years.

Thesis 26. *The teacher of mathematics should have a wide background in the subjects he will be called upon to teach.*

It will not be possible to accomplish this program completely with most prospective teachers during their undergraduate training. However, enough training may be given to enable the teacher to get well on the way to complete accomplishment. This thesis means that the teacher's study of mathematics must include courses in college mathematics and not be merely a review of high school mathematics (algebra, plane and solid geometry, and trigonometry).

A teacher cannot teach mathematics with competence unless he knows enough about the subject to understand what elements are important for pupils in their possible life needs or future study. He cannot intelligently aid in reorganizing the high school curriculum in mathematics without an adequate reserve of mathematical knowledge. Without this kind of training he will not see that pupils need basic understandings as well as manipulative skill if they are to develop power in dealing with quantitative situations.

The mathematical background should include work in trigonometry and solid geometry if these have not been studied in high school. It should also include analytic geometry and calculus (elements of these subjects are taught in many high schools) and a course in college geometry beyond the secondary course in synthetic geometry. Also advisable are a course in the theory of equations and a course in spherical trigonometry with applications to global geometry, astronomy, and mapping; so also is a course in the history of mathematics, with emphasis on the historical development of computation and of elementary mathematics.

Some knowledge of the foundations of mathematics is indispensable for a well-trained teacher of mathematics. It is not likely that students will get it outside of class work. It may easily be included in the courses in college algebra and geometry.

At some time in his training the teacher should learn the use of, and the elementary problems of, the transit, sextant, slide rule, other mechanical computers, and related elementary problems. Not to be neglected is the habit of browsing in the college library that gives a knowledge of those recreational topics so useful in conducting mathematics clubs. College mathematics clubs, and the sponsoring of high school clubs during apprentice teaching will help greatly.

Other courses from which selections may be made and which will widen the teacher's background are: elementary statistics and educational measurements, the elements of non-euclidean geometry, projective or descriptive geometry, and the mathematics of finance. Selections should not, however, be made from these courses at the expense of the other training outlined above in this section.

Thesis 27. *The mathematics teacher should have a sound background in related fields.*

Courses in physics, mechanics, astronomy, navigation, economics, business problems, and the like add much to the teacher's ability to draw upon other fields and to understand and use vital applications from these fields in his teaching.

Thesis 28. *The mathematics teacher should have adequate training in the teaching of mathematics, including arithmetic.*

The background developed in previous paragraphs is of little use to the teacher unless he can teach with skill. Therefore he should take courses in the history and philosophy of education, psychology, and the techniques and problems of teaching in general, as well as specific methods in one or more mathematics subjects.

The mathematics teacher should be thoroughly familiar with the methods of teaching arithmetic. The war has shown a need for emphasis on arithmetic by high school teachers. There is a rather widespread belief among high school teachers that a knowledge of higher mathematics carries with it skill in teaching arithmetic. Such is not the case. A teacher cannot adequately remedy earlier defects in arithmetic teaching without a knowledge of how arithmetic should be taught, nor can he, without such knowledge, devise adequate diagnostic tests or conduct remedial work in arithmetic. The need is for specific training in arithmetic for prospective high-school teachers.

As a part of his training in teaching methods he should become acquainted with those multi-sensory aids that are available through commercial sources, motion pictures, film strips, and models. In time he should become adept in devising and making for his own class use simple models, devices, and even film strips, to aid him in teaching.

Thesis 29. *The courses in mathematical subject matter for the prospective mathematics teacher should be professionalized.*

Since the objectives to be sought in training a high school teacher are obviously not the same as the objectives sought in training a research scholar or an engineer, college instructors in mathematics should be closely connected with the teaching of mathematics in secondary schools, should have an intimate knowledge of the problems that teachers in such schools have to meet, and should be able to tie in the college courses with problems in secondary teaching.

Thesis 30. *It is desirable that a mathematics teacher acquire a background of experience in practical fields where mathematics is used.*

He should have opportunity for experience in such fields as the general shop, machine shop, the making and reading of simple blue prints, and surveying. A few colleges and universities are providing courses for prospective teachers of mathematics which include a semester of experience in holding a job in an industry or a business. It would seem feasible and certainly desirable for a teacher of mathematics to devote at least a summer or two in learning a variety of jobs in one of the large manufacturing plants. All such experiences provide illustrations of mathematical uses.

Thesis 31. *The minimum training for mathematics teachers in small high schools should be a college minor in mathematics.*

This report would not be complete without mention of teachers in the smaller high schools who must teach one or more subjects besides mathematics and who may have a major interest in some subject other than mathematics. Under these circumstances the training outlined for mathematics teachers in larger high schools, whose major interest is in mathematics, cannot be expected or obtained. In suggesting a minimum training for such teachers there is always the chance that the minimum may be misinterpreted as a satisfactory standard. This error must not be made. If these teachers continue to teach mathematics, they should plan to take undergraduate or graduate work to bring their background and training up to the standard suggested in these theses.

Since the training outlined in this thesis must be considered as an absolute minimum, the state should insist that, if the teacher is to continue teaching mathematics, he must improve his preparation. This improvement should follow the suggestions made earlier in this section.

Thesis 32. *Provision should be made for the continuous education of teachers in service.*

Prospective teachers for all grades should have extensive opportunities to engage in student teaching under skillful supervision and guidance. To say that one learns to teach by teaching is not to disparage the more formal and academic aspects of teacher education. It is simply to recognize that such instruction gains greatly in meaning and effectiveness when it is translated into the activities of concrete teaching experience. Ideally, student teaching should be started in a campus or laboratory school where good teaching and competent supervision is, in general, rather easily provided. It should be supplemented by experience in situations involving run-of-the-mill pupils, a feeling of full responsibility for the results produced, and at least reasonably good supervision.

A teacher should serve an internship which will enable him to observe good teaching and, under the guidance of a critic teacher, allow him to practice what he has observed. A training school, no matter how fine, can not provide all the variety of experiences necessary. A student teacher needs an internship under competent supervision in a typical school situation with about half a teaching load and with enough pay so that he can concentrate on becoming a good teacher.

VII. MULTISENSORY AIDS IN MATHEMATICS

Thesis 33. *Mathematics teachers need to give careful consideration to the possibilities of multi-sensory aids.*[16]

The schools of the armed forces have made extensive use of training aids which may be listed as, (1) motion pictures, (2) film strips and slides, (3) graphic charts and pictures, (4) models and other equipment, and (5) recordings. The figures for production and use are fantastic.[17] As of January, 1944, 2200 film-strip subjects had been produced by the Training Film Section of the Navy alone! Figures on the use of other visual aids, charts, graphs, models, recordings, etc., would likewise exceed the imagination.

Training aids are useful in a great variety of testing and learning situations. Training aids are being used in the armed forces in about every type of training and in about every conceivable situation. For example, training aids are used in tests of factual memory, for inspirational purposes, in the development of concepts, in the practice of skills, in orientation to new situations, and especially in teaching the relationships of parts of an operating machine. In fact, the range of applications seems to be limited only by the imagination, the resourcefulness, and the competence of the training personnel.

Since this amazing development of training aids is essentially the product of the thought, research, and effort of professional educators now serving as wartime officers, it is safe to predict that multi-sensory aids will be widely used in the post-war period provided that the public is willing to furnish large funds for materials and personnel. It is also obvious that multi-sensory aids are especially useful in teaching science and mathematics.

Thesis 34. *The resourceful teacher of mathematics should be given competent guidance in the production, selection, and use of slide films.*

There are good reasons for believing that a teacher of mathematics can make a significant improvement in his work by the wider use of slide films. The slide film or film strip consists of a series of "frames" that may be projected on the ordinary wall of a class room. It has the very great advantage that a single slide or frame may be held on the screen or wall for a period of time that is adequate for careful study. Fortunately film strips are not too expensive to produce nor too difficult to design by a resourceful teacher. It is conceivable that a teacher with imagination, in a favorable

16. See *Multi-Sensory Aids in the Teaching of Mathematics.* The 18th Yearbook of The National Council of Teachers of Mathematics. The Bureau of Publications, Teachers College, 525 W. 120th St., New York 27, N. Y. Price, $2.

17. For a more complete picture of the wide use of training aids, the reader may wish to refer to three articles by Lieutenant Commander Francis W. Noel, U.S.N.R., in the *School Executive,* February, March and April, 1944.

school situation, may be disposed to experiment with slide films. If this should happen, the total number of such teachers in the nation will be more than necessary to provide a complete set of slide films for all curriculum units that can be illuminated by this technique, if properly coordinated. The increased interest in multi-sensory aids is likely to produce a vast number of slide films—some excellent, from which the teacher must make a selection.

The Council is the appropriate organization to sponsor, guide, and coordinate the production of an excellent collection or library of slide films. The Council could promote such a program by (a) providing the necessary directions for making a slide film, (b) giving generous recognition and reasonable compensation to the person or persons creating the slide films, (c) utilizing the audience situations at regional and national meetings for the selection of the best slide films, (d) arranging for the effective distribution of its films by an organization that would operate on a low service charge and turn over a small profit on each film to the Council, and (e) giving wide publicity to the film strips sponsored by the Council.

Though the film strip seems at the moment to offer the most promising possibilities for mathematics, it is obviously not the only one of the newer aids that deserves study and experimentation. The fact that the 18th yearbook of the Council deals with the broad topic of multi-sensory aids is evidence of the importance of other aids. Questions and proposals relating to training aids deserve careful study by a special committee of the Council. The Commission, therefore, has recommended to the Board of Directors of the Council, that a standing committee on multi-sensory aids be created to study developments, to keep the council informed and up-to-date, and to make information about the best multi-sensory aids generally available to mathematics teachers.

In conclusion, let it be repeated that the foregoing Report is tentative and provisional. It does not offer final solutions, but submits a set of theses which, it is hoped, will stimulate further deliberation and discussion among the nation's educators, administrators, and teachers of mathematics. It should also be stated that the Report is the result of intensive group conferences and of much correspondence. Such discussions by local groups should resolve differences of opinion as to certain details. Absolute agreement under ordinary circumstances is not to be expected. Nevertheless most of the theses of this report were endorsed unanimously and all others were approved by a substantial majority of the members of the Commission.

Members of the Commission

RALEIGH SCHORLING (Chairman)
The University High School
Ann Arbor, Michigan

WILLIAM L. SCHAAF
Assistant Professor of Education
Brooklyn College
Brooklyn, N. Y.

WILLIAM BETZ
Specialist in Mathematics in the
    Schools of Rochester, N. Y.

WILLIAM A. BROWNELL
Duke University
Durham, N. C.

EUGENIE C. HAUSLE
Chairman of Standing Committee on
    Mathematics in New York City
James Monroe High School, Bronx
    59, New York

VIRGIL S. MALLORY
Professor of Mathematics
State Teachers College
Montclair, N. J.

MARY POTTER
Supervisor of Mathematics
Racine, Wis.

ROLLAND R. SMITH
Coordinator of Mathematics
Public Schools
Springfield, Massachusetts

RUTH SUMNER, MRS.
President, Mathematics Section
State Teachers Association
Oakland, Calif.

F. LYNWOOD WREN
George Peabody College for
    Teachers, Nashville, Tenn.

JAMES H. ZANT
Professor and Acting Head,
    Department of Mathematics
Oklahoma A and M College
Stillwater, Oklahoma

The University of Illinois School Mathematics Program

UICSM Project Staff
University of Illinois High School [1]
Urbana, Illinois

INTRODUCTION

The state of mathematics teaching in secondary schools in this country has received, within the last few years, considerable attention in the public press. The publication of the survey conducted by the Educational Testing Service was followed by severe editorial indictments of the way in which mathematics training is provided in public schools.[2] The American school patron has been bombarded with statistics which purport to show that America's production of scientifically trained personnel is lagging far behind America's needs for such personnel and certainly far behind the production of technically trained people in the Soviet Union. We have also been exposed to statistics which show alleged declines in enrollments in mathematics and science in secondary schools. It has become commonplace to hear mathematics professors deplore the lack of mathematics training in college freshmen students. Despite the fact that much of what we read about mathematics education in the public press may be alarmist propaganda, it is clear to those of us in the mathematics education profession that there is abundant room for improvement in the secondary school mathematics curriculum. We do not think that there was once a "golden age of mathematics instruction" in the public schools and that this period was brought to a close by the depredations of faddists and educationists. Our group at the University of Illinois believes that the mathematics education of high school youth who are preparing for college can be significantly improved if certain fundamental changes are made in the content of the

1. University of Illinois Committee on School Mathematics—Project for the Improvement of School Mathematics: Max Beberman (Director), David A. Page (Editor), Herbert E. Vaughan (Mathematics Consultant), Gertrude Hendrix (Teacher Coordinator), et al. The ideas expressed in this article are to a large extent derived from the texts, teacher commentaries, and teaching program of the project. This article and the other work of the project has been made possible by a grant from the Carnegie Corporation of New York.
2. Henry S. Dyer, Robert Kalin, and Frederic M. Lord, *Problems in Mathematical Education*. Princeton, New Jersey: Educational Testing Service, 1956.

[This report was issued in 1956.]

mathematics curriculum and in the ways in which mathematics is taught. It is the purpose of this article to describe such changes.

BACKGROUND

In the fall of 1951 the University of Illinois issued a bulletin which stated new entrance requirements in mathematics for the College of Engineering.[3] The statement of these requirements—four units or the equivalent of high school mathematics—was accompanied by a set of supporting arguments which demonstrated the need for increasing mathematics competence of beginning engineering students. The bulletin contained a list of topics which attempted to describe this competence. The arguments and list were prepared by a joint committee comprising faculty members from the Colleges of Education and Engineering, and the Department of Mathematics in the College of Liberal Arts and Sciences. The work of this committee is often cited as one of the first cooperative undertakings among several branches of a university with regard to educational problems in mathematics in the public secondary schools.[4]

The success of this joint venture served as impetus for the creation of another committee (UICSM) comprising representatives from the three divisions mentioned above and the University of Illinois (Laboratory) High School. The fundamental charge to this new committee was to search for ways of helping the high schools in the state of Illinois, particularly the small high schools, to develop a mathematics curriculum which would be more effective in preparing students to meet the new requirements for entrance into the College of Engineering. Very early in its work, this Committee concluded that the education of the prospective engineering student was not a separate problem. It was felt that all students who plan to do collegiate work requiring a study of mathematics should have sound mathematical background. There is little need to differentiate at the early adolescent level among prospective engineers, prospective physicists, prospective physicians, prospective accountants, etc. Since the Committee was given considerable freedom to experiment and since it had available to it the laboratory facilities at the University of Illinois High School, it undertook the development of a secondary school mathematics curriculum.[5]

3. *Mathematical Needs of Prospective Students at the College of Engineering of the University of Illinois.* University of Illinois Bulletin, Vol. XLIX, No. 18. Urbana, Illinois: University of Illinois, 1951. [Out of print.]

4. Kenneth B. Henderson and Kern Dickman, "Minimum Mathematical Needs of Prospective Students in a College of Engineering." *The Mathematics Teacher,* XLV (February, 1952), 89–93.

5. Bruce E. Meserve, "The University of Illinois List of Mathematical Competencies," *The School Review,* Vol. LXI, No. 2 (February 1953), 85–92.

One of its basic working principles is that high school mathematics need not be organized in the conventional manner: a year of algebra, followed by a year of geometry, followed by a year of algebra, followed by solid geometry and trigonometry. It is quite possible to take basic and simple ideas from each of the branches of traditional high school mathematics and incorporate them into a beginning course and to follow this beginning course by moving along threads of arithmetic, algebra, and geometry through all years of high school mathematics. An obvious advantage of this approach is that a student tends to view mathematics as a unified discipline. Moreover, through this process of sampling among the various branches of mathematics at the beginning of his high school career, he acquires the ability to make a judicious choice of the subjects he shall elect to concentrate on while in high school.

The UICSM developed a high school freshman course which was taught in one class at the University High School in the academic year 1952–53. The result of this year's experience was encouraging enough to suggest to the Committee and to University officials that the UICSM program be extended to several public schools in the state for experimental trial. Two Illinois public schools entered the UICSM program in the fall of 1953 and taught *First Course* during the academic year 1953–54.

THE NEW MATHEMATICS CURRICULUM

The early attempts of the UICSM to design a new curriculum in high school mathematics were directed largely toward a reorganization of the traditional curriculum. Although the "integration" aim is a laudatory one, the attempt to implement this aim did not result in a product which was entirely satisfactory to the Committee. The curriculum makers of the Committee asked questions such as the following:

> What is a number?
> What is a variable?
> What is a function?
> What is an equation?
> What is geometry?

None of these questions is treated satisfactorily in conventional textbooks, nor does a reshuffling of traditional content help. The Committee members, especially those who had high school teaching experience, were deeply concerned with these questions. They felt that unless such questions could be answered in a consistent fashion, the intellectual content of high school mathematics would remain disjointed and mysterious. In fact, the charge that the traditional high school curriculum in mathematics is riddled with inconsistencies is one which can be easily documented. [Yet, one hears very

657

little of this charge in current criticisms of mathematics education.] To us, the quest for a consistent exposition of high school mathematics is a primary motivation.

But, if in conventional programs, the explanations of basic concepts are confused, how do we explain the fact that some high school graduates appear to be well-grounded in mathematics? A clue to an explanation of this phenomenon is provided, indirectly, by Brownell in a description of research conducted under his supervision.[6] In this particular study, third grade children demonstrated a variety of procedures in arriving at answers to simple questions concerning arithmetic combinations. Although the children were taught in such a manner that one would expect them to respond to questions with answers which they had learned by rote, it was discovered upon interviewing the children that they used many "common sense" techniques to obtain answers, for example, 6 and 4 are 10 because 5 and 5 are 10. Thus, despite what children are actually told in the classroom, they tend to organize their mathematical knowledge in ways which are meaningful to them. We think that this tendency persists throughout a child's elementary and secondary education. Children observe teachers solving problems at the blackboard; they imitate their teachers. However, not all problems can be solved through imitation simply because there is not enough time for teachers to demonstrate the solutions to all problems. Therefore, the *more able* student makes some attempt to systematize his knowledge of mathematics. Sometimes his textbooks will attempt to assist him in this systematization. But textbook statements are so often fraught with semantic confusion that a literal acceptance of them cannot help but confuse a child. Thus, the bright student who is interested in mathematics tends to learn mathematics almost in spite of teacher and textbook. The less able student who is not successful in systematization can operate only in familiar areas. Thus many students who have had several years of mathematical training in high school are at a loss when presented with a mathematics problem which does not resemble closely the ones they learned to do through imitation. Of course, there are some bright students who very quickly detect inconsistencies in textbook explanations and in teacher explanations and so decide that "math is silly" or that "there is the math teacher's way of solving a problem and there is the common sense way of solving it." Such students give up mathematics at a rather early age and move into areas which are more intellectually satisfying to them.

We believe that the students' desire for systematization is ever-present. In fact, it is probable that this desire, and the ability to satisfy it, are the

6. William A. Brownell, "Psychological Considerations in the Learning and the Teaching of Arithmetic," *The Teaching of Arithmetic, The Tenth Yearbook of the National Council of Teachers of Mathematics,* New York City: Bureau of Publications, Teachers College, Columbia University, 1935. 8–10.

important components of what we call *creativity*. We do not think that a program of instruction could be or should be designed to eliminate this desire. Moreover, mathematics courses ought to be such as to capitalize upon the existence of this desire. Whatever the teacher and textbook say about mathematics ought to help the student to make his systematization more inclusive and consistent.

In addition to its thesis that expositions of mathematics should be consistent, the UICSM maintains a second thesis, somewhat related to the first. We believe that high school students have a profound interest in *ideas*. High school students are speculative; they enjoy working with abstractions; they like to exercise their imaginations. Despite the current furor concerning the usefulness of mathematics in various occupations, we believe that high school students are not genuinely stirred by such a "sales campaign." The goal of vocational utility is too remote to make much difference to a ninth grader. He wants to know how mathematics fits into his own world. And, happily enough, his own world is full of fancy and abstractions. Thus, we hold that students become interested in mathematics because it gives them quick access to a kind of intellectual adventure which is enticing and significant. For example, we do not believe in attempting to motivate a student's study of quadratic equations by telling him that engineers make considerable use of them in their everyday work. Even if this statement about engineers were true, a student is interested in how a quadratic equation can be solved because this information can be incorporated into his "internal theory" of equation-solving.

The third thesis of the UICSM is one which provokes opposition from more teachers of mathematics than do either of the other two. There are teachers who believe that the most effective kind of curriculum for the high school student is one which is heavy-laden with manipulative tasks. They feel that the period of adolescence is the best period in which to get students to become adroit in carrying out mathematical routines. Although we do not deny the need for dexterity in carrying out routine mathematical tasks, we do not believe that a curriculum which is based primarily on such tasks is attractive to high school youth. To be sure, manipulative tasks *can* be designed to develop a certain degree of cleverness, and many good mathematicians had their early contact with mathematics in just such a curriculum. However, the creative urge of the adolescent does not find satisfaction in such a curriculum. Moreover, the mathematics teacher who is interested in ideas can hardly find satisfaction in becoming a "drill sergeant." In developing the UICSM program we avoid manipulative tasks which do not cast light on some basic concept. If in teaching the solution of systems of equations we must choose between teaching what it means to solve a system of linear equations and teaching rote methods for solving both systems of linear equations and systems of quadratic equations, our choice is clear.

We have evidence for the belief that a student who *understands* the solution of systems of linear equations can create his own methods for solving systems of quadratic equations. We believe that a student who has been exposed to a diet rich in ideas is more resourceful than one who has been exposed only to manipulative tasks.

In our attempt to develop a curriculum consistent with the aforementioned theses, the UICSM program acquired characteristics which have marked it in the eyes of many mathematicians and educators as one which seeks to introduce modern mathematics into the high school curriculum. This judgment is correct although it should not be interpreted as indicative of a primary motive. We are more concerned with consistency than with "up-to-dateness." But we discovered that in trying to tell a consistent mathematical story we were compelled to seek the advice of the contemporary research mathematician, particularly that of the mathematician who is concerned with discoveries in the foundations of mathematics. This field of research seems to be the most fruitful source of answers to the questions we have raised. Consequently, in the academic year 1954–55 the UICSM developed, purely on an exploratory basis, teaching units which dealt with theoretical treatments of the natural number system, the system of integers, the rational number system, and a Hilbert-like version of plane geometry. Although these units did not meet with unqualified success in all of the schools participating in the program, the experience gained through the trial led to the following conclusions.

1. Contemporary mathematics (material of interest to research mathematicians within the last hundred years) contains much that can be both interesting and valuable to high school students.
2. High school teachers of mathematics, although receptive to these new ideas and anxious to incorporate them in their teaching, are not prepared academically to teach concepts from contemporary mathematics. However, they are capable to doing so when they are given appropriate help both in understanding these ideas and in teaching them.

We shall say more about the implications of the second conclusion in a later section. At this point it is appropriate to present in outline form the content of the four-year curriculum as it is presently conceived by the UICSM. We list below the major topics in our four courses as they are presently being taught.

First Course

Distinction between numbers and their numerals.
Principles of arithmetic (commutative, associative, etc.).
Positive and negative numbers.
Relations of inequality ($\neq, <, >, \leqslant$, etc.).
Variables ("pronumerals"; we sedulously avoid such confusing terms as

'variable number' and 'general number'.).

Generalizations about numbers (Ex. For every x and y, $|x + y| \leqslant |x| + |y|$.).

Equations and inequalities and their loci.

Second Course

Euclidean geometry of the coordinate plane (lines, angles, polygons, circles, etc. are treated as sets of points).

Sets and relations (elementary probability, algebra of sets, relations as sets of ordered pairs, systems of equations and inequalities, equivalence relations, number systems).

Functions (functions as relations, linear and quadratic functions, zeros of functions, inverses of functions).

Third-Fourth Courses

Mathematical induction (generalizations, hereditary properties, recursive definitions, progressions, Σ-notation).

Exponents and logarithms (recursive definitions of exponentials, inductive proofs of laws of exponents, rational and real number exponents, exponential curves).

Complex numbers (ordered pairs of real numbers, field properties, applications to plane geometry).

Functions (integral rational functions, polynomial equations, derivatives, Newton's Method).

Circular functions (winding functions, periodic functions, even and odd functions, cosine and sine and related functions, trigonometry, subtraction formulas, etc., inverses of circular functions, "trigonometric" equations, limit law for sine, loci of composite circular functions).

It should be remarked that the UICSM curriculum has always been in a somewhat fluid state, and that we expect it to remain so for some time. Both major and minor changes in the curriculum are suggested by the classroom experiences of the teachers who are cooperating with us, and by the insights into the structure of elementary mathematics which come to us as we attempt to solve the problems of exposition. For example, our present ninth grade course (*First Course*) is now in its fourth edition, and a comparison with the first edition will reveal scant similarity between the two. Since there have been few really radical experiments in mathematics curriculum construction, we have almost no precedents to go by other than those which we create ourselves.

THE "NEW" TEACHING

It is implicit in the foregoing discussion that we have strong beliefs about how students learn mathematics. The most carefully devised curriculum can be vitiated if teachers utilize techniques which are inappropriate.

We believe that students can perceive their mathematics courses in much the same light as they perceive courses in art and in literature. Just as a good literature teacher leaves students with the belief that literature is a living subject and that students can contribute to it, so does a good mathematics teacher foster in his students the belief that the development of mathematics is a human creation which is not complete and to which each person can make contributions. Such a belief is not cultivated merely by talking about it. It can be fostered, however, through daily experience. The UICSM does not claim to have invented this kind of teaching. On the other hand, it must be admitted that such teaching is not commonplace. We do believe that teachers can be helped to accomplish the result we mentioned above. They need extensive help in developing teaching techniques consonant with this aim, and they need textbook materials which are of real assistance to them. We describe below two examples which illustrate the kind of teaching we advocate.

(a) *Discovery.*—In our treatment of positive and negative numbers we do not give a statement of the rules for operating with such numbers. We know that students can discover such rules on their own. If students are given a reasonable interpretation of the symbols for positive and negative numbers, we have seen that they will develop rules for operating with such numbers and will also develop ways and means of carrying out the rules. If, at an early stage in the student's learning, we ask him to state the rules he has discovered, we are sure that such statements will be ill-conceived and will involve semantical errors. Since such errors are difficult to correct at this early stage and since we do not want students to follow verbalizations which are essentially incorrect, we avoid verbal formulations of these rules. In a later chapter when the concept of numerical variables has been treated, the student is given formulations of the rules and asked to check them.

Now, it is not an easy task to convince teachers that students can operate successfully with positive and negative numbers in the absence of formalized rules. There is a tendency for teachers to "tie things up" in verbalizations. We find it necessary to persuade teachers with whom we work that students can operate without this "tying-up." Usually, the first trial is enough to convince teachers of the soundness of this position. Frequently, beginning students will ask for verbalizations of the rules. They are astounded to learn that it is their job to make up the rules. It is not easy to bring students to the point where they believe that they do not have to depend upon textbooks or teachers in order to operate successfully, but it is possible, and rewarding.

(b) *Freedom.*—It is common to hear high school mathematics students talk about the "arithmetic way of solving a problem," the "algebra way of doing it," or the "geometry way of doing it." Observation gives credence to the belief that many current textbooks and teaching methods engender this attitude. Much of conventional mathematics is taught in an exceedingly formal manner. Often, a formalism is required in the performance of mathematical tasks which bears no relation to the manner in which mathematics is applied outside the classroom or to the way mathematics is studied at more advanced levels. It is no exaggeration to state that some students believe that one has not proved a theorem unless one has divided a sheet of paper into two columns and has placed statements in one column and reasons in the other! It is not surprising that many students develop an aversion to mathematics just because of this petty formalism. We urge that teachers in our program give students much freedom in attacking problems. For example, in our treatment of equations and inequalities in FIRST COURSE, we demonstrate to students several techniques for using equations in solving the familiar "story" problems. Nowhere do we *insist* that students use equations to solve such problems. In fact, we are frequently surprised at the ingenious, so-called "arithmetic" techniques which students discover in solving such problems. Frequently, the problems are too difficult to yield to an arithmetic-type approach; it is for these problems that the so-called "algebraic" method is appropriate. At times a student will bring to class an ingenious arithmetic solution for a problem. His teacher may ask him if he could also solve the problem by using an equation. If he is successful with the second method, both methods can be compared. But in no sense is his first method rejected. We urge students to exercise their intuition in solving problems, in making estimates of answers, and even in making a wild guess and then adjusting the guess in the light of subsequent verification. This attitude of freedom has remarkable results. We have witnessed bursts of creativity which are indicative of genuine mathematical talent.

We do not aim at a passive "permissiveness" on the part of the teacher, but at something much more active: a receptiveness to students' ideas and an attitude of delight in another's intellectual adventure.

[*The report continues with specifics on the organization and future planning within the project.*]

*Report of the Commission
on Mathematics*

Program for
college preparatory
mathematics

*College Entrance Examination Board
New York, 1959*

Commission on Mathematics

Albert W. Tucker, Princeton University[1],
  Chairman
Carl B. Allendoerfer,
  University of Washington
Edwin C. Douglas, The Taft School,
  Watertown, Connecticut[2]
Howard F. Fehr, Teachers College,
  Columbia University
Martha Hildebrandt,
  Proviso Township High School,
  Maywood, Illinois
Albert E. Meder, Jr., Rutgers,
  the State University of New Jersey[3]
Morris Meister,
  Bronx High School of Science,
  New York, New York[4]
Frederick Mosteller, Harvard University
Eugene P. Northrop, University of Chicago
Ernest R. Ranucci, Weequahic High School,
  Newark, New Jersey[5]
Robert E. K. Rourke, Kent School,
  Kent, Connecticut[6]
George B. Thomas, Jr.,
  Massachusetts Institute of Technology
Henry Van Engen,
  Iowa State Teachers College[7]
Samuel S. Wilks, Princeton University

[1]The institutions given are those with which Commission members were affiliated at the time of their appointment to the Commission. Subsequent changes in institutional affiliations are noted below.

[2]An ex officio member of the Commission, first as Chairman of the Examiners in Mathematics of the College Entrance Examination Board and, since October 31, 1956, as Chairman of the Board's Panel of Examiners in Mathematics.

[3]Mr. Meder's ex officio membership on the Commission ceased upon the expiration of his term as Chairman of the Committee on Examinations of the College Board on December 31, 1956. From January 1, 1957 until June 30, 1958, he served as Executive Director of the Commission, on leave from Rutgers University. On July 1, 1958, he again became a member of the Commission.

[4]Subsequently affiliated with Bronx Community College. Mr. Meister's ex officio membership on the Commission began with his appointment as Chairman of the Committee on Examinations on January 1, 1957.

[5]Subsequently affiliated with Newark State College.

[6]Executive Director from July 1, 1958, on leave from Kent School.

[7]Subsequently affiliated with the University of Wisconsin.

Contents

Foreword, ix

Assignment: the Commission's role, xi

*1. Orientation: an urgent need for
curricular revision, 1*

Creation of new mathematics, 1
Reorganization of older mathematics, 2
The nature of contemporary
mathematics, 2
New applications of mathematics, 3
Significance for the secondary school
curriculum, 5
Demand for improved instruction, 6
The national need for mathematical
manpower, 7
Summary of the case for revision, 9

*2. Secondary education:
the Commission's premises, 10*

The role of the secondary school, 10
Mathematics in general education, 10
Mathematics for the "college-capable", 11
Determining course content, 13
The place of calculus, 14
The Advanced Placement Program, 15
The program and the teacher, 15
Summary, 16

*3. Recommendation: the Commission's
program, 17*

Prerequisite mathematics, 18

Mathematics for grades 9, 10, and 11
(Elementary and Intermediate
Mathematics), 20
Mathematics for grade 12
(Advanced Mathematics), 30
Summary, 33

*4. Organization: a proposed sequence
for the Commission's program, 35*

Mathematics for grade 9
(Elementary Mathematics I), 36
Mathematics for grade 10
(Elementary Mathematics II), 38
Mathematics for grade 11
(Intermediate Mathematics), 40
Mathematics for grade 12
(Advanced Mathematics), 42

*5. Implementation: the vital role of
teacher education, 48*

Some comments on the education of
elementary school teachers, 48
The education of secondary school
mathematics teachers, 50
Summary, 58

*6. Articulation: the school and the
college, 59*

College entrance requirements, 59
College curricula, 62
Summary, 62

1. Orientation: An Urgent Need for Curricular Revision

Mathematics is a living, growing subject. The vitality and vigor of present-day mathematical research quickly dispels any notion that mathematics is a subject long since embalmed in textbooks. Mathematics today is in many respects an entirely different discipline from what it was at the turn of the century. New developments have been extensive; new concepts have been revolutionary. The sheer bulk of current mathematical development is staggering.

CREATION OF NEW MATHEMATICS

The American Mathematical Society, the learned society in this country devoted primarily to the advancement of mathematical research, publishes a journal entitled *Mathematical Reviews*, in which brief notice is given of new mathematical results. No proofs are included, nor any expositions, but merely critical factual reports—and still the journal runs to some 1,200 large, double-column pages each year.

Also, the Society holds meetings at which research results are communicated. Over 800 papers are presented annually at such meetings. The Society's membership in the United States and Canada alone numbers more than 5,000. When one realizes that mathematicians are active all over the world, he begins to see why the annual production of new mathematics is formidable.

One inevitable result of this explosive development of mathematics has been the creation of new subject matter. Such fields as mathematical logic, probability and statistical inference, topology, and modern abstract algebra are largely or wholly the products of recent mathematical research. Mathematical logic, for example, was little known to most mathematicians a generation ago. But by 1936 its development was sufficiently extensive, and interest in it sufficiently widespread to warrant the formation of an international learned society, the Association for Symbolic Logic, devoted exclusively to this branch of mathematics. The Association publishes some 200 pages of research annually.

Similarly, the field of probability and statistical inference has been extensively developed in recent years. In this field, too, a research society and research journal have been established in this country: the Institute of Mathematical Statistics, and the *Annals of Mathematical Statistics*, now in its twenty-ninth year. At least 10 other journals, in English, are entirely devoted to the theory and applications of probability and statistics.

These exciting new mathematical developments also receive popular notice. For example, articles on "The New Mathematics" and "The New Uses of the Abstract" by G. A. W. Boehm recently have appeared in *Fortune*, in the issues of June and July 1958.

REORGANIZATION OF OLDER MATHEMATICS

Another result of the recent growth of mathematics has been the reorganization, extension, and transformation of parts of the older mathematics.

Algebra is a branch of mathematics that has been transformed by the mathematical research of the last quarter-century. A first-year graduate school course in algebra today bears little or no resemblance to that of 30 years ago. The key concepts of the earlier course would now be subsumed under newer and broader concepts that had not been formulated in 1928. Yet the corresponding course of 30 years ago differed little or not at all from its predecessor of 1900.

The essence of this transformation is essentially that algebra is now thought of as the study of mathematical structure, or "pattern." For example, high school algebra deals extensively with systems of numbers: positive and negative integers, rational numbers, real numbers, and complex numbers. One rule of combination of numbers is multiplication. In all of these systems, two of the patterns of multiplication are given by the commutative and associative laws:

$$a \times b = b \times a$$

and

$$(a \times b) \times c = a \times (b \times c)$$

Today's algebra encompasses as well systems in which the elements are not numbers at all. And in such systems familiar patterns may not appear—for example, the commutative and associative laws do not hold in some algebras.

Earlier mathematicians often looked upon algebra from a manipulative point of view. Skill in performing the operations within the system frequently was the goal of instruction, rather than an understanding of the properties of the system. The contemporary point of view, while not discounting the manipulative skills necessary for efficient mathematical thought, puts chief emphasis on the structure or pattern of the system and on deductive thinking.

THE NATURE OF CONTEMPORARY MATHEMATICS

The difference in point of view between the older approach and the contemporary conception is well put by W. W. Sawyer: "The mathematician of older times asked, 'Can I find a trick to solve this problem?' If he could not find a trick today, he looked for one tomorrow. But . . . we no longer assume that a trick need exist at all. We ask rather, 'Is there any reason to suppose that this problem can be solved with the means we have at hand? Can it be broken up into simpler problems? What is it that makes a problem soluble, and how can we test for solubility?' We try to discover the nature of the problem we are dealing with."[1]

Today, developments in mathematics are concerned with such patterns of thought and such insights into meaning. Thus, contemporary mathematics is characterized by: (1) a tremendous development quantitatively; (2) the introduction of new content; (3) the reorganization and extension of older content; and (4) renewed, increased, and conscious emphasis upon the view that mathematics is concerned with abstract patterns of thought.

NEW APPLICATIONS OF MATHEMATICS

Not only in pure mathematics are great vitality, new content, and spectacular growth to be found. The same developments are seen in recent applications of mathematics. Mathematics is extending itself, often with dramatic results, into fields in which until recently it had not been used.

There are two aspects to this greatly expanded application of mathematics: first, the new uses of the older mathematics; second, the uses of the newer mathematics.

NEW USES OF OLDER MATHEMATICS

Some idea of the scope and nature of the recent application of mathematics long since known is conveyed by the following statement prepared for the Commission by M. S. Longuet-Higgins, a British expert on fluid dynamics:

"The basic mathematical ideas and methods that have been known for centuries still are as valid, as exciting, and as practically useful as ever. Especially is this true in the fields of calculus and mathematical analysis. Many of the most striking advances of our age, for example the development of supersonic flight and the launching of earth satellites, depend directly on an expert application of fluid dynamics, to which calculus is absolutely fundamental. Current research in geophysics—in the upper atmosphere (ionosphere), in the oceans (discovery of deep ocean currents), and in the interior of the earth (theories of the magnetic field)—are closely associated with advances in mathematical theory. New achievements in mechanical engineering, in automatic control (automation), and in radar communication would be unthinkable but for the work of analysts (such as Norbert Wiener and applied mathematicians (such as Claude Shannon). To all such workers calculus is a basic tool, and analysis is part of their very thought.

1. *Prelude to Mathematics* (Baltimore: Pelican Books, Penguin Books, Inc., 1955), p. 214.

"The close connection between mathematics and physics also should not be forgotten. Most of the great physical discoveries have come from skilled use of mathematical technique. Newton's law of gravitation (on which the Sputniks and Explorers depend) was established by combined use of calculus and physical observation. The more refined Einstein law of gravitation is stated in terms of differential geometry. Theories of the atom are described in terms of Schroedinger's differential equation. A satisfactory theory of the atomic nucleus, still to be formulated, almost certainly will come in a mathematical form.

"Therefore, while the growing character of mathematics may be emphasized, the permanence of traditional mathematical ideas must not be forgotten. Mathematics may be compared to a great tree, ever putting forth green shoots and new branches, still nevertheless, having the same firm trunk of established knowledge. The new shoots are evidence of life, the trunk is essential for the support of the whole."

USES OF NEW MATHEMATICS

In addition to the impressive array of new uses to which the older mathematics is now put, there are also astonishing and rapidly expanding fields of application for contemporary mathematics. Mathematics is no longer reserved for the use of engineers and physical scientists, even though a great many of its applications are still in their hands.

Mathematics and mathematical techniques and modes of thought permeate our lives and activities today to an extent that relatively few people yet perceive. Previous ages regarded mathematics as a worthy handmaiden of science and engineering. Today mathematics exerts actual leadership in natural science, social science, business, industry, and other fields of application.

Mathematics in the social sciences: One of the most important of these new fields of application is that of the social sciences. Social scientists have frequent occasion to deal with large masses of data, usually obtained by sampling. With respect to such data, problems of presentation, description, and inference must be considered. How can extensive data be organized to show essential features and to reval relationships without distortion? How can such a mass of data be accurately summarized without neglecting its dispersion? Under what conditions can inferences be drawn from the data, and how reliable are the inferences? Such mathematical questions are dealt with in the contemporary theory of probability and statistical inference.

Areas of the field of psychology increasingly are using quantitative methods, in the form of statistics and other advanced mathematical techniques. The same is true in sociology—in population and social studies concerning the individual and the community.

670

While economists for some time have found frequent uses for mathematics, especially calculus, in their work, recent years have seen these undergo a startling increase. This increase is reflected not only in the number and variety of problems attacked mathematically, but in the bewildering diversity of mathematics employed. And this is by no means a one-way street. Economics is contributing problems that lead to the development of new mathematics. The theory of games is an example of a branch of mathematics suggested by problems in economics related to competition and cooperation.

Economists have directed much research toward quantitative interrelations among various sectors of industry, toward constructing models of dynamic processes in the national economy, and toward predictions of the behavior of large economic complexes.

Economics and direct industrial applications overlap in the use of mathematical methods to solve complicated problems of management. In this field, sometimes called "operations research," are found specific instances of the application of the theory of games, of input-output analysis, and of programming for problems in machine loading, distribution, allocation, and scheduling.

The Social Science Research Council has set up a committee on the mathematical training of social scientists, and summer seminars have been conducted to help provide training in mathematics for persons active in social science research. Many research projects and organizations in social science have engaged mathematicians either as regular staff members or as consultants.

Mathematics in industry: The use of statistics has expanded greatly in industry. This is especially true in the design and analysis of industrial research experiments, and in statistical quality control and sampling theory. The techniques of statistical quality control, now extensively used in mass production industries, are essentially mathematical answers to questions of reliability of inference.

Samples of products being made are withdrawn for inspection or testing. What inferences as to the quality of the total production can be drawn from the results of the tests of such samples? Are defective items sufficiently few in number to justify acceptance of the product by the purchaser? What is the life expectancy of the product? Are defects, when they occur, caused by chance, by inferior raw material, or by faulty workmanship? Are the defective items the product of particular machines or particular workers? How reliable are the answers to these questions? The techniques of statistical quality control—techniques that are an application of contemporary mathematics—have been developed precisely to solve such problems.

Other applications of contemporary mathematics are found in the design of high-speed computing machines, in the communications industry, and in the theory of learning. The importance of these developments is well emphasized by the following statements quoted from a pamphlet entitled *Mathematics in an Industrial Economy.*[2]

"The growing volume of knowledge and the complexity of our social organization have made necessary an incredible expansion of the application of logical and quantitative methods. Here the automatic computer has greatly facilitated and extended the usefulness of mathematics. The electronic computers and data-processing systems make logical and analytical investigations possible on a scale undreamed of only a few decades ago. . . .

". . . Mathematics offers a medium for expressing complicated and logical relationships. It provides a framework for organizing masses of data and information. Its concepts and symbols display a dynamic dependence of the performance of the whole upon the behavior of its parts."

SIGNIFICANCE FOR THE SECONDARY SCHOOL CURRICULUM

The fact that the new mathematics of the past 50 or 100 years is playing an ever-increasing role in our society is of special importance for the work of the Commission. It has profound implications with respect to curricular revision.

The Commission is concerned, as was the committee of examiners whose recommendations led to its appointment, over the fact that the present secondary school mathematics curriculum has lagged behind the growth and uses of the subject. The development of mathematics and the broadening of its applications have outrun the curriculum. Another way of putting this is to say that the present curriculum rests on a static rather than on a dynamic concept of mathematics. An analogy may help to dramatize the difference.

As a city grows, it becomes increasingly difficult to find adequate transportation from the center of the city to the outlying areas and the suburbs. The center is still the core of the city, but the streets are too narrow and too congested for the newer sections to be reached as quickly as the needs of the residents require. For a time, systems of traffic lights and one-way streets suffice; but ultimately these patchwork methods, too, are found to be inadequate. Then there is constructed a limited-access freeway or expressway from the heart of the city to outlying points, bringing the newer regions effectively closer to the core.

Precisely this process is what the growth of mathematics demands—namely, that new and more efficient routes be found in the foundations of the subject as laid in secondary school to the newer territory of modern mathematics, in order that students may penetrate these newer territories

2. (Detroit, Mich.: Industrial Mathematics Society, 1955 [revised, 1958]), p. 6.

without laboriously traversing all of the older content. In the process some obsolete or obsolescent material will be dropped, as will some material whose omission will cause regret. While still of value, it is of lesser value than the objective of attaining an understanding of the spirit, method, and content of contemporary mathematics. Traditional mathematics—algebra, geometry, trigonometry—is still the great core of the subject, but the distance between the core and the newer developments must be shortened by new methods of approach.

Fortunately, much of the new mathematics suitable for high school is no more difficult, though of course less familiar, than a large part of the older mathematics. This is not surprising. A new topic must of necessity start with ideas that are in some sense elementary, whereas the further development of older topics cannot help but presuppose familiarity with a considerable amount of technical material. Intricate ideas are more likely to be found in the extensive development of any subject than in its beginnings.

It is fortunate that this is so because, as has been suggested, the scope of recent developments in mathematics and in its applications requires that schools and colleges recognize the existence of the new material and its importance. They should include in their courses of instruction at least selections from it or introductions to it. It is entirely feasible to accomplish this since much of the material to be introduced has the added advantage of being in some ways simpler than the traditional content.

Substantial changes in the mathematical curriculum are thus long overdue. But a mere change of subject matter is not sufficient. A poor curriculum well taught is better than a good curriculum badly taught. A good curriculum well taught is the only acceptable goal. With adequate guidance, students will seek courses in mathematics (and in anything else) that present significant, challenging subject matter, interestingly and meaningfully taught. The quality of the curriculum and the skill of the teacher both are vital: this combination alone can effect the kind of improvement in mathematical instruction that the United States must have.

DEMAND FOR IMPROVED INSTRUCTION

There is abundant evidence of public dissatisfaction with mathematics programs, curricula, and instruction. Many writers have claimed that the general quality of mathematics teaching is in need of improvement, and that the level of mathematical competence of American high school graduates is low. Colleges complain that entering freshmen are poorly prepared in mathematics. The requirements in mathematics for high school graduation in many states are exceedingly limited. It is alleged that too small a percentage of high school students is enrolled in mathematics courses, and that many students dislike mathematics. Complaints such as these became very widespread after the launching of the first earth satellite.

It is not appropriate in this report to examine these popular beliefs in detail. No useful end would be served here by an attempt to determine statistically the proportion of secondary school students who dislike mathematics, or how they acquired their dislike. Nor would it assist the Commission, in dealing with its assigned task, if it were to become involved in a consideration of the percentage of students studying a particular course in mathematics today, as compared with some past date. Such a study would not be directly germane to the work of the Commission, nor would a discussion of minimum graduation requirements for mathematics in the high schools of the several states.

If the nation is indeed faced with low levels of mathematical competence —and in fact it is—the Commission thinks that part of the answer may be found in increasing the amount of time devoted to the study of mathematics (in both homework and schoolwork); but a complete solution demands improvements in the effectiveness of instruction and in the appropriateness of course content. Also, while the general quality of mathematics teaching, like the general quality of teaching in any field, is probably in need of improvement, one can cite many examples of excellent classroom technique and exciting—even inspired—mathematical instruction in the American schools.

From the point of view of the Commission, it is not important to determine the precise reasons for public concern about the program of secondary school mathematical instruction, or to support or refute such reasons. It is important to recognize that such a general concern exists, and that the existence of this concern strongly supports the thesis that the time is ripe for the improvement of the high school mathematics program. But improvement should not be conceived merely as a by-product of the post-Sputnik panic. Awareness of the problem, the appointment of the Commission, and the beginning of its study all antedate the Sputniks. The dramatic Soviet achievements serve, helpfully, to create greater public concern and greater awareness and acceptance of what must be done. It is imperative that hasty improvisations be avoided, and that action be based on sound judgment and well-reasoned arguments. As in most concerns of importance, one should beware of the pat answer. Individual differences among human beings are the rule; these differences can be neglected only with peril.

THE NATIONAL NEED FOR MATHEMATICAL MANPOWER

Finally, the fast-growing national need for people skilled in various branches of mathematics provides a compelling reason why an improved mathematics curriculum for college preparation is of the utmost importance.

Americans traditionally have devoted themselves to practical rather than to theoretical knowledge. The names of certain American inventors are household words—Whitney, Morse, McCormick, Edison, and others; the names of great American theoretical scientists, except for Einstein (an American by adoption), are not. Over a century ago, de Tocqueville observed, "Hardly anyone in the United States devotes himself to the theoretical and abstract portion of human knowledge." This same imbalance between practical and theoretical preoccupations remains a serious problem to the United States. The Commission does not wish to support its recommendations by playing on fears, but it is an incontrovertible fact that America does have an undersupply of men and women adequately trained in mathematics and science. For example, a committee of the American Association for the Advancement of Science tells us that, "The progress of basic science does not appear to be keeping pace with the development of applied science." Neither basic nor applied science can develop as they ought without adequate mathematical foundations.

The demand for mathematically trained men and women comes not only from science and engineering, as in the past; it now comes from business, industry, and government as well. Within two decades the employment pattern of persons with mathematical training has changed completely. Twenty years ago, college or secondary school teaching absorbed all but a handful of persons holding master's or doctor's degrees in mathematics; there were no other jobs. Today the applications of mathematics in electronics, in the design and use of computing machinery, in industrial research, in automation, and in a dozen other areas have opened up new opportunities and created new demands. Mathematical journals and even daily newspapers carry "help wanted" advertisements for the mathematically trained; qualified teachers are being attracted from the classroom to the laboratory, plant, or office.

One aspect of this startling demand for mathematical manpower is evidenced in a statement made by George E. Forsythe, professor of mathematics at Stanford University, in a lecture presented before the Mathematical Association of America in Cambridge, Massachusetts, on August 30, 1958:[3]

"There seem to be over 3,000 automatic digital computers now installed in the United States, with more on the way. As a rough estimate, each automatic computer needs to have 10 attendants who serve it as mathematicians—programmers, coders, analysts, supervisors, and so forth. The resulting requirement for 30,000 computer mathematicians should be compared with the combined membership of the American Mathematical Society,

3. "The role of numerical analysis in an undergraduate program."

Mathematical Association of America, Society for Industrial and Applied Mathematics, Association for Computing Machinery, Institute of Mathematical Statistics, and American Statistical Association—under 20,000 persons. While some makeshift arrangements are possible, the disparity in numbers is creating the unprecedented demand . . . for the new A.B. in mathematics."

This pressing national need for what we may call "mathematical manpower" cannot be met merely by training more young men and women in an outmoded curriculum. One well-trained high school graduate may make a more effective contribution to the national manpower need than a half-dozen who are poorly trained.

SUMMARY OF THE CASE FOR REVISION

This then is the case for curricular revision: Mathematics is a dynamic subject, characterized in recent years by such impressive growth and such extensive new applications that these have far outrun the curriculum. Moreover, the traditional curriculum fails to reflect adequately the spirit of contemporary mathematics, which seeks to study all possible patterns recognizable by the mind,[4] and by so striving has tremendously increased the power of mathematics as a tool of modern life. Nor does the traditional curriculum give proper emphasis to the fact that the developments and applications of mathematics have always been not only important but indispensable to human progress.

In order that the school and college curricula meet the needs of mathematics itself and of its applications, there must be a change. A new program, oriented to the needs of the second half of the twentieth century and based on a dynamic conception of mathematics, is required. The national need for mathematical manpower, and a general feeling of dissatisfaction with the present state of affairs, support the early introduction of such a new curriculum.

The necessity for a thorough revision of the program in mathematics (as a basic element of the program in science education) is impressively summarized in the following quotation:

"First, the crisis in our science education is not an invention of the newspapers, or scientists, or the Pentagon. It is a real crisis.

"Second, the U.S.S.R. is not the 'cause' of the crisis. The cause of the crisis is our breath-taking movement into a new technological era. The U.S.S.R. has served as a rude stimulus to awaken us to that reality.

"The heart of the matter is that we are moving with headlong speed into

4. Cf. W. W. Sawyer, *op. cit.,* p. 12.

a new phase in man's long struggle to control his environment, a phase beside which the industrial revolution may appear as a modest alteration of human affairs. Nuclear energy, exploration of outer space, revolutionary studies of brain functioning, important new work on the living cell—all point to changes in our lives so startling as to test to the utmost our adaptive capacities. . . .

"The immediate implications for education may be briefly stated. We need an ample supply of high caliber scientists, mathematicians, and engineers. . . . We need quality and we need it in considerable quantity."[5]

5. *The Pursuit of Excellence; Education and the Future of America* (Special Studies Project Report V, Rockefeller Brothers Fund), (Garden City, N.Y.: Doubleday and Co., Inc., 1958), pp. 27–28.

2. Secondary Education: The Commission's Premises

The Commission was appointed for the avowed purpose of improving the program of college preparatory mathematics in the secondary schools. This goal has been before its members at all times. The Commission has no authority to enforce changes; its role is to recommend and to suggest. By these means, it hopes to influence, but not dictate, the immediate future of the college preparatory mathematics curriculum.

In curriculum building, attention must be paid to the purposes of the schools, their place in society, and their programs; to the nature of the pupils, their maturity, their interests, their objectives; and to the findings of psychology as to how human beings grow, develop, mature, and learn. At this point, therefore, it may be appropriate for us to indicate the general premises within which our recommendations for a new curriculum are made.

THE ROLE OF THE SECONDARY SCHOOL

The members of the Commission recognize that there rests on the American secondary school an obligation to serve "all the children of all the people." We do not believe, however, that this means that the entire school population should be required to take exactly the same program. While we hold that some form of mathematical instruction is needed by every secondary school student, we do not believe that everyone should study the curriculum set forth in this report.

Our program is a college preparatory program, designed for students who can profit from it. We believe the secondary school must meet the needs of this group, as well as the needs of all other groups. *Every* student should have what is for him a challenging and rewarding intellectual experience, marked by sound intellectual content, by appropriate personal and social development, and by preparation for everyday living. All students need not be taught at the same pace, in the same order, or to the same extent, or with the same emphasis.

MATHEMATICS IN GENERAL EDUCATION

In many secondary schools, only a minority of the school population proceeds to college. The Commission realizes that secondary schools must serve the needs of those students who are not bound for college. Many aspects of the Commission's program can be adapted, in terms of general education, to this group of students, though this adaptation is a task that the Commission must perforce leave to other hands.

Instruction in mathematics designed to meet the needs of secondary school students for general education should aim to teach the student the basic mathematical ideas and concepts that every citizen needs to know, and to explain the essential character of mathematics—how it is used to explore and describe physical reality, and how it is used to contribute through its aesthetic values to one's personal intellectual satisfaction. More specifically, some objectives of mathematics in general education are:

1. An understanding of, and competence in, the processes of arithmetic and the use of formulas in elementary algebra. A basic knowledge of graphical methods and simple statistics is also important.

2. An understanding of the general properties of geometrical figures and the relationships among them.

3. An understanding of the deductive method as a method of thought. This includes the ideas of axioms, rules of inference, and methods of proof.

4. An understanding of mathematics as a continuing creative endeavor with aesthetic values similar to those found in art and music. In particular, it should be made clear that mathematics is a living subject, not one that has long since been embalmed in textbooks.

MATHEMATICS FOR THE "COLLEGE-CAPABLE"

There are many secondary schools—usually city or suburban public schools or independent schools—from which a majority of the graduates proceeds to higher education. Whether this group is small or large, in any school it is an important group deserving the most careful consideration. From the college-trained will come the nation's scientists, engineers, physicians, lawyers, teachers, writers, artists, ministers, and other professional men and women—and probably the statesmen who will help shape the world's future.

It is a mistake, in the American educational system, to think in terms of the "college-bound." Financial or other external considerations too often affect the question of who is bound for college. As a policy in education, the nation cannot afford to do less than attempt to recognize and prepare appropriately every student who is capable of college work. The Commission prefers to call such students the "college-capable." Toward this group as a whole, the schools have a major responsibility.

The program set forth in this report is designed to meet the needs in mathematics of college-capable students in the second half of the twentieth century. The Commission believes that bright, young minds will find the material exciting and challenging, demanding and rewarding.

If the Commission is correct in this belief, a task of first importance faces the home and the school: to see that students of college potential tackle this program (or one of similar caliber) for *at least* three years. The shocking inadequacy of the traditional notion that "one year of algebra and one year of geometry" is sufficient college preparation in mathematics should be apparent to all. The handwriting is not only on the wall; it is all over the nation.

Moreover, it should be emphasized that the recommendation of three years of mathematics for the college-capable is minimal. Indeed, the Commission goes much further: it believes that school counselors, teachers, and parents have a duty to see that as many as possible of the college-capable should study mathematics in high school for four years. The most talented should attempt the Advanced Placement Program (described on p. 15) if it can be made available.

These convictions of the Commission are generally supported by a statement recently appearing in one of the Rockefeller Reports and based partly on a study by Dr. James B. Conant and partly on the findings of a conference sponsored by the National Education Association:

"In addition to the general education prescribed for all—four years of English, three to four years of social studies, one year of mathematics, and one year of science—the academically talented student should have two to three additional years of science, three additional years of mathematics, and at least three years of a foreign language. For certain students, the study of a second foreign language, for at least three years, might replace the fourth year of mathematics and the third year of science."[1]

There are cogent reasons for urging that the college-capable student should study mathematics for four years. Young people in high school do not always know what careers they will follow. What they should know beyond all doubt is that lack of mathematical preparation closes many doors—not only doors that open the way to engineering and the natural sciences, but also newer doors that lead to important areas of the social sciences, biological sciences, business, and industry. Many a college professor can testify to the frustrations of graduate students who face formidable roadblocks in sociology, economics, biology, and psychology—roadblocks caused by inadequate high school preparation in mathematics. Every indication points to wider and even more striking uses of mathematics in the immediate future. It is not too much to say that many of the college-capable will find their mathe-

---

1. *The Pursuit of Excellence; Education and the Future of America* (Special Studies Project Report V, Rockefeller Brothers Fund), (Garden City, N. Y.: Doubleday and Co., Inc., 1958), p. 27.

matical needs bounded only by the limits of their talent.

The Commission is aware of the importance of breadth in the high school curriculum. Indeed, all of its members would deplore specialization at the expense of sound, liberal training. But certain subjects occupy special levels in the scale of liberal knowledge. Mathematics (like a foreign language) comes easier to the young. The study of some subjects may be postponed for a while without serious loss; indeed, age makes their appreciation much easier. The study of mathematics is different—for the young, it is now or never. The implications of this fact must be faced squarely. For experience proves that high school is the place where most of our great scientists and mathematicians first acquired the interest that spurred them on to high achievement.

It would be most unfortunate to attempt to justify the four-year study of mathematics solely as preparation for a wide and ever-increasing range of applications. Mathematics is eminently worthy of study in its own right: it is a vital and shining example of mankind's creativity, one of the great cultural achievements of the ages. Few subjects can rival its ability to stimulate the inquiring mind. Every educated man and woman should have an opportunity to know at first hand something of the intellectual excitement and deep satisfaction that mathematics can offer.

Two important points: Two of the Commission's premises regarding mathematics for the college-capable should be made clear. First, students studying college preparatory mathematics should, in our opinion, be taught in groups with similar interests and similar intellectual abilities. We believe that instruction so given increases the challenge to the student and the likelihood of his developing his talents and ability to the full.

The injustice done to capable students by failure to use ability grouping is well pointed out in the Rockefeller Report: "Because many educators reject the idea of grouping by ability, the ablest students are often exposed to educational programs whose content is too thin and whose pace is too slow to challenge their abilities."[2]

In their programs of physical education, schools commonly find no difficulty in reconciling a program of physical training for all with provision of more intensive activity for students with sufficient ability to make school "varsity" or "junior varsity" teams. We see no reason why analogous considerations should not be considered valid in intellectual pursuits as well.

Second, college-capable students who follow the recommendations of this report will not be exposed to certain so-called "practical" courses such as consumer mathematics, installment buying, principles of insurance, and so forth. The Commission does not regret this fact. For it believes that these students will ordinarily develop sufficient mathematical power to acquire

2. *Ibid.*, pp. 22–23.

such information independently if they need it. One must not assume that an individual's knowledge consists solely of what he has been specifically taught in school.

DETERMINING COURSE CONTENT

The Commission believes that it is not the responsibility of the mathematicians and teachers of mathematics alone to solve all the problems relating to the mathematical instruction of any individual or group. The motivation, vocational objectives, interest, and ability of students all enter into the picture. Hence, the advice of experts in educational psychology is likely to be helpful in many respects.

We submit, however, that no decision with respect to the appropriateness of including some particular mathematical topic in a curriculum ought to be made without considering the opinions of professional mathematicians and teachers of mathematics. They must decide whether subject matter is obsolete, obsolescent, important, significant, educationally meaningful, likely to be increasingly important, and so on. Just as philosophers and psychologists must be heard as to aims, objectives, learning theory, grade placement of material, methodology, and the like, so the mathematicians and teachers must be heard as to the mathematical content of a program.

It is such advice that the Commission has undertaken to give. Our recommendations are based on the needs of mathematics, on its uses, and on the anticipated needs of the students and of society, insofar as we can determine them.

The Commission believes also that content in mathematics or any other subject, for that matter, must be appropriate to the level of maturity of the student. Otherwise there can be no meaningful learning. The number of questions that can be asked with respect to the "readiness" of pupils of different levels of intellectual, physical, and emotional maturity to deal with particular concepts in mathematics is exceedingly great. Even for traditional subject matter, psychological research has barely scratched the surface. Since we are suggesting the introduction of some new material, the problem is compounded.

In these circumstances, the Commission has taken a middle course between detailed experimental studies and pronouncements based on a priori judgments. We decided to subject ideas that seemed valid or desirable to at least limited tests of their practicality. We have convened several writing groups, composed of Commission members and other teachers of mathematics, to write instructional units dealing with new materials, or new presentations of older materials. These units have been taught experimentally with satisfactory results, indicating the realistic and practical nature of this program as the beginning of the solution of an urgent problem, work toward which cannot be delayed.

The attitude of the Commission is reflected independently in sentiments expressed in an article by Dael Wolfle:

"There are . . . educational changes that lend themselves to experimental study, but many of the current efforts to improve the teaching of science and mathematics do not. . . . There is still room for the exercise of good judgment in attempting to bring about social and educational improvements. If we have what we think is a good song to breathe into the air, let us go ahead and breathe it, without trying to fool ourselves by pretending to be carrying out an experiment."[3]

THE PLACE OF CALCULUS

The Commission takes the position, held generally in the United States at present, that calculus is a college-level subject. A reasonable immediate goal for most high schools is a strong college-preparatory mathematics curriculum that will have students ready to begin calculus when they enter college. Such is the curriculum described in this report. At the same time, however, the Commission recommends that well-staffed schools offer their ablest students a year of college-level calculus and analytic geometry as recommended in the Advanced Placement Program.[4] It is essential, though, that such a year be firmly based on a full pre-calculus program, completed early by some form of acceleration. In the long run, improvements in the curriculum (beginning with the first grade) and in teachers' qualifications may eventually make it possible to move such a calculus course into the normal program for grade 12 of most schools.

A few schools now teach calculus effectively in their regular programs. But schools that can do this are unusual at the present time. In regarding calculus as a college-level subject, the Commission does not want to discourage those with exceptional facilities from attempting exceptional tasks. Rather, it warns against premature general acceptance of a curricular responsibility for which all too few schools are now adequately prepared.

The Commission cannot recommend the practice of exposing college preparatory students to formal calculus for a short time at the end of the twelfth grade. Such anticipation tends to breed overconfidence and blunt the exciting impact of a thorough presentation. The Commission's program for grade 12 includes some concepts close to calculus—limit, difference quo-

---

3. "The Fetish of Experiment," *Science,* vol. 125, no. 3,240 (Feb. 1957), p. 177.

4. The program is described on p. 15. An encouraging fact is the rapid increase in the number of schools offering Advanced Placement courses in mathematics. In 1956, 45 schools had 386 candidates for the Advanced Placement Examination in mathematics; in 1959, according to an advance estimate, over 360 schools will have over 3,200 candidates.

tient, and slope of a curve. But it intends that these should be taught as informal preparation for calculus, rather than as preliminary calculus employing formal language and notation (such as "derivative" and "dy/dx").

THE ADVANCED PLACEMENT PROGRAM

Under the Advanced Placement Program, which is sponsored by the College Entrance Examination Board, high schools are encouraged to offer to their ablest students college-level courses in the senior year. As has already been suggested, the objectives and philosophy of the Program are in complete accord with those of the Commission. The mathematics course recommended by the Advanced Placement Program is a college-level course in calculus and analytic geometry for twelfth-grade students who have already completed a full high school program, such as the one set forth in this report. The recommendations of the Commission and those of the Advanced Placement Program are therefore quite consistent.

Many larger schools will be interested both in reorganizing their college preparatory work along the lines recommended by the Commission, and also in organizing Advanced Placement courses for their ablest students. The Commission strongly endorses such a plan, provided that students admitted to the Advanced Placement course will have completed, prior to their senior year, the program set forth in the following chapter at least to the end of the course entitled "Elementary Functions."

THE PROGRAM AND THE TEACHER

The role of the teacher is vital: curricular change must be accompanied by effective, meaningful teaching, directed toward the development of mathematical power and understanding. Hence, the Commission has made numerous suggestions and recommendations with respect to teacher education, both for the pre-service preparation of teachers for improved programs, and for the in-service training that may produce similar competence. These are set forth in Chapter 5 of this report. We commend them to the attention of school boards, superintendents, teachers' associations, colleges, and universities.

The Commission regards as one of the most important advantages of its approach to curricular revision the fact that it does not demand an "all or none" approach. It does not propose closing the books on the old curriculum on a certain date and beginning a totally new program when the schools next open, but rather that teachers may introduce modifications as the way opens, and as their knowledge and experience permit them to do so.

The interest of teachers in its work and their reactions to its progress reports have confirmed the Commission in its belief that many high school teachers of mathematics are aware of the need to improve the secondary school curriculum, and are receptive to the introduction of new ideas, provided only that they are given suitable assistance in comprehending them and in adapting them to classroom instruction.

SUMMARY

The secondary school has an obligation to serve the needs of all young people, including the college-capable. In providing for this latter group, cognizance must be taken of the high potential for worthwhile academic achievement. The times demand a program in mathematics that exploits this potential—a program that provides for the full development of the individual and meets the needs of the nation. Schools must provide such programs. Parents, teachers, and counselors must face squarely the implied responsibilities. For, as many as possible of the college-capable must be urged to study challenging mathematics for four years in high school; none of them should study mathematics for less than three years, and the most gifted should accelerate their studies in mathematics so as to undertake the Advanced Placement Program. The Commission believes that such studies are likely to be most effective under some system of ability grouping.

It follows that development of programs in high school mathematics suitable for our college-capable students in the last half of the twentieth century is an urgent, present need. As a first approximation to such a program, the Commission decided to make recommendations based on the judgment of experienced mathematicians and teachers, supplemented by some experimentation. The resulting program aims to infuse the spirit of contemporary mathematics into some traditional topics, and to include some new topics important to mathematicians and accessible to high school students. Calculus is regarded as a college-level subject, available in secondary schools through the Advanced Placement Program.

The major demands of any curricular revision fall on the shoulders of the teachers. In appreciation of this fact, the Commission advocates a new program that grows out of the old in a manner that makes reasonable demands on teachers, allowing them to implement the recommendations gradually as their training permits.

3. Recommendation: The Commission's Program

In the present chapter, the Commission sets forth recommendations that we believe will achieve the objective of improving the program of college preparatory mathematics in secondary schools. Before discussing these recommendations in detail, we shall make some general comments about their nature.

While the direction of the proposed changes is oriented to the future, the changes themselves are not radical. No attempt has been made to uproot the traditional curriculum. The Commission has tried to have new ideas and new subject matter grow out of the old through reasonable modifications and additions. The result is a revision that the Commission believes can begin at once gradually and move forward rapidly. This revision is designed to meet imperative present needs; the demands of the more distant future in college preparatory mathematics will require further adjustments. But, for the present, the Commission feels that its recommendations offer a goal that is both challenging and attainable.

Furthermore, the Commission's recommendations as to mathematical content have been kept flexible, so that they may be adapted to the varying needs of many different types of schools or groups of students. It is possible to organize the proposed subject matter in a variety of ways. Writers of textbooks will undoubtedly develop the program in accordance with their own understanding of learning theory and their own philosophies of secondary education.

This flexibility of the recommended program includes its manner of presentation. Members of the Commission would decry an authoritarian approach to method and practice, but a teacher who believes that such an approach is most effective may present this material in the same way that he has, presumably, taught the traditional content. Most if not all of the Commission members would prefer to see a developmental approach, which would encourage the student to discover as much of the mathematical subject matter for himself as his ability and the time available (for this is a time-consuming method) will permit.

Although most of the Commission would like to see the interrelations among the various topics of the program pointed out and stressed, no one of them would say that there is one and only one way of accomplishing this. Questions about methods of teaching and patterns of organization; questions as to whether algebra, geometry, trigonometry, coordinate geometry, and other areas should be presented as separate courses or units, or should constitute a single, integrated fabric; questions about grade placement of material—such questions as these have no ideal answers, valid at all times and in all schools. They are best left to teachers and supervisors, authors and editors. The Commission's hope is that many diverse proposals will be formulated and will compete in the market place of ideas as well as in the textbook market.

In the material that follows, the mathematics supposed to have been covered prior to the program recommended for grades 9 through 12—in grades 7 and 8, whether in junior high or elementary school—is presented first. Second, the mathematics recommended by the Commission for grades 9, 10, and 11 is discussed. Recommendations for the revision of content and the Commission's reasons for making them are both set forth. Although this statement is presented in terms of traditional subject matter—algebra, geometry, and trigonometry—the form of its presentation does not necessarily represent the order in which the Commission believes these topics should be organized or taught. Third, the program recommended for the twelfth grade is described.

In the next chapter, the Commission outlines a suggested sequence of topics that incorporates its recommendations for the mathematics of grades 9 through 12. The purpose of this sequence is to exemplify one possible course of study that reflects the spirit of the Commission's proposals. Both the proposals of this chapter and the sequence of the next are amplified, clarified, and elucidated in the volume of appendices to this report.

PREREQUISITE MATHEMATICS

The Commission's program is necessarily predicated on certain learnings expected of students before they begin the program. There are in the United States a number of different arrangements of school organization, commonly known as 8-4, 6-3-3, 6-6, and 7-5, where the numbers indicate, respectively, years of study in each division of an elementary and secondary school system. Presumably, regardless of school organization, the mathematics studied year by year should be practically the same under all plans. This is not the case, however. Textbooks written for the seventh and eighth year of study in an eight-year elementary program (8-4) stress arithmetic more, and informal geometry much less, than books written explicitly for a junior high school program (6-3-3).

The Commission recognizes the need for a careful study of the mathematics program of grades 7 and 8 (and, indeed, of the earlier grades as well). But this is not the task of the Commission. To fill this gap, it must rely on other groups such as the School Mathematics Study Group, the University of Maryland Mathematics Project, and the Curriculum Committees of the

National Council of Teachers of Mathematics.

This much can be said: regardless of the form of school organization, in order to give students in grades 7 and 8 the type of mathematics study that will form a proper foundation for the Commission's program, the following subject matter is regarded as essential. The Commission is convinced that it can be mastered by all college-capable students during grades 7 and 8. The better students can cover this work in one to one-and-a-half years and move on to the Commission's program during the eighth school year.

ARITHMETIC

Fundamental operations and numeration: Mastery of the four fundamental operations with whole numbers and fractions, written in decimal notation and in the common notation used for fractions. This includes skill in the operations at adult level (i.e., adequate for ordinary life situations) and an understanding of the rationale of the computational processes. Understanding of a place system of writing numbers, with use of binary notation (and perhaps other bases) to reinforce decimal notation. Ability to handle very large numbers (greater than 1,000,000) and very small numbers (less than one ten-thousandth). The meaning and use of an arithmetic mean. In addition, a knowledge of square root and the ability to find approximate values of square roots of whole numbers is desirable. (The process of division and averaging the divisor and quotient—Newton's method—is suggested.)

Ratio: Understanding of ratio as used in comparing sizes of quantities of like kind, in proportions, and in making scale drawings. Per cent as an application of ratio. Understanding of the language of per cent (rate), percentage, and base. In particular the ability to find any one of these three designated numbers, given the other two. Ability to treat with confidence per cents less than 1 and greater than 100. Applications of per cent to business practices, interest, discount, and budgets should be given moderate treatment.

GEOMETRY

Measurement: The ability to operate with and transform the several systems of measure, including the metric system of length, area, volume, and weight. Geometric measurements, including length of a line segment, perimeter of a polygon, and circumference of a circle, areas of regions enclosed by polygons and circles, surface areas of solids, volumes of solids, measure of angles (by degrees). The use of a ruler and protractor. The student should know the difference between the process of measuring and the measure of the quantity. Ability to apply measurement to practical situations. Use of measurement in drawing to scale and finding lengths indirectly.

Relationships among geometric elements: These include the concepts of parallel, perpendicular, intersecting, and oblique lines (in a plane and in a space); acute, right, obtuse, complementary, supplementary, and vertical angles; scalene, isosceles, and equilateral triangles; right triangles and the Pythagorean relation; sum of the interior angles of a triangle. The use of instruments in constructing figures; ideas of symmetry about a point and a line.

ALGEBRA AND STATISTICS

Graphs and formulas: Use of line segments and areas to represent numbers. Reading and construction of bar graphs, line graphs, pictograms, circle graphs, and continuous line graphs. Meaning of scale. Formulas for perimeters, areas, volumes, and per cents—introduced as generalizations as these concepts are studied. Use of symbols in formulas as placeholders for numerals arising in measurement. Simple expressions and sentences involving "variables."

MATHEMATICS FOR GRADES 9, 10, AND 11
(ELEMENTARY AND INTERMEDIATE MATHEMATICS)

In this discussion and throughout this report, the work of grades 9 and 10 will often be designated as Elementary Mathematics I and II, and the work of grade 11 as Intermediate Mathematics. This work ordinarily will be covered in grades 9 through 11, but schools may, of course, begin the work earlier or extend it later. Indeed, it is precisely because of the Commission's desire to provide for as much flexibility in organization as possible that we have adopted such generalized descriptive terms as Elementary Mathematics, Intermediate Mathematics, and Advanced Mathematics, adaptable to various grade designations.

ALGEBRA

The Commission recommends increased attention to algebra as a part of the secondary school curriculum, but couples it with an equally earnest recommendation that the point of view from which the material is presented be that of contemporary mathematics, as explained in the opening chapter (p. 2). The goal of instruction in algebra should not be thought of exclusively or even largely as the development of manipulative skills. Rather instruction should be oriented toward the development and understanding of the properties of a number field. At this point it is probably well to digress and present two points to guard against possible misunderstanding.

First, in stating that the material of algebra should be presented from the point of view of contemporary mathematics and that instruction should be oriented toward the properties of a number field, the Commission is *not* advocating the outright presentation of elementary algebra from an abstract point of view. Nor does it advocate the teaching of abstraction before concrete or intuitive notions have been established as a point of departure.

Development of generalized abstract concepts is difficult, too difficult to be a point of departure for the beginner, but nevertheless it is absolutely necessary if any true understanding of mathematics is to be attained. It cannot be used as a starting point until the proper intuitive foundation has been laid and the students are ready for it. Many of the "laws" of algebra (the axioms of a number field) are easier to understand and much more useful than the arbitrary "rules" usually found in elementary text-books. These laws should be taught and used—at an appropriate stage in the instructional process. Such ideas are more fully set forth and illustrated in the first appendix to this report, "An introduction to algebra" (see separate *Appendices* volume).

Second, the Commission fully realizes the necessity of teaching appropriate manipulative skills. Its members are as concerned as anyone that students entering college mathematics courses should be able to solve quadratic equations and systems of linear equations, perform the fundamental operations upon polynomials and rational fractions, and deal routinely with the other simple algebraic operations necessary for comfortable progress in a course in calculus and analytic geometry. But the development of these manipulative skills should not be the most important nor the only goal of instruction in algebra; many college professors would no doubt share the view of one who stated recently that he would gladly forego such skills if he could be assured instead of a genuine understanding of deductive reasoning.

It is not, however, an alternative of *either* skill *or* understanding that confronts teachers. *Both* skills *and* concepts are essential. The Commission is not alone in insisting that the development of manipulative skill should not be the primary goal of instruction in algebra. Nor is this a novel idea. The National Committee on Mathematical Requirements, writing in 1923, stated: "The excessive emphasis now commonly placed on manipulation is one of the main obstacles to intelligent progress. . . . Drill in algebraic manipulation should be limited to those processes and to the degree of complexity required for a thorough understanding of principles and for probable applications either in common life or in subsequent courses which a substantial proportion of the pupils will take. It must be conceived throughout as a means to an end, not as an end in itself. Within these limits, skill in algebraic manipulation is important, and drill in this subject should be extended far enough to enable students to carry out the essential processes accurately and expeditiously." [Italics omitted.] [1]

This statement is as valid today as it was a generation ago when first written. It applies with special significance to the study of college prepara-

1. National Committee on Mathematical Requirements, *The Reorganization of Mathematics in Secondary Education* (n.p.: The Mathematical Association of America, 1923), p. 11.

tory mathematics. Strong skills are surely needed; but they must be based on understanding and not merely on rote memorization. Once meaning has been achieved, then drill should be provided to establish skills—skills that can be performed, as Whitehead says, "without thinking." In this way, the mind is liberated to grapple with new ideas.

The new with the old: In making its recommendations for increased emphasis upon algebra and for instruction oriented toward a more contemporary point of view, the Commission is influenced by the fact that algebra is a subject that has been largely transformed by the mathematical research of the past quarter-century. This transformation has been brought about through the systematic axiomatic development of algebra or, more accurately, of algebras, and the light thus thrown on the study of mathematical structures. Such structures, or patterns, have been thrown into sharp relief. The Commission is influenced too by the fact that many recent applications of mathematics to areas hitherto regarded essentially as non-mathematical are algebraic in character.

In the proposed program, the mechanics or formal manipulations in algebra are the same as hitherto taught, and the subject matter is largely the same. The difference is principally in concept, in terminology, in some symbolism, and in the introduction of a rather large segment of new work dealing with inequalities treated both algebraically and graphically. Solution sets of inequalities involving two variables are also studied.

The new emphasis in the study of algebra is upon the understanding of the fundamental ideas and concepts of the subject, such as the nature of number systems and the basic laws for addition and multiplication (commutative, associative, distributive). The application of these laws in various number systems, with emphasis on the generality of the laws, the meanings of conditional equations and identities and inequalities, is stressed. The nature of a function—in particular, the linear, quadratic, exponential, and logarithmic functions—is also discussed.

As an example of the use of a fundamental concept in illuminating algebra, the distributive law may be cited. This law is the basic idea behind much mental arithmetic, the use of parentheses, factoring, multiplication of polynomials, and the manipulation of fractions. If it is understood, most of the special methods of handling these topics can be eliminated.

Deductive reasoning in algebra: One way to foster an emphasis upon understanding and meaning in the teaching of algebra is through the introduction of instruction in deductive reasoning. The Commission is firmly of the opinion that deductive reasoning should be taught in all courses in school mathematics and not in geometry courses alone.[2]

---

2. As a specific example of how instruction in deductive reasoning may be introduced into algebra, even very early in the course, the Commission has prepared a classroom booklet entitled, *Informal deduction in algebra.*

A student who understands the nature of a subject is more likely to be able to solve problems that present an element of novelty than one who lacks this understanding. The ability to solve such problems involves more than merely the blind application of rules or techniques to typical problems preclassified as to form.

Moreover, in their ability to perform algebraic manipulations, students who study algebra from the point of view advocated in this report should be the equal of students who study more traditional curricula. When algebra (or any subject, for that matter) is studied or taught with an eye to the fundamental nature of the subject, this more general point of view tends to make the whole subject more understandable. Diverse bits of information support one another and "hang together" so to speak, thereby promoting understanding and assisting memory.

For example, one sometimes reads: "If the discriminant of a quadratic equation is a perfect square, then the roots of the equation are rational." Yet the equation $2x^2 + 2\sqrt{6x} + 1 = 0$ has a discriminant equal to 16, and irrational roots. Wherein lies the discrepancy? A student who approaches algebra from the contemporary point of view is accustomed to thinking in terms of the set of numbers admissible in a particular problem. The quoted statement holds only for quadratic equations with rational coefficients: it fails for the given example because $2\sqrt{6}$ is not a member of the set of rationals.

GEOMETRY

Objectives of geometric study: The inclusion of geometry in the high school curriculum has three main objectives.

The first objective is the acquisition of information about geometric figures in the plane and in space. Since geometry originated as, and still essentially is, a mathematical model of the physical world, the student needs to know the facts of geometry if he is to be able to deal effectively with the world about him. This knowledge is important for the everyday citizen and essential for the prospective scientist. Moreover, little progress can be made in trigonometry or calculus without an understanding of geometric facts.

The second objective is the development of an understanding of the deductive method as a way of thinking, and a reasonable skill in applying this method to mathematical situations. For historical reasons, the deductive method has been emphasized in geometry but not elsewhere in high school mathematics. However, it is now possible and desirable to use the deductive method in all mathematical subjects, and consequently the time devoted to it in geometry can be somewhat reduced.

Not all reasoning is syllogistic or deductive. Training in mathematics based on deductive logic does not necessarily lead to an increased ability to argue logically in situations where insufficient data exist, and where strong emotions are present. It is a disservice to the student and to mathematics for geometry to be presented as though its study would enable a student to solve a substantial number of his life problems by syllogistic and deductive reasoning.

Deductive methods are taught primarily to enable the pupil to learn mathematics. Mathematics, and consequently deductive methods, can be applied to life only in those life-situations that are capable of accurate transformation into mathematical models. These situations, though of tremendous importance, are far from frequent in the everyday lives of high school students.

A third important objective of the geometry course is the provision of opportunities for original and creative thinking by students. The material of elementary geometry affords an uncommonly good opportunity for students to think along lines that are original for them. Its elements are sufficiently simple to be grasped readily, and its consequences sufficiently complex to challenge students of varying abilities, no matter how high. Therefore a large part of the course should be devoted to original exercises involving, if possible, both the discovery of relationships and their proofs.

Defects and possible remedies: Geometry must continue to play a large role in secondary school mathematics. The Commission recommends, however, that the character of the course in geometry be drastically changed. Recent developments in geometric thinking have disclosed grave faults in the logical structure of Euclid, thus calling attention to the need for a modification in the traditional approach to high school geometry.

There are essentially three defects in the Euclidean development of geometry that make it unsuitable as the basis for modern high school instruction. Since these are discussed at length in Appendices 10 ("Some reasons for modifying the traditional treatment of geometry") and 18 ("Order relations in plane geometry"), they receive only brief mention here. The first defect is Euclid's failure to formulate explicitly the axiomatic basis on which the congruence theorems rest. Although there is in the *Elements* an extensive argument in support of the superposition of line segments, the less obvious matter of justifying the superposition of angles is completely neglected. A remedy for this defect is the outright assumption of the congruence theorems.

The second defect is the difficulty introduced into some phases of the development because of the lack of an adequate algebra. Today, of course, these difficulties can be avoided by the use of coordinate geometry based on a one-to-one correspondence between ordered pairs of real numbers and points in the plane.

The third defect is the failure of Euclid to recognize the necessity of making formal assumptions concerning "betweenness," an omission recognized by Gauss 125 years ago and first corrected by Pasch in 1882. For any complete logical formulation of geometry, there must be postulates concerning the *order* of points on a line and the matter of regions in the plane, neither of which is mentioned in Euclid's *Elements*. A discussion of order relations that illustrates the kind of treatment needed to make Euclid logically rigorous is given in Appendix 18 ("Order relations in plane geometry").

What should be done to remedy the situation created by the foregoing logical defects in Euclid's development? One possibility is that of developing a logically unimpeachable treatment of Euclidean geometry suitable for use in secondary schools. Although some distinguished mathematicians, among them D. Hilbert, O. Veblen, G. D. Birkhoff, R. L. Moore, and S. MacLane, have undertaken this task, the Commission feels that at present no presentation suitable for high school exists. The danger is that of boring students with logical subtleties of little or no interest to most of them, and with proofs of theorems that seems quite obvious.

The Commission hopes that mathematicians will continue to strive for the development of a logically sound basis for Euclidean geometry in a form suitable for high school use. However, for the present, it recommends that textbook writers and teachers should feel free to modify the Euclidean development to attain a more incisive and interesting program.

A mathematical science, when put in final form, consists of a set of undefined terms and unproved propositions, in terms of which all other concepts are defined and all other propositions are proved. It is, of course, a mark of mathematical elegance to reduce the number of undefined concepts and simple unproved propositions to a minimum. Moreover, if in an axiomatic treatment of any branch of mathematics, one takes as an assumption a proposition that might have been proved on the basis of the other assumptions, the beauty or elegance of the structure is somewhat marred. One cannot tell whether the proposition is an assumption or a theorem. But there is nothing erroneous about this situation, so long as the assumptions are consistent with one another.

For secondary school purposes it is clearly not necessary that the set of unproved propositions be reduced to the theoretical minimum; it is better to assume propositions which seem so obvious that proving them seems meaningless to the student, even though proofs of them could be effected in terms of the other assumptions. Furthermore, the geometry course need not consist of a single chain of deductions from a set of primitive terms and primitive propositions lasting through the entire course; and it certainly should not be based on an axiomatic treatment like that of Euclid, which without modification involves serious defects.

SPECIFIC PROPOSALS FOR GEOMETRY

As has already been set forth, it is felt that a substantial introduction to

694

geometry on an intuitive and informal basis should be accomplished in the seventh and eighth grades. A sense of geometric form, a knowledge of simple geometric facts, and skill in simple geometric constructions are all appropriate achievements for junior high school or upper grade-school pupils. Deductive proofs will contribute little at best to the understanding of these aspects of geometry. In a sense, this intuitive geometry may be thought of as the physical geometry of the space in which we live, rather than as an abstract mathematical system. These remarks should not be taken to imply that deductive thinking is to be considered unimportant in geometry instruction, but merely that it is not an appropriate aim for the introductory course *preceding* the ninth grade. However, it is to be regarded as a major aim of the senior high school program in geometry.

With respect to the latter course in geometry, the Commission has several observations to make.

The number of theorems should be reduced: It has been traditional in geometry courses for students to be held responsible for the formal proofs of a considerable number of theorems arranged in a precise, sequential order. Often the number of such theorems has been substantial. The Commission believes that the number of basic theorems should be drastically reduced, and that the geometry course should consist of several short sequences, rather than a single long sequence of theorems.

It should be emphasized that these basic theorems are not the only theorems that would be proved. All that is being said is that there would be only 10 or 12 propositions whose proofs would be required as part of an inviolable deductive chain. All other propositions would be treated as originals. A student might offer different proofs on different occasions, and order would be relatively unimportant. Of course, no teacher would accept such circular reasoning as basing the proof of two propositions each upon the other.

In making this recommendation for drastically reduced deductive sequences, the Commission is independently in agreement with a report recently issued in England by representatives of examining bodies and teachers' associations. The report recommended that students he held responsible in examinations for only certain "key-theorems," on the ground that otherwise too much teaching time will be sacrificed to learning the proofs of theorems. The key-theorems suggested by the group are only six in number, and the report comments that "The proposed list . . . is not necessarily the best possible selection, but it is of about the right length if there are to be theorems at all." [3]

The sequences of theorems suggested by the Commission are set forth

3. G. B. Jeffery, *School Certificate Mathematics* (London: Cambridge University Press, 1944), p. 3.

in the following chapter ("Mathematics for grade 10," section III, p. 38; section V, p. 39). The objective of the first sequence, it will be noted, is to reach the Pythagorean Theorem at an early stage.

Coordinate geometry should be introduced: The Commission proposes that some coordinate geometry be introduced early in the geometry course. An ideal time is immediately after the first sequence of theorems ("Mathematics for grade 10," section III, p. 38). The student will then be able to combine the geometric facts of the sequence with his earlier experiences in graphical algebra, and thus have the satisfaction of seeing two rivers of knowledge join to form a mightier mathematical stream. The student will also need coordinate geometry to deal with trigonometry in the manner recommended in this report. But there are deeper reasons for introducing some coordinate geometry at this time. The discovery by Descartes that the position of any point in the plane can be fixed by an ordered pair of real numbers is one of the most momentous in the history of mathematics. The student will be ready to use this idea at the point indicated, and the intellectual opportunity should not be postponed.

It has been mentioned that coordinate geometry avoids the defects in the Euclidean development that stem from Euclid's lack of an adequate algebra. There are other advantages: the student gains new power because he has a general method for studying geometry; and he achieves results that later can be extended to three and more dimensions. Moreover, he is laying firm foundations for the future: college work, from calculus on, employs geometric material in analytic form.

Whitehead has underlined the important role of coordinate geometry in mathematical thought:

"No one can have studied even the elements of elementary geometry without feeling the lack of some guiding method. Every proposition has to be proved by a fresh display of ingenuity; and a science for which this is true lacks the great requisite of scientific thought, namely, method. Now the essential point of coordinate geometry is that for the first time it introduced method. . . . [It] relates together geometry, which started as the science of space, and algebra, which has its origin in the science of number." [4]

Once coordinate geometry has been introduced, the Commission advocates the use of analytic (algebraic) as well as synthetic methods in proving geometric theorems and exercises. Indeed, certain propositions might advantageously be given both analytic and synthetic proofs. Simple examples of propositions amenable to such treatment are: (1) the diagonals of a square bisect each other at right angles; (2) the medians of a triangle are concurrent at a point that divides each median in the ratio 2:1; and (3)

---

4. Albert North Whitehead, *Introduction to Mathematics,* (London: Oxford University Press, 1948), pp. 83–84.

the line segment joining the mid-points of two sides of a triangle is parallel to the third side and equal to half of it (these and others are given and commented on in the volume of appendices, Appendix 15, "Theorems having easy analytic proofs").

Place of solid geometry: The geometry course need not and probably should not be sharply divided into two parts on the basis of dimensionality. It is not necessary completely to separate plane and solid geometry. On the contrary, it is both possible and desirable to teach certain material of solid geometry along with the analogous content of plane geometry. For example, the locus of all points equidistant from two fixed points can be considered in two dimensions and then in three dimensions. Similarly, the treatment of the sphere may be coordinated with the treatment of the circle, developing new insights by the comparative study of properties in two and three dimensions.

Time equivalent to about one-third of a semester should be devoted to solid geometry. The objective should be the development of concepts of spatial relations, and of spatial perception. Mensuration should have been covered intuitively earlier; however, lengths, areas, and volumes of standard figures should be reviewed. Deductive proofs of mensuration formulas are not in order at this time: such demonstrations are properly a part of integral calculus. Theorems in spherical geometry are particularly suitable material, since they can be compared and contrasted with theorems in plane geometry.

Coverage of solid geometry should include the basic facts about lines, planes, angles, dihedral angles, and spheres. There is neither time to establish all these facts deductively, nor virtue in so doing. A clear understanding of the relationships is essential, however. This can best be attained by an intuitive approach. An outline of the material the Commission considers essential is given in the volume of appendices (Appendix 16, "Outline of a unit in solid and spherical geometry").

Other geometries: It has been known for over a century that Euclidean geometry is not the only possible geometry of congruence. This is an important fact for students to appreciate. Although time will not permit doing much about these "non-Euclidean" geometries, some ideas can be suggested to students by using spherical geometry as a foil. For example, on a sphere the sum of the angles of a triangle always exceeds two right angles, and two triangles are congruent if corresponding angles are equal.

There are still other types of geometry—such as projective geometry and topology—that are not concerned with congruence. Simple pictorial material from these geometries provides intriguing foils to stimulate the imagination. For example, on a torus (the surface of a doughnut) a cut along a circle through the hole leaves the surface still in one piece; but in a plane a cut along any circle severs the plane into two pieces (see accompanying figures).

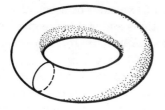 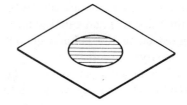

Summary of the proposed course in geometry: In brief, the program proposed by the Commission envisages an informal and intuitive introduction to geometric ideas, followed by an informal discussion of the nature of deductive reasoning. The course would then take up a short but important sequence of theorems, studied deductively, culminating in the Pythagorean Theorem. In the treatment of this sequence, both the geometric and the logical ideas previously introduced informally would be illustrated, consolidated, and confirmed by more formal study. Specific postulates, including in addition to the usual assumptions the congruence properties of triangles, would be introduced.

With the Pythagorean Theorem and theorems about similar triangles established, it is possible to proceed with coordinate geometry. The essential topics to cover are:

1. Location of points by coordinates
2. Length and slope of a line segment
3. Division of a segment in a given ratio
4. Equation of a line
5. Equation of a circle

(For a discussion of these topics, see Appendix 14, "Introduction to coordinate geometry.")

The remainder of plane geometry can now be developed using both synthetic and analytic methods. Emphasis should be placed on the development of skill in analyzing a situation and constructing a valid proof of either kind. Additional short sequences of theorems are suggested in the next chapter (p. 39, section V, "Mathematics for grade 10").

Since the scope of the analytic method may be unfamiliar to some teachers, a list of important theorems that have simple analytic proofs is presented in the volume of appendices (Appendix 15, "Theorems having easy analytic proofs"). Suitable exercise material can be found in almost any textbook on analytic geometry.

In recommending the introduction of relatively short deductive chains of theorems and a mixture of synthetic geometry with coordinate geometry, the Commission is aware that some teachers may regret the loss of an opportunity to develop an extended sequence of theorems. The Commission does not share the regret, nor do we believe that any important loss to the student is involved. Able students need not lose the opportunity for the appreciation of a complex mathematical structure derived from a set of assumptions. Books in which they can encounter this particular form of mathematical beauty are easily available. Moreover, able students, and others as well, will benefit from the greater power and the increased opportunities for original thinking provided by the new organization of subject matter.

TRIGONOMETRY

Trigonometry is the part of school mathematics related most clearly to technical applications. In the past, these had mainly to do with surveying and navigation. Therefore, much attention was paid to methods of solving plane and spherical triangles by logarithmic computation. But that era has passed. Special tables, computing machines, and other equipment have made the logarithmic solution of triangles an almost obsolete tool. Instead, there are more substantial and challenging applications of trigonometry now evident in many areas of science and technology—especially, in statics and dynamics, electromagnetic waves, and vibration problems of all sorts.

Trigonometry must be reorganized to meet these contemporary needs. Computational emphasis should shift from triangles to vectors, and analytic emphasis from identities to functional properties. Of course, some triangles will still be solved (by direct use of the laws of sines and cosines), and simple identities still treated. However, the vital material of the reorganized trigonometry lies in the rectangular and polar description of points, vectors, and complex numbers, and in the addition theorems and periodic character of the circular functions. In particular, the one-to-one correspondence between the set of ordered pairs of real numbers, and the set of points of the plane, or the set of vectors drawn from the origin, or the set of complex numbers, provides a superlative example of the manner in which important mathematical ideas coalesce.

In the sequence outline suggested by the Commission in the following chapter there are four trigonometric units, here briefly indicated in the following manner:

1. Rudimentary trigonometry of right triangles
2. Trigonometry of x, y, r, θ—coordinates, vectors, complex numbers
3. Cosine and sine laws, addition theorems, identities
4. Circular measure, circular functions and their wave nature.

The first is an optional unit at the end of grade 9, the second and third occur at the end of grade 11 (about a third of a semester), and the fourth forms the final part of the semester course in elementary functions in grade 12. The first unit might be anticipated in grade 8, or combined with unit two in grade 11.

Mathematicians now put much stress on the definition of the circular functions in terms of real numbers. One way of developing this idea is by winding a line around a unit circle. The Commission recommends that this be done in unit four. On the other hand, unit two treats functions of angles (in degrees)—the entities that occur in direct applications to physical vector quantities. Radian measure might be introduced in unit three, but it is not essential at that stage. It is essential at the beginning of unit four as the natural means of transition from the functions of angles used in vector computation to the functions of real numbers used in trigonometric analysis. (As a physicist says, the radian measure of an angle is the ratio of two lengths and so is a pure number.)

Treatment of complex numbers as vectors is a most important mathematical by-product of the reorganized trigonometry. Reinforcing the student's earlier contact with complex numbers in the study of quadratic equations, this trigonometric treatment should round out a good basic knowledge of complex numbers in grade 11. At the end of unit four, an informal discussion of Euler's formula ($e^{ix} = \cos x + i \sin x$) and series expansion serves to relate the exponential and circular functions in striking fashion, and to free the latter from angles without a shadow of doubt.

It is also possible to develop the essentials of trigonometry (included in units two through four) by starting with the circular functions in terms of real numbers and ending with angles, radian measure, and degree measure. Such passage from "pure" to "applied" trigonometry may have greater brevity and mathematical elegance, but it presents a higher level of abstraction to the learner. The Commission's proposed treatment of trigonometry should not be construed as a dogmatic judgment in favor of angles over real numbers. Rather, it reflects the Commission's decisions to stress coordinates, vectors, and complex numbers in grade 11, and functional properties in grade 12.

AN INTRODUCTION TO STATISTICAL THINKING

Just as mathematics deals with situations in which the facts can be determined, it also provides ways to study, understand, and control uncertainty. Many of the newer applications of mathematics use the theories of probability and statistical reasoning. Increasingly, modern science—physics, biology, social science—makes use of probabilistic descriptions of phenomena.

The Commission believes that it is desirable that material in these areas be introduced into the high school curriculum. Statistical thinking is playing more and more of a part in the daily lives of educated men and women. An introduction to statistical thinking is an important supplement to an introduction to deductive thinking.

This introduction may well begin in the ninth grade or earlier with a unit on descriptive statistics (like that outlined on p. 37, section X, "Mathematics for grade 9") ; it would cover numerical data, frequency tables, averages (median, mean), and simple measures of dispersion (range, quartiles). A more formal unit on probability, designed for grade 12, is discussed later in this chapter.

MATHEMATICS FOR GRADE 12
(ADVANCED MATHEMATICS)

The subject matter of a fourth high school year is treated separately because this course will not necessarily be pursued by all students who have completed the work of the earlier years. College entrance requirements for students wishing to take nontechnical or nonscientific courses in college frequently do not demand more than Elementary and Intermediate Mathematics. The Advanced Mathematics course will be taken by students whose personal interest in mathematics impels them to elect this course. Because there is a certain element of natural selection about the enrollment, it is possible to suggest content for this course that can properly be described as Advanced (high school) Mathematics.

Many possibilities for topics: It should be noted that the character of the study of mathematics undergoes a change at about the twelfth-grade level: the sequential aspect of the study of mathematics begins to break down. In the early grades, one can be reasonably certain about many parts of the sequence—arithmetic before algebra, algebra before trigonometry, and so forth. But by about the middle of the twelfth grade the student's mathematical journey has brought him to a point from which he can proceed in many directions, all of them inviting. Consequently, there are many topics that might be included in Advanced Mathematics, far more than could be taught in the allotted time. The Commission has had to determine which of these many topics seems to be the most desirable, and make its recommendations accordingly. Following the procedure used in the discussion of Elementary and Intermediate Mathematics, both the Commission's recommendations and its reasons for making them will be given.

The Commission has decided to recommend a course to be called Elementary Functions as the core of the Advanced Mathematics program. This course can be taught either for a semester or enlarged to a full year by adding a selection of topics from the list on page 47. If Elementary Functions is given for a semester, the Commission proposes that the second semester be devoted either to introductory probability with statistical applications or to an introduction to modern algebra (fields and groups).

There are other possibilities that could be suggested. One promising alternative is an introduction to linear algebra and matrices. Indeed, any serious mathematics, creatively and imaginatively taught, would be appro-

701

priate. Schools with unusual facilities and specially trained teachers may wish to try other combinations of subject matter. The prime requisite is that such subject matter be real mathematics, challenging to the students and contributing substantially to the development of their mathematical power.

Some schools may at first find it too difficult a task to complete the entire program of Elementary and Intermediate Mathematics by the end of grade 11. In such cases, the Commission suggests that a *minimal* four-year program consist of Elementary Mathematics, Intermediate Mathematics, and Advanced Mathematics through the Elementary Functions course.

ELEMENTARY FUNCTIONS

The core of the proposed work in Advanced Mathematics consists of a modification of the traditional advanced algebra course with stress placed upon the study of certain functions: polynomials, the exponential and logarithmic functions, and the circular functions. This course may be regarded as one that picks up certain concepts from Intermediate Mathematics, builds on them, and deepens their meaning. In this course, there is also a more formal treatment of sets, relations, and functions than that given in Elementary and Intermediate Mathematics.

The study of polynomial functions includes an intuitive introduction to the nation of slope of a curve. This knowledge makes it possible to draw graphs of polynomials rapidly and with increased accuracy. Time-consuming work in locating the real roots of a polynomial equation can then be replaced by graphical methods. This approach has the dual advantage of being thoroughly practical and promoting genuine theoretical understanding. The emphasis in the work on polynomials and polynomial equations carried over into this course from the traditional advanced algebra course is to be placed on polynomials as functions, and on their functional properties. Material on roots of polynomial equations is to be regarded as an application of these properties. As already indicated, the study of polynomial functions is to be followed by a study of exponential, logarithmic, and circular functions (for an exposition of the latter, see Appendix 22, "Circular functions"). Permutations and combinations and mathematical induction are included in the course on Elementary Functions and also in Selected Topics (p. 47).

Such topics as the solution by formula of cubic and biquadratic equations, Descartes' rule of signs, Horner's method, determinants, and partial fractions are omitted.

INTRODUCTORY PROBABILITY WITH STATISTICAL APPLICATIONS

One of the semester courses recommended for grade 12 offers an introduction to probability with statistical applications. The title is a matter of some significance. It is not intended that this course be a more elaborate presentation of descriptive statistics than the optional unit in Elementary Mathematics I (see p. 37, section X). Neither is it intended to be a course in which techniques for gathering data and similar non-mathematical aspects of statistics are discussed. This course is a course in mathematics, built around concepts of great importance for our modern technological society—the theory of probability. The objectives of the course are: (1) to introduce the student to probability concepts and to the mathematics involved in these ideas; and (2) to illustrate ways in which these concepts apply to certain common statistical problems.

The introduction of this unit is one of the more novel suggestions of the Commission. Since the material is new and unfamiliar to many teachers, an experimental textbook giving a detailed presentation of the material recommended for inclusion in the course has been prepared.[5] This textbook has been undergoing classroom trial, but enough evidence is already at hand to indicate that the material is entirely suitable for students in grade 12. Many of them find it exciting. In the light of experimental reports a revision of the book is being issued.

So great is the current scientific and industrial importance of probability and statistical inference that the Commission does not believe valid objections based on theoretical considerations can be offered to its inclusion in the curriculum. The value of having instruction in probability with statistical applications included in college preparatory mathematics should be recognized immediately. Not only is there a great demand in a wide variety of occupations for persons with sound competence in these areas, but this material, more than most secondary school mathematics, is closely related to problems of daily living. Most people, whether they realize it or not, must frequently make decisions based upon data that are essentially statistical in character. The Commission, therefore, believes there will be general recognition of the validity of its recommendation that some of this material be taught in the secondary school; dissent can only arise, it feels, on the ground of the difficulty of carrying out the task. It is for this reason that steps have been taken to insure that the probability unit is teachable in secondary schools. Though no more intricate than some traditional topics in algebra, the theory of probability is tremendously more vital and important, and fully as valuable in developing and keeping alive algebraic skills. Since an appreciation of the ideas involved requires some maturity, we recommend that the study of probability be undertaken in grade 12. The Commission believes that many of the nation's mathematics teachers

5. Commission on Mathematics, *Introductory Probability and Statistical Inference* (revised preliminary ed.; New York: College Entrance Examination Board, 1959).

will want to familiarize themselves and their students with this important subject matter of contemporary mathematics.

Finally, a course on probability with statistical applications has an important contribution to make to the mathematical growth and development of students. The theory of probability is an example of a small axiomatic system that has remarkably extensive consequences: it takes its place beside the deductive systems recommended for geometry and for algebra. Moreover, the theory of probability provides a natural use for the important notions of sets—so central to contemporary mathematics; it also exploits and brings perspective to the traditional algebraic treatment of permutations and combinations. The binomial expansion takes on new significance when it is used to construct mathematical models for a variety of physical situations.

In addition, the proposed material provides the student with much valuable practice: in the translation of situations in real life into mathematical problems; in the construction and manipulation of functions, operations with sets, algebraic equations, and inequalities; in the use of mathematical tables (including interpolation and the extension of tables); and in the development and use of approximations, as well as of bounds. Occasions for practice with limits, maxima, minima, subscripts and exponents, and with the factoring and expanding of algebraic expressions, arise naturally in the work.

Apart from these specific mathematical values, the student will meet in this course the same challenge to his intellectual capabilities and his mathematical maturity that is presented by every other part of the mathematical curriculum.

INTRODUCTION TO MODERN ALGEBRA

Throughout the first three years of the high school course recommended by the Commission, the field and group properties of the real numbers (i.e., commutativity, associativity, etc.) are highlighted. These properties are now studied in detail for their inter-relations and consequences. Specifically, the axioms for an abstract field are extracted from the earlier experiences of the student and other properties are deduced from them. The abstract group—a still simpler system—is treated similarly. The axioms for real numbers are developed in full, and the study of transformations and their composition solidifies the concept of function. Thus algebra will be seen, indeed, as the study of mathematical structure, and this final semester's work will serve as a capstone for much of the entire secondary school course.

An additional virtue of the proposed course in groups and fields is that it makes inescapably clear to the student that deduction is not only something that is done in geometry, but is a powerful means for organizing the subject matter of other branches of mathematics. Moreover, the availability of numerous models of groups provides a fertile field for the examination of dissimilar and interesting systems.

Indeed, groups—and, to a lesser extent, fields—are so pervasive in mathematics generally that they have interesting and important applications in such diverse fields as quantum mechanics, crystallography, aesthetics, and geometry.

The subject matter of this course is of comparatively recent development in mathematics. In the early 1940's the study of groups and fields filtered down into the upper undergraduate years from the graduate school, and more recently, into the lower courses. Still more recently, carefully selected material of this sort has been found to be within the grasp of able high school students. Experience has indicated that these students have found this subject matter both challenging and interesting. A course in modern algebra in the high school can serve as an admirable means by which to bridge the gap between high school and college mathematics.

SUMMARY

The major proposals of the Commission are outlined in the following nine points:

1. Strong preparation, *both* in concepts *and* in skills, for college mathematics at the level of calculus and analytic geometry

2. Understanding of the nature and role of deductive reasoning—in algebra, as well as in geometry

3. Appreciation of mathematical structure ("patterns")—for example, properties of natural, rational, real, and complex numbers

4. Judicious use of unifying ideas—sets, variables, functions, and relations

5. Treatment of inequalities along with equations

6. Incorporation with plane geometry of some coordinate geometry, and essentials of solid geometry and space perception

7. Introduction in grade 11 of fundamental trigonometry—centered on coordinates, vectors, and complex numbers

8. Emphasis in grade 12 on elementary functions (polynomial, exponential, circular)

9. Recommendation of additional alternative units for grade 12: *either* introductory probability with statistical applications *or* an introduction to modern algebra

Finally, as a close scrutiny of the full report will show, the Commission's recommendations embody relatively minor changes in content, but tremendously important changes in the points of view of instruction, and major changes in teaching emphases. None of these changes is simply for the sake of change. The Commission, as stated before, has tried to produce a curriculum suitable for students and oriented to the needs of mathematics, natural science, social science, business, technology, and industry in the second half of the twentieth century. This has been the overriding objective. Whatever of the old has disappeared, whatever of the traditional yet remains, whatever of the new appears, is in or out of the curriculum solely to effect necessary modification and improvement.